TEACHER'S EDITION

# MODELING with MATHEMATICS
## A Bridge to Algebra II

# MODELING with MATHEMATICS

## A Bridge to Algebra II

SECOND EDITION

**Nancy Crisler**

**Gary Simundza**
Wentworth Institute of Technology

region4®
Educated Solutions
Houston, TX

**COMAP Inc.**
Lexington, VA

WH Freeman and Company/BFW
New York

| | |
|---|---|
| *National Sales Manager, Director High School:* | Craig Bleyer |
| *Publisher:* | Ann Heath |
| *Associate Editor:* | Dora Figueiredo |
| *Freelance Development Editor:* | Ann Stollenwerk |
| *Media Editor:* | Laura Capuano |
| *Assistant Media Editor:* | Catriona Kaplan |
| *Executive Marketing Manager:* | Cindi Weiss |
| *Photo Editor:* | Bianca Moscatelli |
| *Photo Researcher:* | Deborah Anderson |
| *Cover Designer:* | Vicki Tomaselli |
| *Text Designer:* | Marsha Cohen |
| *Cover Image:* | Suzanne DeChillo/*The New York Times/* Redux |
| *Project Editor:* | Teresa Christie |
| *Illustrations:* | Precision Graphics, Network Graphics |
| *Illustration Coordinator:* | Bill Page |
| *Production Manager:* | Paul Rohloff |
| *Composition:* | MPS Limited |
| *Printing and Binding:* | RR Donnelley and Sons |

Library of Congress Control Number:   2012930466
ISBN-13: 978-1-4292-8344-1
ISBN-10: 1-4292-8344-0
© 2012, 2006 by W. H. Freeman and Company
First printing
Printed in the United States of America

**W. H. Freeman and Company**
41 Madison Avenue
New York, NY 10010
Houndmills, Basingstoke RG21 6XS, England
www.whfreeman.com

# About the Authors

**NANCY CRISLER**, a Presidential Awardee for Excellence in Mathematics Teaching, has taught mathematics at many levels including middle school, high school, and college. She has also worked as the Curriculum Specialist for the Pattonville School District in the St. Louis area for several years. In addition to full-time teaching, Nancy has been a lead teacher in numerous summer institutes dealing with topics of discrete mathematics for high school students and developmental mathematics for college-level students. She has also coauthored several articles and books that focus on topics in mathematical modeling, activity-based learning, and discrete mathematics.

**GARY SIMUNDZA** is Professor of Mathematics at Wentworth Institute of Technology in Boston, MA, where he teaches both mathematics and physics after having previously been a high school science teacher. He has directed several faculty workshops for the Mathematics Association of America aimed at helping teachers create activity-based, applied developmental mathematics courses. He has also coauthored modeling-oriented algebra textbooks and other curriculum materials for the high school and college levels.

Nancy and Gary are the authors of *Developing Mathematics through Applications: Elementary and Intermediate* (2003), *Activities for Introductory College Mathematics* (2009), and *A New Beginning: Introductory College Mathematics through Applications* (2010).

**REGION 4** Education Service Center (ESC) is the largest Texas educational service center. It provides services to 53 school districts, representing over 1,000,000 students and more than 83,000 professional educators. Region 4 provides nationally recognized professional development, technical assistance services, and quality, economical products to districts and businesses.

**COMAP**, the Consortium for Mathematics and Its Applications, is an award-winning non-profit organization whose mission is to improve mathematics education for students of all ages. Since 1980, COMAP has worked with teachers, students, and business people to create learning environments where mathematics is used to investigate and model real issues in our world.

# Contents

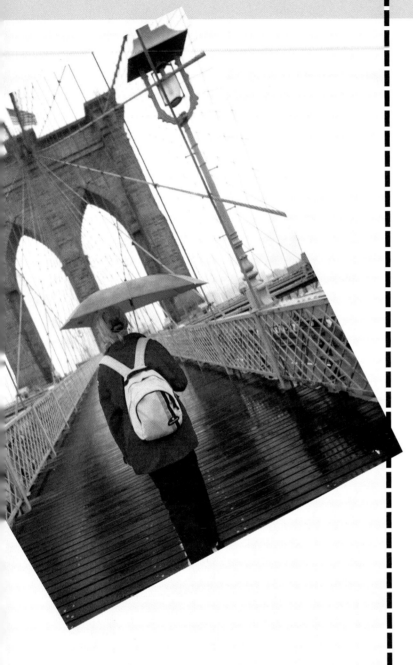

## To the Teacher

### I. WHY?

Many students complete their Algebra I and Geometry coursework with only a partial mastery of the fundamentals that are needed for further study. *Modeling with Mathematics: A Bridge to Algebra II* is intended to help students solidify their understanding of Algebra I and Geometry by providing a different kind of learning experience. In this course, students build mathematical models of real-world applications, using a functions approach that imparts a deeper grasp of the concepts and enables them to see their world from a mathematical perspective. In doing so, they will also reinforce their algebra and geometry skills. For students that leave Algebra I with an unstable foundation in algebraic thinking, this reinforcement helps to clarify their mathematical understanding and empowers them for success in Algebra II.

### II. WHAT?

*Modeling with Mathematics: A Bridge to Algebra II* focuses on incorporating topics that are essential to student achievement in Algebra II. Before beginning work on this new edition, the authors carefully reviewed Algebra II content and listed prerequisite topics that are needed for success in that course. Linearity and linear models form the algebraic core of the first part of the text, followed by linear systems, exponential and quadratic functions, and a brief introduction to other functions. Geometry-related topics are interspersed. Chapters on data analysis, probability, and finance are also included.

This structure and choice of topics reflects the content of the Common Core State Standards in Mathematics (*www.corestandards.org/the-standards/mathematics*). The CCSS mission statement states, "The Common Core State Standards provide a consistent, clear understanding of what students are expected to learn, so teachers and parents know what they need to do to help them. The standards are designed to be robust and relevant to the real world, reflecting the knowledge and skills that our young people need for success in college and careers." Because individual states who adopt the CCSS may add 15 percent of their own standards to the CCSS, it is likely that they will continue to vary in their emphasis of certain topics. The last few chapters of *Modeling with Mathematics: A Bridge to Algebra II* allow for such variation. The optional Extensions included at the end of most chapters provide opportunities for further customization.

The text assumes that students begin the course with prior knowledge of topics from arithmetic and elementary data analysis, as well as the rudiments of working with algebraic expressions and simple equations. For ease of reference, these prerequisites are reviewed in the Appendices in the back of the book and are cited where appropriate in this Annotated Teacher's Edition.

## III. HOW?

**Mathematical modeling** is the unifying theme of this textbook. It is the process by which students encounter a real-world situation, pose a question regarding the situation, and use mathematics to seek an answer to that question. In order to provide a fresh encounter with mathematics in this course, an engaging problem is presented that allows students to explore data and generate a function that best models the situation. Through a process of guided discovery, they apply their mathematical model to answer critical questions and solve meaningful, relevant problems related to the context. By repeating this approach for a variety of contexts and mathematical topic areas, students learn that mathematical modeling involves

- identifying the relevant features of a real-world situation,

- representing those features symbolically,

- analyzing the model, and

- considering the accuracy and limitations of the model.

**Cooperative learning** encourages the exchange of mathematical ideas in a safe environment for the testing of conjectures. Many of the lessons in *Modeling with Mathematics: A Bridge to Algebra II*, particularly those labeled *Activity* or *Investigation*, encourage cooperative group work. Since the analysis of gathered data is the basis for forming many types of mathematical models, group data collection is a recurring emphasis. Having students collect their own data makes learning more concrete and interesting. Engaging in mathematical discussions within their group helps students see the value of a team-oriented approach to problem-solving, an essential part of the modern workplace.

The use of **multiple representations** is emphasized throughout the text. Students are encouraged to use tables, graphs, diagrams, and equations to view problem situations in a variety of ways. Each representation brings a different insight into the structure of a problem and allows for students' diverse learning styles. Graphical analysis can often be abetted through the use of graphing calculators, which is suggested where appropriate throughout the text.

**Four primary types of lessons** are used in this edition:

- *Activities* usually involve group experimentation or other data collection to introduce new topics and often appear as the first lesson in a chapter.

- *Investigations* typically consist of pencil-and-paper explorations of new or previously introduced topics and are also performed in groups.

- *Regular lessons* are more traditionally structured presentations of course material.

- *Review and Practice* (R.A.P.) lessons are skill-building exercise sets that revisit previously learned and prerequisite topics.

Stepped-out *Examples* are included to help students, parents, and teachers with methodology, and *Practice* exercises in each lesson emphasize problem solving, critical thinking, and writing about mathematics. The Practice exercises have been carefully chosen. It is suggested that *all* exercises in each lesson be assigned to students to be completed either in class or as homework.

Each chapter also includes a brief preparatory reading that introduces a principal context of the chapter, as well as a *Modeling Project* and a *Chapter Review*. Additionally, many chapters conclude with an *Extension* lesson that introduces an optional topic to be assigned at the teacher's discretion.

The components of the **5E Instructional Model** (Engage, Explore, Explain, Elaborate, and Evaluate) form the backbone of the text. The 5E Model is described later in this preface.

## IV. WHAT'S NEW?

In response to suggestions from users of the first edition, the mathematics content has been made more transparent in this new edition of *Modeling with Mathematics: A Bridge to Algebra II*, as can be seen from the Table of Contents and the brief opening paragraph of each lesson. Activities and Investigations are directly connected to the mathematical development that follows, and there is greater emphasis on direct explanation of concepts and skills. Exercise sets provide more skill practice than in the first edition, with the first several exercises in each lesson usually consisting of a non-contextual focus on skill development.

Students often experience difficulty in Algebra II because they lack the skills and conceptual development necessary for success. To help students improve their basic algebra and geometry skills, one lesson in each chapter of this edition is a R.A.P. (**R**eview **A**nd **P**ractice) lesson. These lessons, *as* distinct from the chapter reviews, are designed to review topics previously taught in the text along with the prerequisite skills that are reviewed in the appendices. If students have trouble with any exercises in a R.A.P. lesson, refer them to the appropriate appendix or previous lesson as indicated in the teacher's edition wrap.

Some teachers were concerned with the amount of reading in the first edition, so, the reading level of this edition has been consciously addressed. Nonetheless, we believe that students should be encouraged to improve their reading skills as they develop mathematical facility. Many of the contextual situations in the text require students to read for mathematical content. Indeed, an essential part of acquiring the ability to model the world with mathematics is learning to see how mathematics is embedded in those situations. We hope students will be encouraged to read carefully, as that helps them achieve mathematical competence. To this end, unfamiliar concepts are clearly explained in terms that students are able to understand.

## V. WHAT'S HERE?

This Annotated Teacher's Edition consists of an easy-to-follow wrap-around structure. A detailed description of the various features of the ATE is provided in the following pages.

Since group work is an important aspect of the text, you should become familiar with features of cooperative learning. Simply placing students in a group does not promote a greater understanding of mathematical principles or the ability to communicate one's reasoning to others. Cooperative learning involves small groups of 2, 3, or 4 students working together to make sense of their own and each other's learning. Basic elements of cooperative learning (Johnson, D.W., R.T. Johnson, and E.J. Holubec, *The Nuts and Bolts of Cooperative Learning*, Edina, MN: Interaction Book Co., 1994) include:

- There must be a clear task and group goal.

- Students support and help each other to become successful.

- Each group member must be held accountable for contributing to the group's goals.

- Teamwork skills must be taught alongside academic skills.

- Groups must evaluate how well they are working together.

The *Activities* and *Investigations* that appear in each chapter are fundamental to the approach used in this text. The table below suggests strategies for using them.

| Before the *Activity* or *Investigation* | During the *Activity* or *Investigation* | After the *Activity* or *Investigation* |
|---|---|---|
| Students should:<br><br>Read the Chapter Opener or material preceding the *Activity* or *Investigation* and discuss the material in their group or as a class. | Students should:<br><br>Actively participate in performing the calculations and answering the questions posed in the *Activity* or *Investigation*. Take notes about the group's responses, and prepare a written report if requested. | Students should:<br><br>Ask questions about anything that remains unclear after completing the *Activity* or *Investigation*. |
| Instructors should:<br><br>Facilitate a class discussion of the Chapter Opener or reading material and have the members of each group write down their ideas. If possible, have students work at tables or arrange their chairs so that they can easily work together. | Instructors should:<br><br>Ensure that every student contributes and that each student's ideas are considered by the group. Guide group discussions so that the important mathematical concepts are correctly brought out. | Instructors should:<br><br>Bring the class back together for a follow-up discussion. Make sure that all of the important objectives covered in the *Activity* or *Investigation* have been addressed and are understood. |

# Features

## Chapter 1
## Mathematical Modeling

### Mathematical Overview

This chapter opens the door for students to better understand the use of mathematical modeling when presented with a situation or problem to solve. They begin by examining a presentation of different forms of mathematical models and proceed to using ratios and proportions to create a model for estimating animal populations. Then students explore how proportions can be used to model a variety of other real-world situations. In the last lesson of this chapter, students examine the use of words, graphs, and tables as models to relate one real-world quantity to another. Understanding which model best describes a situation, looking closely at that model, discovering patterns in the model, and describing the patterns mathematically are steps students will use throughout this book to solve problems.

### Lesson Summaries

**Lesson 1.1   *Activity: Animal Populations***
In this Activity, students use beans to represent a wild horse population. Each bean represents one wild horse in a population to be estimated. During the Activity, students simulate a technique known as *capture-recapture* to estimate how many horses there are without actually counting each horse. Students write ratios, set up proportions using a variable to represent the total number in the horse population, and then solve for the variable.

**Lesson 1.2   *Proportions as Models***
In this lesson, students extend their knowledge of proportions by representing and solving a variety of real-world situations. The first real-world situation they examine is the cost of driving a given distance when the cost per mile is constant. Then students examine using a scale from a scale drawing to find the actual width of a room. A third situation draws on students' recall of geometry. Students use corresponding sides of similar polygons to calculate the scale factor, set up a proportion, and then solve for an unknown length for one of the polygons.

**Lesson 1.3   *R.A.P.***
In this lesson, students **R**eview **A**nd **P**ractice solving problems that require the use of skills and concepts taught in previous math levels. The skills reviewed in this lesson are skills that are needed as a basis for solving problems throughout this course.

**Lesson 1.4   *Investigation: Patterns and Explanations***
In this Investigation, students are given a situation and asked to choose a graph or a table that best models the relationship between the variables in the situation. They discuss the features of several qualitative graphs and identify the two variables in each situation. They also examine patterns in graphs and tables to better understand how to use mathematics to describe the relationship between the variables in a given situation.

Two pages of overview and lesson planning material precede each chapter in the Teacher's Edition. The first page provides an overview of the mathematics development in the chapter.

### Lesson Guide

| Lesson/Objectives | Materials | |
|---|---|---|
| **Chapter 1 Opener: What Is a Mathematical Model?**<br>• recognize that many different representations can be used to model real-world situations. | | |
| **1.1 Activity: Animal Populations**<br>• use ratios and proportions to create mathematical models.<br>• use mathematical models to estimate the sizes of populations.<br>• solve proportions. | *Per groups:*<br>• white beans or other small objects that can be marked with a marker (about 150)<br>• small paper bag or other container for holding the beans<br>• permanent marker | *Optional:*<br>• TRM table shell for Question 5. |
| **1.2 Proportions as Models**<br>• use proportions to model real-world situations.<br>• solve problems that involve scale drawings.<br>• solve problems that involve similar polygons. | | *Optional:*<br>• TRM shell for the Vocabulary Organizer<br>• an item that shows a scale (map, blueprint, model car, etc.) |
| **1.3 R.A.P. (Review and Practice)**<br>• solve problems that require previously learned concepts and skills. | | |
| **1.4 Investigation: Patterns and Explanations**<br>• use multiple representations to model real-world situations. | | |

### Pacing Guide

| | Day 1 | Day 2 | Day 3 | Day 4 | Day 5 | Day 6 |
|---|---|---|---|---|---|---|
| **Basic** | p. 2, 1.1 | 1.2 | 1.3 | 1.4 | project | review |
| **Standard** | p. 2, 1.1 | 1.2 | 1.3 | 1.4 | project | review |
| **Block** | p. 2, 1.1, 1.2 | 1.3, 1.4 | project, review | | | |

### Supplement Support
See the Book Companion Website at www.highschool.bfwpub.com/ModelingwithMathematics and the Teacher's Resource Materials (TRM) for additional resources.

The second page contains useful information for class preparation. *Objectives* are listed for each lesson in the text, as well as *Materials* that are needed to complete Activities and Investigations. Relevant *Optional* materials that are available, including blackline masters and table shells, are also listed. A *Pacing Guide* assists with lesson planning.

## CHAPTER 1 OPENER

**5e**   Engage

### Lesson Objective
• recognize that many different representations can be used to model real-world situations.

### Vocabulary
• mathematical modeling
• mathematical models

### Description
This chapter sets the stage for the entire course. The chapter is purposely short, yet it shows most of the different types of lessons: Activities, Investigations, R.A.P. lessons, Modeling Projects, and Chapter Reviews. The mathematical skills reviewed in this chapter are necessary for student success in future chapters.

### What Is a Mathematical Model?

The process of starting with a situation or problem and gaining understanding about the situation through the use of mathematics is known as **mathematical modeling**. The mathematical descriptions obtained in the process are called **mathematical models**. These models are often built to explain why things happen in a certain way. They are also created to make predictions about the future.

Mathematical models can take many different forms. Among them are:

"The U.S. Postal Service accepts a package for mailing only if the sum of its length and girth is not more than 108 inches."

→ verbal descriptions

→ tables of information

| Time (minutes) | Temperature (°F) |
|---|---|
| 0 | 40 |
| 5 | 48 |
| 10 | 54 |
| 15 | 59 |
| 20 | 62 |

→ equations

$$h = 2 + 1.5n$$

→ graphs

→ formulas

The *Chapter Opener* is designed to stimulate thought and discussion. It introduces a major context in the chapter and often leads directly into the first Activity or Investigation lesson.

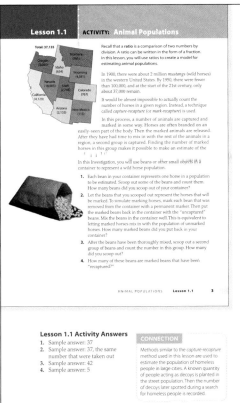

At the beginning of each Lesson, the wraparound text provides guidance on executing the lesson successfully. *Lesson Objectives* are followed by a list of new mathematical *Vocabulary* terms and a list of *Materials* needed (if appropriate). A *Description* of what is accomplished in the lesson includes suggestions for preparing and wrapping up Activities and Investigations.

The wraparound also includes answers for all questions and exercises (in red print). For open-ended questions, sample answers are provided.

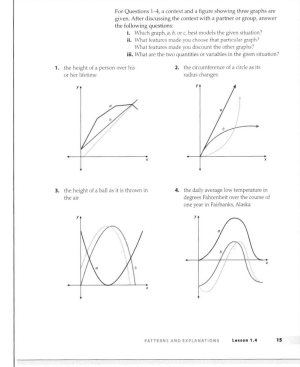

## TEACHING TIP

After students have read the Chapter Opener and examined the examples of the different types of representations discussed in the reading, lead a whole-class discussion asking students to give other examples of each type of model.

## CONNECTION

**Exercise 5** The English scientist Robert Hooke discovered the law named after him in the late 17th century. The constant ratio $k$ in the equation $F = kx$ is called a *spring constant*.

## COMMON ERROR

**Exercise 1** Remind students about the need for uniform scales.

*Teaching Tips* and *Connections* to historical background or other contexts are also included in the wrap. Tips related to exercises, including *Common Errors* that you can help students avoid, are inserted next to the relevant exercises from the student edition.

---

### E X A M P L E  2

The graph below shows the medication dosage function $d = 25w$ from Lesson 2.3.

Find the slope of the line.

**Solution:**

As the weight increases from 0 to 60 kg, the dosage rises from 0 to 1,500 mg. The slope of the line is

$$\frac{\text{rise}}{\text{run}} = \frac{1{,}500 \text{ mg}}{60 \text{ kg}}$$
$$= 25 \text{ mg/kg}$$

Notice that in this case, the slope has units of milligrams per kilogram.

### ADDITIONAL EXAMPLE  2

The graph below shows the cost of having various amounts of clothes cleaned at a drop-off laundry. Find the slope of the line.

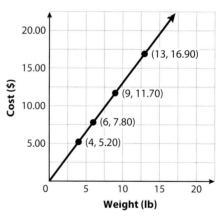

$$\frac{11.70 - 5.20}{9 - 4} = 1.30 \, \frac{\text{dollars}}{\text{pound}}$$

For each Example in the student text, an *Additional Example* is provided for your use in further illustrating problem-solving techniques.

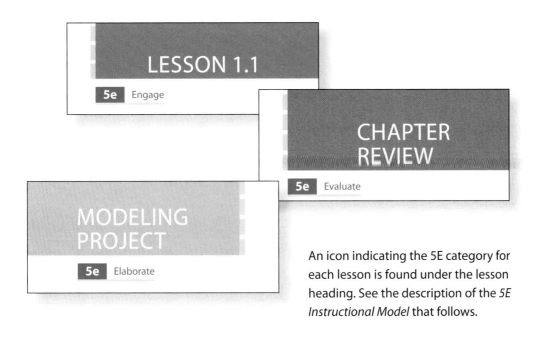

An icon indicating the 5E category for each lesson is found under the lesson heading. See the description of the *5E Instructional Model* that follows.

## WHAT IS THE 5E MODEL?

The lessons contained in *Modeling with Mathematics: A Bridge to Algebra II* reflect the 5E Instructional Model, which was developed and modified by Roger W. Bybee (Bybee et al., 2006), past executive director of the National Research Council and Center for Science, Mathematics, and Engineering Education. According to the model, instructional materials should

- actively **Engage** students by stimulating their curiosity,

- guide students to **Explore** new concepts in cooperative groups,

- provide instruction to **Explain** those concepts as well as related skills,

- allow opportunities to **Elaborate** and extend their learning, and

- **Evaluate** students' understanding.

**5e** Engage : The Chapter Opener is designed to pique students' interest. Teachers can build on this by asking well-chosen questions as suggested in this Annotated Teacher's Edition. The first lesson of each chapter is often an Activity that further engages students and makes connections between past and present learning.

**5e** Explore : Guided Investigations allow students to become involved more deeply with new concepts presented in the chapter. These usually require students to probe, inquire, and question while working on group problem solving. The exploration phase fosters critical thinking and writing about mathematics. Teachers' observation and probing questions help students clarify their understanding.

**5e** Explain : The teacher uses this phase to offer further explanation and provide additional meaning or information, including formalizing correct terminology. Giving labels or correct terminology is far more meaningful and helpful for retention if it is done after the learner has had direct experience with the topic.

**5e** Elaborate : This phase allows students to extend and expand what they have learned in the chapter. Each chapter contains a Modeling Project that gives students an opportunity to apply what they have learned in researching a subject of interest. Most chapters conclude with an Extension lesson that can

be assigned at the teacher's discretion to provide an in-depth treatment of a topic that may be required in some states and/or to supply enrichment.

**5e** Evaluate : While Practice exercises are included in most lessons to provide an ongoing evaluative process, there are two lessons in each chapter that are primarily intended for evaluation. The R.A.P. lessons provide a regular cumulative review of skills, while the Chapter Review contains a Test Review section that consists of a comprehensive evaluation of students' understanding of the concepts presented in the chapter. As part of this review, students write about the mathematics and reflect on what they have learned.

## VI. WHAT ELSE?

Additional resources for teachers:

### Teacher's Resource Materials

This ancillary resource includes classroom handouts, blackline masters, and more! All resources in this binder may be copied for class distribution and multiple uses.

### Printed Test Bank

The printed test bank provides a wide range of questions and question types for assessing student comprehension, interpretation, analysis, and synthesis skills. This test bank includes over 1,000 questions. The questions are organized by chapter and lesson.

### ExamView® Software

New to the 2nd edition, the Printed Test Bank is now available in computerized format with ExamView® Assessment Suite. ExamView Test Generator guides teachers through the process of creating online or paper tests and quizzes quickly and easily. Users may select from the extensive bank of more than 1,000 questions or write their own. Tests may be printed or administered online using the ExamView Player. Questions may be sorted according to various information fields and scrambled to create different versions of tests and results may be sent to the course management component in ExamView Test Manager.

## Teacher's Resource CD-ROM

The CD-ROM includes all text figures (in JPEG and PPT formats) and the entirety of the Teacher's Resource Materials in PDF. Using the CD-ROM, the teacher may easily create classroom presentations, enhance instructional time, and improve online courses. Icons referencing the TRM and TRCD material are found throughout the Teacher's Edition.

## Book Companion Website

www.highschool.bfwpub.com/ ModelingwithMathematics

The companion Web site helps instructors by including access to the contents of the Teacher's Resource CD, and suggestions for additional resources.

All of us involved in the development of this book think that you will find that this approach will help your students see the value of using mathematical models and strategies. As they become actively involved in investigating the role of mathematics in a variety of applied contexts, they will be more motivated and better able to master the skills necessary to succeed in future mathematics courses. Students who are involved in approaching mathematics in this way will also be more likely to transfer those skills to situations that require mathematical problem solving ability in their other current and future studies, as well as in their eventual careers.

# Preface

The central purpose of this text is to help students solidify their understanding of Algebra I and Geometry concepts in preparation for Algebra II by providing a different kind of experience. We believe that by modeling real-world applications with a functions approach, students will gain a deeper grasp of important concepts.

Although the principal goal of preparing students for success in Algebra II through a modeling approach has not changed in the second edition, we have restructured the content and pedagogy to insure that all prerequisite topics for Algebra II are addressed. This new look helps to make the mathematics more transparent and provides better pacing for both students and teachers.

The components of the **5E Instructional Model** (Engage, Explore, Explain, Elaborate, and Evaluate) continue to form the backbone of the text. These are identified on the first page of each lesson in the teacher's edition.

## CHANGES TO THE SECOND EDITION

### More Connections

Many of the same topics, contexts, and activities from the previous edition remain in this edition. This new edition clarifies and streamlines these topics to make them easier for students to follow. The revision is purposely designed so that students can more easily make the connections from the Activities and Investigations to the mathematical skills and concepts being taught.

### Additional Content

This new standards-based edition focuses on incorporating topics that are essential to student success in Algebra II. Before beginning this new edition, we examined Algebra II content and listed prerequisite topics that were needed for success in that course. As a result, more topics from geometry and Algebra I appear in this new edition.

Emphasis is placed on student use of algebraic, graphical, numerical, and geometric reasoning to model information and solve problems. It is through the use of the modeling process that connections are made to many real-life situations.

**Focus on the important topics**

- Linearity and linear models form the algebraic core of the first part of the text. The solution of linear equations and systems is part of that core.

- Functions (including linear, exponential, and quadratic) are emphasized throughout, as they are essential to mathematical modeling.

- Geometry-related chapters are thoughtfully interspersed where they fit in the flow of the algebraic development.

- Separate chapters targeting data analysis, probability, and finance are also included, as these topics are of increasing importance in many fields of study as well as in modern life.

**Make the mathematics more transparent**

Although the content is highly contextual, the mathematics is transparent. This is evident from the Table of Contents and the vocabulary and objective lists at the end of each chapter. Such transparency makes it easier to correlate the text with individual state-specific standards and/or the new Common Core State Standards.

**Provide remediation, if needed**

Sixteen short appendices provide a quick review of key skills such as order of operations, working with fractions, decimals, percent, ratios, and so forth. Each appendix features worked examples and exercise sets that provide opportunities to check for comprehension.

**New Format**

Most chapters are divided into four different types of well-paced lessons that make teaching and learning from the book easier. The various types of lessons help engage students through hands-on learning, and reflect upon and practice what they have learned

through integrated exercises that facilitate connections between past and future learning. The four core lesson types are:

- **Activities** – These lessons provide opportunities for students to perform experiments and/or collect data in order to develop new concepts. Throughout these lessons, they are actively engaged in learning as well as reflecting upon and writing about their learning

- **Investigations** – These lessons provide opportunities for students to analyze real-world situations, hypothesize about solutions, and justify conclusions. Students are asked to talk and write about their ideas as they engage in mathematical thinking. While some Investigations could be done by students studying at home, we recommend that students work through these Investigations in collaborative groups during class.

- **Regular lessons** – These lessons are designed to teach specific skills. Highlighted examples offer detailed, annotated solutions making it easier for students to learn, teachers to teach, and parents to help facilitate their child's learning.

- **Review and Practice (R.A.P.)** – Students often experience difficulty in Algebra II because they lack the skills and conceptual development necessary for success. To help students improve on their basic algebra and geometry skills, one lesson in each chapter is specifically designed to review topics and practice skills previously taught in the text along with the prerequisite skills that are reviewed in the appendices.

**In addition to core lessons, most chapters include:**

- **Modeling Projects** – These lessons provide students with opportunities to apply the skills that they have acquired in the chapter to more open-ended situations. These projects vary in focus, but each is designed to develop higher-order thinking skills. Some projects ask students to do research and report on what they have found while in others they create and use good models to solve specific problems.

- **Extensions** – These lessons are designed to "extend" the chapter for those teachers or students who want to explore concepts beyond those presented in the chapter itself.

Each chapter includes a Chapter Opener, which is a brief preparatory reading that is designed to help students make connections between the mathematics they are going to learn about in the chapter and familiar real-world contexts. Each chapter also includes a Review which features lists of the Lesson Objectives and Vocabulary and a Test Review.

## Thoughtful Practice

The Practice section of each lesson has been thoughtfully designed. Some of the Exercises provide practice similar to the Examples in the lesson while others contain new ideas and new contexts. Some even use a guided discovery approach similar to the Investigations. It is our hope that through these Exercises, students come to understand the usefulness of the math that they just learned by seeing it applied to new situations. It is our intention that all exercises be assigned, as each was created with student practice, understanding, and learning in mind.

## Readability

Many of the contextual situations presented in this text require students to read for mathematical content. Indeed, an essential part of acquiring the ability to model the world with mathematics is learning to see how mathematics is embedded in those situations. We hope students will be encouraged to read carefully, as that helps them achieve mathematics competence. To this end, attention has been paid to the reading level of the text, and unfamiliar concepts are clearly explained in terms that students are able to understand.

## Technology

The use of calculators, computers, and data collection devices is encouraged where appropriate throughout this book. However, alternatives are frequently provided for users of the book who lack access to some of the technology.

For a detailed list of supplements available to support *Modeling with Mathematics: A Bridge to Algebra II,*

*Second Edition,* go to: www.highschool.bfwpub.com/bridgetoalgebra2_2e

## Acknowledgements

Although we have made many changes to the second edition, we owe a debt of gratitude to the individuals who shaped the first edition:

From Region 4 ESC: Jo Ann Wheeler, David Eschberger, Gary Cosenza, Paul Grey, Julie Horn, and Sharon Benson.
From COMAP: Soloman Garfunkel and Roland Cheney.

The following individuals were also instrumental in creating content used in the first edition:

Marsha Davis, Eastern Connecticut State University, Williamantic, CT
Juliann Doris, Seguin High School, Seguin, TX
Anne Konz, Cypress-Fairbanks Independent School District, Cypress, TX
Jerry Lege, COMAP, Inc., Lexington, MA
Jennifer May, Independent Consultant
Paul Mlakar, St. Mark's School, Dallas, TX
Sandra Nite, Texas A&M University, College Station, TX
Richard Parr, Rice University, Houston, TX
Ann Worley, Spring Branch Independent School District, Houston, TX

We offer our heartfelt thanks to the following teachers and school districts who piloted the first edition of *Modeling with Mathematics: A Bridge to Algebra II* 1e and provided essential feedback:

Kim Armstrong, Lindale High School, Lindale, Texas
Toni Ericson, Hallsville High School, Hallsville, Texas
Jason Hendricks, Madison High School, San Antonio, Texas
Sara Kamphaus, Summit High School, Mansfield, Texas
Mary Ann Knight, Mansfield High School, Mansfield, Texas
Connie Koehn, Elsik High School, Houston, Texas
Garnette Lamm, Madison High School, San Antonio, Texas

For the second edition, we were fortunate to benefit from the excellent counsel of the following reviewers:

Pamela Bailey, Spotsylvania County Schools, Fredericksburg, VA
Maleika Brown, Grand Rapids Public, Grand Rapids, MI
Wendy Clark, Renaissance High School, ID
Tim Dalton, Victor J. Andrew High School, IL
Vicki Greenberg, Woodward Academy, College Park, GA
Wendy Hoglund, Sepulveda Middle School, North Hills, CA
Ellen House, Hope High School, Providence, RI
Nancy Jacobson, Central High School, Rapid City, SD

Tawnia King, Celina High School, Celina, TX
Kara Leaman, Glenwood High School, Chatham, IL
Catherine Martin, Denver Public Schools, CO
Sylvia Olinger, Central High School, Rapid City, SD
Sherry Oyler, Central High School, Rapid City, SD
Marty Prentice, Rapid City Central High School, Rapid City, SD
Cindy Schimek, Katy ISD, Houston, TX
David Trotter, Franklin High School, Portland, OR

Jennifer Walton, Half Moon Bay High School, Half Moon Bay, CA
Debra Ward, Anne Arundel County Public Schools, MD

We would like to extend a special thank you to our friend, colleague, and developmental editor, Ann Stollenwerk. Without her editorial skills, mathematical knowledge, and attention to detail this book would not have been possible.

# How to get the most from your text...

*If you think math is just about numbers, think again!*

**Read** the **Chapter Opener** to learn about an interesting, real-world application of mathematics.

Chapter 2 looks at the context of bungee jumping to set the stage for the study of direct variation.

---

### How Is Mathematics Related to Bungee Jumping?

A bungee cord is an elastic cord that can be used to secure objects without tying knots. Specialized bungee cords are used in the sport of bungee jumping. One end of the cord is attached to a bridge or tower, and the other end is attached to the jumper. As the jumper falls, the cord stretches and slows the fall. At the bottom of the jump, the cord recoils and the jumper bounces up and down at the end of the cord.

The strength of the cord used for a bungee jump must be accurately known. The cord must be adjusted for the height of the jump and for the weight of the jumper. Otherwise, the consequences can be disastrous. In one well-publicized case, a woman died practicing for a bungee jump exhibition for the 1997 Super Bowl halftime show. The bungee cord was supposed to stop her 100-foot fall just above the floor of the Superdome in New Orleans. At the time, officials were quoted in *The Boston Globe* as saying:

> Apparently, she made an earlier jump and didn't come as close as they wanted. They made some adjustments, and somebody made a miscalculation. I think it was human error.

> Bungee safety is a product of simple mathematics that factors height and weight in its calculations. It's so predictable.

Ratios can be used to model bungee jumping. Knowing how much the cord stretches for different jumper weights can help ensure that bungee jumps are safe.

---

### Lesson 2.1    ACTIVITY: Bungee Jumping

Constructing a mathematical model to describe a relationship between two variables often begins with collecting data and recording the values in a table. The data can then be graphed with a scatter plot.

A bungee cord is *elastic*, meaning that it can be stretched and then returned to its original length. You can use a large rubber band to simulate a bungee cord.

1. Start with an empty can, such as a soup can, that has two small holes punched opposite each other near the rim. Insert the end of a large opened paper clip in each of the holes. Insert a large rubber band through the free ends of the clips so that the can hangs from the rubber band.
2. Hang the rubber band so that the bottom of the can is at least 6 inches above a flat desk, a table, or the floor. Use a ruler to measure the height of the bottom of the can to the nearest $\frac{1}{8}$ inch.
3. Find the weight (in ounces) of one of the identical objects provided.
4. Make a table like the one shown here. Leave the last column blank for use in Lesson 2.2. Record the height of the bottom of the can above the flat surface.

| Total Weight (ounces) | Height (inches) | Total Length of Stretch (inches) | |
|---|---|---|---|
| 0 | | 0 | |
| | | | |
| | | | |
| | | | |
| | | | |
| | | | |

5. Then place one object in the can. Record the weight of the object in the can and the new height of the bottom of the can.
6. Continue adding weight, one object at a time, until 6 objects are in the can. After each object is added, record the total weight of the objects in the can and the height of the bottom of the can.

---

*Get your hands "dirty" and experiment.*

Each chapter of the text has at least one **Activity**. Many of these activities use simple physical models such as this soup can on a rubber band to model complex situations, such as bungee jumping.

---

*Practice what you learned.*

A set of **exercises** at the end of each lesson lets you practice the skills you learned. It is very important for you to work ALL of the exercises at the end of each lesson to make sure that you understand the concepts and skills.

---

### Practice for Lesson 2.1

**For Exercises 1–3, use the following information.**

Boiling water is poured over a teabag in a cup. The temperature is measured every 2 minutes. The results are shown in the table at the left.

| Time (min) | Temperature (°F) |
|---|---|
| 0 | 205 |
| 2 | 158 |
| 4 | 122 |
| 6 | 108 |
| 8 | 96 |

1. Make a scatter plot of the data in the table. Let time be the variable on the horizontal axis, and let temperature be the variable on the vertical axis. Plot points for (*time, temperature*). Label the axes with variable names, units, and uniformly increasing scales.
2. Describe the pattern in your graph.
3. What do you think would happen to the temperature after another 10 minutes?
4. The table below shows a comparison of several 2010 sporty cars. It lists acceleration as the time it takes to go from 0 to 60 miles per hour, as well as highway gas mileage.

| Car | Time from 0 to 60 mph (seconds) | Gas Mileage (miles per gallon) |
|---|---|---|
| Mini Cooper S Clubman | 8.1 | 34 |
| Ford Mustang GT Coupe | 5.2 | 24 |
| Volkswagen Hatchback | 7.6 | 31 |
| Mitsubishi Eclipse Coupe | 8.7 | 28 |
| Chrysler Sebring Sedan | 8.5 | 30 |
| MazdaSpeed3 | 6.3 | 25 |

SOURCE: HTTP://WWW.AUTOS.COM/PASSENGER_CARS/SPORTY_CARS/ACCELERATION

## Dig a little deeper.

**Investigations** give you another chance to explore important math concepts. You will often work with classmates to share ideas and learn from others.

Be sure to work all of the **Practice Exercises** that follow the Investigation to make sure you stay on track.

---

**Lesson 2.2**  **INVESTIGATION: Proportional Relationships**

An equation is one of the most useful kinds of mathematical models. It can allow you to predict the value of one quantity when you know the value of another. In this lesson, you will use ratios to find an equation that models the relationship between the weight on a rubber band and how much the band stretches.

**Note**
In some situations, neither variable is dependent on the other. In such cases, either variable can be placed on the horizontal axis. For example, if heights and weights of people are graphed, either height or weight could correctly go on the horizontal axis.

### INDEPENDENT AND DEPENDENT VARIABLES

In the Activity in Lesson 2.1, you chose the values for the amount of weight. But you did not choose values for the length of the stretch. The stretch is called the **dependent variable** because its value depends on the value of the weight. Since values of weight can be freely chosen, weight is called the **independent variable**. The independent variable is almost always represented on the horizontal axis of a graph.

### A PROPORTIONAL RELATIONSHIP

In the Activity in Lesson 2.1, the points on your scatter plot most likely fell in a nearly straight-line pattern. A straight line drawn through the origin may be a good visual model for the data. When a clear pattern exists on a graph of two variables, it is often possible to find an equation that relates the variables. Clues to an equation may sometimes be found by examining the ratios of the values of the variables.

1. Return to your data table from the Activity in Lesson 2.1. Label the fourth column "Stretch-to-Weight Ratio." Calculate the ratio of the total stretch to the total weight for each row of the table and record it. Write your ratios as decimals.

| Total Weight (ounces) | Height (inches) | Total Length of Stretch (inches) | Stretch-to-Weight Ratio |
|---|---|---|---|
| 0 | | 0 | ----- |

2. How do the ratios in your table compare to each other?
3. If the ratio of stretch $S$ to weight $W$ is always equal to the same constant value, there is a **proportional relationship** between $S$ and $W$. The constant ratio is called the **constant of proportionality**. The letter $k$ is often used to represent such a constant. So, $\frac{S}{W} = k$ is an equation relating the variables $S$ and $W$.

---

**Practice** for Lesson 2.2

1. How is the value of $k$ in the Investigation related to the points in your scatter plot from the Activity in Lesson 2.1?

**For Exercises 2–7, use the following information.**
Most high-definition television sets have wider screens than other sets. Here is an example.

---

## Review and Practice.

As the saying goes, "Practice Makes Perfect." To learn new skills it is very important to review frequently and practice what you have learned.

**R.A.P.** lessons appear once in every chapter. They review topics previously taught and also check your mastery of the prerequisite skills that are reviewed in the appendices.

---

**Lesson 2.4**  **R.A.P.**

**Fill in the blank.**

1. For two variables $x$ and $y$, if the ratio $\frac{y}{x}$ is constant, then $y$ is _____ to $x$.

2. In the equation $y = kx$, $k$ is called the _____.

3. An input/output relationship in which each input value has exactly one output value is called a(n) _____.

4. The shape of the graph of a direct variation function is a(n) _____.

**Choose the correct answer.**

5. Which of the following is *not* a correct way of writing the ratio "3 to 4"?

   A. $3 : 4$    B. $\frac{3}{4}$    C. $3 \times 4$    D. 3 to 4

6. Given that 1 kilogram weighs approximately 2.2 pounds, rewrite 10 pounds as an equivalent number of kilograms.

   A. 22 kilograms    B. 4.5 kilograms
   C. 7.8 kilograms    D. 0.22 kilograms

**Change the decimal to a fraction in lowest terms.**

7. 0.4    8. 0.15    9. 0.22

**Change the fraction to a decimal.**

10. $\frac{5}{8}$    11. $\frac{7}{25}$    12. $\frac{3}{11}$

**Evaluate the expression.**

13. $|-8| + 2$    14. $-|-2|$    15. $4 - 2|-10|$

**The value of the square root is between which two integers?**

16. $\sqrt{30}$    17. $\sqrt{78}$    18. $\sqrt{108}$

## Read the text and study the worked Examples.

Each chapter includes lessons that focus on mathematical concepts. Read the explanations and then study the **Examples** including the detailed solutions.

---

### SLOPE AND RATE OF CHANGE

For a direct variation function of the form $y = kx$, the constant of proportionality $k$ is equal to the slope of the graph of the function.

### E X A M P L E  ②

The graph below shows the medication dosage function $d = 25w$ from Lesson 2.3.

Find the slope of the line.

---

## Need extra help?

If you are struggling, talk to your teacher or consult this book's **Appendices** for extra help.

---

You have seen that the graph of a direct variation function is a straight line. The slope of a line is a measure of its steepness. In this lesson, you will learn how to find the slope of a line and to interpret it as a rate of change.

### SLOPE OF A LINE

The *rise* of a staircase is defined as the vertical distance between landings. The horizontal distance from the edge of the bottom step to the top landing is called the *run*.

The steepness of the red line in the figure above can be described by a ratio known as the **slope** of the line.

$$\text{slope} = \frac{\text{rise}}{\text{run}}$$

### E X A M P L E  ①

Find the slope of a staircase that rises 64 inches over a run of 80 inches.

**Solution:**

The slope of the staircase is the ratio of rise to run.

$$\text{Slope of staircase} = \frac{\text{rise}}{\text{run}}$$
$$= \frac{64 \text{ in.}}{80 \text{ in.}}$$
$$= \frac{4}{5}$$

The slope is $\frac{4}{5}$ or 0.8.

**Connection**

Staircases are usually built with slopes between 0.6 and 0.9.

---

A **ratio** is a comparison of two numbers by division. Ratios can be written in three ways. For example, the ratio of the number of red squares to the number of gray squares is 3 to 4 or 3 : 4 or $\frac{3}{4}$.

### FINDING A RATIO

**To find the ratio between two quantities**, show the two quantities as a fraction. Then write the fraction in simplest form.

#### Examples

**1.** Your class has 20 books and 25 students. Find the ratio of the number of books to the number of students.

**Solution:**

Write the ratio of the number of books to the number of students.

$$\frac{20 \text{ books}}{25 \text{ students}}$$

Simplify.

$$\frac{20}{25} = \frac{20 \div 5}{25 \div 5}$$
$$= \frac{4}{5}$$

The ratio can be written in three ways.  4 to 5, 4 : 5, or $\frac{4}{5}$

---

## Make your own model.

Once you master the topics in the chapter, try building a model of your own.

**CHAPTER**

**2**

## Modeling Project

### It's Only Water Weight

In this chapter, you have learned to identify proportional relationships and to model them with direct variation functions. You are now ready to construct and analyze a model beginning with data that you collect.

You will need a scale, such as a bathroom scale, a large pot, a measuring cup, and a source of water.

- Place the pot on the scale and record its weight.
- Add measured volumes of water to the pot. After each added amount, record the total volume of water and the weight of the pot and water.
- Continue adding water until the pot is almost full.

Conduct an investigation of the weight vs volume relationship.

1. Make a table and graph comparing the total weight of the pot and water with the total volume of water in the pot.
2. Determine whether a direct variation function provides a good model for the relationship, and explain how you know. If so, find a direct variation function that models your data. If not, then find a way you can analyze the data in a different way so that a direct variation model is appropriate.

Prepare a report of your findings. Use what you have learned about proportions, as well as the calculation and interpretation of slope, to describe your model.

---

## Chapter 2 Review

**You Should Be Able to:**

**Lesson 2.1**
- collect experimental data.
- make a scatter plot of experimental data.

**Lesson 2.2**
- identify proportional relationships.
- identify independent and dependent variables.
- find a constant of proportionality.
- write an equation that expresses a proportional relationship.

**Lesson 2.3**
- identify direct variation.
- write direct variation equations.

**Lesson 2.4**
- solve problems that require previously learned concepts and skills.

**Lesson 2.5**
- find the slope of a line given rise and run.
- find the slope of a line given two points on the line.
- interpret the slope of a line as a rate of change.

**Key Vocabulary**

dependent variable (p. 26)
independent variable (p. 26)
proportional relationship (p. 26)
constant of proportionality (p. 26)
direct proportion (p. 32)
variation (p. 32)
direct variation (p. 32)
varies directly (p. 32)

origin (p. 33)
function (p. 33)
input value (p. 33)
output value (p. 33)
direct variation function (p. 35)
slope (p. 40)
rate of change (p. 42)

**Chapter 2 Test Review**

**Fill in the blank.**

1. A relationship between two variables such that there is exactly one output value for each input value is called a(n) _____.

2. The slope of a line is equal to the ratio of the _____ to the _____ between any two points on the line.

---

## Test yourself.

Look closely at the **Chapter Review**.

Do you know how to do everything in the bulleted list under each Lesson?

Are you familiar with all of the terms listed in the **Key Vocabulary**?

How well did you do on the **Test Review**?

---

## Challenge yourself.

Once you have mastered all of the topics in the chapter, turn to the **Chapter Extension** to learn a little more.

**CHAPTER**

**2**

## Chapter Extension
### Inverse Variation

Variables can be related to each other in many different ways. In this chapter, you have explored direct variation in some detail. Direct variation is one of the most common types of variation between two quantities. This extension consists of an activity that involves another frequently found type of variation.

When you look through a telescope, the amount you can see changes as the length of the telescope changes. The size of the *viewing circle* depends on the length of the telescope.

- Make a simple telescope by cutting a paper towel tube from one end to the other so that a second paper towel tube can fit inside of it. Do the same with a third paper towel tube. Insert the uncut tube inside one of the cut tubes. Then put these two inside the other cut tube. Now you can vary the length of your scope from one tube to nearly three.
- Tape a meter stick to a wall in a horizontal position. Back away from the wall and look at the stick through your scope. If you align the left edge of your viewing circle with the left end of the meter stick, you can estimate the diameter of the viewing circle. If you change the length of your scope, the diameter of your viewing circle should also change.

# To the Student

This book is probably different from the mathematics textbooks you have used in the past. We believe that mathematics should be learned by seeing how it is used day to day. The reason for learning the mathematics presented here is not simply to prepare you for the next math course, but also to prepare you to be able to use mathematics to solve problems that arise in other areas of your life. Yes, the mathematics that you learn will help prepare you for further schoolwork. But it is also important as a life skill, something you will use and value.

This book encourages active exploration of mathematics. You will learn to construct a variety of mathematical explanations of real problems. To do this, you will use equations, graphs, tables, verbal descriptions, geometry, and statistics. Here are a few tips that will help you use this book successfully:

- Every chapter of the book includes *Activities and Investigations*, which will most likely be done during class time. Discussions with other students will help you grasp new mathematical concepts.
- You will have to read carefully in order to understand the connections between mathematics and the world around you. This is especially important in some of the *Practice* exercises.
- Many of the *Activities, Investigations*, and *Practice* exercises require written responses. Try to write clearly and in complete sentences in order to show your understanding of the mathematics.
- When appropriate, use a graphing calculator or computer.
- Each chapter contains a *Review and Practice (R.A.P.)* lesson. Use the exercises in the *R.A.P.* to reinforce your learning of skills from earlier chapters, and even from past math courses.
- Use each chapter's *Modeling Project* to apply the mathematics you have learned to situations outside the classroom.
- The *Chapter Review* summarizes the mathematics in each chapter and allows you to test your knowledge of all the main concepts and skills from the chapter. As is the case with each lesson in the book, you should work *all* of the exercises.
- Some of the chapters end with an *Extension* lesson that goes beyond the regular chapter material. Your teacher may ask you to study some or all of these lessons.

In order to use mathematics to describe the world around you, you need to see how mathematics is part of that world. Our goal is that you will be able to recognize certain mathematical principles when you are outside the classroom. We hope that you enjoy using this text to develop your mathematical skills and understanding.

*The Authors*

# Chapter 1
# Mathematical Modeling

## Mathematical Overview

This chapter opens the door for students to better understand the use of mathematical modeling when presented with a situation or problem to solve. They begin by examining a presentation of different forms of mathematical models and proceed to using ratios and proportions to create a model for estimating animal populations. Then students explore how proportions can be used to model a variety of other real-world situations. In the last lesson of this chapter, students examine the use of words, graphs, and tables as models to relate one real-world quantity to another. Understanding which model best describes a situation, looking closely at that model, discovering patterns in the model, and describing the patterns mathematically are steps students will use throughout this book to solve problems.

## Lesson Summaries

### Lesson 1.1    *Activity: Animal Populations*

In this Activity, students use beans to represent a wild horse population. Each bean represents one wild horse in a population to be estimated. During the Activity, students simulate a technique known as *capture-recapture* to estimate how many horses there are without actually counting each horse. Students write ratios, set up proportions using a variable to represent the total number in the horse population, and then solve for the variable.

### Lesson 1.2    *Proportions as Models*

In this lesson, students extend their knowledge of proportions by representing and solving a variety of real-world situations. The first real-world situation they examine is the cost of driving a given distance when the cost per mile is constant. Then students examine using a scale from a scale drawing to find the actual width of a room. A third situation draws on students' recall of geometry. Students use corresponding sides of similar polygons to calculate the scale factor, set up a proportion, and then solve for an unknown length for one of the polygons.

### Lesson 1.3    *R.A.P.*

In this lesson, students **R**eview **A**nd **P**ractice solving problems that require the use of skills and concepts taught in previous math levels. The skills reviewed in this lesson are skills that are needed as a basis for solving problems throughout this course.

### Lesson 1.4    *Investigation: Patterns and Explanations*

In this Investigation, students are given a situation and asked to choose a graph or a table that best models the relationship between the variables in the situation. They discuss the features of several qualitative graphs and identify the two variables in each situation. They also examine patterns in graphs and tables to better understand how to use mathematics to describe the relationship between the variables in a given situation.

## Lesson Guide

| Lesson/Objectives | Materials | |
|---|---|---|
| **Chapter 1 Opener: What Is a Mathematical Model?**<br>• recognize that many different representations can be used to model real-world situations. | | |
| **1.1 Activity: Animal Populations**<br>• use ratios and proportions to create mathematical models.<br>• use mathematical models to estimate the sizes of populations.<br>• solve proportions. | *Per group:*<br>• white beans or other small objects that can be marked with a marker (about 150)<br>• small paper bag or other container for holding the beans<br>• permanent marker | *Optional:*<br>• TRM table shell for Question 5. |
| **1.2 Proportions as Models**<br>• use proportions to model real-world situations.<br>• solve problems that involve scale drawings.<br>• solve problems that involve similar polygons. | | *Optional:*<br>• TRM shell for the Vocabulary Organizer<br>• an item that shows a scale (map, blueprint, model car, etc.) |
| **1.3 R.A.P. (Review and Practice)**<br>• solve problems that require previously learned concepts and skills. | | |
| **1.4 Investigation: Patterns and Explanations**<br>• use multiple representations to model real-world situations. | | |

## Pacing Guide

| | Day 1 | Day 2 | Day 3 | Day 4 | Day 5 | Day 6 |
|---|---|---|---|---|---|---|
| **Basic** | p. 2, 1.1 | 1.2 | 1.3 | 1.4 | project | review |
| **Standard** | p. 2, 1.1 | 1.2 | 1.3 | 1.4 | project | review |
| **Block** | p. 2, 1.1, 1.2 | 1.3, 1.4 | project, review | | | |

**Supplement Support**

See the Book Companion Website at www.highschool.bfwpub.com/ModelingwithMathematics and the Teacher's Resource Materials (TRM) for additional resources.

# Mathematical Modeling

## CONTENTS

## Lesson Objective

- recognize that many different representations can be used to model real-world situations.

## Vocabulary

- mathematical modeling
- mathematical models

## Description

This chapter sets the stage for the entire course. The chapter is purposely short, yet it shows most of the different types of lessons: Activities, Investigations, R.A.P. lessons, Modeling Projects, and Chapter Reviews. The mathematical skills reviewed in this chapter are necessary for student success in future chapters.

This reading introduces students to the process of mathematical modeling and the different forms that mathematical models can take.

### TEACHING TIP

After students have read the Chapter Opener and examined the examples of the different types of representations discussed in the reading, lead a whole-class discussion asking students to give other examples of each type of model.

## What Is a Mathematical Model?

The process of starting with a situation or problem and gaining understanding about the situation through the use of mathematics is known as **mathematical modeling**. The mathematical descriptions obtained in the process are called **mathematical models**. These models are often built to explain why things happen in a certain way. They are also created to make predictions about the future.

Mathematical models can take many different forms. Among them are:

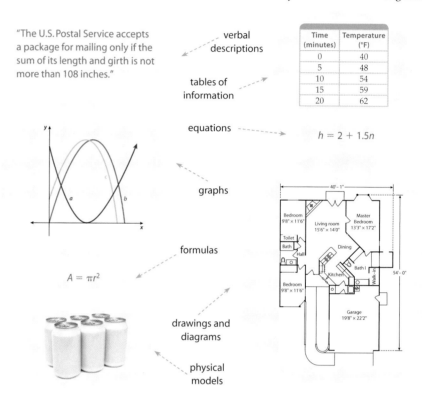

"The U.S. Postal Service accepts a package for mailing only if the sum of its length and girth is not more than 108 inches."

verbal descriptions

tables of information

| Time (minutes) | Temperature (°F) |
|---|---|
| 0 | 40 |
| 5 | 48 |
| 10 | 54 |
| 15 | 59 |
| 20 | 62 |

equations

$$h = 2 + 1.5n$$

graphs

formulas

$$A = \pi r^2$$

drawings and diagrams

physical models

A good mathematical model is one that helps you better understand the situation under investigation.

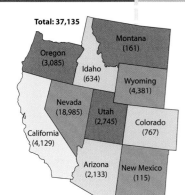

**Total: 37,135**

Montana (161)

Oregon (3,085)

Idaho (634)

Wyoming (4,381)

Nevada (18,985)

Utah (2,745)

Colorado (767)

California (4,129)

Arizona (2,133)

New Mexico (115)

Recall that a **ratio** is a comparison of two numbers by division. A ratio can be written in the form of a fraction. In this lesson, you will use ratios to create a model for estimating animal populations.

In 1900, there were about 2 million *mustangs* (wild horses) in the western United States. By 1950, there were fewer than 100,000, and at the start of the 21st century, only about 37,000 remain.

It would be almost impossible to actually count the number of horses in a given region. Instead, a technique called *capture-recapture* (or *mark-recapture*) is used.

In this process, a number of animals are captured and marked in some way. Horses are often branded on an easily-seen part of the body. Then the marked animals are released. After they have had time to mix in with the rest of the animals in a region, a second group is captured. Finding the number of marked horses in this group makes it possible to make an estimate of the entire population.

In this Investigation, you will use beans or other small objects in a container to represent a wild horse population.

1. Each bean in your container represents one horse in a population to be estimated. Scoop out some of the beans and count them. How many beans did you scoop out of your container?

2. Let the beans that you scooped out represent the horses that will be marked. To simulate marking horses, mark each bean that was removed from the container with a permanent marker. Then put the marked beans back in the container with the "uncaptured" beans. Mix the beans in the container well. This is equivalent to letting marked horses mix in with the population of unmarked horses. How many marked beans did you put back in your container?

3. After the beans have been thoroughly mixed, scoop out a second group of beans and count the number in this group. How many did you scoop out?

4. How many of these beans are marked beans that have been "recaptured?"

ANIMAL POPULATIONS    **Lesson 1.1**    **3**

## Lesson 1.1 Activity Answers

1. Sample answer: 37
2. Sample answer: 37, the same number that were taken out
3. Sample answer: 42
4. Sample answer: 5

### CONNECTION

Methods similar to the *capture-recapture* method used in this lesson are used to estimate the population of homeless people in large cities. A known quantity of people acting as decoys is planted in the street population. Then the number of decoys later spotted during a search for homeless people is recorded.

## Lesson Objectives

- use ratios and proportions to create mathematical models.
- use mathematical models to estimate the sizes of populations.
- solve proportions.

## Vocabulary

- proportion
- ratio
- variable

## Materials List

*Per group:*

- white beans or other small objects that can be marked with a marker (about 150)
- small paper bag or other container for holding the beans
- permanent marker

## Description

*Preparation:*

This lesson is designed as a whole class/small group activity (2–4 students). Prior to class, place an unknown number of white beans in each bag (one bag of about 120–150 beans per group).

*During the Activity:*

Give each group one bag of beans and point out that the number of beans is unknown. Explain that the object is to determine the number of beans in the bag without counting them.

As students remove some of their beans, have them count and mark them with a permanent marker. Once done, they should place all of the marked beans back into the bag.

*Closing the Activity:*

Remind students that this procedure is used when you are physically unable to count an unknown population. Reinforce the modeling aspect of this Activity by asking students to explain why they think this procedure provides them with a reasonable estimate of the number of beans in their bag.

**5.** Sample answer:

| First Captured Group | |
|---|---|
| Number captured and marked | 37 |
| Total population size | Unknown ($p$) |
| **Second Captured Group** | |
| Number that were marked | 5 |
| Number captured | 42 |

**6.** Sample answer: $\dfrac{5}{42}$

**7.** Sample answer: $\dfrac{5}{42} = \dfrac{37}{p}$

**8.** Sample answer: $p = 310.8$ or about 311 beans

**9.** Sample answer: First estimate: 42 beans, 5 marked; estimated population of 311. Second estimate: 40 beans, 6 marked; estimated population of 247. The estimates vary by 64 beans.

**5.** Complete the table to summarize your findings so far.

| First Captured Group | |
|---|---|
| Number captured and marked | |
| Total population size | Unknown ($p$) |
| **Second Captured Group** | |
| Number that were marked | |
| Number captured | |

**6.** What is the ratio of the number of marked (recaptured) beans to the total number of beans in the second captured group?

**7.** If the marked beans were well mixed with the unmarked beans, any captured group should contain about the same $\dfrac{\text{marked beans}}{\text{total beans captured}}$ ratio as the entire population.

A statement that two ratios are equal is called a **proportion**.

Complete the proportion below by comparing the ratio of marked beans to total beans captured for the second captured group and the ratio of marked beans to total beans for the whole population.

$$\frac{\text{marked beans (in second captured group)}}{\text{total beans captured (in second captured group)}} = \frac{\text{marked beans (in whole population)}}{\text{total beans (in whole population)}}$$

$$\frac{?}{?} = \frac{?}{p}$$

When values of quantities are unknown, **variables** can be used to represent their values. Notice that the variable $p$ is used to represent the total number of beans in the whole population because that number is unknown.

**8.** To estimate the total number of beans in the container, solve your proportion.

**9.** Repeat Questions 3–8 to find a second estimate of the bean population. Is the result similar to your first estimate?

**Recall**

To solve proportions, use cross products and Properties of Equality. For example,

Original equation $\dfrac{x}{8} = \dfrac{3}{4}$

Find the cross products. $\quad 4(x) = 3(8)$

Simplify. $\quad 4x = 24$

Divide each side by 4. $\quad \dfrac{4x}{4} = \dfrac{24}{4}$

Simplify. $\quad x = 6$

**Practice** for Lesson 1.1

Solve each proportion. If necessary, round any decimal answers to the nearest tenth.

1. $\dfrac{15}{y} = \dfrac{5}{6}$     2. $\dfrac{c}{12} = \dfrac{2}{7}$

3. $\dfrac{10}{2.8} = \dfrac{a}{4.2}$     4. $\dfrac{3}{4} = \dfrac{7}{n}$

5. $\dfrac{x}{2} = \dfrac{15}{6}$     6. $\dfrac{7.1}{3} = \dfrac{t}{2}$

7. Suppose a similar *capture-recapture* procedure is used to find the number of horses in a large grassland. Twenty horses are captured and marked. Then they are released into the grassland. After a week, 80 horses are captured. Five of those horses are found to be marked.

   a. Write a proportion that models this situation.
   b. Use your proportion to estimate the population of horses in this region.

ANIMAL POPULATIONS   **Lesson 1.1**   5

**Practice for Lesson 1.1 Answers**

1. 18
2. $\dfrac{24}{7}$ or $3\dfrac{3}{7}$
3. 15
4. $9\dfrac{1}{3}$
5. 5
6. 4.7
7a. $\dfrac{5}{80} = \dfrac{20}{n}$
7b. 320 horses

**COMMON ERROR**

**Exercise 7** If students incorrectly write the order of the quantities in their proportion, suggest that they state the units aloud. For example,

$$\dfrac{\text{marked in captured group}}{\text{total number in captured group}} = \dfrac{\text{marked in total population}}{\text{total number in total population}}$$

## Lesson Objectives

- use proportions to model real-world situations.
- solve problems that involve scale drawings.
- solve problems that involve similar polygons.

## Vocabulary

- congruent
- polygon
- scale
- scale factor
- sides
- similar figures
- similar polygons
- vertex

## Description

In this lesson students explore writing proportions to solve problems. Special attention is given to writing and solving proportions for scale models, drawings, and maps. Solving for an unknown side in similar polygons is also investigated.

> **TEACHING TIP**
>
> Guide students as they work through each of the three examples. Use the following additional examples as extra in-class practice.

## ADDITIONAL EXAMPLE

Walking at a fast pace burns 5.6 Calories per minute. How many minutes of walking at a fast pace are needed to burn the 500 Calories consumed by eating a dish of ice cream? about 89 minutes

---

| Lesson 1.2 | **Proportions as Models** |

As you saw in the previous lesson, proportions can be used as mathematical models to help estimate animal populations. In this lesson, you will explore how proportions can be used to model a variety of other real-world situations.

### WRITING AND SOLVING PROPORTIONS

When you write a proportion to represent a given situation, be sure that the quantities in each ratio are written in the same order. For example, you know that there are 12 inches in 1 foot and there are 36 inches in 3 feet. You can write a proportion to model how these quantities are related.

$$\text{inches} \rightarrow \quad \frac{12 \text{ inches}}{1 \text{ foot}} = \frac{36 \text{ inches}}{3 \text{ feet}} \quad \leftarrow \text{ inches}$$
$$\text{feet} \rightarrow \qquad\qquad\qquad\qquad\qquad \leftarrow \text{ feet}$$

Notice that because the ratio on the left is expressed as "inches to feet," the ratio on the right must also be expressed as "inches to feet."

### EXAMPLE 1

According to the American Automobile Association (AAA), the overall cost of owning and operating a passenger vehicle averages $7,834 based on 15,000 miles of driving. If the cost per mile is constant, about what would it cost to drive 12,000 miles?

**Solution:**

Let $c$ represent the cost of driving 12,000 miles.

Write a proportion for the problem.

$$\text{average cost} \rightarrow \quad \frac{\$7,834}{15,000} = \frac{c}{12,000} \quad \leftarrow \text{ average cost}$$
$$\text{number of miles} \rightarrow \qquad\qquad\qquad\qquad \leftarrow \text{ number of miles}$$

Solve for $c$.

| | |
|---|---|
| Original equation | $\dfrac{7,834}{15,000} = \dfrac{c}{12,000}$ |
| Find the cross products. | $15,000c = (7,834)(12,000)$ |
| Simplify. | $15,000c = 94,008,000$ |
| Divide each side by 15,000. | $\dfrac{15,000c}{15,000} = \dfrac{94,008,000}{15,000}$ |
| Simplify. | $c = 6,267.20$ |

So, the average cost of driving 12,000 miles is about $6,267.

---

> **TEACHING TIP**
>
> Vocabulary organizers, such as the one below, are particularly helpful for this chapter.

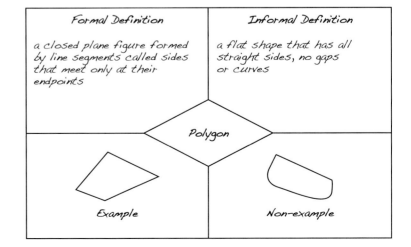

## SCALE DRAWINGS

Scale drawings are used in many types of design work to accurately model the shapes of objects. A **scale** is a ratio that compares the size of a model to the actual size of an object. Scales are often found on drawings, maps, and models.

### E X A M P L E ②

A typical scale for a house plan is $\frac{1}{4}$ inch to 1 foot. If the width of a room on such a plan measures $3\frac{1}{2}$ inches, what is the actual width of the room?

**Solution:**

Let $w$ represent the actual width of the room.

Write a proportion to model the situation.

$$\begin{array}{ll} \text{drawing (in.)} & \to & \dfrac{1}{4} \quad 3\dfrac{1}{2} & \leftarrow & \text{drawing (in.)} \\ \text{actual room (ft)} & \to & 1 \quad\;\; w & \leftarrow & \text{actual room (ft)} \end{array}$$

Solve for $w$.

| | |
|---|---|
| Original equation | $\dfrac{\frac{1}{4}}{1} = \dfrac{3\frac{1}{2}}{w}$ |
| Find the cross products. | $\dfrac{1}{4}w = 3\dfrac{1}{2}(1)$ |
| Multiply each side by 4. | $(4)\dfrac{1}{4}w = (4)\left(3\dfrac{1}{2}\right)$ |
| Simplify. | $w = 14$ |

So, the width of the room is 14 feet.

## SIMILAR POLYGONS

Two figures that have the same shape, but not necessarily the same size, are said to be **similar**.

> Two polygons are **similar polygons** if their corresponding angles are equal in measure and the lengths of their corresponding sides are proportional.

**Recall**

A **polygon** is a closed plane figure formed by line segments called **sides** that meet only at their endpoints. Each point where the sides meet is called a **vertex**.

## ADDITIONAL EXAMPLE ②

A plan for an office building uses a scale of $\frac{1}{16}$ inch to 1 foot. How long would a 35-foot wall appear on the plan? $2\frac{3}{16}$ in.

### TEACHING TIP

When a scale is written as a ratio, it usually takes this form:

$$\text{scale} = \frac{\text{dimensions of model}}{\text{dimensions of actual object}}$$

### CONNECTION

Bring to class an item that shows a scale (map, blueprint, model car, etc.) or suggest that students share items they might have.

## ADDITIONAL EXAMPLE ❸

Given: $ABCDE \sim RSTUV$. Find the value of $x$. 5 in.

It is also the case that if two polygons are similar, then you know that the corresponding angles are congruent and the corresponding sides are proportional.

If two polygons are similar, the ratio of the lengths of two corresponding sides is called the **scale factor**.

**Recall**

**Congruent** figures have the same size and shape.

**Recall**

When similar polygons are named, the corresponding vertices are listed in the same order.

## E X A M P L E ❸

Given: $ABCD \sim KLMN$

a. What is the scale factor of $ABCD$ to $KLMN$?

b. Find the value of $x$.

**Solution:**

a. $\overline{AB}$ and $\overline{KL}$ are corresponding sides of the two quadrilaterals. So, the scale factor is $\dfrac{AB}{KL} = \dfrac{4}{6} = \dfrac{2}{3}$.

b. Since the polygons are similar, you know the following:

$\angle A \cong \angle K$, $\angle B \cong \angle L$, $\angle C \cong \angle M$, and $\angle D \cong \angle N$.

Also, $\dfrac{AB}{KL} = \dfrac{BC}{LM} = \dfrac{CD}{MN} = \dfrac{DA}{NK}$.

To find the value of $x$, write a proportion and solve.

| | |
|---|---|
| Corresponding sides of similar polygons are proportional. | $\dfrac{AB}{KL} = \dfrac{BC}{LM}$ |
| $AB = 4$, $BC = 5$, $KL = 6$, $LM = x$ | $\dfrac{4}{6} = \dfrac{5}{x}$ |
| Find the cross products. | $4x = (5)(6)$ |
| Simplify. | $4x = 30$ |
| Divide each side by 4. | $\dfrac{4x}{4} = \dfrac{30}{4}$ |
| Simplify. | $x = 7.5$ |

**Practice for Lesson 1.2**

For Exercises 1–3, choose the correct answer.

1. Which proportion *cannot* be used to solve the following problem?

   How many milligrams (mg) of medication should you give to a 120-pound person if you should give 50 mg for every 10 pounds?

   **A.** $\dfrac{50 \text{ mg}}{10 \text{ lb}} = \dfrac{x}{120 \text{ lb}}$ 　　　　**B.** $\dfrac{10 \text{ lb}}{50 \text{ mg}} = \dfrac{120 \text{ lb}}{x}$

   **C.** $\dfrac{50 \text{ mg}}{x} = \dfrac{120 \text{ lb}}{10 \text{ lb}}$ 　　　　**D.** $\dfrac{10 \text{ lb}}{120 \text{ lb}} = \dfrac{50 \text{ mg}}{x}$

2. Triangles *ABC* and *XYZ* are similar. Which statement is *not* true?

   **A.** $\dfrac{AB}{XY} = \dfrac{BC}{YZ}$ 　　　　**B.** $\dfrac{XZ}{AC} = \dfrac{YZ}{BC}$

   **C.** $\dfrac{CB}{ZY} = \dfrac{AC}{XZ}$ 　　　　**D.** $\dfrac{XY}{AB} = \dfrac{ZY}{CA}$

3. *ABCD* is a rectangle.

   Which set of dimensions produces a rectangle that is similar to rectangle *ABCD*?

   **A.** 36.4 mm, 11 mm 　　　　**B.** 44 mm, 9.1 mm
   **C.** 176 mm, 72.8 mm 　　　　**D.** 91 mm, 66 mm

4. If your new car goes 320 miles on 10 gallons of gas, how far will it go on 6 gallons of gas?

5. The Tannery Mall in Massachusetts is partially powered by an array of 375 solar panels. They produce 60 kilowatts of electrical power. How many panels would be needed to produce 84 kilowatts of power?

## Practice for Lesson 1.2 Answers

1. C
2. D
3. C
4. 192 miles
5. 525 panels

**6.** 87.5 acres

**7.** 31.5 inches

**8.** 18 miles

**9.** 1.25 inches

**10a.** $\dfrac{3}{1.5}$ or $\dfrac{2}{1}$

**10b.** 2 cm

**11.** 1.2 m

**6.** An airplane sprays 16 gallons of liquid fertilizer on 5 acres of crops. If the plane's tank can hold 280 gallons, how many acres of crops can be sprayed?

**7.** Most conventional TV screens have a width : height ratio of 4 : 3. If a screen has a width of 42 inches, what is its height?

**8.** The scale on a map is 1 inch : 6 miles. Find the actual length of a road if it is 3 inches long on the map.

**9.** A drawing's scale is 0.5 inch : 20 feet. If a banquet room's length is 50 feet, what is the length of the room in the drawing?

**10.** Given: $\triangle ABC \sim \triangle RST$

**a.** What is the scale factor of triangle $ABC$ to triangle $RST$?

**b.** Find the value of $x$.

**11.** Trapezoid $PQRS$ is similar to trapezoid $KLMN$. Find the value of $x$.

12. The ratio of the corresponding sides of two similar rectangles is 4 : 9. The length of the smaller rectangle is 16 cm and its width is 12 cm. What is the perimeter of the larger rectangle?

13. Suppose that $a$, $b$, $c$, and $d$ represent four numbers that form the proportion $\frac{a}{b} = \frac{c}{d}$. If $a$ is doubled while $b$ remains the same, how would $c$ or $d$ have to change for the proportion to stay true?

12. 126 cm
13. Sample answer: $c$ could be doubled; $d$ could be divided by 2.

# LESSON 1.3

## Lesson Objective

- solve problems that require previously learned concepts and skills.

## Exercise Reference

## Lesson 1.3
## R.A.P. Answers

1. ratio
2. proportion
3. B
4. D
5. $6\frac{3}{8}$
6. $1\frac{19}{40}$
7. $3\frac{7}{8}$
8. $\frac{1}{18}$
9. 12
10. 16
11. 0
12. 44
13. 10
14. $-2$
15. $-6$
16. 12
17. $-112$
18. 3
19. $-16$
20. $-8$
21. Distributive Property
22. Identity Property of Addition
23. 8
24. 72
25. 10

---

**Fill in the blank.**

1. A comparison of two numbers by division is called a(n) _____.

2. A statement that two ratios are equal is called a(n) _____.

**Choose the correct answer.**

3. Which ratio is equivalent to $\frac{3}{4}$?

   A. $\frac{4}{3}$    B. $\frac{6}{8}$    C. $\frac{6}{4}$    D. $\frac{3}{8}$

4. Which expression is equivalent to $3(5x - 6)$?

   A. $15x - 6$    B. $18x - 15$    C. $15x + 30$    D. $15x - 18$

**Add or subtract. Write your answer in simplest form.**

5. $3\frac{1}{2} + 2\frac{7}{8}$      6. $\frac{3}{5} + \frac{7}{8}$

7. $6\frac{1}{8} - 2\frac{1}{4}$      8. $\frac{1}{2} - \frac{4}{9}$

**Evaluate the expression.**

9. $10 + 8 \div 4$      10. $(2 + 18) \div 5 + 12$

11. $(8 - 3)^2 - 100 \div 4$      12. $71 - 24 + (-3)$

13. $|-8| + 2$      14. $-|-2|$

**Add, subtract, multiply, or divide.**

15. $17 + (-23)$      16. $-5 - (-17)$

17. $14(-8)$      18. $-18 \div (-6)$

19. $5 + (-3) - 18$      20. $4(-6) + 2(8)$

**Identify the property illustrated in each equation.**

21. $5(3 + x) = 15 + 5x$

22. $11 + 0 = 11$

**Solve.**

23. $2x + 7 = 23$      24. $\frac{2n}{3} = 48$      25. $18 = 5t - 32$

**Solve the proportion.**

**26.** $\dfrac{6}{n} = \dfrac{18}{33}$     **27.** $\dfrac{20}{8} = \dfrac{x}{16}$

**28.** $\dfrac{a}{7.2} = \dfrac{1.8}{5.4}$     **29.** $\dfrac{6}{4} = \dfrac{8}{y}$

**30.** There are 8 males and 14 females in the school choir.
  **a.** Write the ratio of the number of males to the number of females.
  **b.** Write the ratio of the number of females to the total number of students in the choir.

**31.** Animal biologists wanted to estimate the deer population in a large wildlife area. Initially, 15 deer were captured and tagged. Then the tagged deer were returned to the area. After a week, 60 deer were observed by the biologist. Four of those deer were found to be tagged. About how many deer were in the region?

**32.** If 50 milliliters of water are used for 100 grams of plaster to make a dental model, how much water should be used for 150 grams of plaster?

**33.** Rectangle *KLMN* is similar to rectangle *RSTU*. Find the value of *x*.

26. 11
27. 40
28. 2.4
29. $5\dfrac{1}{3}$
30a. $\dfrac{8}{14} = \dfrac{4}{7}$
30b. $\dfrac{14}{22} = \dfrac{7}{11}$
31. 225 deer
32. 75 ml
33. 4.8 m

# LESSON 1.4

**5e** Explore

## Lesson Objective

- use multiple representations to model real-world situations.

## Vocabulary

## Materials List

## Description

This lesson is designed as a whole class/small group investigation (2–4 students). Have students read the information about finding patterns. Then, as a class, discuss the graph in the Example. Review the parts of graphs as needed so that students will recognize that the scale on the vertical axis is missing. Also discuss the two variables shown on the graph. Point out the pattern and other features of the graph that provide the information needed to answer the question.

In groups, have students read through the three questions that they need to answer for each of the four situations on page 15.

Once all groups have completed the Investigation, discuss their results for **Questions 1–4** by talking about why they chose a particular graph and discounted others. Pay particular attention to the identification of the two variables in each situation. Ask how they know which variable is on the horizontal axis and which is on the vertical axis.

## Wrapping Up the Investigation:

Point out that they have seen two different types of models in this lesson, graphs and tables. Ask students why they think that graphs are often used as models. Reinforce that graphs are used to provide visual models of situations and that patterns often become apparent when information is shown in a graph or table.

---

When a mathematical model and a real-world situation are well matched, the information obtained from the model is meaningful in the real-world situation. In this lesson, you will explore several situations and the graphs and tables that model them.

### FINDING PATTERNS

When developing a model, modelers often look for patterns in the real world. Frequently these patterns involve numbers. Describing these patterns mathematically helps produce useful information.

Among the simplest patterns are those that relate one real-world quantity to another. Sometimes these patterns are more obvious if they are shown on a graph.

### E X A M P L E

Does the line graph below show hourly daytime temperatures (8:00 a.m. – 7:00 p.m.) or hourly nighttime temperatures (8:00 p.m. – 7:00 a.m.)? Explain.

**Hourly Temperatures-Dallas, TX January 30, 2012**

**Solution:**

Even though the graph does not give you the exact temperatures, the pattern of the graph is apparent at a glance. The graph shows that the temperatures rise, and then fall. Since daytime temperatures usually increase around midday, and are followed by a drop in temperature in the evening, it is likely that this graph shows daytime temperatures (8:00 a.m. – 7:00 p.m.).

**14**   Chapter 1   MATHEMATICAL MODELING

---

## ADDITIONAL EXAMPLE

Describe the situation that might be modeled by the line graph.

**Daily High Temperatures—Deviations from Normal January 2012**

A sample answer for the Additional Example can be found on page 15.

For Questions 1–4, a context and a figure showing three graphs are given. After discussing the context with a partner or group, answer the following questions:

 **i.** Which graph, *a*, *b*, or *c*, best models the given situation?
 **ii.** What features made you choose that particular graph? What features made you discount the other graphs?
 **iii.** What are the two quantities or variables in the given situation?

**1.** the height of a person over his or her lifetime

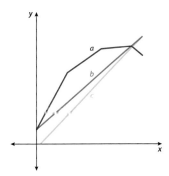

**2.** the circumference of a circle as its radius changes

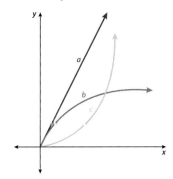

**3.** the height of a ball as it is thrown in the air

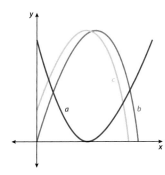

**4.** the daily average low temperature in degrees Fahrenheit over the course of one year in Fairbanks, Alaska

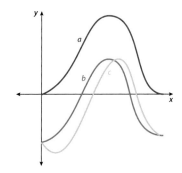

## ADDITIONAL EXAMPLE

Sample answer: The temperatures during the first week in January were below normal. During the second week of the month, temperatures were above normal until the last day of the week. The high temperature on Day 6 was the closest to normal. Overall, temperatures for about half the days were below normal and half were above normal.

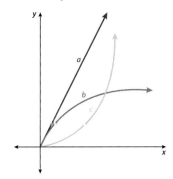

## Lesson 1.4 Investigation Answers

**1** **i.** Graph *a*
  **ii.** Sample answer: A person's growth slows with age and might even decrease as shown in graph *a*.
  **iii.** height, time, or age

**2** **i.** Graph *a*
  **ii.** Sample answer: The circumference of a circle increases at a constant rate as the radius increases.
  **iii.** radius, circumference

> **TEACHING TIP**
>
> Since time is not specifically mentioned in **Question 3**, students may have difficulty determining that time is the second variable. If that is the case, toss an object into the air and have the student describe in words what happened.

**3** **i.** Graph *c*
  **ii.** Sample answer: The ball is thrown upward, so graph *a* is not correct, and it is thrown from a location above the ground, so graph *b* is not correct.
  **iii.** height, time

**4** **i.** Graph *c*
  **ii.** Sample answer: Temperatures in January in Fairbanks will probably be below zero, so graph *a* is not correct. It is unlikely that all January and February temperatures will be warmer than the temperature on January 1, so graph *b* is not correct.
  **iii.** time, temperature

# LESSON 1.4

**5.** Sample answer: Table 1 best describes the growth of a plant. As time increases, the height of the plant should increase, not decrease as shown in Table 2.

## Practice for Lesson 1.4 Answers

1. Sample answers: Important features include: when the graph is increasing and when it is decreasing, whether the graph goes through the origin, and whether it ever has negative values.
2. Sample answers: In Question 1, people eventually die; in Question 3, the ball hits the ground and no longer moves; and in Question 4, a specific time frame was given in the situation.
3. In Question 4, temperature can be negative.
4a. Graph *c*

---

> **TEACHING TIP**
>
> **Exercise 4** If students have difficulty determining which graph best represents the growing mold, have them examine each graph individually and discuss what that graph would indicate. For example, Graph *b* would indicate that the mold grew very slowly for a while. Then the amount of mold would decrease slowly and then more rapidly.

---

**5.** Which of the tables below better models the height of a kudzu plant over time? Explain.

| Table 1 | |
|---|---|
| Time (days) | Height (cm) |
| 0 | 0 |
| 4 | 3 |
| 8 | 6 |
| 12 | 9 |
| 16 | 12 |

| Table 2 | |
|---|---|
| Time (days) | Height (cm) |
| 0 | 12 |
| 4 | 9 |
| 8 | 6 |
| 12 | 3 |
| 16 | 0 |

## Practice for Lesson 1.4

1. Examine the graphs in Questions 1–4 of the Investigation. List some of the important features of the graphs that helped you choose the one that best modeled the given situation.
2. In Question 2, arrows were drawn on the ends of the graphs to show that the graphs continue indefinitely. Explain why arrows were not always used in Questions 1, 3, and 4.
3. In Questions 1–4, you identified the variables. For which of those situations does it make sense for either of the variables to have a negative value? Explain.
4. Consider the relationship between the amount of observable mold on a piece of bread and the time from when it was baked until several months later.
   a. Which graph, *a*, *b*, or *c*, best models the given situation?

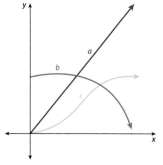

**16**    **Chapter 1**    MATHEMATICAL MODELING

b. What features made you choose that graph, and what features made you discount the other graphs?

c. What are the two quantities or variables in the given situation?

5. Water is pumped from a plastic cylinder at a constant rate. Which representation shown below, *words, graph,* or *table,* best models this situation? Explain.

| Words | Graph | Table |
|---|---|---|

**Words**

The height of the water decreases for a few minutes, stays at the same height for a while, then increases again.

**Graph**

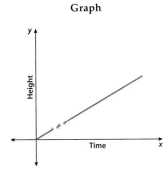

**Table**

| Time (min) | Height (in.) |
|---|---|
| 0 | 18 |
| 1 | 14 |
| 2 | 10 |
| 3 | 6 |
| 4 | 2 |
| 5 | 0 |

**4b.** Sample answer: The mold grows rapidly at first then slows down as it covers the bread. So, only graph *c* can be correct.

**4c.** time, amount of mold

**5.** The table best describes the situation because the height of the water will decrease until there is no water left in the container.

## Materials List

• magazines and newspapers

## Description

This project is designed to reinforce the idea that there are multiple ways to represent real-world situations. In this case, students are looking for and making connections between words and tables or graphs.

Students are asked to look through magazines and newspapers for models in the form of tables or graphs. Once they find a graph or table of interest, they are to write about how their particular representation reflects what the article is trying to say.

Once the projects are complete, you may want to have students share what they found with the entire class. This project works best when students work individually.

## Sample Answer

Answers will vary depending on the articles chosen.

---

## A Picture Is Worth a Thousand Words

Look through magazines and newspapers for articles that contain tables and/or graphs. Once you have found a table or graph of interest, look at the article to see how the table or graph represents the ideas in the article.

Then write a short explanation about how a particular graph or table represents or is connected to the words in the article. Bring both a copy of your article and your written explanation to class.

# Chapter 1 Review

## You Should Be Able to:

### Lesson 1.1

- use ratios and proportions to create mathematical models.
- use mathematical models to estimate the sizes of populations.
- solve proportions.

- solve problems that involve scale drawings.
- solve problems that involve similar polygons.

### Lesson 1.3

- solve problems that require previously learned concepts and skills.

### Lesson 1.2

- use proportions to model real-world situations.

### Lesson 1.4

- use multiple representations to model real-world situations.

## Key Vocabulary

mathematical modeling (p. 2)

mathematical models (p. 2)

ratio (p. 3)

proportion (p. 4)

variable (p. 4)

scale (p. 7)

similar figures (p. 7)

similar polygons (p. 7)

polygon (p. 7)

sides (p. 7)

vertex (p. 7)

congruent (p. 8)

scale factor (p. 8)

## Chapter 1 Test Review

**Fill in the blank.**

1. A(n) _____ is the comparison of two numbers by division.

2. If two figures have the same shape and size, then they are _____.

3. A statement that two ratios are equal is called a(n) _____.

**Solve each proportion.**

4. $\dfrac{8}{x} = \dfrac{2}{3}$

5. $\dfrac{n}{0.3} = \dfrac{9}{0.6}$

6. $\dfrac{5}{3} = \dfrac{11}{a}$

## Chapter 1 Test Review Answers

1. ratio
2. congruent
3. proportion
4. 12
5. 4.5
6. $6\dfrac{3}{5}$

# CHAPTER REVIEW

**7a.** $\dfrac{7}{56} = \dfrac{42}{p}$

**7b.** 336 turtles

**8.** $16.20

**9.** 360 ft

**10.** 65 mm

**11.** about 6.2 cm

**12a.** $\dfrac{5}{3}$

**12b.** $11\dfrac{2}{3}$

**13.** Sample answer: Most likely the times shown on the graph are 5:00 a.m. to 3:00 p.m. as traffic is slowed during the rush hours in the early morning.

---

**7.** The *capture-recapture* method is used to find the number of turtles in a small stream. Forty-two turtles are captured. Their shells are marked with green paint. Then the turtles are released back into the stream. Later in the summer, 56 turtles are captured. Of those captured, 7 had green paint on their shells.

  **a.** Write a proportion that models this situation.
  **b.** About how many turtles are in the stream?

**8.** If 18 greeting cards cost $24.30, what is the cost of 12 cards?

**9.** The floor plan for an office building has a scale of $\frac{1}{8}$ in. = 1 ft. If the length of the main hallway measures 45 inches on the drawing, how long is the actual hallway?

**10.** The ratio of the corresponding sides of two similar triangles is 2 : 5. The sides of the smaller triangle are 6 mm, 8 mm, and 12 mm. What is the perimeter of the larger triangle?

**11.** A computer image-processing program can be used to change the size of a digital photograph. If a 4.0 cm × 5.5 cm photo is enlarged so that its length is 8.5 cm, what is its new width?

**12.** *ABCDE ~ LMNOP*

  **a.** What is the scale factor of *ABCDE* to *LMNOP*?

  **b.** Find the value of $x$.

**13.** The graph below shows the average speed of vehicles on a freeway of a large city at specific times of day.

Does the graph show times from 5:00 a.m. to 3:00 p.m. or from 10 a.m. to 8 p.m.? Explain.

---

#2: Incorrect ✓

#3: Incorrect ✓

#7A: ✓ Incorrect. Doesn't deal ✓ with unknown variable of total population of turtles in stream.

7b: ✓ Correct answer for weaqe answer. Also, answer lacks units.

8: ✓ Proportion and final ✓ answer lacks units. Correct

#9: ✓ Proportion lacks units. Correct.

#10: "p = ..." (correct)

#11: ✓ Proportion lacks units. ✓ Final answer is not simplified.

12b: ✓ Careless error. Find and ✓ correct.

13: ✓ Good answer. Improve with "rely in the moving day rush hour."

# Chapter 2
## Direct Variation

## Mathematical Overview

Proportional relationships are introduced by having students conduct an Activity and an Investigation that relate stretch to weight using bungee jumping simulations. Students learn that an equation of the form $y = kx$, where $k$ is the constant of proportionality, represents a direct variation function and that all graphs of direct variation functions are straight lines that pass through the origin. Students look for patterns in their data that can be described by the equation $y = kx$. They also use their equations to find unique output values for possible input values. The connection between $k$ and the slope of the graph of their function is made. Students use the formula $\frac{\Delta y}{\Delta x} = \frac{y_2 - y_1}{x_2 - x_1}$ to calculate the slope of a line that passes through any two points $P_1(x_1, y_1)$ and $P_2(x_2, y_2)$ on a coordinate grid. One other type of variation, inverse variation, of the form $y = \frac{k}{x}$, is presented in the Extension to this chapter.

## Lesson Summaries

### Lesson 2.1    Activity: Bungee Jumping

In this Activity, student groups use an empty can, large paper clips, and a rubber band to simulate the testing of a bungee jump cord. Students first measure and record the weight of an object, put the object in the can, then measure and record the height of the bottom of the can. As students continue adding identical objects to the can and recording weights and heights in their tables, they create a set of data that they use to make a scatter plot. From their plot they identify a pattern and use that pattern to predict what might happen if they continued to add objects to the can. This data table and scatter plot will be used again in Lesson 2.2.

### Lesson 2.2    Investigation: Proportional Relationships

During the Activity in Lesson 2.1, students collected data and created tables of the data. In this lesson, students extend their tables to include a column of "stretch-to-weight ratios." They then use the ratios to find an equation that models the relationship between the weight on the rubber band and how much the band stretches. As students progress through this Investigation, they come to understand how the value of $k$, the constant of proportionality, is related to the points they plotted in their scatter plot and are able to write an equation relating stretch to weight. They also use their equation to predict the length of stretch for a weight they did not test.

### Lesson 2.3    Direct Variation Functions

In this lesson, students learn to recognize direct proportion relationships, and how to write equations that express direct variation. Students explore a context in which a regulating line is used to estimate the dimensions of similar rectangles. Students are given tables of data and asked to determine if one variable is directly proportional to the other variable. They also write equations that model direct variation functions and use their equations to make predictions.

### Lesson 2.4    R.A.P.

In this lesson, students **R**eview **A**nd **P**ractice solving problems that require the use of skills and concepts taught in previous math levels. The skills reviewed in this lesson are skills that are needed as a basis for solving problems throughout this course.

### Lesson 2.5    Slope

In this lesson, students learn that the slope (ratio of the rise to the run) of a line is a measure of its steepness. They also calculate the slope of a line and interpret it as a rate of change. A connection is made between the value of the constant of proportionality $k$ and the slope of the graph of a function. Students conclude that the slope of a line is a constant and use a formula to calculate the slope of a line that passes through any two points on a coordinate grid. They also interpret the meaning of slope for real-world relationships.

### Chapter 2    Extension: Inverse Variation

In this Extension, students turn paper towel tubes into "telescopes." They use their "telescopes" to collect data on the diameter of the viewing circle and the length of the telescope. They describe the pattern they see in their data and learn that the variables vary inversely. This type of relationship is called an inverse variation and can be represented by an equation of the form $y = \frac{k}{x}$.

## Lesson Guide

| Lesson/Objectives | Materials | |
|---|---|---|
| **Chapter 2 Opener: How Is Mathematics Related to Bungee Jumping?**<br>• recognize that safety in bungee jumping depends on a knowledge of mathematics. | | |
| **2.1 Activity: Bungee Jumping**<br>• collect experimental data.<br>• make a scatter plot of experimental data. | *Per group:*<br>• ruler<br>• stand with hook, or other means of hanging the rubber band<br>• long rubber bands* ($7'' \times \frac{1}{8}''$)<br>• metal can such as a soup can with two small holes punched in it<br>• 2 jumbo paper clips<br>• 6 identical objects such as "C" batteries, each weighing about 2 to 3 ounces<br>• scale for measuring weight in ounces, accurate to 0.1 ounce<br>* If long rubber bands are not available, a chain of three or four shorter $\left(3\frac{1}{2}'' \times \frac{1}{4}''\right)$ rubber bands can be used. | *Optional:*<br>• nail and hammer<br>• TRM table shell for Question 4.<br>• TRM table shell for Exercise 5.<br>• grid paper |
| **2.2 Investigation: Proportional Relationships**<br>• identify proportional relationships.<br>• identify independent and dependent variables.<br>• find a constant of proportionality.<br>• write an equation that expresses a proportional relationship. | *Per student:*<br>• students' tables and scatter plots from the Activity in Lesson 2.1 | *Optional:*<br>• TRM table shell for Question 2<br>• grid paper |
| **2.3 Direct Variation Functions**<br>• identify direct variation.<br>• write direct variation equations. | | *Optional:*<br>• TRM table shell for Exercise 4.<br>• grid paper |
| **2.4 R.A.P.**<br>• solve problems that require previously learned concepts and skills. | | *Optional:*<br>• grid paper |
| **2.5 Slope**<br>• find the slope of a line given rise and run.<br>• find the slope of a line given two points on the line.<br>• interpret the slope of a line as a rate of change. | | *Optional:*<br>• grid paper |
| **Chapter 2 Extension: Inverse Variation**<br>• use inverse variation to model experimental data. | *Per group:*<br>• 3 paper towel tubes<br>• masking tape<br>• meter stick<br>• tape measure<br>• scissors | *Optional:*<br>• TRM table shell for Question 1.<br>• grid paper |

## Pacing Guide

| | Day 1 | Day 2 | Day 3 | Day 4 | Day 5 | Day 6 | Day 7 | Day 8 |
|---|---|---|---|---|---|---|---|---|
| **Basic** | p. 22, 2.1 | 2.1, 2.2 | 2.2, 2.3 | 2.3, 2.4 | 2.5 | project | review | |
| **Standard** | p. 22, 2.1 | 2.1, 2.2 | 2.2, 2.3 | 2.3, 2.4 | 2.5 | project | review | extension |
| **Block** | p. 22, 2.1 | 2.2, 2.3 | 2.3, 2.4 | 2.5, project | review, extension | | | |

### Supplement Support

See the Book Companion Website at www.highschool.bfwpub.com/ModelingwithMathematics and the Teacher's Resource Materials (TRM) for additional resources.

CHAPTER

# 2

# Direct Variation

## CONTENTS

## Lesson Objective

- recognize that safety in bungee jumping depends on a knowledge of mathematics.

## Vocabulary

## Description

This reading helps students see that mathematics can be involved in the design and coordination of safe recreational activities.

### TEACHING TIP

After students have read the Chapter Opener, ask the class if they are familiar with the sport of bungee jumping, and whether they know anyone who has done a bungee jump. Also have them discuss what kind of knowledge might have helped prevent the disaster mentioned in the reading.

## How Is Mathematics Related to Bungee Jumping?

A bungee cord is an elastic cord that can be used to secure objects without tying knots. Specialized bungee cords are used in the sport of bungee jumping. One end of the cord is attached to a bridge or tower, and the other end is attached to the jumper. As the jumper falls, the cord stretches and slows the fall. At the bottom of the jump, the cord recoils and the jumper bounces up and down at the end of the cord.

The strength of the cord used for a bungee jump must be accurately known. The cord must be adjusted for the height of the jump and for the weight of the jumper. Otherwise, the consequences can be disastrous. In one well-publicized case, a woman died practicing for a bungee jump exhibition for the 1997 Super Bowl halftime show. The bungee cord was supposed to stop her 100-foot fall just above the floor of the Superdome in New Orleans. At the time, officials were quoted in *The Boston Globe* as saying:

> Apparently, she made an earlier jump and didn't come as close as they wanted. They made some adjustments, and somebody made a miscalculation. I think it was human error.
>
> Bungee safety is a product of simple mathematics that factors height and weight in its calculations. It's so predictable.

Ratios can be used to model bungee jumping. Knowing how much the cord stretches for different jumper weights can help ensure that bungee jumps are safe.

Constructing a mathematical model to describe a relationship between two variables often begins with collecting data and recording the values in a table. The data can then be graphed with a scatter plot.

A bungee cord is *elastic*, meaning that it can be stretched and then returned to its original length. You can use a large rubber band to simulate a bungee cord.

1. Start with an empty can, such as a soup can, that has two small holes punched opposite each other near the rim. Insert the end of a large opened paper clip in each of the holes. Insert a large rubber band through the free ends of the clips so that the can hangs from the rubber band.

2. Hang the rubber band so that the bottom of the can is at least 6 inches above a flat desk, a table, or the floor. Use a ruler to measure the height of the bottom of the can to the nearest $\frac{1}{8}$ inch.

3. Find the weight (in ounces) of one of the identical objects provided.

4. Make a table like the one shown here. Leave the last column blank for use in Lesson 2.2. Record the height of the bottom of the can above the flat surface.

| Total Weight (ounces) | Height (inches) | Total Length of Stretch (inches) | |
|---|---|---|---|
| 0 | | 0 | |
| | | | |
| | | | |
| | | | |
| | | | |
| | | | |
| | | | |

5. Then place one object in the can. Record the weight of the object in the can and the new height of the bottom of the can.

6. Continue adding weight, one object at a time, until 6 objects are in the can. After each object is added, record the total weight of the objects in the can and the height of the bottom of the can.

## Lesson 2.1 Activity Answers

1. Check students' set ups.
2. Sample answer: $8\frac{1}{2}$ inches
3. Sample answer: 2.3 ounces (size C battery)
4–7. See sample table to the right.

| Total Weight (ounces) | Height (inches) | Total Length of Stretch (inches) |
|---|---|---|
| 0 | $8\frac{1}{2}$ | 0 |
| 2.3 | 8 | $\frac{1}{2}$ |
| 4.6 | $7\frac{5}{8}$ | $\frac{7}{8}$ |
| 6.9 | $7\frac{1}{4}$ | $1\frac{1}{4}$ |
| 9.2 | $6\frac{3}{4}$ | $1\frac{3}{4}$ |
| 11.5 | $6\frac{1}{4}$ | $2\frac{1}{4}$ |
| 13.8 | $5\frac{3}{4}$ | $2\frac{3}{4}$ |

**5e**   Engage

## Lesson Objectives
- collect experimental data.
- make a scatter plot of experimental data.

## Vocabulary

## Materials List

*Per group:*
- ruler
- stand with hook, or other means of hanging the rubber band
- long rubber bands* ($7'' \times \frac{1}{8}''$)
- metal can such as a soup can with two small holes punched in it
- 2 jumbo paper clips
- 6 identical objects such as "C" batteries, each weighing about 2 to 3 ounces
- scale for measuring weight in ounces, accurate to 0.1 ounce

\* If long rubber bands are not available, a chain of three or four shorter ($3\frac{1}{2}'' \times \frac{1}{4}''$) rubber bands can be used.

## Description

*Preparation:*

Have students work in groups of 2 to 4. Make sure that students suspend their rubber band in such a way that they can use a ruler to measure the stretch of the rubber band. Stands and scales may be available from a science lab. Another possibility is hanging the rubber band from a doorknob. A nail and hammer can be used to punch two small holes on opposite sides near the top of the can, large enough for the paper clips to pass through.

Any identical weights may be used. Choose weights so that 6 of them will cause a stretch of a few inches.

*During the Activity:*

If students measure the height of the rubber band to $\frac{1}{8}$-inch precision, their scatter plots should look roughly linear. Perfectly linear data rarely occur, and students should be made aware of this fact.

*Closing the Activity:*

If necessary, prompt students to observe that their scatter plot has a nearly linear pattern. Even though a linear relationship is expected, some points in the scatter plot may deviate from a straight line. Point out to students that a straight line may be appropriate despite some minor fluctuations.

Remind students to keep their tables and graphs, which will be needed for Lesson 2.2.

**TEACHING TIP**

If necessary in **Question 7**, point out to students that they must subtract each measured height from their initial height measurement to find the total stretch of the rubber band.

**TEACHING TIP**

**Question 8** Ask students how they know that the point (0, 0) belongs on their scatter plot.

**TEACHING TIP**

**Question 8** Remind students that the scale on each axis of a graph must increase uniformly. Also check to make sure they have included units with the variable names.

**COMMON ERROR**

**Exercise 1** Remind students about the need for uniform scales.

**TEACHING TIP**

Students may not be aware that graphs will only reveal true mathematical patterns in data if their scales are uniform. **Exercise 4** is intended to emphasize this fact. Graph A shows a misleading linear pattern because the scales are not uniformly increasing.

7.  See sample table on page 23.

---

7.  Use the data in your Height column to complete the Total Length of Stretch column.

8.  Make a scatter plot of (*weight, stretch*) for your data. Let weight be the variable on the horizontal axis. Let stretch be the variable on the vertical axis. Label the axes with the variable names. Include their units. Also, label the axes with uniformly increasing scales for each variable.

9.  Describe the pattern of points on your graph.

10. What do you think would happen if you continued to add more and more objects?

Save your data table and scatter plot for use in Lesson 2.2.

**Practice** **for Lesson 2.1**

**For Exercises 1–3, use the following information.**

| Time (min) | Temperature (°F) |
|---|---|
| 0 | 205 |
| 2 | 158 |
| 4 | 122 |
| 6 | 108 |
| 8 | 96 |

Boiling water is poured over a teabag in a cup. The temperature is measured every 2 minutes. The results are shown in the table at the left.

1.  Make a scatter plot of the data in the table. Let time be the variable on the horizontal axis, and let temperature be the variable on the vertical axis. Plot points for (*time, temperature*). Label the axes with variable names, units, and uniformly increasing scales.

2.  Describe the pattern in your graph.

3.  What do you think would happen to the temperature after another 10 minutes?

4.  The table below shows a comparison of several 2010 sporty cars. It lists acceleration as the time it takes to go from 0 to 60 miles per hour, as well as highway gas mileage.

| Car | Time from 0 to 60 mph (seconds) | Gas Mileage (miles per gallon) |
|---|---|---|
| Mini Cooper S Clubman | 8.1 | 34 |
| Ford Mustang GT Coupe | 5.2 | 24 |
| Volkswagen Hatchback | 7.6 | 31 |
| Mitsubishi Eclipse Coupe | 8.7 | 28 |
| Chrysler Sebring Sedan | 8.5 | 30 |
| MazdaSpeed3 | 6.3 | 25 |

SOURCE: HTTP://WWW.AUTOS.COM/AUTOS/PASSENGER_CARS/SPORTY_CARS/ACCELERATION

**24**     **Chapter 2**     DIRECT VARIATION

---

8.  Sample answer:

9.  Sample answer: The points lie very close to a straight line that passes through the origin.

10. Sample answer: The rubber band would continue to stretch by about half an inch for each additional object, until it might break or the can might touch the floor.

**Practice for Lesson 2.1 Answers**

1–4  See answers on page 25.

Identify the graph that is the best model for the data. Explain why it is the best one and why each of the others does not accurately model the data.

**A**
**Mileage and Acceleration**
Gas Mileage (mpg) vs Time 0 to 60 (seconds)

**B**
**Mileage and Acceleration**
Gas Mileage (mpg) vs Time 0 to 60 (seconds)

**C**
**Mileage and Acceleration**
Gas Mileage (mpg) vs Time 0 to 60 (seconds)

**For Exercises 5–8, use the following information.**

A bungee cord has a length of 60 feet when it hangs with no weight on it. To test its strength, increasing amounts of weight are attached to its end. After each weight is added, the total length of the cord is measured. The results are shown in the table.

| Total Weight (pounds) | Total Length (feet) | Length of Stretch (feet) |
|---|---|---|
| 0 | 60 | |
| 64 | 76 | |
| 144 | 96 | |
| 176 | 104 | |
| 280 | 130 | |

5. Complete the column labeled "Length of Stretch."
6. Make a scatter plot of (*weight, stretch*). Label the axes with variable names, units, and uniformly increasing scales.
7. Describe the pattern of points on your graph.
8. What do you think would happen if more and more weight were added?

BUNGEE JUMPING     **Lesson 2.1**     **25**

5.

| Length of Stretch (feet) |
|---|
| 0 |
| 16 |
| 36 |
| 44 |
| 70 |

6. Sample scatter plot:

Stretch (ft) vs Weight (lb)

**CONNECTION**

The data for **Exercises 5–8** are an idealization. Real bungee cords may not have a perfectly linear response over their entire usable length.

**TEACHING TIP**

**Exercise 5** Point out that the stretch of the cord must be found by subtracting 60 feet from each length in the table.

7. Sample answer: The points all lie on a straight line that passes through the origin.
8. Sample answer: The bungee cord would continue to stretch by about 1 foot for each 4 pounds of additional weight, until it might break.

1. Sample answer:

Temperature (°F) vs Time (min)

2. Sample answer: The graph is slightly curved.

3. Sample answer: The temperature would continue to drop, but it would level off at room temperature.
4. Scatter plot C is correct. Both scales are uniform, so the plot correctly shows how gas mileage varies with acceleration. In A, points are just plotted in the order the data appear in the table, and the scales are jumbled. In B, the scales are both increasing but are not uniform, so the data are distorted.

25

**5e** Explore

## Lesson Objectives

- identify proportional relationships.
- identify independent and dependent variables.
- find a constant of proportionality.
- write an equation that expresses a proportional relationship.

## Vocabulary

- constant of proportionality
- dependent variable
- independent variable
- proportional relationship

## Materials List

- students' tables and scatter plots from the Activity in Lesson 2.1

## Description

This lesson is designed as a small group investigation (2–4 students), using the same groups as in the Activity in Lesson 2.1. Students should work through **Questions 1–6** to extend their work from the previous lesson and discover that the ratios of stretch to weight for their rubber band are approximately constant. The ratios may not all be exactly equal, but they should be close.

**Question 7** asks students to use their equation to make a prediction, which demonstrates the value of solving their first equation for $S$ and expressing the relationship between $S$ and $W$ in the form of a function. Functions are discussed in Lesson 2.3.

*Wrapping Up the Investigation:*

Ask students to compare their analysis of the elasticity of their rubber band to what further information might be needed to prevent an accident like the one discussed in the Chapter Opener. For example, in addition to the stretching produced by hanging weights, the additional dynamic stretching due to the initial jump height would have to be considered.

---

### Lesson 2.2 INVESTIGATION: Proportional Relationships

An equation is one of the most useful kinds of mathematical models. It can allow you to predict the value of one quantity when you know the value of another. In this lesson, you will use ratios to find an equation that models the relationship between the weight on a rubber band and how much the band stretches.

**Note**

In some situations, neither variable is dependent on the other. In such cases, either variable can be placed on the horizontal axis. For example, if heights and weights of people are graphed, either height or weight could correctly go on the horizontal axis.

#### INDEPENDENT AND DEPENDENT VARIABLES

In the Activity in Lesson 2.1, you chose the values for the amount of weight. But you did not choose values for the length of the stretch. The stretch is called the **dependent variable** because its value depends on the value of the weight. Since values of weight can be freely chosen, weight is called the **independent variable**. The independent variable is almost always represented on the horizontal axis of a graph.

#### A PROPORTIONAL RELATIONSHIP

In the Activity in Lesson 2.1, the points on your scatter plot most likely fell in a nearly straight-line pattern. A straight line drawn through the origin may be a good visual model for the data. When a clear pattern exists on a graph of two variables, it is often possible to find an equation that relates the variables. Clues to an equation may sometimes be found by examining the ratios of the values of the variables.

1. Return to your data table from the Activity in Lesson 2.1. Label the fourth column "Stretch-to-Weight Ratio." Calculate the ratio of the total stretch to the total weight for each row of the table and record it. Write your ratios as decimals.

| Total Weight (ounces) | Height (inches) | Total Length of Stretch (inches) | Stretch-to-Weight Ratio |
|---|---|---|---|
| 0 | | 0 | ----- |
| | | | |

2. How do the ratios in your table compare to each other?
3. If the ratio of stretch $S$ to weight $W$ is always equal to the same constant value, there is a **proportional relationship** between $S$ and $W$. The constant ratio is called the **constant of proportionality**. The letter $k$ is often used to represent such a constant. So, $\frac{S}{W} = k$ is an equation relating the variables $S$ and $W$.

---

**TEACHING TIP**

**Question 1** Remind students that division by 0 is undefined, so the first cell in the fourth column of the table must be left blank.

**TEACHING TIP**

**Questions 2 and 3** Remind students that real data rarely yield ratios that are exactly equal even when a relationship is proportional. Approximate equality of ratios, combined with a scatter plot that appears to follow a straight-line pattern, provide evidence of proportionality.

### Lesson 2.2 Investigation Answers

1. Sample answer:

| Total Weight (ounces) | Height (inches) | Total Length of Stretch (inches) | Stretch-to-Weight Ratio |
|---|---|---|---|
| 0 | $8\frac{1}{2}$ | 0 | — |
| 2.3 | 8 | $\frac{1}{2}$ | 0.217 |
| 4.6 | $7\frac{5}{8}$ | $\frac{7}{8}$ | 0.190 |
| 6.9 | $7\frac{1}{4}$ | $1\frac{1}{4}$ | 0.181 |
| 9.2 | $6\frac{3}{4}$ | $1\frac{3}{4}$ | 0.190 |
| 11.5 | $6\frac{1}{4}$ | $2\frac{1}{4}$ | 0.196 |
| 13.8 | $5\frac{3}{4}$ | $2\frac{3}{4}$ | 0.199 |

For your data, $k$ equals the average value of the ratios in the fourth column of your table. Find the constant of proportionality for your data.

4. Use your answer to Question 3 to write an equation relating $S$ and $W$.

5. Solve your equation for $S$.

6. What are the units of the constant of proportionality $k$ for your equations in Questions 4 and 5?

7. You can use your equation from Question 5 to predict the length of stretch for a weight that was not tested in your experiment. Choose a value for $W$. Then predict how much it would stretch your rubber band.

### Practice for Lesson 2.2

1. How is the value of $k$ in the Investigation related to the points in your scatter plot from the Activity in Lesson 2.1?

**For Exercises 2–7, use the following information.**

Most high-definition television sets have wider screens than other sets. Here is an example.

Screen dimensions for a range of models are given in the table.

| Height (in.) | Width (in.) |
|:---:|:---:|
| 18 | 32 |
| $22\frac{1}{2}$ | 40 |
| 27 | 48 |
| $31\frac{1}{2}$ | 56 |

2. For the dimensions of the first two TV models listed in the table, do the heights and widths form a proportion? Explain.

3. Is there a proportional relationship between width and height? Why or why not?

2. Sample answer: They are all equal to approximately 0.19.

3. Sample answer: 0.196

4. Sample answer: $\frac{S}{W} = 0.196$

5. Sample answer: $S = 0.196\,W$

6. inches per ounce, or in./oz

7. Sample answer: For $W = 3.0$ ounces, $S = (0.196)(3) = 0.588$ inches.

### TEACHING TIP

**Exercise 1** lays the groundwork for the study of slope in Lesson 2.5. Remind students that the coordinates of a point on a scatter plot represent the distances of the point from the axes.

### TEACHING TIP

Make sure students see that proportional relationships are revealed by both constant ratios (**Exercises 2 and 11**) and linear patterns in graphs (**Exercises 6 and 9**).

## Practice for Lesson 2.2 Answers

1. For each point, it approximately equals the ratio of the point's height to its distance to the right of the Stretch axis.

2. Sample answer: Yes, the ratios of height to width are equal: $\frac{18}{32} = \frac{22\frac{1}{2}}{40}$.

3. Yes, the ratio of width to height is always 16 to 9, or about 1.78. Or, the ratio of height to width is 9 to 16, or about 0.56.

**4.** $w = \frac{16}{9}h$ or $h = \frac{9}{16}w$

**5.** They cannot be identified because neither variable depends on the other.

**6.** Sample answer:

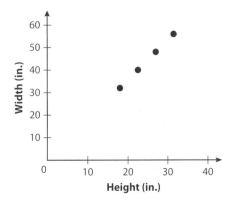

**7.** Sample answer: No, there are no TV sets with dimensions of 0 inches and 0 inches.

**8.** The dependent variable is height, and the independent variable is time. The height of the plant depends on how long it has been growing.

**9.** Sample answer:

**4.** Write an equation to model the relationship between width $w$ and height $h$.

**5.** If possible, identify the dependent variable and the independent variable. Explain.

**6.** Make a scatter plot for these data.

**7.** Does it make sense to include the point $(0, 0)$ on your scatter plot? Why or why not?

**For Exercises 8–13, use the following information.**

For their science project, students plant a kudzu vine seed in order to investigate how quickly it grows. Every four days after the seed sprouts, they measure and record the height of their plant. Their results are shown in the table.

| Time (days) | Height (cm) |
|---|---|
| 0 | 0 |
| 4 | 3 |
| 8 | 6 |
| 12 | 9 |
| 16 | 12 |
| 20 | 15 |

**8.** If possible, identify the dependent variable and the independent variable. Explain.

**9.** Make a scatter plot for these data.

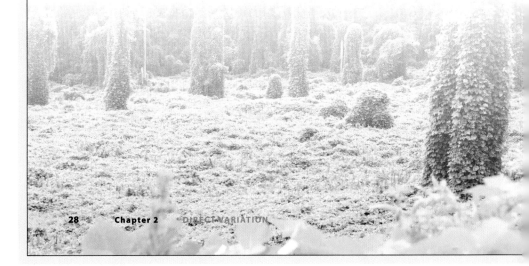

10. Does it make sense to include the point (0, 0) on your scatter plot? Why or why not?

11. Is there a proportional relationship between height and time? Why or why not?

12. Find the constant of proportionality, including units, for this situation.

13. Write an equation to model the relationship between height $h$ and time $t$.

**For Exercises 14–16, use the following information.**

The amounts of a family's electric bills for four months are shown in the table.

| Electricity Used (kilowatt-hours) | Amount of Bill |
|---|---|
| 54 | $14.56 |
| 120 | $23.80 |
| 210 | $36.40 |
| 285 | $46.90 |

14. If possible, identify the dependent variable and the independent variable. Explain.

15. Make a scatter plot for these data.

16. Is there a proportional relationship between the variables? Why or why not?

10. Sample answer: Yes, because when the seed first sprouts, its height is 0 cm.

11. Yes, the ratio of height to time is constant.

12. $\dfrac{3 \text{ centimeters}}{4 \text{ days}} = 0.75$ centimeter per day

13. $h = \dfrac{3}{4}t$ or $h = 0.75t$

14. Electricity used is the independent variable. The bill amount is the dependent variable because it depends on how much electricity was used.

15. Sample answer:

16. No, the ratios of $\dfrac{\text{amount of bill}}{\text{electricity used}}$ are not constant.

# LESSON 2.3

## Lesson Objectives
- identify direct variation.
- write direct variation equations.

## Vocabulary
- direct proportion
- direct variation
- direct variation function
- function
- input value
- origin
- output value
- variation
- varies directly

## Description

In this lesson, students are introduced to the concept of a function. They identify direct variation functions that arise from proportional relationships and learn to recognize their graphs.

Two variables have a proportional relationship if their ratio is constant. In this lesson, you will learn how to recognize direct proportion relationships, as well as how to write functions that express direct variation.

### DIRECT PROPORTION

Architects and other designers often use *proportioning systems* to give structure to their work. A proportioning system can help ensure that the different parts of a design have shapes that fit together in a visually pleasing way.

The photograph at the left shows the Cathedral of Notre Dame in Paris, France. Many rectangular shapes can be seen in the design of the cathedral. A few of these are outlined in red in Figure 1.

**Figure 1**

These rectangles have different sizes. But they all have the same shape. They are therefore similar to each other.

The entire front or *facade* of Notre Dame is about 304 feet high and 190 feet wide. The small rectangle in the upper-left tower is about 88 feet high and 55 feet wide. The height-to-width ratios of the building's front and the small rectangle form a proportion.

$$\frac{304}{190} = \frac{88}{55}$$

Both ratios are equal to $\frac{8}{5}$. The same is true for the other rectangles outlined in the figure. Since the ratio of height to width is constant, height and width are proportional to each other.

In Figure 2, all of the rectangles shown in Figure 1 are drawn with their lower-left corners at the same position. Notice that their upper-right corners all lie on the same slanted line, which contains the diagonals of all of the rectangles.

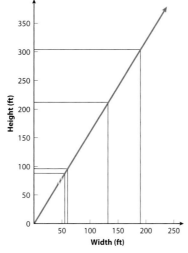

**Figure 2**

Designers call such a line a *regulating line*. Since all of the rectangles having their corners on this line are similar, such a line can be used to provide a uniform structure in a design.

 **E X A M P L E ❶**

The Notre Dame proportioning system can be used to find rectangles similar to the ones shown in Figure 1.

  **a.** Use the regulating line in Figure 2 to *estimate* the height of a similar rectangle that has a width of 85 feet.

  **b.** Use a proportion to *calculate* the height.

**TEACHING TIP**

As students examine the graph that shows the regulating line, have them look back at the rectangles in Figure 1. If necessary, point out where the diagonals of the rectangles are in the figure.

**ADDITIONAL EXAMPLE ❶**

**a.** Use the regulating line for the Notre Dame proportioning system in Figure 2 to estimate the width of a similar rectangle with a height of 200 feet. about 120 ft

**b.** Use a proportion to calculate the width. 125 ft

**Solution:**

**a.** Estimate the height by drawing the rectangle so that its diagonal is on the regulating line.

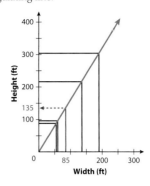

The height of the similar rectangle appears to be about 135 feet.

**b.** Write a proportion for the problem.

$$\text{height} \rightarrow \quad \frac{8}{5} = \frac{h}{85 \text{ feet}} \quad \leftarrow \text{height}$$
$$\text{width} \rightarrow \qquad\qquad\qquad\qquad \leftarrow \text{width}$$

Solve for $h$.

| | |
|---|---|
| Original equation | $\dfrac{8}{5} = \dfrac{h}{85}$ |
| Find the cross products. | $5h = (8)(85)$ |
| Simplify. | $5h = 680$ |
| Divide each side by 5. | $\dfrac{5h}{5} = \dfrac{680}{5}$ |
| Simplify. | $h = 136$ |

So, for a width of 85 feet, the height should be 136 feet.

Most of the relationships you have been exploring in this chapter are examples of **direct proportions**.

- One quantity is *directly proportional* to another if the ratios of the two quantities are constant.
- A graph of the quantities is a line that includes the point $(0, 0)$.

There are several types of **variation** between two quantities. In general, the equation $y = kx$ expresses **direct variation**. The equation can be read "$y$ is directly proportional to $x$" or "$y$ **varies directly** with $x$."

**TEACHING TIP**

Point out to students the distinction between the use of the letters $y$ and $x$ that are used to represent variables and the letter $k$ that is used to represent an unknown constant.

The stretch $S$ of a rubber band is directly proportional to the weight $W$ that is hung from it. This relationship can also be expressed as "$S$ varies directly with $W$."

All direct variation graphs are straight lines that pass through the **origin** $(0, 0)$. Another kind of variation is explored in this chapter's Extension.

## FUNCTIONS

Recall that a mathematical model uses mathematics to describe relationships. In the stretch and weight relationship $S = kW$ from the bungee jump activity, for each value of $W$ there is exactly one value of $S$. This kind of model is an example of a function.

> A **function** is a relationship between input and output in which each **input value** has exactly one **output value**.

A function provides a way of finding a unique output value for every possible input value.

The equation $S = kW$ expresses stretch as a function of weight. The input values are those of the independent variable $W$. For each value of the independent variable, the function returns an output value for the dependent variable $S$.

 E X A M P L E ❷

Nurses, doctors, and other types of caregivers often dispense medications. In many cases, the amount of medication depends on the weight of the person taking the medication. The table shows the dosage of a medication for various weights.

a. Verify that dosage is directly proportional to weight.

b. Write an equation that gives dosage $d$ as a function of weight $w$.

c. Draw a graph of dosage versus weight.

d. Use your equation to determine the dosage for a person weighing 43 kilograms.

| Weight (kg) | Dosage (mg) |
|---|---|
| 10 | 250 |
| 20 | 500 |
| 30 | 750 |
| 40 | 1,000 |
| 50 | 1,250 |
| 60 | 1,500 |

**Note**

In graphs, the term *versus* (or the abbreviation *vs*) describes the position of the variables. The first variable (the dependent variable) is associated with the vertical axis and the second variable (the independent variable) with the horizontal axis.

DIRECT VARIATION FUNCTIONS    **Lesson 2.3**    33

**CONNECTION**

**Example 2** refers to "weight in kilograms." A kilogram is actually a unit of mass, but some people (pharmacists, for example) in the U.S. often refer to weight in kilograms, grams, or milligrams.

## ADDITIONAL EXAMPLE ❷

The table shows the cost of having various amounts of clothes washed at a drop-off laundry.

| Weight of Clothes (lb) | Cost ($) |
|---|---|
| 4 | 5.20 |
| 6 | 7.80 |
| 9 | 11.70 |
| 13 | 16.90 |

a. Verify that cost is directly proportional to weight. The ratios of cost to weight all equal 1.30.

b. Write an equation that models cost $C$ as a function of weight $w$. $C = 1.30w$

c. Draw a graph of cost vs weight.

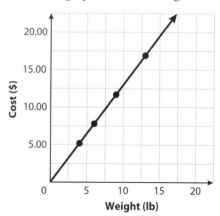

d. Use your equation to determine the cost for a load of 8 pounds of clothes. $10.40

**TEACHING TIP**

**Example 2** You may want to point out that drawing a line through the points on the scatter plot makes sense because all intermediate weights and dosages are feasible. For some graphs, only certain discrete values make sense, so a line may not be appropriate even though lines are often drawn in such cases.

**Solution:**

**a.** Find the ratios of dosage to weight.

| Weight (kg) | Dosage (mg) | $\dfrac{\text{Dosage}}{\text{Weight}}$ (mg/kg) |
|:---:|:---:|:---:|
| 10 | 250 | $\dfrac{250}{10} = 25$ |
| 20 | 500 | $\dfrac{500}{20} = 25$ |
| 30 | 750 | $\dfrac{750}{30} = 25$ |
| 40 | 1,000 | $\dfrac{1,000}{40} = 25$ |
| 50 | 1,250 | $\dfrac{1,250}{50} = 25$ |
| 60 | 1,500 | $\dfrac{1,500}{60} = 25$ |

The ratios of dosage $d$ to weight $w$ all equal 25 milligrams per kilogram (mg/kg). So, $d$ is directly proportional to $w$.

**b.** Since $\dfrac{d}{w} = 25$, the equation $d = 25w$ is a function that models the relationship between the two variables.

**c.** Plot the data from the table. Then draw a line through the points.

**d.** To find the dosage for a person weighing 43 kg, use the equation $d = 25w$.

Original equation   $d = 25w$
Substitute.     $d = 25(43)$
Simplify.      $d = 1,075$

So, a dosage of 1,075 mg is needed.

The equations $S = kW$ and $d = kw$ both express direct variation relationships. And both produce unique output values for each input value. They therefore represent **direct variation functions**.

## Practice for Lesson 2.3

1. The "triple-decker" apartment building shown here is another example of a proportioning system in architecture. Many of the rectangles have a length-to-width ratio of 7 to 4.
   a. Write an equation that models the length $l$ of a rectangle as a function of width $w$.
   b. Use this proportioning system to find the length of a window that has a width of 30 inches.

**For Exercises 2–5, tell whether the relationship is an example of a direct variation. If it is, explain how you know. Then write an equation relating the variables. If the relationship is not an example of direct variation, explain why.**

2. The table shows travel times for driving on a highway.

| Time Elapsed (h) | Distance Traveled (mi) |
|---|---|
| 0 | 0 |
| 3 | 180 |
| 6 | 360 |
| 9 | 540 |

3. The table lists some temperature conversions.

| Celsius Scale (°C) | Fahrenheit Scale (°F) |
|---|---|
| 5 | 41 |
| 10 | 50 |
| 15 | 59 |
| 20 | 68 |

4. It costs $2.00 to begin a trip in a taxicab and an additional $0.20 for each $\frac{1}{4}$ mile traveled. (*Hint*: Make a table of distances and costs.)

5. The graph shows the force $F$ needed to stretch a spring by $x$ inches. This is an example of *Hooke's Law* for an elastic spring.

F (lb) vs x (in.), point (2.5, 7)

DIRECT VARIATION FUNCTIONS    Lesson 2.3    35

## Practice for Lesson 2.3 Answers

**1a.** $l = \frac{7}{4}w$

**1b.** 52.5 inches

2. This is a direct variation, since the ratio of distance traveled $d$ to time $t$ is always 60. An equation is $d = 60t$.

3. The relationship is not a direct variation. The ratios of °C to °F are not constant: $\frac{41}{5} = 8.2$, $\frac{50}{10} = 5$, $\frac{59}{15} \approx 3.9$, $\frac{68}{20} = 3.4$.

4. The relationship is not a direct variation. Sample table:

| Distance Traveled (mi) | Cost ($) | Cost/Distance Ratio |
|---|---|---|
| 0 | $2.00 | |
| $\frac{1}{4}$ | $2.20 | $8.80 per mile |
| $\frac{1}{2}$ | $2.40 | $4.80 per mile |
| $\frac{3}{4}$ | $2.60 | $3.47 per mile |

The cost-to-distance ratio is not constant.

**CONNECTION**

**Exercise 5** The English scientist Robert Hooke discovered the law named after him in the late 17th century. The constant ratio $k$ in the equation $F = kx$ is called a *spring constant*.

5. This is a direct variation, since the graph is a straight line that passes through the origin. The equation must have the form $F = kx$, and $k = \frac{F}{x}$ for every point on the line. Using the given point, $k = \frac{7}{2.5} = 2.8$, so $F = 2.8x$.

**6a.** Sample answer: The ratios of strength to width are all very close to 24. Also, a scatter plot of strength vs width is approximately a straight line that passes through the origin.

**6b.** Sample answer: $S = 24w$

**6c.** Sample answer:

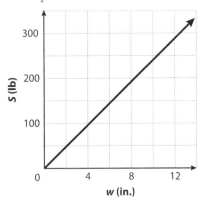

**6d.** $S = 24(7) = 168$ lb

---

**TEACHING TIP**

**Exercise 7** Students need to recognize the patterns in the table in order to see that the length of a sheet of A7 paper is 105 mm.

---

**7a.** Sample answer: Yes, the ratio of width to length is very close to 0.71 for all the papers listed.

**7b.** $w = 0.71l$

**7c.** Sample answer: 105 mm long, 75 mm wide

**6.** The table contains data relating the breaking strength of pine boards to their widths. The boards all have the same thicknesses and lengths.

| Width (in.) | Breaking Strength (lb) |
|---|---|
| 4 | 94 |
| 6 | 145 |
| 8 | 196 |
| 10 | 241 |
| 12 | 289 |

  **a.** Verify that strength is directly proportional to width for these boards.
  **b.** Write an equation that models strength $S$ as a function of width $w$.
  **c.** Draw a graph of strength vs width.
  **d.** Use your equation to determine the strength of a board that is 7 inches wide.

**7.** Outside the United States, most countries use "metric" paper. International paper sizes are listed in the table.

| Paper Size | Width (mm) | Length (mm) |
|---|---|---|
| A0 | 841 | 1,189 |
| A1 | 594 | 841 |
| A2 | 420 | 594 |
| A3 | 297 | 420 |
| A4 | 210 | 297 |
| A5 | 148 | 210 |
| A6 | 105 | 148 |

  **a.** Does width vary directly with length for these papers? Explain.
  **b.** Write an equation that models width $w$ as a function of length $l$.
  **c.** Find the dimensions of the next smaller size, the A7 paper.

**8.** On the average, 1 pound of recycled aluminum contains 33 cans.

   **a.** Write an equation expressing the number of cans $N$ as a function of the weight $w$ (in pounds) of recycled aluminum.

   **b.** In a recent year, 1,938,000,000 pounds of cans were recycled. How many cans were recycled?

**9.** A person's red blood cell count can be estimated by looking at a drop of blood under a microscope. The number of cells inside the circular field of the microscope is counted.

If the area of the circle is known, then area can be used as a measure of the number of blood cells. The number of cells varies directly with area.

   **a.** Assume that a 0.01 mm$^2$ viewing field contains 23 red blood cells. Find an equation for the number $N$ of red blood cells as a function of area $A$.

   **b.** Use your equation from Part (a) to determine how many red blood cells are contained in an area of 50 mm$^2$.

**10.** Variable $y$ is directly proportional to $x$, and $y$ is 28 when $x$ is 6.

   **a.** Write an equation that gives $y$ as a function of $x$.

   **b.** Find the value of $y$ when $x$ is 15.

**11.** Variable $r$ is directly proportional to $t$, and $r$ is 12.84 when $t$ is 42.8.

   **a.** Write an equation that gives $r$ as a function of $t$.

   **b.** Find the value of $r$ when $t$ is 21.7.

   **c.** Find the value of $t$ when $r$ is 15.9.

**8a.** $N = 33w$

**8b.** $33(1{,}938{,}000{,}000) = 63{,}954{,}000{,}000$ cans

**9a.** $N = kA$; $N = 23$ for $A = 0.01$, so $k = 23/0.01 = 2{,}300$ cells/mm$^2$, and $N = 2{,}300A$.

**9b.** $N = 2{,}300(50) = 115{,}000$

**10a.** $y = \dfrac{14}{3}x$

**10b.** $\dfrac{14}{3}(15) = 70$

**11a.** $r = 0.3t$

**11b.** $(0.3)(21.7) = 6.51$

**11c.** 53

# LESSON 2.4

**5e** Evaluate

## Lesson Objective

- solve problems that require previously learned concepts and skills.

## Exercise Reference

## Lesson 2.4
## R.A.P. Answers

1. directly proportional
2. constant of proportionality
3. function
4. straight line
5. C
6. B
7. $\frac{2}{5}$
8. $\frac{3}{20}$
9. $\frac{11}{50}$
10. 0.625
11. 0.28
12. $0.\overline{27}$
13. 10
14. $-2$
15. $-16$
16. 5 and 6
17. 8 and 9
18. 10 and 11

---

**Fill in the blank.**

1. For two variables $x$ and $y$, if the ratio $\frac{y}{x}$ is constant, then $y$ is _____ to $x$.

2. In the equation $y = kx$, $k$ is called the _____.

3. An input/output relationship in which each input value has exactly one output value is called a(n) _____.

4. The shape of the graph of a direct variation function is a(n) _____.

**Choose the correct answer.**

5. Which of the following is *not* a correct way of writing the ratio "3 to 4"?

   **A.** $3 : 4$    **B.** $\frac{3}{4}$    **C.** $3 \times 4$    **D.** 3 to 4

6. Given that 1 kilogram weighs approximately 2.2 pounds, rewrite 10 pounds as an equivalent number of kilograms.

   **A.** 22 kilograms    **B.** 4.5 kilograms
   **C.** 7.8 kilograms    **D.** 0.22 kilograms

**Change the decimal to a fraction in lowest terms.**

7. 0.4      8. 0.15      9. 0.22

**Change the fraction to a decimal.**

10. $\frac{5}{8}$      11. $\frac{7}{25}$      12. $\frac{3}{11}$

**Evaluate the expression.**

13. $|-8| + 2$      14. $-|-2|$      15. $4 - 2|-10|$

**The value of the square root is between which two integers?**

16. $\sqrt{30}$      17. $\sqrt{78}$      18. $\sqrt{108}$

**Solve the proportion.**

**19.** $\dfrac{5}{6} = \dfrac{x}{42}$

**20.** $\dfrac{1.2}{n} = \dfrac{60}{45}$

**21.** $\dfrac{7}{19} = \dfrac{14}{a}$

**22.** The table shows the temperature of a glass of juice at different times after being removed from a refrigerator.

| Time (min) | Temperature (°F) |
|---|---|
| 0 | 40 |
| 5 | 48 |
| 10 | 54 |
| 15 | 59 |
| 20 | 62 |

Make a well-labeled scatter plot of temperature versus time.

**23.** The table shows the pressure due to water at various depths below the surface.

| Depth (feet) | Pressure (pounds per square foot) |
|---|---|
| 0 | 0 |
| 2 | 125 |
| 5 | 312 |
| 10 | 624 |
| 20 | 1,248 |

Make a scatter plot of pressure versus depth and draw a smooth line through the points.

**State whether there is a proportional relationship between the variables. Explain.**

**24.** temperature and time in Exercise 22

**25.** pressure and depth in Exercise 23

**19.** 35

**20.** 0.9

**21.** 38

**22.** Sample answer:

**23.** Sample answer:

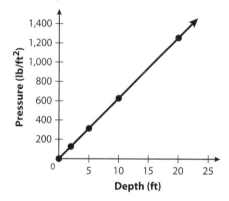

**24.** No, the ratios are not constant, and the scatter plot has a curved shape.

**25.** Yes, the ratio of pressure to depth is approximately constant, and the graph is a straight line that passes through the origin.

# LESSON 2.5

## Lesson Objectives

- find the slope of a line given rise and run.
- find the slope of a line given two points on the line.
- interpret the slope of a line as a rate of change.

## Vocabulary

- rate of change
- slope

## Description

In this lesson students explore the concept of slope as a measure of the steepness of a line and relate it to the concept of rate of change.

---

### TEACHING TIP

To help students connect the concept of slope to their real world, ask them to give other examples (besides staircases) for which the word slope is used to describe steepness. These may include roofs, streets, ski trails, etc.

---

### CONNECTION

The line used to define the slope of a staircase is not the same as the *pitch* of the staircase. Pitch refers to the ratio of tread depth to riser height for an individual stair.

---

## ADDITIONAL EXAMPLE ❶

Find the slope of a staircase that rises 90 inches over a run of 120 inches.
$\frac{3}{4}$ or 0.75

---

You have seen that the graph of a direct variation function is a straight line. The slope of a line is a measure of its steepness. In this lesson, you will learn how to find the slope of a line and to interpret it as a rate of change.

### SLOPE OF A LINE

The *rise* of a staircase is defined as the vertical distance between landings. The horizontal distance from the edge of the bottom step to the top landing is called the *run*.

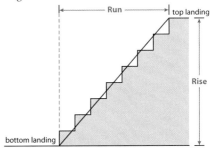

The steepness of the red line in the figure above can be described by a ratio known as the **slope** of the line.

$$\text{slope} = \frac{\text{rise}}{\text{run}}$$

Find the slope of a staircase that rises 64 inches over a run of 80 inches.

**Solution:**

The slope of the staircase is the ratio of rise to run.

$$\text{Slope of staircase} = \frac{\text{rise}}{\text{run}}$$
$$= \frac{64 \text{ in.}}{80 \text{ in.}}$$
$$= \frac{4}{5}$$

The slope is $\frac{4}{5}$ or 0.8.

### Connection

Staircases are usually built with slopes between 0.6 and 0.9.

# LESSON 2.5

For a direct variation function of the form $y = kx$, the constant of proportionality $k$ is equal to the slope of the graph of the function.

 **2**

The graph below shows the medication dosage function $d = 25w$ from Lesson 2.3.

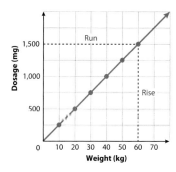

Find the slope of the line.

**Solution:**

As the weight increases from 0 to 60 kg, the dosage rises from 0 to 1,500 mg. The slope of the line is

$$\frac{\text{rise}}{\text{run}} = \frac{1,500 \text{ mg}}{60 \text{ kg}}$$

$$= 25 \text{ mg/kg}$$

Notice that in this case, the slope has units of milligrams per kilogram.

The ratio of the *change* in dosage to the *change* in weight for any two points on the graph of dosage vs weight is also equal to the slope of the line.

- Consider the points (20, 500) and (30, 750).

$$\frac{\text{change in dosage}}{\text{change in weight}} = \frac{750 \text{ mg} - 500 \text{ mg}}{30 \text{ kg} - 20 \text{ kg}} = 25 \text{ mg/kg}$$

- Also, consider the points (20, 500) and (50, 1,250).

$$\frac{\text{change in dosage}}{\text{change in weight}} = \frac{1,250 \text{ mg} - 500 \text{ mg}}{50 \text{ kg} - 20 \text{ kg}} = 25 \text{ mg/kg}$$

## ADDITIONAL EXAMPLE **2**

The graph below shows the cost of having various amounts of clothes cleaned at a drop-off laundry. Find the slope of the line.

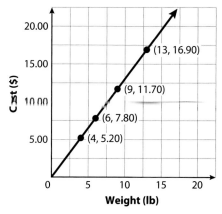

$$\frac{11.70 - 5.20}{9 - 4} = 1.30 \frac{\text{dollars}}{\text{pound}}$$

**Note**

The symbol $\Delta$ (pronounced "delta") is the equivalent of a capital *D* in the Greek alphabet. It stands for a change or *difference* between two values of a variable.

In these calculations, the change in dosage can be represented by $\Delta d$, read "change in $d$." The change in weight can be represented by $\Delta w$, read "change in $w$." So, the slope of the line can also be thought of as the ratio of these changes $\dfrac{\Delta d}{\Delta w}$, or the **rate of change** of dosage with respect to weight.

$$\frac{\Delta d}{\Delta w} = \frac{750 \text{ mg}}{30 \text{ kg}} = 25 \text{ mg/kg}$$

And again, any two points on the line can be used to determine the slope.

$$\frac{\Delta d}{\Delta w} = \frac{500 \text{ mg}}{20 \text{ kg}} = 25 \text{ mg/kg}$$

The dosage increases by 25 milligrams for each kilogram of increase in weight.

In general, the slope of the graph of a direct variation function of the form $y = kx$ can be symbolized as $\dfrac{\Delta y}{\Delta x}$, read as "the change in $y$ divided by the change in $x$."

1. A school staircase has a total vertical rise of 96 inches and a horizontal run of 150 inches.
   a. For this staircase, what is the rise when the run is 50 inches?
   b. What is the slope of the staircase?

2. The Americans with Disabilities Act (ADA) requires that a straight ramp have a slope no greater than $\frac{1}{12}$.
   a. What is the slope of the ramp in the figure? Does it meet the ADA requirement?

   b. Find the coordinates of a point that is halfway up the ramp.
   c. Find the slope from the halfway point to the top of the ramp.
   d. What can you say about the slope between any two points along a straight ramp?

3. Roofers describe the steepness of a roof by its *pitch*, the number of inches of rise for each 12 inches of run. A "3 in 12" roof rises 3 inches for every 12 inches of run.
   a. What is the slope of a "3 in 12" roof?
   b. A roof rises 100 inches over a run of 20 feet. Find the slope of the roof.

4. In Lesson 2.3, you learned that architects often use a regulating line to unify a design. The corners of three similar rectangles are on the regulating line shown here.

   Find the slopes of line segments joining two different pairs of points to show that the slope of the regulating line is constant.

## Practice for Lesson 2.5 Answers

**1a.** $\frac{96}{150} = \frac{\text{rise}}{50}$; rise = 32 inches

**1b.** $\frac{16}{25}$ or 0.64

**2a.** $\frac{30}{400} = \frac{3}{40}$ or 0.075; Yes, since $\frac{1}{12} \approx 0.083$ and $0.075 < 0.083$.

**2b.** (200, 15)

**2c.** $\frac{(30 - 15)}{(400 - 200)} = \frac{15}{200} = \frac{3}{40}$ or 0.075

**2d.** Sample answer: The slope is the same between any two points.

**Exercise 3** If students give the slope of the roof as "5 inches per foot," point out that, for comparison to the roof in Part (a), 20 feet must be converted to 240 inches.

**3a.** $\frac{1}{4}$ or 0.25

**3b.** $\frac{100 \text{ inches}}{240 \text{ inches}} = \frac{5}{12}$ or about 0.42

**4.** Sample answer: $\frac{75 - 0}{45 - 0} = \frac{5}{3}$; $\frac{50 - 25}{30 - 15} = \frac{5}{3}$; The slopes are equal.

# LESSON 2.5

5. $\dfrac{-136}{189} \approx -0.72$

6. $\dfrac{1 \text{ inch}}{240 \text{ inches}} = \dfrac{1}{240}$ or about 0.0042;

   also $\dfrac{1}{20}$ or 0.05 inches per foot

5. If a line slopes downward from left to right, its rise is negative, and so is its slope.

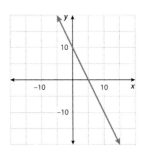

For example, the line in the figure above falls from 10 units to 0 as $x$ increases from 0 to 5 units. It has a slope of $\dfrac{-10}{5} = -2$.

The White Heat trail at Sunday River Ski Resort in Maine is one of the steepest ski trails in the eastern United States. It falls 136 feet over a horizontal distance of 189 feet. What is the slope of White Heat?

6. A roof gutter should be installed so that it slopes about 1 inch in 20 feet. What is the slope of such a gutter?

7. The general expression $\dfrac{\Delta y}{\Delta x}$ for slope can be written another way. For two points $P_1(x_1, y_1)$ and $P_2(x_2, y_2)$ on a line, the change in $x$, or $\Delta x$, equals the difference $(x_2 - x_1)$ of the $x$-coordinates. Similarly, $\Delta y = (y_2 - y_1)$.

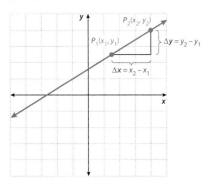

So, the formula $\dfrac{\Delta y}{\Delta x} = \dfrac{y_2 - y_1}{x_2 - x_1}$ can be used to calculate the slope for a line that passes through any two points $P_1$ and $P_2$.

**a.** Use the formula to find the slope of the line containing points $P_1(-4, 1)$ and $P_2(4, 3)$.

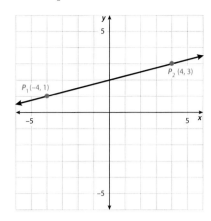

**b.** Now switch the names of the points. Let the point on the left be $P_2(-4, 1)$ and let the point on the right be $P_1(4, 3)$. Once again, use the formula to calculate the slope.

**c.** Explain what the results of Parts (a) and (b) suggest about the use of the slope formula.

**For Exercises 8–11, find the slope of each line. Use the two points with integer coordinates indicated on each graph.**

**8.**

**9.**

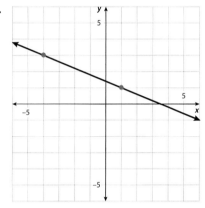

**7a.** $\dfrac{\Delta y}{\Delta x} = \dfrac{y_2 - y_1}{x_2 - x_1} = \dfrac{3 - 1}{4 - (-4)} = \dfrac{2}{8} = \dfrac{1}{4}$

**7b.** $\dfrac{\Delta y}{\Delta x} = \dfrac{y_2 - y_1}{x_2 - x_1} = \dfrac{1 - 3}{(-4) - 4}$

$= \dfrac{-2}{-8} = \dfrac{1}{4}$

**7c.** Sample answer: The order of the subtractions in the formula is not important, as long as $x_1$ and $y_1$ are coordinates of the same point (and similarly for $x_2$ and $y_2$).

**8.** $\dfrac{3}{4}$

**9.** $-\dfrac{2}{5}$

**10.** 3

**11.** 0

**12.** Sample answer: All points on a horizontal line have the same $y$-coordinate. Therefore, the rise is always 0, and $\frac{0}{\Delta x} = 0$.

**13.** Sample answer: All points on a vertical line have the same $x$-coordinate. Therefore, the denominator in the slope formula is always 0, and division by 0 is undefined.

**14a.** Sample graph:

**14b.** Sample answer: Yes, the ratio of sales tax to purchase amount is always 0.04, and the graph is a straight line that passes through the origin.

**14c.** Sample answer:
$$\frac{\$1.40 - \$0.48}{\$35 - \$12} = \frac{\$0.92}{\$23} = 0.04$$

**14d.** Sample answer: For each dollar spent, the sales tax is $0.04. So, the sales tax rate in this state is 4 percent.

**15a.** $\dfrac{760 \text{ kilobytes}}{8 \text{ seconds}} = 95$ kilobytes per second

**15b.** The computer can download files at a rate of 95 kilobytes per second.

---

**10.**

**11.**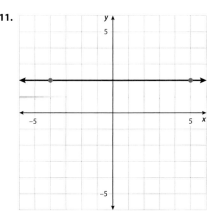

**12.** Explain the statement "Every horizontal line has the same slope."

**13.** Explain why the slope of any vertical line is undefined.

**14.** The table shows the amount of sales tax paid on various purchases in a particular state.

    **a.** Make a graph of sales tax vs purchase amount.

    **b.** Is this a direct variation function? Why or why not?

    **c.** Find the slope of the line on the graph.

    **d.** Write a sentence that interprets the meaning of the slope.

| Purchase Amount | Sales Tax |
|---|---|
| $12 | $0.48 |
| $35 | $1.40 |
| $57 | $2.28 |
| $86 | $3.44 |

**For Exercises 15–17, answer Parts (a) and (b).**

    **a.** Find the slope of the graph, including units.

    **b.** Interpret the meaning of the slope as a rate of change.

**15.** The graph shows the size of a file that can be downloaded from the Internet by a particular computer in a given number of seconds.

**46**    **Chapter 2**    DIRECT VARIATION

**16.** The graph below shows the force needed to stretch a spring to different lengths.

**17.** The graph below shows the *depreciation*, or decrease in value over time, of a piece of office equipment.

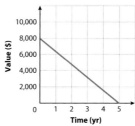

**18.** The table shows the data for the stretching of a bungee cord from Exercise 5 of Lesson 2.1.

| Total Weight (pounds) | Total Length (feet) | Length of Stretch (feet) |
|---|---|---|
| 0 | 60 | 0 |
| 64 | 76 | 16 |
| 144 | 96 | 36 |
| 176 | 104 | 44 |
| 280 | 130 | 70 |

  **a.** Make a graph of stretch vs weight.
  **b.** Is this a direct variation function? Why or why not?
  **c.** Find the slope of the line, including units.
  **d.** Write a sentence that interprets the slope as a rate of change.

**19.** Find the slope of the line that passes through the points (−3, 2) and (1, 0).

**20.** A line passes through the point (1, 5) and has a slope of $\frac{2}{3}$.
  **a.** Find another point on the line.
  **b.** Graph the line.

**16a.** $\dfrac{7 \text{ pounds}}{2.5 \text{ inches}} = 2.8$ lb/in.

**16b.** It requires 2.8 pounds of force to stretch a spring for each inch of stretch. The rate of change of force with respect to length is 2.8 lb/in.

**17a.** $\dfrac{-\$8{,}000}{5 \text{ years}} = -1{,}600$ dollars per year

**17b.** The equipment depreciates at a rate of 1,600 dollars per year. The rate of change of value with respect to time is −1,600 dollars per year.

**18a.** Sample graph:

**18b.** Sample answer: Yes, the ratios of stretch to weight are all equal to $\frac{1}{4}$, and the graph is a straight line that passes through the origin.

**18c.** $\frac{1}{4}$ ft/lb or 0.25 ft/lb

**18d.** Sample answer: The bungee cord stretches one-fourth of a foot for every pound of weight suspended from it. The rate of change of stretch with respect to weight is 0.25 ft/lb.

**19.** $-\dfrac{1}{2}$

**20a.** Sample answer: (−2, 3)

**20b.** Sample answer:

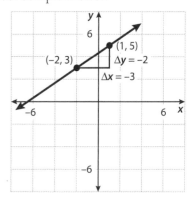

## Materials List

- bathroom scale
- large pot
- measuring cup
- water

## Description

In this project students examine the relationship between the volume of water added to a pot and the total weight of pot plus water. They are asked to find a way of analyzing the relationship that involves direct variation. This project works well when students work together in small groups of two or three.

## Sample Answers

The data in the students' reports will vary, but the conclusions should all be similar. The relationship between the weight of the pot plus water and the volume of the water is a linear relationship, but it is not direct variation.

Students should recognize that by subtracting the weight of the pot from the total weight of pot plus water, they can model the relationship between the weight of the water and the volume of the water with a direct variation function. The ratio of weight to volume, which equals the slope of a graph of weight of water vs volume of water, provides an experimental value for the density of water. For comparison purposes, the true density of water is 62.4 pounds per cubic foot, or about 0.13 pounds per fluid ounce.

If students have trouble seeing how to analyze the data to find a direct variation, suggest they look at the treatment of the data in the Activity in Lesson 2.1. There, the heights of the can were subtracted from the original height to find the amount of stretch.

CHAPTER

# 2

# Modeling Project

## It's Only Water Weight

In this chapter, you have learned to identify proportional relationships and to model them with direct variation functions. You are now ready to construct and analyze a model beginning with data that you collect.

You will need a scale, such as a bathroom scale, a large pot, a measuring cup, and a source of water.

- Place the pot on the scale and record its weight.
- Add measured volumes of water to the pot. After each added amount, record the total volume of water and the weight of the pot and water.
- Continue adding water until the pot is almost full.

Conduct an investigation of the weight vs volume relationship.

1. Make a table and graph comparing the total weight of the pot and water with the total volume of water in the pot.

2. Determine whether a direct variation function provides a good model for the relationship, and explain how you know. If so, find a direct variation function that models your data. If not, decide how you can analyze the data in a different way so that a direct variation model is appropriate.

Prepare a report of your findings. Use what you have learned about proportions, as well as the calculation and interpretation of slope, to describe your model.

# Chapter 2 Review

## You Should Be Able to:

### Lesson 2.1
- collect experimental data.
- make a scatter plot of experimental data.

### Lesson 2.2
- identify proportional relationships.
- identify independent and dependent variables.
- find a constant of proportionality.
- write an equation that expresses a proportional relationship

### Lesson 2.3
- identify direct variation.
- write direct variation equations.

### Lesson 2.4
- solve problems that require previously learned concepts and skills.

### Lesson 2.5
- find the slope of a line given rise and run.
- find the slope of a line given two points on the line.
- interpret the slope of a line as a rate of change.

## Key Vocabulary

dependent variable (p. 26)

independent variable (p. 26)

proportional relationship (p. 26)

constant of proportionality (p. 26)

direct proportion (p. 32)

variation (p. 32)

direct variation (p. 32)

varies directly (p. 32)

origin (p. 33)

function (p. 33)

input value (p. 33)

output value (p. 33)

direct variation function (p. 35)

slope (p. 40)

rate of change (p. 42)

## Chapter 2 Test Review

**Fill in the blank.**

1. A relationship between two variables such that there is exactly one output value for each input value is called a(n) _____.

2. The slope of a line is equal to the ratio of the _____ to the _____ between any two points on the line.

## Chapter 2
## Test Review Answers

1. function
2. rise, run

**3.** $x$ or horizontal, $y$ or vertical

**4.** ratio

**5.** Sample plot:

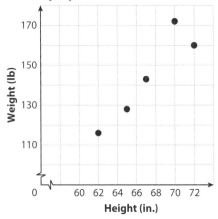

**6.** The number scales on the axes are not uniformly increasing.

**3.** On the graph of a function, the independent variable is on the _____ axis and the dependent variable is on the _____ axis.

**4.** For a direct variation function, the _____ of the variables is constant.

**5.** The table lists heights and weights for the starters on a high school girls' basketball team.

| Height (inches) | Weight (pounds) |
|---|---|
| 67 | 143 |
| 62 | 116 |
| 65 | 128 |
| 72 | 160 |
| 70 | 172 |

Make a scatter plot of weight vs height for the data. Label the axes appropriately.

**6.** In a geometry class, students measured the diameters and circumferences of a variety of circular objects. What is wrong with the scatter plot of their data?

**For Exercises 7–9, state whether the relationship between the variables is proportional. If it is, complete Parts (a), (b), (c), and (d). If it is not, explain how you know.**

   **a.** Identify the independent and dependent variables.

   **b.** Make a graph of the relationship.

   **c.** Find the constant of proportionality, including units if appropriate.

   **d.** Write an equation for a direct variation function that models the data.

**7.** The table shows the speed of a ball after falling for various times.

| Time (seconds) | Speed (meters per second) |
| --- | --- |
| 0.25 | 2.45 |
| 0.50 | 4.90 |
| 0.75 | 7.35 |
| 1.00 | 9.80 |
| 1.25 | 12.25 |

**8.** The table shows the period (time between bounces) for people of different weights on a bungee cord.

| Weight (lb) | Period (s) |
| --- | --- |
| 100 | 8.0 |
| 140 | 9.5 |
| 180 | 10.7 |
| 200 | 11.3 |

**9.** The table shows the weight of different volumes of water in a pitcher.

| Volume (oz) | Weight (lb) |
| --- | --- |
| 16 | 2.1 |
| 20 | 2.6 |
| 30 | 3.9 |
| 42 | 5.5 |
| 60 | 7.8 |

**10.** Variable $y$ is directly proportional to variable $x$, and $y$ is 128 when $x$ is 5.

    **a.** Write an equation that gives $y$ as a function of $x$.

    **b.** Find the value of $y$ when $x$ is 12.

**11.** A house sewer drain must fall at least $\frac{1}{4}$ inch for each foot of length. What is the slope of a house sewer drain?

**12.** Find the slope of a line that passes through the points $(-2, 1)$ and $(3, 8)$.

**7.** proportional

**7a.** independent variable: time; dependent variable: speed

**7b.** Sample graph:

**7c.** 9.80 meters per second per second

**7d.** Sample equation: $s = 9.80t$

**8.** not proportional; The ratios of period to weight are not constant.

**9.** proportional

**9a** independent variable: volume; dependent variable: weight

**9b.** Sample graph:

**9c.** 0.13 lb/oz

**9d.** $W = 0.13V$

**10a.** $y = 25.6x$

**10b.** 307.2

**11.** $\dfrac{-\frac{1}{4}\text{ inch}}{12\text{ inch}} = -\dfrac{1}{48}$ or about $-0.021$

**12.** $\dfrac{7}{5}$

**13.** $-\dfrac{1}{3}$

**14a.** 400 square feet per gallon

**14b.** Each gallon of paint covers 400 square feet of wall area. The rate of change of painted area with respect to paint volume is 400 square feet per gallon.

**13.** Find the slope of the line. The coordinates of the indicated points are integers.

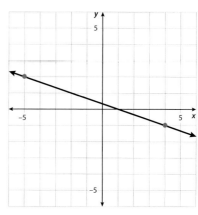

**14.** The graph shows the relationship between wall area covered and volume of paint from a certain manufacturer.

a. Find the slope of the graph, including units.

b. Write a sentence that interprets the slope as a rate of change.

# Chapter Extension
## Inverse Variation

Variables can be related to each other in many different ways. In this chapter, you have explored direct variation in some detail. Direct variation is one of the most common types of variation between two quantities. This extension consists of an activity that involves another frequently found type of variation.

When you look through a telescope, the amount you can see changes as the length of the telescope changes. The size of the *viewing circle* depends on the length of the telescope.

- Make a simple telescope by cutting a paper towel tube from one end to the other so that a second paper towel tube can fit inside of it. Do the same with a third paper towel tube. Insert the uncut tube inside one of the cut tubes. Then put these two inside the other cut tube. Now you can vary the length of your scope from one tube to nearly three.

- Tape a meter stick to a wall in a horizontal position. Back away from the wall and look at the stick through your scope. If you align the left edge of your viewing circle with the left end of the meter stick, you can estimate the diameter of the viewing circle. If you change the length of your scope, the diameter of your viewing circle should also change.

1. Stand at the farthest distance from the wall that still allows you to read the numbers on the meter stick. Start with the telescope at its shortest length. Measure that length. Then measure the diameter of the viewing circle. Record both measurements in the first row of a table like the one shown.

| Telescope Length (cm) | Diameter of Viewing Circle (cm) | |
|---|---|---|
| | | |
| | | |
| | | |
| | | |
| | | |
| | | |

2. Pull on the outer tube of the telescope to increase the telescope's length by 10 centimeters. Again, record the telescope length and the diameter of the viewing circle.

---

## Lesson Objective
- use inverse variation to model experimental data.

## Vocabulary
- inverse variation
- vary inversely

## Materials List
*Per group:*
- 3 paper towel tubes
- masking tape
- meter stick
- tape measure
- scissors

## Description

Students should work in groups of 2 or 3 on this lesson. They investigate the relationship between the length of a simulated telescope and the diameter of the resulting viewing circle.

> **TEACHING TIP**
>
> **Questions 1-3** The validity of the data will be improved if each student in a group estimates the diameters independently and an average is determined for each telescope length.

## Chapter 2 Extension Answers
1. See table in Question 9.
2. See table in Question 9.

# CHAPTER 2 EXTENSION

**TEACHING TIP**

**Question 9** The products of diameter and length will not be exactly constant, but they should be approximately constant to the nearest 100 centimeters, which is roughly the accuracy of the calculations.

**TEACHING TIP**

**Question 11** provides an opportunity to anticipate the discussion of the domain of a function in Chapter 5. Ask students to identify the minimum and maximum values for telescope length. Although the domain of an inverse variation function is all positive numbers, the *problem domain* for this experiment includes any length between 0 and the maximum length of students' telescopes.

**3.** See table in Question 9.

**4.** Sample graph:

**5.** Sample answer: The scatter plot has a curved shape, and the diameters decrease as the length of the telescope increases.

**6.** Sample answer: No, the diameter-to-length ratios are not constant, and the point (0, 0) does not fit the trend of the plot.

**7.** Sample answer: The diameter of the viewing circle would get smaller but would level off.

**8.** Sample answer: The diameter would get larger and larger.

**3.** Continue to increase the telescope's length 10 centimeters at a time. Record each new length and the corresponding diameter of the viewing circle.

**4.** Make a scatter plot of diameter of viewing circle vs length of telescope.

**5.** Describe the shape of your scatter plot.

**6.** Could the relationship between diameter and length be one of direct variation? Explain.

**7.** What do you expect would happen to the diameter of the viewing circle if the length of the telescope could get longer and longer?

**8.** What do you expect would happen to the diameter of the viewing circle if the length of the telescope got shorter and shorter?

**9.** Label the third column of your table "Product of Length and Diameter (cm²)." Then multiply each length and diameter pair and record the results in this column.

**10.** Describe any pattern you see in the Product of Length and Diameter column.

**Note**
Inverse variation is sometimes called *inverse proportion* or *indirect variation*.

**11.** When the product of two variables is always equal to the same number, the variables are said to **vary inversely** with each other. This type of relationship is called **inverse variation**. In general, if $y$ varies inversely with $x$, the relationship can be expressed by the equation $y = \frac{k}{x}$. The number $k$ is the constant product of the variables. Assume that your variables vary inversely with each other. Write an equation that models viewing circle diameter $d$ as a function of telescope length $L$.

**12.** Use your equation to predict the diameter of the viewing circle when telescope length is half of the shortest length you recorded in your table. You might even cut one of your tubes in half to check your prediction.

**13.** In the 17th century, the English scientist Robert Boyle found that the pressure $P$ of a gas varies inversely with the volume $V$ of the gas. This relationship is now known as *Boyle's Law*.
  **a.** Use a constant $k$ to write an equation for Boyle's Law.
  **b.** A particular sample of gas has a volume of 30 cubic inches at a pressure of 0.2 pound per square inch. Use this information along with Boyle's Law to write an equation giving pressure as a function of volume for this gas sample.
  **c.** Use your equation to find the pressure when the gas is compressed to a volume of 10 cubic inches.

**54**     **Chapter 2**     **DIRECT VARIATION**

**9.** Sample answer:

| Telescope Length (cm) | Diameter of Viewing Circle (cm) | Product of Length and Diameter (cm²) |
|---|---|---|
| 29 | 43 | 1,247 |
| 39 | 33 | 1,287 |
| 49 | 24 | 1,176 |
| 59 | 21 | 1,239 |
| 69 | 18 | 1,242 |
| 79 | 16 | 1,264 |

**10.** Sample answer: The products vary, but all are between 1,176 and 1,287.

**11.** Sample answer: The average product of $d$ and $L$ is 1,242.5. An equation is $(d)(L) = 1{,}242.5$, which is equivalent to the function $d = \frac{1{,}242.5}{L}$.

**12.** Sample answer: For $L = 14.5$ cm, $d = \frac{1{,}242.5}{14.5} \approx 86$ cm.

**13a.** $P = \frac{k}{V}$ or $PV = k$

**13b.** $k = PV = (0.2)(30) = 6$, so $P = \frac{6}{V}$.

**13c.** $P = \frac{6}{10} = 0.6$ pound per square inch

# Chapter 3
## Solving Equations and Inequalities

## Mathematical Overview

In this chapter, students use algebraic expressions as the building blocks for writing equations and inequalities. Arrow diagrams are introduced as a way to represent expressions and then later as a way to model the steps used when solving equations. The order of operations guidelines and the **TABLE** feature on a calculator, as well as the Properties of Equality and the Properties of Inequality, are all explored in the context of finding solutions for real-world problems. Students note that whereas a single number solution is graphed as a point on a number line, the graph of an inequality is an interval on the line. The concept of an inequality is extended to include compound inequalities. Students also transform statements into inequalities and graph the solution sets on number lines.

## Lesson Summaries

### Lesson 3.1    *Activity: Tree Growth*

In this Activity, students measure the heights of drawings of a tree in six different years of growth. They then use a proportion to compute the actual height of the tree for each of those six years. Using their tables of data, students write expressions that represent the height of the tree for any year of growth and use them to make predictions about the height of the tree. Students are introduced to arrow diagrams and use them to represent/evaluate expressions. They also review the order of operations guidelines to help them evaluate expressions that contain many mathematical operations.

### Lesson 3.2    *Investigation: From Expression to Equation*

In this Investigation, students build on their work with simple expressions from Lesson 3.1 and construct equations that model a second stage of tree growth. They learn that an equation is a statement that two expressions are equal. Students become aware that solving some problems may require different strategies than they normally use. The process of using equations to model real-world problems that are unlike problems students have solved in the past is the main focus of this lesson.

### Lesson 3.3    *Using Arrow Diagrams and Tables to Solve Equations*

In this lesson, the use of arrow diagrams is expanded to represent two-step equations. Students solve equations by using a completed diagram to tell them which operations to perform and in which order. Students also learn to use the calculator **TABLE** feature to solve equations. The methods used in this lesson illustrate important algebraic properties, the Properties of Equality, which are used to solve many types of equations.

### Lesson 3.4    *R.A.P.*

In this lesson, students **R**eview **A**nd **P**ractice solving problems that require the use of skills and concepts taught in previous math levels. The skills reviewed in this lesson are skills that are needed as a basis for solving problems throughout this course.

### Lesson 3.5    *Investigation: Solving Multi-Step Equations and* 3.6   *Investigation: Solving Inequalities*

In Lesson 3.5, students explore using expressions and equations to model, evaluate, and solve real-world problems. Emphasis is placed on finding and combining like terms and isolating the variable. In Lesson 3.6 students apply this same knowledge to solving and graphing inequalities. The main purpose of the Investigation in this lesson is to provide students with a review of the Properties of Inequality.

### Lesson 3.7    *Compound Inequalities*

In this lesson, students use what they learned in Lessons 3.5 and 3.6 to write, solve, and graph compound inequalities. Students learn that the intersection of two graphs consists of all points that are common to both graphs, and the union of two graphs consists of all the points in one or the other or in both. Absolute value inequalities are included in some of the practice exercises.

## Lesson Guide

| Lesson/Objectives | Materials | |
|---|---|---|
| **Chapter 3 Opener: How Can We Care for Our Forests?**<br>• recognize that equations can be used to help maintain and protect our country's forests. | | |
| **3.1 Activity: Tree Growth**<br>• use arrow diagrams to represent expressions.<br>• evaluate expressions.<br>• write expressions to model real-world situations. | *Per pair:*<br>• inch ruler | *Optional:*<br>• TRM table shell for Question 2.<br>• TRM table shell for Exercises 6 and 9. |
| **3.2 Investigation: From Expression to Equation**<br>• write an equation that models a real-world situation. | | *Optional:*<br>• TRM table shells for Exercises 1 and 18.<br>• grid paper |
| **3.3 Using Arrow Diagrams and Tables to Solve Equations**<br>• use arrow diagrams to solve two-step equations.<br>• use tables to solve equations. | | |
| **3.4 R.A.P.**<br>• solve problems that require previously learned concepts and skills. | | |
| **3.5 Investigation: Solving Multi-Step Equations**<br>• combine like terms in an expression.<br>• solve equations.<br>• use equations to solve real-world problems. | | *Optional:*<br>• algebra tiles |
| **3.6 Investigation: Solving Inequalities**<br>• solve inequalities.<br>• graph inequalities. | | |
| **3.7 Compound Inequalities**<br>• write compound inequalities.<br>• graph compound inequalities on a number line.<br>• solve compound inequalities. | | |

## Pacing Guide

| | Day 1 | Day 2 | Day 3 | Day 4 | Day 5 | Day 6 | Day 7 | Day 8 | Day 9 | Day 10 |
|---|---|---|---|---|---|---|---|---|---|---|
| **Basic** | p. 56, 3.1 | 3.2 | 3.3 | 3.4 | 3.5 | 3.5 | 3.6 | 3.7 | project | review |
| **Standard** | p. 56, 3.1 | 3.2 | 3.3 | 3.4 | 3.5 | 3.5 | 3.6 | 3.7 | project | review |
| **Block** | p. 56, 3.1, 3.2 | 3.2, 3.3 | 3.3, 3.4 | 3.5 | 3.6, 3.7 | 3.7, project | review | | | |

**Supplement Support**

See the Book Companion Website at www.highschool.bfwpub.com/ModelingwithMathematics and the Teacher's Resource Materials (TRM) for additional resources.

# CHAPTER

# 3

# Solving Equations and Inequalities

## CONTENTS

# CHAPTER 3 OPENER

**5e** Engage

## Lesson Objective

- recognize that equations can be used to help maintain and protect our country's forests.

## Vocabulary

## Description

This reading helps students see that sustainable forest management involves planting large numbers of trees, and that mathematics can be used to predict the rate at which they will grow.

> **TEACHING TIP**
>
> After students have read the Chapter Opener, lead a class discussion on the importance of forests to their state and/or community. Ask students to name products that they use that come from trees. Examples could include furniture, paper, and books.

## How Can We Care for Our Forests?

One-third of the United States is covered with trees. In some states, the majority of land consists of forests. For example, in Virginia, 62% or 16 million acres is forested. Altogether, the United States contains about 230 billion trees or about 1,000 trees per person.

We often hear about problems related to the loss of forests, such as rain forests, throughout the world. In the United States, efforts are made to maintain a balance between the removal of trees for commercial and other purposes, and the natural or controlled regrowth of trees. One company that supplies wood for paper products, J. D. Irving Limited, has planted over 800 million trees over the past fifty years. A nonprofit organization called Sustainable Forestry Initiative, Inc., certifies forest lands in the United States and Canada to help ensure that responsible forest management is practiced.

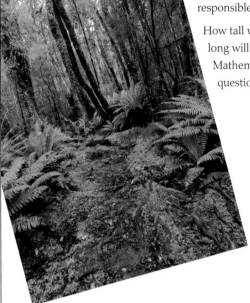

How tall will a tree be after ten years of growth? How long will it take a tree to reach 50 feet in height? Mathematical equations can be used to answer questions like these.

Algebraic expressions are some of the basic building blocks of mathematics. They allow us to describe real-world situations in such a way that the power of mathematics can be applied to them. In this Activity, you will write expressions to describe the growth of trees.

New trees arise naturally in a forest, from seeds that come from existing trees. In the United States, over 2 billion trees are planted each year by the forest products industry, tree farmers, and government agencies. Many of these plantings consist of small seedlings or saplings that are already more than a foot tall.

The figure below shows several stages in the growth of a tree. The first drawing on the left represents a newly planted sapling. This sequence of drawings shows successive years in the tree's growth.

Year 0   Year 1   Year 2   Year 3   Year 4   Year 5

| Year | Height on Drawing | Actual Height |
|------|-------------------|---------------|
| 0    |                   |               |
| 1    |                   |               |
| 2    |                   |               |
| 3    |                   |               |
| 4    |                   |               |
| 5    |                   |               |

1. The scale of the drawings is $\frac{1}{4}$ inch = 1 foot. Measure the height of the drawing of the newly planted sapling on the left to the nearest eighth of an inch. Then use a proportion to find the actual height of the tree.

2. Complete the table to the left by measuring each of the drawings and using a proportion to find the actual height of each tree.

3. Describe any pattern you see in the third column of your table.

4. If the pattern in the table continues, what do you expect the height of the tree to be after 6 years? After 10 years?

5. Let the variable $n$ represent any number of years of tree growth. Assuming the pattern continues, what do you expect the height of the tree to be after $n$ years?

## Lesson 3.1 Activity Answers

1. $\frac{1}{2}$ inch; 2 feet

2. Sample answer:

| Year | Height on Drawing | Actual Height |
|------|-------------------|---------------|
| 0    | $\frac{1}{2}$ inch | 2 feet |
| 1    | $\frac{7}{8}$ inch | $3\frac{1}{2}$ feet |
| 2    | $1\frac{1}{4}$ inches | 5 feet |
| 3    | $1\frac{5}{8}$ inches | $6\frac{1}{2}$ feet |
| 4    | 2 inches | 8 feet |
| 5    | $2\frac{3}{8}$ inches | $9\frac{1}{2}$ feet |

3. Sample answer: The heights increase by a constant amount of $1\frac{1}{2}$ feet each year.

4. 11 feet; 17 feet

5. Sample answer: $2 + 1.5n$ feet

## Lesson Objectives
- use arrow diagrams to represent expressions.
- evaluate expressions.
- write expressions to model real-world situations.

## Vocabulary
- algebraic expression
- coefficient
- evaluate an expression
- order of operations

## Materials List
- rulers

## Description
*Preparation:*

Have students work in pairs. Provide each pair with a ruler.

*During the Activity:*

Students should measure the heights of the trees in the drawing to the nearest eighth of an inch and then use the $\frac{1}{4}$ inch = 1 foot scale to compute the corresponding tree heights.

*Closing the Activity:*

Make sure students see that the construction of an arrow diagram is based on the *Order of Operations Guidelines*. Write an expression, such as $\frac{x+4}{7}$, on the board. Ask students to represent the expression with an arrow diagram. Then have them evaluate the expression for different values of $x$.

### TEACHING TIP

Ask students how they converted measurements from the drawing to actual tree heights.

**6a.** 1.5; It is the yearly rate of tree growth.

**6b.** 2; It represents the height of the tree when planted, 2 feet.

**7.**

Multiply by 1.5   Add 2

$n$      $1.5n$      $1.5n + 2$

**8.** $2 + 1.5(15) = 24.5$ feet

---

**TEACHING TIP**

Point out to students that the *Order of Operations Guidelines* for algebraic expressions are the same as those for arithmetic.

---

**TEACHING TIP**

Remind students that the fraction bar is a grouping symbol, as are parentheses, brackets, and braces.

---

Your answer to Question 5 is an example of an algebraic expression.

An **algebraic expression** contains one or more variables. It can also include numbers, grouping symbols, and operation symbols.

Other examples of algebraic expressions include the following:

$25w$ $\qquad$ $4t - 3$ $\qquad$ $5(2x + 7y)$

**6.** A number that is multiplied by a variable in an expression is called the **coefficient** of that variable. Look at the expression you wrote for Question 5.

  **a.** What is the coefficient of $n$? What does it represent?

  **b.** What is the constant term? What does it represent?

**7.** An *arrow diagram* is one way to represent an expression. In an arrow diagram, arrows are used to show the order in which operations are performed. For example, this arrow diagram represents the expression $5x - 3$.

Multiply by 5    Subtract 3

$x$      $5x$      $5x - 3$

Draw an arrow diagram to represent the expression in your answer to Question 5.

**8.** To **evaluate**, or find the value of, an algebraic expression, substitute a numerical value for the variable. Then simplify the resulting expression. Predict the height of the tree after 15 years by evaluating your expression for $n = 15$. Use your arrow diagram as a guide.

## ORDER OF OPERATIONS

When you evaluate expressions that contain many mathematical operations, guidelines must be followed. These guidelines tell you the order in which the operations must be performed.

> **Order of Operations Guidelines**
>
> To evaluate an expression that contains more than one operation, the following order is used:
>
> 1. Perform the operations within any grouping symbols, which include parentheses, brackets, and fraction bars.
>
> 2. Evaluate powers.
>
> 3. Perform multiplications and divisions in order from left to right.
>
> 4. Perform additions and subtractions in order from left to right.

# E X A M P L E

Evaluate the expression $(a + 7) + 4(3 - a) - a^3$ for $a = 2$.

**Solution:**

| | |
|---|---|
| Substitute 2 for $a$. | $(a + 7) + 4(3 - a) - a^3 = (2 + 7) + 4(3 - 2) - 2^3$ |
| Perform operations within parentheses. | $= 9 + 4(1) - 2^3$ |
| Evaluate powers. | $= 9 + 4(1) - 8$ |
| Multiply and divide from left to right. | $= 9 + 4 - 8$ |
| Add and subtract from left to right. | $= 5$ |

## Practice for Lesson 3.1

**For Exercises 1–2, draw an arrow diagram to represent the expression. Then evaluate the expression for $m = 21$.**

1. $\dfrac{m}{3} + 12$

2. $\dfrac{m + 12}{3}$

**For Exercises 3–5, evaluate the expression.**

3. $4(b - 2) + 3b - b^2$ for $b = 5$

4. $3k - k^4 + 5(k + 1) - k$ for $k = -1$

5. $5 - \dfrac{2y + 1}{3} + y^3 - 10y$ for $y = 4$

**For Exercises 6–8, use the following information.**

A landscaper plants a tree that is 5 feet tall. The tree grows 2 feet taller each year.

6. Complete the table to show the height of the tree during the first 6 years of growth.

| Years of Growth | Height of Tree (ft) |
|---|---|
| 0 | |
| 1 | |
| 2 | |
| 3 | |
| 4 | |
| 5 | |
| 6 | |

6.

| Height of Tree (ft) |
|---|
| 5 |
| 7 |
| 9 |
| 11 |
| 13 |
| 15 |
| 17 |

## ADDITIONAL EXAMPLE

Evaluate the expression

$4t + 8 - 2t^2 + \dfrac{t + 1}{3}$ for $t = 5$. $-20$

### TEACHING TIP

For some students, it may be helpful to review some of the properties of real numbers such as the Commutative, Associative, and Distributive Properties. (See Appendix J.)

### TEACHING TIP

**Exercises 1–2** ask students to draw arrow diagrams and use them to evaluate simple expressions. This is an important preparation for using arrow diagrams to solve two-step equations in Lesson 3.3. While arrow diagrams are of limited utility in representing more involved expressions and equations, they can be very helpful to students who have difficulty with order of operations and the fundamentals of solving equations.

## Practice for Lesson 3.1 Answers

1. $\dfrac{21}{3} + 12 = 19$

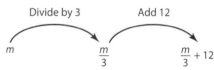

2. $\dfrac{21 + 12}{3} = 11$

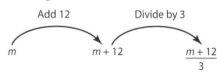

3. 2
4. −3
5. 26

**7.** $5 + 2n$ or $2n + 5$

**8.** $5 + 2(8) = 21$ feet

**9.**

| Length of Beach (ft) |
| --- |
| 50 |
| 48 |
| 46 |
| 44 |
| 42 |
| 40 |

**10.** Sample answer: Start with a length of 50 feet, then subtract 2 feet three times.

**11.** $L = 50 - 2t$

**12.** $50 - 2(15) = 20$ ft

**13.** 19,500

**14.** It represents the population of the town in 2000.

**15.** It represents the yearly growth rate of the town.

**16.** It represents his weight at the beginning of October.

**17.** It represents the number of pounds he loses each week.

**7.** Write an expression for the height of the tree after $n$ years.

**8.** Use your expression to find the height of the tree after 8 years.

**For Exercises 9–12, use the following information.**

An ocean beach extends out into the ocean a length of 50 feet, but erosion causes it to lose 2 feet of length a year.

**9.** Complete the table to show the length of the beach during the first 5 years of erosion.

| Years of Erosion | Length of Beach (ft) |
| --- | --- |
| 0 | |
| 1 | |
| 2 | |
| 3 | |
| 4 | |
| 5 | |

**10.** Explain the process you used to find the length of the beach after 3 years of erosion.

**11.** Write an equation that models the length $L$ of the beach after $t$ years.

**12.** Find the length of the beach after 15 years if erosion continues at the same rate.

**For Exercises 13–15, use the following information.**

The expression $12{,}500 + 700n$ describes the population of a town $n$ years after the year 2000.

**13.** What was the town's population in 2010?

**14.** What does 12,500 represent in the expression?

**15.** What does 700 represent in the expression?

**For Exercises 16–17, use the following information.**

A wrestler is trying to lose a little weight in preparation for wrestling season. The expression $152 - 3t$ gives his weight (in pounds) during October, where $t$ represents time in weeks.

**16.** What does 152 represent in the expression?

**17.** What does 3 represent in the expression?

Expressions can be used to form equations, which are useful mathematical representations. They allow people to predict what will happen in a certain situation or how to achieve a particular objective. In this lesson, you will use expressions as building blocks for writing equations.

As you saw in Lesson 3.1, the numerical value of an expression depends on the value or values given to the variables in the expression. If two expressions are known to have the same value, they can be written as part of an equation.

> An **equation** is a statement that two expressions are equal.

You found in Lesson 3.1 that the expression $2 + 1.5n$ represents the height of the tree after $n$ years. The equation

$$\text{height} = 2 + 1.5n$$

models the relationship between age and height for all possible ages and heights of the tree. You could also write this as $h = 2 + 1.5n$.

1. Coast redwood trees include the tallest individual organisms that ever existed on Earth. For the first 20 years of its life, a coast redwood might grow 3 feet each year. Write an equation that models the height $h$ of a coast redwood at age $n$ years after being grown from a seed.

2. If grown from a sapling that is planted when it is 2 feet tall, what would be an equation for a coast redwood's height at any age?

After 20 years, a redwood's growth rate typically slows. Suppose that a particular tree begins to grow at only 1.4 feet a year after year 20. Finding an equation that models the tree's height for ages beyond 20 years requires careful thought.

3. You can often begin modeling a situation like this by using words to express the total amount described in the problem. The total height of the coast redwood includes the growth during both parts of the growing cycle. Begin an equation with "$h =$" and use words to describe the two portions of the tree's growth for any age greater than 20 years.

$$h = \underline{\hspace{4cm}} + \underline{\hspace{4cm}}$$

## Lesson Objective

- write an equation that models a real-world situation.

## Vocabulary

- equation

## Materials List

## Description

This lesson is designed as a small group investigation (2–4 students). In **Questions 1–6** students build on their work with simple expressions from Lesson 3.1 and construct equations that model a second stage of tree growth.

**Question 7** asks students to use their equation to predict tree growth.

*Wrapping Up the Investigation:*

Ask students to share their models with the class to see if there are any differences. If any groups have written their equation in the simplified form $h = 34 + 1.4n$, point out that this form would be difficult to find directly. This should help convince students of the value of the incremental model-building process in the Investigation.

### CONNECTION

The growth pattern discussed in **Question 3** is a simplification. Actual tree growth rates would not change so abruptly.

### TEACHING TIP

Beginning with **Question 3**, caution students to resist the urge to jump immediately to a symbolic equation. Point out that the process of *building* a model is the objective here.

## Lesson 3.2 Investigation Answers

1. $h = 3n$
2. $h = 3n + 2$
3. Sample answer: $h =$ (growth during first 20 years) + (growth after 20 years)

# LESSON 3.2

**TEACHING TIP**

In **Question 6**, if students have trouble writing a symbolic equation, suggest that they build a table to look for a pattern in heights for individual years beyond 20.

**TEACHING TIP**

Discuss the list of strategies for model construction with students. Point out that **Questions 3–6** of the Investigation provide an example of the first strategy listed. Remind students that the second strategy listed was used in the Activity in Lesson 3.1.

4. $3(20) + 2 = 62$; $h = 62 +$ (growth after 20 years)
5. Sample answer: $h = 62 + 1.4$ (number of years greater than 20)
6. $h = 62 + 1.4(n - 20)$
7. 97 feet

4. Your answer to Question 2 about the growth of a tree from a sapling provides a way to calculate the tree's height after 20 years. Find that height and use it to simplify part of your word equation from Question 3.

5. Another way to describe the growth after 20 years might be "After 20 years, the tree grows 1.4 feet per year." Revise your equation to take this fact into account. Include the number 1.4, but use words to express the number of years after 20 that your expression will represent.

6. Express the number of years greater than 20 in terms of the total age $n$ of the tree. Then write a completely symbolic equation that models the height of the tree for any age $n$ greater than 20 years.

7. Use your equation to find the height of the tree after 45 years.

## STRATEGIES FOR CONSTRUCTING MATHEMATICAL MODELS

Some situations are simple enough that they can be easily modeled by comparing them to known models. Many real-world applications involve an initial value of some quantity that then grows at a constant rate, just like the growth of the redwood during its first 20 years. For example, a baseball weighs about one-third of a pound. So, a 2-pound box containing $n$ baseballs would have a total weight of $w = 2 + \frac{1}{3}n$ pounds.

But other problems may be unique, or at least unlike situations more familiar to a modeler. The growth of the redwood tree after 20 years is an example. In such cases some of the following strategies may be useful.

- **Write a simple "word equation."**
  Make sure your words state the big idea of the problem. Then gradually add smaller pieces of the problem until you have a symbolic equation.
- **Make a table.**
  Your table should contain specific values for the quantities that you are investigating. Once your table is complete, look for a pattern.
- **Draw a sketch or diagram.**
  This strategy is often used in situations that include aspects of geometry.
- **Check your model.**
  When you have found a model you think is a good one, substitute values for any variables in the model to see if they predict reasonable results.

## E X A M P L E

A girl is 36 inches tall at age 3. She grows $2\frac{1}{2}$ inches each year up to age 8. Find an equation that models her height $h$ at any age $A$ from 3 to 8 years.

### Solution:

*Make a table* to show the girl's height from ages 3 to 8 years.

| Age (years) | Height (inches) |
|---|---|
| 3 | 36 |
| 4 | $38\frac{1}{2}$ |
| 5 | 41 |
| 6 | $43\frac{1}{2}$ |
| 7 | 46 |
| 8 | $48\frac{1}{2}$ |

The pattern in the table shows that height increases by $2\frac{1}{2}$ inches for each year beyond 3 years of age.

*Write a word equation*: "Her height at any age is 36 inches plus $2\frac{1}{2}$ inches for each year of age beyond 3."

The word *is* can be replaced by an equal sign. The number of years beyond 3 can be written as the expression $(A - 3)$. So, the relationship between age and height can be modeled by the equation

$$h = 36 + 2\frac{1}{2}(A - 3)$$

*Check the model:* At age 7, the model predicts a height $h = 36 + 2\frac{1}{2}(7 - 3)$ or 46 inches.

This checks with the corresponding value in the table.

## Practice for Lesson 3.2

**For Exercises 1–8, use the following information.**

A tree is planted as a 3-foot sapling and grows $1\frac{3}{4}$ feet per year.

| Time (years) | Height (feet) |
|---|---|
| 0 | |
| 1 | |
| 2 | |
| 3 | |
| 4 | |
| 5 | |

1. Complete the table to show the tree's growth for the first 5 years.

2. Identify the independent and dependent variables. Explain your choices.

3. Make a scatter plot of the data in your table. Does it make sense to draw a line through the plot? Explain. If it does, find the slope of the line.

4. Is this a direct variation function? Explain.

FROM EXPRESSION TO EQUATION    **Lesson 3.2**    63

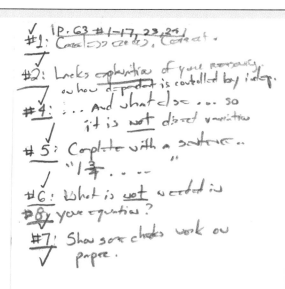

### ADDITIONAL EXAMPLE

A giant sequoia tree has an initial diameter of 4.320 meters and it grows 0.003 meters in diameter each year thereafter.

a. Find an equation that models the diameter $d$ of the tree after $t$ years.
   $d = 4.320 + 0.003t$

b. Find the diameter of the tree after 100 years.
   4.620 m

### Practice for Lesson 3.2 Answers

1.

| Height (feet) |
|---|
| 3 |
| $4\frac{3}{4}$ |
| $6\frac{1}{2}$ |
| $8\frac{1}{4}$ |
| 10 |
| $11\frac{3}{4}$ |

2. Sample answer: Time (years) is the independent variable and height (feet) is the dependent variable, because the height of the tree depends on how much time it has been growing.

3. Sample answer: It makes sense to draw a line, because the rate of change of height should remain constant at all times. The slope is $1\frac{3}{4}$ feet/year.

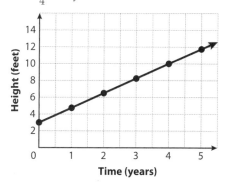

4. No, the ratios of time to height are not constant and the graph does not pass through the origin.

5.  Sample answer: $1\frac{3}{4}$ inches for every year of growth
6.  $h = 3 + 1.75t$ or $h = 1.75t + 3$
7.  Sample answer: After 5 years, the model gives $h = 3 + 1.75(5) = 11.75$, which agrees with the table.
8.  $h = 3 + 1.75(10) = 20.5$ ft
9.  Sample answer: Time (hours) is the independent variable and snow height (inches) is the dependent variable, because the height of the snow depends on how much time it has been snowing.
10. Sample answer: Yes, if snow continues to fall, it would gradually build up. The slope is 2.3 inches per hour.

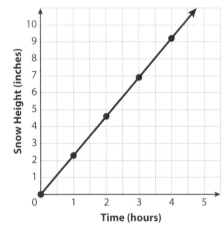

11. Sample answer: Yes, the graph is a straight line that passes through the origin. The ratios of height to time are constant.
12. $h = 2.3t$
13. $h = 2.3(8) = 18.4$ in.
14a. $C = 6.99n + 12$
14b. $67.92
15a. $I = 800 + 0.06s$
15b. $920

5.  Complete the following sentence to describe the way the tree's height changes: "Its height at any time is 3 feet plus _____."
6.  Write an equation that models the height $h$ of the tree after $t$ years.
7.  Check your model against the values in your table.
8.  Find the height of the tree after 10 years if the same rate of growth continues.

**For Exercises 9–13, use the following information.**

The table shows the amount of snow that accumulated on the ground during a snowstorm.

| Time (hours) | Snow Height (inches) |
|---|---|
| 0 | 0 |
| 1 | 2.3 |
| 2 | 4.6 |
| 3 | 6.9 |
| 4 | 9.2 |

9.  Identify the independent and dependent variables. Explain your choices.
10. Make a scatter plot of the data. Does it make sense to draw a line through the plot? Explain. If it does, find the slope of the line.
11. Is this a direct variation function? Explain.
12. Write an equation that models the height $h$ of the snow after $t$ hours.
13. Find the height of the snow after 8 hours if the same rate of snowfall continues.
14. DVDs can be bought from an Internet retailer for $6.99 each. The shipping cost for the entire order is $12, no matter how many DVDs are ordered.
    a.  Write an equation that models the total cost $C$ of an order of $n$ DVDs.
    b.  Find the total cost of an order of 8 DVDs.
15. A salesperson makes a salary of $800 a week plus a commission of 6 percent on the value of all goods sold.
    a.  Write an equation that models the salesperson's total income $I$ for a week in which her sales amount is $s$ (in dollars).
    b.  Find the salesperson's total income if she sells $2,000 worth of goods.

√#9: Lacks explanation of how dependent is controlled by indep.

#16b: What is missing in final answer?

√#17b: What number convention is missing in your final answer?

#23 a & b: Good job! But, variable typically placed on left side.

√#24 a & b: Fabulous work!! But constants ($0.45 and $0.20) customarily placed to left of parentheses ... to the right

16. In one airline's frequent-flyer program, a passenger receives two credits for each round-trip flight. Also, 0.5 credits are awarded for each approved car rental.
   a. Write an equation that models the total number of credits $C$ received if the number of round-trip flights is $f$ and the number of car rentals is $r$.
   b. Find the number of credits received if a person made 5 round-trip flights and rented a car twice.

17. The assembly shop of a custom furniture manufacturer has just produced a set of 8 chairs. Each chair must be sanded 3 times. Then 2 coats of finish must be applied.
   a. Write an equation that models the total time $t$ needed to complete a set of 8 chairs if it takes $s$ minutes to sand a chair one time and $f$ minutes to apply a coat of finish.
   b. Find the time it takes to complete a set of chairs if it takes 35 minutes to sand a single chair one time and 25 minutes to apply one coat of the finish.

**For Exercises 18–22, use the following information.**

In one state, for speeding on a 65-mile-per-hour highway a person may be fined $50 as well as an additional $10 for each mile per hour over the speed limit.

18. Complete the table to show the total fine $F$ for various speeds $s$.

| Speed (mph) | Fine ($) |
|---|---|
| 65 | 0 |
| 66 | |
| 67 | |
| 68 | |
| 69 | |
| 70 | |

19. Identify the independent and dependent variables. Explain your choices.

20. Complete the following sentence to describe the way the fine depends on speed: "The total fine is $50 plus _____."

21. Write an equation that models the total fine $F$ (in dollars) for any speed $s$ that is at least 65 mph.

22. Find the total fine if a person is caught going 78 miles per hour.

**16a.** $C = 2f + 0.5r$
**16b.** 11 credits
**17a.** $t = 8(3s + 2f)$
**17b.** 1,240 minutes
**18.**

| Fine ($) |
|---|
| 0 |
| 60 |
| 70 |
| 80 |
| 90 |
| 100 |

19. Sample answer: Speed (mph) is the independent variable and the fine ($) is the dependent variable, because the amount of the fine depends on how fast a person is traveling.
20. Sample answer: $10 for every mile per hour of speed above 65 mph
21. $F = 50 + 10(s - 65)$
22. $F = 50 + 10(78 - 65) = \$180$

**COMMON ERROR**

In **Exercise 21**, students may be tempted to write "10(miles per hour over 65)" and then have trouble seeing where to go from there. Suggest they pick a speed that is over 65 mph and compute the difference to see that $(s - 65)$ is the appropriate expression.

**23a.** $A = \dfrac{84 + 72 + 65 + 90 + T}{5}$

**23b.** 81

**24a.** $C = 39.99 + 0.45(m - 450)$

**24b.** $C = 39.99 + 0.45(m - 450) + 9.99 + 0.20(d - 25)$

**25a.** $L = 20[2h + 2(w + 3)]$ or
$L = 20[2(h + 3) + 2w]$

**25b.** 2,520 in. or 210 ft

---

**23.** Suppose that your scores on the first four tests in a course are 84, 72, 65, and 90. There is one test remaining, and all tests have equal weight.
  **a.** Write an equation that relates your score $T$ on the final test to your final average $A$ for all 5 tests.
  **b.** Calculate your average if the score on your final test is 94.

**24.** One cell-phone plan costs $39.99 a month for 450 minutes of talking and unlimited texting. Each additional minute over 450 costs 45 cents.
  **a.** Write an equation that models the relationship between the total cost $C$ of the plan and the number of minutes $m$ talked during a month in which more than 450 minutes are used.
  **b.** Another plan has the same features and costs. But it also includes a $9.99 charge for up to 25 megabytes of data transfer. Each additional megabyte of data costs 20 cents. Revise your answer to part (a) to reflect the inclusion of the data feature, using $d$ to represent the number of megabytes of data transferred. Assume that at least 25 megabytes of data are transfered.

**25.** The figure below shows a window and its frame.

  **a.** Write an equation that relates the height $h$ and width $w$ of the inside dimensions of the window to the total length $L$ of framing material needed for 20 identical windows in a house. (Assume that the frame is $1\frac{1}{2}$ inches wide.)
  **b.** How much framing material is needed if each window is 2 feet wide and 3 feet high?

Once a situation has been modeled by an equation, the power of mathematics can be used to analyze the problem. In this lesson, you will examine some basic techniques for solving equations.

### INVERSE OPERATIONS AND ARROW DIAGRAMS

In the last lesson, you found that the equation $h = 3n$ could be used to model the growth in height of a coast redwood grown from a seed. If you want to find how many years it will take for a tree grown from seed to reach a height of 40 feet, you can use the equation $3n = 40$.

This simple equation can be modeled with an arrow diagram.

**Recall**

**Inverse operations** are operations that undo each other. Multiplication and division are inverse operations. Addition and subtraction are also inverse operations.

You can add a reverse arrow to this diagram to show how to solve the equation for $n$.

The reversed lower arrow indicates that division by 3 will undo the multiplication represented by the upper arrow.

Then, to solve the equation $3n = 40$ for $n$, use division (the inverse of multiplication) to undo the operation on the variable.

$$\frac{3n}{3} = \frac{40}{3}$$
$$n = \frac{40}{3} \text{ or } 13\frac{1}{3}$$

So, it will take $13\frac{1}{3}$ years for the tree to grow to 40 feet.

# LESSON 3.3

**5e** Explain

## Lesson Objectives
- use arrow diagrams to solve two-step equations.
- use tables to solve equations.

## Vocabulary
- equivalent equations
- inverse operations
- Properties of Equality

## Description

This lesson introduces the use of arrow diagrams and calculator tables as aids to solving two-step equations. Arrow diagrams are especially helpful for students who have difficulty deciding which operations to use at any stage of solving an equation.

**TEACHING TIP**

If students need to review solving simple one- and two-step equations, take time to review Appendix L.

**TWO-STEP EQUATIONS**

The equation $h = 2 + 1.5n$ gives the height of a particular tree grown from a 2-foot sapling. An arrow diagram can be drawn to represent this equation.

To find how many years it will take for a 2-foot sapling to grow to a height of 35 feet, rewrite the equation as $1.5n + 2 = 35$. Then replace $h$ with 35 in the arrow diagram.

Reverse each arrow by using the corresponding inverse operation.

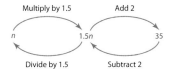

The completed diagram shows that the equation can be solved for $n$ by first subtracting 2 from 35 and then dividing the result by 1.5.

Arrow diagrams are helpful in solving equations because they tell you which operations to perform, and in what order.

| | |
|---|---|
| Original equation | $1.5n + 2 = 35$ |
| Subtract 2. | $1.5n + 2 - 2 = 35 - 2$ |
| Simplify. | $1.5n = 33$ |
| Divide by 1.5. | $\dfrac{1.5n}{1.5} = \dfrac{33}{1.5}$ |
| Simplify. | $n = 22$ |

$$\text{Check:} \qquad 1.5(22) + 2 \overset{?}{=} 35$$
$$33 + 2 \overset{?}{=} 35$$
$$35 = 35 \checkmark$$

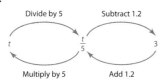

**a.** Draw an arrow diagram that models the solution of the equation $\frac{t}{5} - 1.2 = 3$.

**b.** Solve the equation for $t$.

**Solution:**

**a.**

Divide by 5      Subtract 1.2

$t$    $\frac{t}{5}$    $3$

Multiply by 5      Add 1.2

**b.**

| | |
|---|---|
| Original equation | $\frac{t}{5} - 1.2 = 3$ |
| Add 1.2. | $\frac{t}{5} - 1.2 + 1.2 = 3 + 1.2$ |
| Simplify. | $\frac{t}{5} = 4.2$ |
| Multiply by 5. | $5\left(\frac{t}{5}\right) = 5(4.2)$ |
| Simplify. | $t = 21$ |

*Check:* $\qquad \frac{21}{5} - 1.2 \overset{?}{=} 3$

$4.2 - 1.2 \overset{?}{=} 3$

$3 = 3 \checkmark$

### USING A TABLE TO SOLVE AN EQUATION

Equations can often be solved by examining a table of values. Some calculators have a **TABLE** feature that simplifies this approach.

**ADDITIONAL EXAMPLE**

**a.** Draw an arrow diagram that models the solution of the equation $\frac{a - 2.6}{3} = 1.8$.

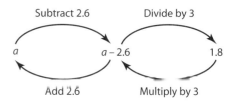

Subtract 2.6      Divide by 3

$a$    $a - 2.6$    $1.8$

Add 2.6      Multiply by 3

**b.** Solve the equation for $a$.    $a = 8$

## ADDITIONAL EXAMPLE

Use a calculator table to solve
$$\frac{a - 2.6}{3} = 1.8.$$

### TEACHING TIP

On many calculators, the only variables allowed are X and Y. Remind students that they should interpret calculator output in the context of the given situation.

Use a calculator table to solve the equation $\frac{t}{5} - 1.2 = 3$ for $t$.

**Solution:**

Enter the expression $\frac{t}{5} - 1.2$ on the function screen $\boxed{Y=}$ of a calculator.

On the **TABLE SETUP** screen [**TBLSET**], choose a starting value (**TblStart**) and the increment (**∆Tbl**) for the variable.

Examine the [**TABLE**] screen to see if the expression equals 3 for any of the input values that first appear.

If not, scroll up or down until the value in the **Y1** column equals 3.

### Note

Sometimes you may not be able to find the exact number you are looking for in the **Y1** column. In such cases, you may have to refine your table. (See Exercise 4, page 71.)

The solution is $t = 21$.

**4b.** Sample answer: The value of $h$ is 60 for some value of $n$ between 22 and 23.

**4c.** The value of $h$ is 60 when $n = 22.8$ years.

## PROPERTIES OF EQUALITY

The methods used in this lesson illustrate important algebraic properties that are used to solve many types of equations. All of the steps in solving an equation involve changing it to an **equivalent equation**. Equations are equivalent if they have the same solution (or solutions).

> The **Properties of Equality** state that an equation can be changed into an equivalent equation by
> - exchanging the expressions on the two sides of the equation;
> - adding the same number to each side of the equation;
> - subtracting the same number from each side of the equation;
> - multiplying each side of the equation by the same non-zero number;
> - dividing each side of the equation by the same non-zero number.

### Practice for Lesson 3.3

**For Exercises 1–3, complete Parts (a), (b), and (c).**
  a. Draw an arrow diagram that models the solution of the equation.
  b. Use a calculator table to solve the equation for the given variable.
  c. Use the Properties of Equality to solve the equation algebraically.

1. Solve $6b - 5 = 19$ for $b$.

2. Solve $3(x + 10) = 6$ for $x$.

3. Solve $\dfrac{d - 10}{5} = 7$ for $d$.

4. The equation $h = 3 + 2.5n$ models the height $h$ (in feet) of a tree after $n$ years. Suppose that you want to use a table to determine how many years it will take the tree to grow to a height of 60 feet.
  a. Enter the expression $3 + 2.5n$ on the function screen of a calculator.
  b. Create a table and scroll to find where the value of $h$ is approximately 60. Describe what you find.
  c. To search for a more accurate answer, go to the **TABLE SETUP** screen. Enter a starting value of 22 and an increment of 0.1. Then return to the table and search for an $h$-value of 60. Describe what you find.

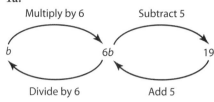

## Practice for Lesson 3.3 Answers

**1a.**

Multiply by 6         Subtract 5

$b$                    $6b$                    19

Divide by 6           Add 5

**1b.**

| X | Y₁ |
|---|---|
| 0 | -5 |
| 1 | 1 |
| 2 | 7 |
| 3 | 13 |
| **4** | **19** |
| 5 | 25 |
| 6 | 31 |

X=4

**1c.** Original equation     $6b - 5 = 19$
  Add 5 to both sides.        $6b = 24$
  Divide both sides by 6.      $b = 4$

> **TEACHING TIP**
>
> **Exercise 2** If students have trouble finding negative solutions, point out that they may sometimes have to scroll upward on their table screens if they start with an $x$-value of 0.

> **TEACHING TIP**
>
> While an exact solution for **Exercise 4** can be found using a calculator table, you may wish to remind students that sometimes only an approximate solution can be found. Such a situation is addressed in **Exercise 27** of **Lesson 3.5**.

**2a.**

Add 10                Multiply by 3

$x$                    $x + 10$                6

Subtract 10           Divide by 3

**2b.**

| X | Y₁ |
|---|---|
| **-8** | **6** |
| -7 | 9 |
| -6 | 12 |
| -5 | 15 |
| -4 | 18 |
| -3 | 21 |
| -2 | 24 |

X=-8

**2c.** Original equation     $3(x + 10) = 6$
  Divide both sides by 3.  $x + 10 = 2$
  Subtract 10 from both sides. $x = -8$

**3a.**

Subtract 10           Divide by 5

$d$                    $d - 10$                7

Add 10                Multiply by 5

**3b.**

| X | Y₁ |
|---|---|
| 39 | 5.8 |
| 40 | 6 |
| 41 | 6.2 |
| 42 | 6.4 |
| 43 | 6.6 |
| 44 | 6.8 |
| **45** | **7** |

X=45

**3c.** Original equation     $\dfrac{d - 10}{5} = 7$
  Multiply both sides by 5. $d - 10 = 35$
  Add 10 to both sides.     $d = 45$

**4a.**

```
Plot1  Plot2  Plot3
\Y1■3+2.5X■
\Y2=
\Y3=
\Y4=
\Y5=
\Y6=
\Y7=
```

**4b.–4c.** Answers can be found on page 70.

71

For Exercises 5–11, solve the given equation for the variable. Draw an arrow diagram or use a table, if needed, to help you.

5. The equation $L = 50 - 2t$ models the erosion over time of a beach that extends 50 feet into the ocean and erodes at a rate of 2 feet per year. After how many years will the beach extend only 37 feet?

6. The diameter $d$ (in meters) of a giant sequoia tree after $t$ years is modeled by the equation $d = 4.320 + 0.003t$. After how many years will the tree's diameter be 4.590 meters?

7. The total cost, including shipping, of buying $n$ DVDs from a certain Internet retailer is modeled by the equation $C = 6.99n + 12$. How many DVDs can be bought for $80?

8. A salesperson earns a weekly income of $I = 800 + 0.06s$ dollars on sales with a value of $s$ dollars. How much must she sell to earn a total of $1,500 in a week?

9. A boy borrowed $2,200 from his uncle to buy a billiard table. He plans to pay his uncle back $150 a week from his summer job earnings.
   a. Write an equation that models the amount $A$ that the boy will owe his uncle after $w$ weekly payments.
   b. How much will the boy still owe after 8 weeks?
   c. How many weeks will it take to pay off the loan?

10. When real estate is purchased, the value of buildings is determined by subtracting the value of the land from the purchase price. A three-unit apartment building is purchased for $800,000. If each apartment unit is valued at $225,000, then the dollar value of the land $L$ is given by the equation
$$\frac{800,000 - L}{3} = 225,000$$
Find the value of the land for this building.

11. The velocity $v$ (in meters per second) of an object that is thrown straight upward with an initial velocity $v_0$ is given by $v = v_0 - 9.8t$, where $t$ represents time in seconds. If a ball is thrown upward at 30 meters per second, when will its velocity drop to 5 meters per second? Round to the nearest tenth of a second.

---

5. $6\frac{1}{2}$ years
6. 90 years
7. $n \approx 9.728$, so 9 DVDs can be bought
8. $11,666.67
9a. $A = 2,200 - 150w$
9b. $1,000
9c. 14.7 weeks or 15 weeks to pay off the loan
10. $125,000
11. after 2.6 seconds

**Fill in the blank.**

1. The word _____ means parts per hundred.

2. A statement that two expressions are equal is called a(n) _____.

3. Subtraction and _____ are called *inverse operations*.

**Choose the correct answer.**

4. Which percent is equivalent to $\frac{3}{4}$?

   A. 34%            B. 133%

   C. 0.75%          D. 75%

5. Which percent is equivalent to 0.025?

   A. 25%            B. 2.5%

   C. 0.025%         D. 0.0025%

**Multiply or divide. Write your answer in simplest form.**

6. $\frac{7}{9} \times \frac{3}{4} \times \frac{8}{9}$

7. $3\frac{3}{5} \times 4\frac{2}{3}$

8. $\frac{9}{10} \div \frac{3}{5}$

9. $8 \div 1\frac{1}{3}$

**Add or subtract.**

10. $4.5 - 12.14 + 0.78$

11. $125.98 - 42.176$

12. $0.4 + 0.04 + 0.004$

13. $14 - 1.76$

**Write the phrase as a variable expression.**

14. the sum of 6 and a number

15. a number multiplied by 8

16. 8 subtracted from a number

17. twice a number divided by 3

**For Exercises 18–21, evaluate the expression.**

18. $4d + 3(d - 1) - d^2$ for $d = 3$

19. $6x - x^2 + y - 8$ for $x = 3$ and $y = 4$

20. $a^2 - (2a + 6) + 1$ for $a = 5$

21. $\frac{5 + m^2}{m^3 - 5}$ for $m = 2$

## Lesson Objective

- solve problems that require previously learned concepts and skills.

## Exercise Reference

Exercise 1: Appendix E

Exercise 2: Lesson 3.2

Exercise 3: Lesson 3.3

Exercises 4–5: Appendix E

Exercises 6–9: Appendix A

Exercises 10–13: Appendix B

Exercises 14–21: Lesson 3.1

Exercise 22: Lesson 2.5

Exercises 23–28: Appendix K

Exercises 29–33: Appendix N

## Lesson 3.4 R.A.P. Answers

1. percent
2. equation
3. addition
4. D
5. B
6. $\frac{14}{27}$
7. $16\frac{4}{5}$
8. $\frac{3}{2}$ or $1\frac{1}{2}$
9. 6
10. $-6.86$
11. 83.804
12. 0.444
13. 12.24
14. $6 + n$
15. $8n$
16. $n - 8$
17. $\frac{2n}{3}$
18. 9
19. 5
20. 10
21. 3

**22.**  2
**23.**  $5.12 \times 10^8$
**24.**  $6.28 \times 10^2$
**25.**  $1.8025 \times 10^3$
**26.**  520,000
**27.**  7,000
**28.**  522,700,000
**29.**  14 low temperatures
**30.**  9 degrees
**31.**  34°F
**32.**  33°F and 37°F
**33.**  about 34.1°F

**22.** Find the slope of a line that passes through the points (4, 8) and (−3, −6).

**Write the number in scientific notation.**
**23.** 512,000,000     **24.** 628     **25.** 1,802.5

**Write the number in standard form.**
**26.** $5.2 \times 10^5$     **27.** $7 \times 10^3$     **28.** $5.227 \times 10^8$

**For Exercises 29–33, use the line plot.**

**Daily Low Temperature (°F)**

**29.** How many low temperatures are recorded in the line plot?

**30.** Find the range of the data.

**31.** What is the median of the data?

**32.** What is the mode of the data?

**33.** What is the mean of the data? (Round to the nearest tenth.)

**INVESTIGATION: Solving Multi-Step Equations**

In Lesson 3.3, you used the Properties of Equality to solve two-step equations. In this lesson, you will apply what you know about solving equations to solving equations with many steps.

### MULTI-STEP EQUATIONS

Suppose that your school's environmental club wants to travel to the state capital to participate in an Earth Day festival. Rental of a bus for the day will cost $895. Lunch and festival activities will cost $25 per student. Your club advisor thinks that the fee for participating should not be more than $60. How many students must be recruited for the trip?

1. To solve this problem, notice that the total fees collected must equal the total cost for the trip. If each of $n$ students pays $60 to attend, write an expression for the total number of dollars collected.

2. The total cost includes the fixed cost of $895 for the bus plus the cost for all the students. Write an expression for the total cost.

3. Form an equation from your expressions in Questions 1 and 2.

The solution to this equation represents the number of students $n$ that must be recruited in order to pay for the trip. Notice that this equation is different from the kind you solved in Lesson 3.3. The variable $n$ appears on both sides of the equation.

4. You can explore a solution to the equation using a calculator. Enter your expressions from Questions 1 and 2 separately as **Y1** and **Y2** on the function screen of a calculator.

5. Create a table on your calculator using an increment of 1 for $n$. Search for a value of $n$ that makes the two expressions approximately equal. Describe what you see.

6. Interpret your answer to Question 5 in the context of this situation.

7. There are two terms in the equation from Question 3 that contain $n$. One is on the left side of the equation and one is on the right side. To solve the equation algebraically for $n$, you must find an equivalent equation in which $n$ appears on only one side of the equation.

Perform an operation that will do this while leaving the constant term (895) by itself.

**Recall**

A **term** in an expression or equation is a variable, a number, or a product or quotient of variables or numbers.

4.

5. Sample answer: The values of the expressions are closest for $n = 26$.

| X | Y1 | Y2 |
|---|---|---|
| 22 | 1320 | 1445 |
| 23 | 1380 | 1470 |
| 24 | 1440 | 1495 |
| 25 | 1500 | 1520 |
| 26 | 1560 | 1545 |
| 27 | 1620 | 1570 |
| 28 | 1680 | 1595 |

X=26

6. Sample answer: For 25 students, the total cost of the trip is $1,520, but the total payments are only $1,500. For 26 students, the total cost is $1,545 and the total payments are $1,560. So, when the fee to participate is $60, 26 students are needed to pay for the trip. There will be $15 left over.

7. Subtract $25n$; $60n - 25n = 895$

## Lesson Objectives

- combine like terms in an expression.
- solve equations.
- use equations to solve real-world problems.

## Vocabulary

- like terms
- term

## Materials List

## Description

This lesson is designed as a small group investigation (2–4 students). Students should work through **Questions 1–9** to explore solving equations that involve more than two steps. In this case they will be combining like terms.

Because of the importance of these equation-solving skills and the large number of exercises, you may wish to devote two days to this lesson.

*Wrapping Up the Investigation:*

Make sure students understand that terms are like terms only if their variable parts are exactly the same.

---

**TEACHING TIP**

Notice that an arrow diagram is not useful for the equation in **Question 3**. These diagrams are rarely helpful for solving equations that require more than two steps.

---

**TEACHING TIP**

For **Question 5**, students need not try for greater accuracy than the nearest whole number, since fractions make no sense in this context.

---

## Lesson 3.5 Investigation Answers

1. $60n$
2. $895 + 25n$
3. $60n = 895 + 25n$

**8.** $35n = 895$

**9.** $n = \dfrac{895}{35}$ or about 25.57; Sample explanation: Since the number of students must be a whole number, at least 26 students must make the trip when the fee to participate is set at $60.

## ADDITIONAL EXAMPLE ❶

Combine like terms in each expression.

**a.** $12d - 7d\ 5d$

**b.** $5m - 2n - 4m\ m - 2n$

**c.** $14x + 2y\ \ 3x + x\ \ 6y\ 15x\ \ 4y\ \ 3x$

---

**8.** Each term containing $n$ can be thought of as a count of $n$'s. Simplify the equation by combining the two terms into one term giving the total count of $n$'s.

**9.** Solve your equation for $n$. Write a sentence explaining the meaning of the solution.

It is not unusual for an equation to contain several terms that may have to be combined. The Properties of Equality can then be used to solve the equation.

### COMBINING LIKE TERMS

If the variable parts of two terms are exactly the same, the terms are called **like terms**. For example, in the expression $5x + 3x + 9y$, the $5x$ and the $3x$ are like terms. In the expression $3t^2 + 4t - 10$, there are no like terms: $t^2$ and $t$ are not the same.

The expression $5a + 2a$ contains two like terms. You can use the Distributive Property to combine like terms.

$$5a + 2a = (5 + 2)a$$
$$= 7a$$

### E X A M P L E ❶

Combine like terms in each expression.

**a.** $8p - 6p$

**b.** $3b + 4c - 7b$

**c.** $10t - 3w + t + 6w - 2t$

**Solution:**

**a.** The variable parts are the same for both terms, so subtract the coefficients.

$$8p - 6p = (8 - 6)p$$
$$= 2p$$

**b.** First, rewrite the expression so that like terms are together.

$$3b + 4c - 7b = 4c + 3b - 7b$$
$$= 4c + (3 - 7)b$$
$$= 4c - 4b$$

**c.** Again, rewrite the expression so that like terms are together.

$$10t - 3w + t + 6w - 2t = 10t + t - 2t - 3w + 6w$$
$$= (10 + 1 - 2)t + (-3 + 6)w$$
$$= 9t + 3w$$

## HINTS FOR SOLVING EQUATIONS

The operations of addition, subtraction, multiplication, and division can be performed on both sides of an equation to produce an equivalent equation with the same solution.

- Simplify the expression on each side of the equation.
- Use addition and/or subtraction to isolate the variable in a single term on one side of the equation.
- Use multiplication and division to solve the equation.
- If an equation contains fractions, it is often helpful to eliminate the fractions by multiplying both sides of the equation by a common denominator.

 **EXAMPLE**

Solve $3p - 9 + 2p = 21$ for $p$.

**Solution:**

First, combine like terms. Reverse the usual order of operations. Undo the subtraction by adding 9 to both sides of the equation. Then divide both sides of the equation by 5.

| Original equation | $3p - 9 + 2p = 21$ |
| --- | --- |
| Combine like terms. | $5p - 9 = 21$ |
| Add 9 to both sides. | $5p - 9 + 9 = 21 + 9$ |
| Simplify. | $5p = 30$ |
| Divide both sides by 5. | $\dfrac{5p}{5} = \dfrac{30}{5}$ |
| Simplify. | $p = 6$ |

*Check*:
$$3(6) - 9 + 2(6) \overset{?}{=} 21$$
$$18 - 9 + 12 \overset{?}{=} 21$$
$$9 + 12 \overset{?}{=} 21$$
$$21 = 21 \checkmark$$

**ADDITIONAL EXAMPLE**

Solve $7b + 12 + 3b = 4$ for $b$. $-\dfrac{4}{5}$

## ADDITIONAL EXAMPLE 3

Solve $12t - 2(3t - 1) = 44$ for $t$. 7

## ADDITIONAL EXAMPLE 4

Solve $8q - 10 = q + 4$ for $q$. 2

## E X A M P L E 3

Solve $5x - 3(7 - 2x) = 23$ for $x$.

**Solution:**

| | |
|---|---|
| Original equation | $5x - 3(7 - 2x) = 23$ |
| Distributive Property. | $5x - 3(7) - 3(-2x) = 23$ |
| Simplify. | $5x - 21 + 6x = 23$ |
| Combine like terms. | $11x - 21 = 23$ |
| Add 21 to both sides. | $11x = 23 + 21$ |
| Simplify. | $11x = 44$ |
| Divide both sides by 11. | $\dfrac{11x}{11} = \dfrac{44}{11}$ |
| Simplify. | $x = 4$ |

*Check:*

$$5(4) - 3[7 - 2(4)] \overset{?}{=} 23$$
$$20 - 3(-1) \overset{?}{=} 23$$
$$20 + 3 \overset{?}{=} 23$$
$$23 = 23 \checkmark$$

## E X A M P L E 4

Solve $5B + 3 = 2B + 11$ for $B$.

**Solution:**

Begin by isolating the variable on one side of the equation.

| | |
|---|---|
| Original equation | $5B + 3 = 2B + 11$ |
| Subtract $2B$ from both sides. | $5B + 3 - 2B = 2B + 11 - 2B$ |
| Combine like terms. | $3B + 3 = 11$ |
| Subtract 3 from both sides. | $3B + 3 - 3 = 11 - 3$ |
| Simplify. | $3B = 8$ |
| Divide both sides by 3. | $\dfrac{3B}{3} = \dfrac{8}{3}$ |
| Simplify. | $B = \dfrac{8}{3}$ |

*Check:*

$$5\left(\frac{8}{3}\right) + 3 \overset{?}{=} 2\left(\frac{8}{3}\right) + 11$$
$$\frac{40}{3} + 3 \overset{?}{=} \frac{16}{3} + 11$$
$$\frac{49}{3} = \frac{49}{3} \checkmark$$

Notice that if you use 2.67 to approximate $\frac{8}{3}$, the left and right sides of the equation are not exactly equal. Only $\frac{8}{3}$ is an *exact* solution to the equation.

p. 79 #1-8, 13-19, 23-25

#1: 'define variable "s" → okay
didn't ask you to solve. Since you solved, what are correct units?

#2: Review and discuss with Dad. Confusing question.

#3: Review table with Dad. Okay

#6: Confusing like #2. Discuss with Dad.

#8: What is not right in final answer?

#23 n 6b: Correct. Review logic with Dad gives further challenge of weighnomets.

## Practice for Lesson 3.5

**For Exercises 1–4, use the following information.**

In one state, the fine $F$ for speeding on a 65-mile-per-hour highway is modeled by the equation $F = 50 + 10(s - 65)$, where $s$ is the speed.

1. Write an equation that you could solve to find the speed that would result in a fine of $270.

2. To use a table to solve for $s$, what would you use for a starting value for $s$? Explain.

3. Use a table to find the speed for a fine of $270.

4. Use the Properties of Equality to solve algebraically for $s$.

**For Exercises 5–8, use the following information.**

One cell-phone plan costs $39.99 a month for 450 minutes of talking and unlimited texting. Each additional minute over 450 costs 45 cents. The total monthly cost for any number of minutes $m$ that is greater than 450 can be modeled by $C = 39.99 + 0.45(m - 450)$.

5. Write an equation that you could solve to find how many talk minutes were used in a month for which the total bill is $136.74.

6. To use a table to solve for $m$, what would you use for a starting value for $m$? Explain.

7. Use a table to find the number of talk minutes for a bill of $136.74.

8. Use the Properties of Equality to solve algebraically for $m$.

**For Exercises 9–12, combine like terms.**

9. $8s + 12 - 3s + 20$

10. $p + 3q + 2p^2 - 8p - q$

11. $M^2 - 2M + 3M^2 + M$

12. $6x^2 + x^2y - xy^2 - 4x^2$

**For Exercises 13–19, solve for the variable, then check.**

13. $5y - 9 = 3y$

14. $4R + 8 = 6R - 4$

15. $18 + 10(w - 1) = 6w$

16. $7z = 15 - 6(z - 4)$

17. $4(y + 5) = 2y + 28$

18. $3 - 5(t + 6) = 8t - (4 - 2t)$

19. $8.6 + 2.1m = 3.7m - 4.2$

SOLVING MULTI-STEP EQUATIONS    Lesson 3.5    79

---

## Practice for Lesson 3.5
## Answers

1. $50 + 10(s - 65) = 270$

2. Sample answer: You could start with 66, since there will be no fine unless the speed is more than 65 mph.

3. The speed is 87 mph.

**TEACHING TIP**

**Exercises 6 and 7** If students find it tedious to scroll all the way down the table, suggest that they start with an increment of 10 and then refine their search.

**TEACHING TIP**

If students struggle with **Exercise 14**, you may want to have them use algebra tiles to help them visualize the operations involved in solving equations.

**TEACHING TIP**

In **Exercise 19**, students may find it helpful to begin by multiplying every term on both sides of the equation by 10 to eliminate decimal numbers.

4.
Original equation $50 + 10(s - 65) = 270$
Subtract 50 from
    both sides.        $10(s - 65) = 220$
Divide both sides by 10.   $s - 65 = 22$
Add 65 to both sides.       $s = 87$

5. $39.99 + 0.45(m - 450) = 136.74$

6. Sample answer: You could start with a number higher than 450, since the bill for 450 minutes would only be $39.99.

---

7. 665

8.
Original equation
    $39.99 + 0.45(m - 450) = 136.74$
Subtract 39.99 from both sides.
    $0.45(m - 450) = 96.75$
Divide both sides by 0.45.
    $m - 450 = 215$
Add 450 to both sides.   $m = 665$

9. $5s + 32$

10. $2p^2 - 7p + 2q$

11. $4M^2 - M$

12. $2x^2 + x^2y - xy^2$

13. $y = \dfrac{9}{2}$ or $4\dfrac{1}{2}$

14. $R = 6$

15. $w = -2$

16. $z = 3$

17. $y = 4$

18. $t = -\dfrac{23}{15}$ or $t \approx -1.53$

19. $m = 8$

**20.** 65 years
**21.** 1989
**22.** 1.6 L
**23a.** $L = 2s + 2(s - 3)$ or $L = 4(s - 1.5)$
**23b.** $49\frac{1}{2}$ inches or 4 feet $1\frac{1}{2}$ inches
**24a.** Sample answer: 6
**24b.** $3(y + 1) - 30 = 4y$
**24c.** $y = -27$
**25.** $x = -\frac{1}{2}$
**26.** $n = \frac{17}{2}$

---

**20.** In Lesson 3.2, you found that the equation $h = 62 + 1.4(n - 20)$ can be used to model the height of a coast redwood for ages greater than 20 years. How many years would it take a coast redwood to grow to a height of 125 feet?

**21.** For people born after 1975, average life expectancy $L$ can be found using the equation $L = 72.6 + 0.17(B - 1975)$, where $B$ represents year of birth. For what birth year is the average life expectancy 75 years?

**22.** Lab technicians often mix two solutions to make one solution with a required concentration. To find the volume $V$ of a 75% solution that must be added to 2 liters of a 30% solution in order to make a 50% solution, solve the equation $0.50(2 + V) = 0.30(2) + 0.75V$.

**23.** A square sandbox is made with lumber that is 1.5 inches thick.

  **a.** If the outside dimensions of the sandbox are of length $s$ (in inches), write an equation that models the total length $L$ of lumber needed.
  **b.** How long is a side of the largest sandbox that can be made from a single 16-*foot* long piece of lumber?

**24.** Consider the equation $\dfrac{y + 1}{2} - 5 = \dfrac{2}{3}y$. To avoid having to combine fractions, you can multiply both sides of the equation by a common denominator.
  **a.** What is a common denominator for the fractions in the equation?
  **b.** Multiply both sides of the equation by your answer to Part (a) and simplify the result.
  **c.** Solve your equation from Part (b) for $y$.

**25.** Solve $\dfrac{2 - x}{5} = \dfrac{4x + 3}{2}$ for $x$, then check.

**26.** Solve $\dfrac{2n - 3}{4} = \dfrac{n + 5}{3} - 1$ for $n$, then check.

**27.** The equation $5B + 3 = 2B + 11$ was solved algebraically in Example 4 (on p. 78). But if you try using a table to solve the equation, you will not be able to find the exact solution even if you refine the **TABLE SETUP [TBLSET]** by using a smaller increment. Explain.

**For Exercises 28–29, use the following information.**

The equation $|a| = 3$ contains an *absolute value* expression. Recall that $|a| = 3$ means $a = 3$ or $-a = 3$, depending on whether the value inside the absolute value symbols is positive or negative. The graph of $|a| = 3$ is

The graph shows that $|a| = 3$ can be interpreted as follows: "$a$ is a number whose distance from 0 on a number line is 3 units."

To solve an absolute value equation such as $|x - 7| = 4$, you first need to rewrite the equation as a compound sentence:

$$x - 7 = 4 \text{ or } -(x - 7) = 4$$

Then both of these equations must be solved in order to find the complete solution to $|x - 7| = 4$. For this equation, the solution set is $x = 3$ or $x = 11$.

**28.** Graph the solution set for $|x - 7| = 4$ on a number line.

**29.** Write a sentence that explains the meaning of $|x - 7| = 4$ in terms of a number line.

**For Exercises 30–31, complete Parts (a) and (b).**
   **a.** Solve the equation.
   **b.** Graph the solution set on a number line.

**30.** $|x + 7| = 4$

**31.** $|D + 8| = 36$

SOLVING MULTI-STEP EQUATIONS    **Lesson 3.5**    81

**27.** Sample answer: The solution to the equation is $\frac{8}{3}$. This fraction cannot be written as an exact decimal. Using a table, you could determine that the solution is between 2.6 and 2.7, but you could never find a decimal value of $B$ that makes both sides of the equation identical. The answer would have to be found to some required accuracy.

**28.**

**29.** Sample answer: $x$ is a number whose distance from 7 on a number line is 4.

**30a.** $x = -3$ or $-11$

**30b.**

**31a.** $D = -44$ or 28

**31b.**

#24b: What calc are a did you make in step 1?

#24c: What calc are did you make?

81

# LESSON 3.6

## Lesson Objectives
- solve inequalities.
- graph inequalities.

## Vocabulary
- Properties of Inequality

## Materials List
none

## Description

The main purpose of the Investigation in this lesson is to provide students with a review of the Properties of Inequality. This lesson can be used as a whole-class investigation, or students can work together in small groups as they review.

*Wrapping Up the Investigation:*

Discuss **Question 11 a–d** with the class to make sure everyone has correctly identified the Properties of Inequality.

## Lesson 3.6 Investigation Answers

1. Sample answer: 15 > 10
2. Yes.
3. Yes.
4. Yes.
5. Yes.
6. Yes.
7. No.
8. Yes.
9. The new inequality is false.

---

## Lesson 3.6    INVESTIGATION: Solving Inequalities

In the previous lessons in this chapter, you explored using expressions and equations to model real-world situations. You also learned to evaluate the expressions and solve the equations. In this lesson, you will apply your knowledge to solving inequalities.

In Lesson 3.5, you used the equation $60n = 895 + 25n$ to determine the number of students that must be recruited for the Earth Day trip. This problem could have been thought of in a different way. *Any* number of students could have gone on the trip as long as there was at least enough money to pay for the bus and other expenses.

So instead of using an equation, the problem is more accurately modeled with the *inequality*:

$$60n \geq 895 + 25n$$

Methods for solving inequalities are slightly different from methods for solving equations. To see how they differ, start with a simple example.

### Recall
Recall the definitions of the following inequality symbols:

| Symbol | Meaning |
|--------|---------|
| < | is less than |
| ≤ | is less than or equal to |
| > | is greater than |
| ≥ | is greater than or equal to |
| ≠ | is not equal to |

1. Pick any two different positive numbers. Then use those numbers and either a less-than symbol (<) or a greater-than symbol (>) to write a true statement.
2. Now add the same positive number to each side of your inequality. Does the inequality remain true?
3. Add the same negative number to each side of your original inequality. Is this new inequality statement true?
4. Subtract the same number from each side of your inequality. Does the inequality remain true?
5. Multiply each side of your original inequality by the same positive number. Is this new inequality true?
6. Divide each side of your original inequality by the same positive number. Does the inequality remain true?
7. Now multiply each side of your original inequality by the same negative number. Is this new statement true?
8. If you reverse the direction of the inequality symbol in your statement from Question 7, is your inequality true?
9. What do you think will happen if you divide each side of your original inequality by a negative number? Check to see if you are correct.

**10.** Now reverse the direction of the inequality in your statement from Question 9. Is your inequality true?

**11.** Summarize your findings from Questions 1–10 by filling in the blanks.

  **a.** If any number is added to each side of a true inequality, then the resulting inequality is _____.

  **b.** If any number is subtracted from each side of a true inequality, then the resulting inequality is _____.

  **c.** If each side of a true inequality is multiplied or divided by the same positive number, the resulting inequality is _____.

  **d.** If each side of a true inequality is multiplied or divided by the same negative number, the direction of the inequality symbol must be _____ so that the resulting inequality is also true.

**10.** Yes.
**11a.** also true
**11b.** also true
**11c.** also true
**11d.** reversed

The solution set for an inequality is usually a range of numbers rather than a single number. But the method for solving an inequality, such as solving $60n \geq 895 + 25n$ for $n$, is very similar to the method for solving its associated equation.

| | |
|---|---|
| Original inequality | $60n \geq 895 + 25n$ |
| Subtract $25n$ from both sides. | $60n - 25n \geq 895 + 25n - 25n$ |
| Simplify. | $35n \geq 895$ |
| Divide both sides by 35. | $\dfrac{35n}{35} \geq \dfrac{895}{35}$ |
| Simplify. | $n \geq \dfrac{895}{35}$ or $n \geq 25.57$ |

Any value for $n$ that is a whole number greater than 25.57 satisfies the inequality. So at least 26 students must go on the trip in order to meet expenses; but 27, 28, or more students will also satisfy the requirement.

To solve an inequality, use the **Properties of Inequality** that are summarized as follows:

**Properties of Inequality**

- Any number can be added to or subtracted from both sides of an inequality without changing the direction of the inequality.
- When both sides of an inequality are multiplied or divided by a positive number, the direction of the inequality is unchanged.
- When both sides of an inequality are multiplied or divided by a negative number, the direction of the inequality is reversed.

## ADDITIONAL EXAMPLE

Solve the inequality $5 - 4x^3 \geq 1$ for $x$.
$x \leq 1$

---

### TEACHING TIP

Point out to students that any number in the solution interval (except an endpoint of a closed interval) can be used to check whether the direction of the inequality symbol in the solution is correct.

---

Solve the inequality $8 - 3x > 2$ for $x$.

**Solution:**

| | |
|---|---|
| Original inequality | $8 - 3x > 2$ |
| Subtract 8 from both sides. | $8 - 3x - 8 > 2 - 8$ |
| Simplify. | $-3x > -6$ |
| Divide both sides by $-3$ and reverse the direction of the inequality. | $\dfrac{-3x}{-3} < \dfrac{-6}{-3}$ |
| Simplify. | $x < 2$ |

As with equations, inequalities should be checked. One way to check if a solution makes sense is to choose any number in the solution interval. Then substitute the number for the variable in the original inequality and see if it is satisfied. In this example, you could try the number 1 because it is less than 2.

$$Check: \qquad 8 - 3(1) \overset{?}{>} 2$$
$$8 - 3 \overset{?}{>} 2$$
$$5 > 2 \checkmark$$

### GRAPHING INEQUALITIES

The solution set in Example 1 can be graphed on a number line. But whereas a single number is graphed as a point, the graph of an inequality is an *interval* on the line. The graph of $x < 2$ is shown below.

The open circle at $x = 2$ indicates that 2 is not included in the solution interval. The arrow means that the interval extends indefinitely to the left without limit.

The graph of $x \geq 1$ is shown below.

Notice that the endpoint at $x = 1$ is treated differently. Because the interval includes 1, a filled circle is placed at $x = 1$.

**E X A M P L E** ❷

a. Solve the inequality $4y - 3(y - 6) \leq 16 - y$.
b. Graph the solution set on a number line.

**Solution:**

a.

| | |
|---|---|
| Original inequality | $4y - 3(y - 6) \leq 16 - y$ |
| Distributive Property | $4y - 3y + 18 \leq 16 - y$ |
| Simplify. | $y + 18 \leq 16 - y$ |
| Add $y$ to both sides. | $y + 18 + y \leq 16 - y + y$ |
| Simplify. | $2y + 18 \leq 16$ |
| Subtract 18 from both sides. | $2y + 18 - 18 \leq 16 - 18$ |
| Simplify. | $2y \leq -2$ |
| Divide both sides by 2. | $\dfrac{2y}{2} \leq \dfrac{-2}{2}$ |
| Simplify. | $y \leq -1$ |

b.

## Practice for Lesson 3.6

For Exercises 1–6, solve the inequality for the variable. Check your solution and graph it on a number line.

1. $8 < 5t - 6$
2. $4x - 7 \geq 3 - 2x$
3. $-5m + 3 \leq 18$
4. $10p \leq \dfrac{30p - 1}{2}$
5. $8h + 3 < 3(h - 4)$
6. $-8q + 24 < -20$

For Exercises 7–9, complete Parts (a) and (b).
  a. Write an inequality to model the sentence.
  b. Solve the inequality.

7. Eleven is no more than the sum of twice a number $n$ and five.
8. One-half a number $n$, increased by five, is at least twenty.
9. The sum of six times a number $n$ and twelve is more than the product of that number and three.

## ADDITIONAL EXAMPLE ❷

a. Solve the inequality $6z < 1 - 4(3 - 2z)$
   for $z$. $z > \dfrac{11}{2}$

b. Graph the solution set on a number line.

**COMMON ERROR**

In **Exercises 3 and 6**, students may need to be reminded that the direction of the inequality symbol must be reversed when an inequality is multiplied or divided by a negative number.

## Practice for Lesson 3.6 Answers

1. $t > \dfrac{14}{5}$

2. $x \geq \dfrac{5}{3}$

3. $m \geq -3$

4. $p \geq \dfrac{1}{10}$

5. $h < -3$

6. $q > 5.5$

7a. $11 \leq 2n + 5$
7b. $n \geq 3$

8a. $\dfrac{1}{2}n + 5 \geq 20$

8b. $n \geq 30$
9a. $6n + 12 > 3n$
9b. $n > -4$

**10.** $n \geq 3.8$ gallons, so a minimum of 4 cans of paint are needed.

**11a.** $l + 2w + 2t < 108$

**11b.** $t \leq 7$ inches

**12a.** $2.40C + 2.00S \leq 48.00$

**12b.** $S \leq 12$ bottles

**13.** Sample answer: A table can be made that includes values of the expression $14 - 3x$. The value of the expression is 2 when $x = 4$. But for values of $x$ less than 4, the value of the expression is greater than 2.

**10.** A gallon of a certain brand of paint will cover a maximum area of 450 square feet. The inequality $450n \geq 2(860)$ models the number of one-gallon cans $n$ of paint needed to give two coats of paint to 860 square feet of wall space. Solve for $n$.

**11.** The U.S. Postal Service will accept a package for mailing only if the sum of its length and *girth* (distance around) is not more than 108 inches. The girth of a package equals twice its width plus twice its thickness.

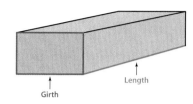

a. Write an inequality that models the Postal Service requirement. Use $l$ for length, $w$ for width, and $t$ for thickness.
b. If a package is 50 inches long and 22 inches wide, how thick can it be?

**12.** A student wants to buy chips and soda for his party. Each large bag of chips costs $2.40, and each large bottle of soda costs $2.00. He wants to spend no more than $48.00.

a. Write an inequality that models the number of bags of chips $C$ and bottles of soda $S$ that he can buy.
b. If he buys 10 bags of chips, solve for $S$ to find how many bottles of soda he could buy.

**13.** Consider the inequality $14 - 3x > 2$. Explain how a table can be used to solve the inequality.

#10: Need full sentence answer for
p.86 Minimum number of full-gallon
cans of paint required

p. 89:
#7: Two inequalities must overlap
or number live in compound
"and" inequality to have
any solution
$N \geq 4$ and $N \leq 3$
do not overlap
↓
No solution
(read p. 87 in textbook)

You have learned to solve equations and inequalities and use them to model real-world situations. In this lesson, you will use what you know to write, solve, and graph compound inequalities.

## WRITING COMPOUND INEQUALITIES

Two inequalities that are joined by the word *and* or the word *or* form a **compound inequality**.

| Compound Inequalities Joined by *and* | Compound Inequalities Joined by *or* |
|---|---|
| $x > -1$ and $x \leq 3$ | $x \leq 0$ or $x > 2$ |

A solution to a compound inequality joined by the word *and* is any number that makes *both* inequalities true.

Its graph is the *intersection* of the graph of the two inequalities. To find the intersection of the two graphs, graph each inequality and find where the two graphs overlap.

The graph of $x > -1$ is

and the graph of $x \leq 3$ is

So, the graph of $x > -1$ and $x \leq 3$ is

These inequalities can be combined and written without using *and*.

$$-1 < x \leq 3$$

A solution to a compound inequality joined by the word *or* is any number that makes *at least one* of the inequalities true.

Its graph is the *union* of the graphs of the two inequalities. To find the union of the two graphs, graph each inequality.

The graph of $x \leq 0$ is

and the graph of $x > 2$ is

So, the graph of $x \leq 0$ or $x > 2$ is

These inequalities cannot be combined. They must be written using the word *or*.

**5e**   Explain

## Lesson Objectives

- write compound inequalities.
- graph compound inequalities on a number line.
- solve compound inequalities.

## Vocabulary

- compound inequality

## Description

This lesson builds on Lesson 3.6 and discusses writing, graphing, and solving compound inequalities. Absolute value inequalities are included in **Exercises 11–13**.

> **TEACHING TIP**
>
> Students may need to be reminded of the meaning of "intersection" and "union." Explain that every point included in the intersection of two graphs must appear on *both* of the graphs, but a point in the union of two graphs has to appear on *at least one* of the graphs.

> **TEACHING TIP**
>
> Inequalities are sometimes stated using the word "but," as in "x is greater than −1 but less than 3." In this context, "but" is interpreted as being operationally equivalent to "and."

## ADDITIONAL EXAMPLE

Write an inequality for each statement.

**a.** $t$ is less than 4 and greater than 0.
$0 < t < 4$

**b.** $p$ is greater than 1 and no more than 5. $1 < p \le 5$

**c.** $q$ is less than $-2$ or greater than 1.
$q < -2$ or $q > 1$

**d.** $b$ is between 0 and 6 inclusive.
$0 \le b \le 6$

## ADDITIONAL EXAMPLE

Graph each compound inequality on a number line.

**a.** $-4 \le t < 1$

**b.** $w \le 1$ or $w \ge 2$

## ADDITIONAL EXAMPLE

Solve $-6 \le 2(d - 3) \le 4$ for $d$.
$0 \le d \le 5$

---

## E X A M P L E ❶

Write an inequality for each statement.

**a.** $n$ is between $-2$ and 5.
**b.** $m$ is at least 0 and less than 10.
**c.** $d$ is less than 3 or greater than 8.
**d.** $h$ is at most 1 or at least 5.

**Solution:**

**a.** $-2 < n < 5$
**b.** $0 \le m < 10$
**c.** $d < 3$ or $d > 8$
**d.** $h \le 1$ or $h \ge 5$

## E X A M P L E ❷

Graph each compound inequality on a number line.

**a.** $-2 \le b < 3$
**b.** $x < -3$ or $x > 0$

**Solution:**

**a.**

**b.**

### SOLVING COMPOUND INEQUALITIES

To solve a compound inequality, solve each inequality separately.

## E X A M P L E ❸

Solve $-5 < t + 1 < 11$ for $t$.

**Solution:**
Write the compound inequality as two inequalities joined by the word *and*.

| | | | |
|---|---|---|---|
| Original inequalities | $-5 < t + 1$ | and | $t + 1 < 11$ |
| Solve each inequality. | $-5 - 1 < t + 1 - 1$ | and | $t + 1 - 1 < 11 - 1$ |
| Simplify. | $-6 < t$ | and | $t < 10$ |

The solution set is all real numbers greater than $-6$ *and* less than 10. This can be written as $-6 < t < 10$.

**E X A M P L E** ❹

**a.** Solve $3x + 4 < -2$ or $2x + 8 \geq 10$ for $x$.

**b.** Graph the solution.

**Solution:**

**a.**

| Original inequalities | $3x + 4 < -2$ | or | $2x + 8 \geq 10$ |
|---|---|---|---|
| Subtract. | $3x + 4 - 4 < -2 - 4$ | or | $2x + 8 - 8 \geq 10 - 8$ |
| Simplify. | $3x < -6$ | or | $2x \geq 2$ |
| Divide. | $\dfrac{3x}{3} < \dfrac{-6}{3}$ | or | $\dfrac{2x}{2} \geq \dfrac{2}{2}$ |
| Simplify. | $x < -2$ | or | $x \geq 1$ |

The solution set is all real numbers less than –2 *or* greater than or equal to 1.

**b.**

## Practice for Lesson 3.7

**For Exercises 1–4, write an inequality for each statement. Then graph the solution set on a number line.**

1. $y$ is greater than or equal to –2 and less than 0.
2. $q$ is either less than 1 or at least 4.
3. $a$ is at least 5 and no more than 8.
4. $z$ is between –3 and 3.

**For Exercises 5–7, solve the compound inequality.**

5. $-2a - 3 > -1$ or $3a - 1 \geq 5$
6. $-2 \leq 4(x - 6) \leq 7$
7. $3n - 2 \geq 10$ and $2n + 1 \leq 7$
8. A tree has a medium growth rate if its rate of increase in height $r$ is more than 12 inches per year and no more than 24 inches per year.
   a. Write a compound inequality that describes the medium growth rates.
   b. Graph the inequality.

COMPOUND INEQUALITIES  **Lesson 3.7**  **89**

# LESSON 3.7

## ADDITIONAL EXAMPLE ❹

**a.** Solve $3 - 2b \geq 1$ or $b - 6 > 4$ for $x$.

**b.** Graph the solution.

**a.** $b \leq 1$ or $b > 10$

**b.**

## COMMON ERROR

In **Exercises 2 and 5**, students may be tempted to try to combine the inequalities in a manner similar to that for "and" inequalities. But $4 \leq q < 1$ makes no sense, since 4 is greater than 1. Solutions to these exercises must be stated as two separate inequalities.

## Practice for Lesson 3.7 Answers

1. $-2 \leq y < 0$; also $y \geq -2$ and $y < 0$

2. $q < 1$ or $q \geq 4$

3. $5 \leq a \leq 8$; also $a \geq 5$ and $a \leq 8$

4. $-3 < z < 3$; also $z > -3$ and $z < 3$

5. $a < -1$ or $a \geq 2$

6. $\dfrac{11}{2} \leq x \leq \dfrac{31}{4}$

⑦ no solution

8a. $r > 12$ and $r \leq 24$; also $12 < r \leq 24$

8b.

89

**9a.** $h \geq 4$ and $h \leq 7$; also $4 \leq h \leq 7$

**9b.**

**10.** $8$ mph $\leq s \leq 38$ mph

**11.** $n < -4$ or $n > 14$

**12.** $x \geq \dfrac{1}{4}$ and $x \leq \dfrac{5}{4}$; also $\dfrac{1}{4} \leq x \leq \dfrac{5}{4}$

**13.** $t < -3$ or $t > 1$

---

9. Most states have building codes that provide standards for construction. For public buildings in Massachusetts, the height of a step in a staircase must be at least 4 inches but cannot be greater than 7 inches.
   a. Write a compound inequality that describes the height $h$ of a legal stair step in Massachusetts.
   b. Graph the inequality.

10. On many interstate highways, a driver must drive at least 40 mph and no more than 70 mph. If a car is traveling 32 miles per hour, what increase in speed would allow the car's speed to be in the legal limit?

**SPEED LIMIT 70 MINIMUM 40**

**Recall**

The quantity $|x|$ equals either $x$ or $-x$, depending on whether $x$ is positive or negative.

**For Exercises 11–13, use the following information.**

In order to solve an absolute value inequality, such as $|x + 3| < 6$, you need to rewrite the inequalities as a compound sentence.

- If the absolute value is on the left of the inequality symbol and the symbol is $<$ or $\leq$, use *and* to write the compound sentence.
- If the absolute value is on the left of the inequality symbol and the symbol is $>$ or $\geq$, use *or* to write the compound sentence.

So, $|x + 3| < 6$ can be rewritten as a compound sentence with *and*.

$$x + 3 < 6 \text{ and } -(x + 3) < 6$$

Then both of these inequalities must be solved in order to find the complete solution to $|x + 3| < 6$. When you solve this inequality, you get $x < 3$ and $x > -9$. This solution set can also be written as $-9 < x < 3$.

**Solve the inequality and graph the solution set.**

11. $|n - 5| > 9$

12. $|4x - 3| \leq 2$

13. $5|t + 1| > 10$

## Algebra's Next Top Model

In this chapter, you have written expressions, equations, and inequalities to model many types of situations that were presented to you. Now it is time to apply your modeling skills to situations of your own choosing.

Remember where the parts of expressions come from.

- Constant terms represent quantities that do not change in a given situation. For example, the initial value of the height of a tree when planted is a constant value in an expression.
- A variable represents a quantity that can change and take on different values. For tree growth, $n$ or $t$ may represent the variable number of years after planting.
- If only the number above a certain value is needed, a constant may be subtracted from the variable. For example, $(s - 65)$ counts the number of miles per hour of speed over 65.
- The coefficient of a variable often represents a constant rate of change. If a tree grows 2 feet each year, then the term $2n$ represents the total growth over $n$ years. The coefficient 2 represents the rate of growth per year.

Also, remember that an equation results from setting two expressions equal to each other.

Think about situations in your experience that involve changing quantities. You may want to talk to people you know and find out the kinds of questions they deal with in their job. For example, you might ask truck farmers what kinds of considerations help them determine their profit when they take goods to market. Or contact tree nurseries in your state to find out about their procedures and how they plan for future tree growth. Be creative and find situations that are important to you or to people in the area where you live.

Choose three situations that can be modeled by equations. For each situation,

- write a question someone might ask that has a numerical answer;
- write an equation that models the situation;
- explain the meaning of any constants, variables, or coefficients in your model; and
- use your model to make predictions for several reasonable values of your variable or variables.

MODELING PROJECT    **Chapter 3**    **91**

### Materials List

### Description

In this project students are asked to think creatively about ways in which real situations can be modeled with mathematics. This project can be completed by individual students, although they may prefer to work in pairs if their project involves research with local companies.

### Sample Answers

Students' reports may vary, depending on the situations they choose to investigate. If students have difficulty thinking of situations to model, you may wish to give them suggestions. In addition to the nursery and truck farming suggestions on the student page, other situations might include modeling cell phone plans, gym membership fees, small business costs or profits, real estate office expenses and commissions, etc.

Regardless of the situations chosen, students' models should reflect an understanding of their work with expressions and equations in this chapter. Not all models need to be linear models, but students should justify the components of their models in any case.

## Chapter 3 Review

### You Should Be Able to:

#### Lesson 3.1

- use arrow diagrams to represent expressions.
- evaluate expressions.
- write expressions to model real-world situations.

#### Lesson 3.2

- write an equation that models a real-world situation.

#### Lesson 3.3

- use arrow diagrams to solve two-step equations.
- use tables to solve equations.

#### Lesson 3.4

- solve problems that require previously learned concepts and skills.

#### Lesson 3.5

- combine like terms in an expression.
- solve equations.
- use equations to solve real-world problems.

#### Lesson 3.6

- solve inequalities.
- graph inequalities.

#### Lesson 3.7

- write compound inequalities.
- graph compound inequalities on a number line.
- solve compound inequalities.

### Key Vocabulary

algebraic expression (p. 58)

coefficient (p. 58)

evaluate an expression (p. 58)

order of operations (p. 58)

equation (p. 61)

inverse operations (p. 67)

equivalent equation (p. 71)

Properties of Equality (p. 71)

term (p. 75)

like terms (p. 76)

Properties of Inequality (p. 83)

compound inequality (p. 87)

### Chapter 3 Test Review

**For Exercises 1–2, draw an arrow diagram to represent the expression.**

1. $4y - 6$
2. $4(y - 6)$

## Chapter 3 Test Review Answers

1.

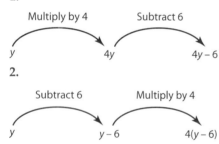

2.

**3.** Evaluate the expression $3t - 4(t - 5) + \frac{t}{2}$ for $t = 6$.

**4.** A student opens a college savings account with a gift from her grandmother. She then makes regular deposits every month from her babysitting earnings. The expression $80n + 500$ models the total balance in her account after $n$ months.

    **a.** Interpret the meaning of the number 80 in the expression.

    **b.** Interpret the meaning of the number 500 in the expression.

**5.** A vendor at the state fair will buy 600 cans of juice for $140. He will charge $1.50 for each can he sells. If he has to pay a $25 fee to the fair, which of these expressions represents the amount of money he makes, after expenses, for selling $n$ cans of juice?

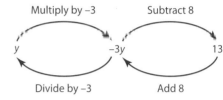

    **A.** $600n - 140 - 25$

    **B.** $140n - 600 - 25$

    **C.** $1.5n - 600 - 25$

    **D.** $1.5n - 140 - 25$

**6.** Main floor seats for the school musical are sold for $8 and balcony seats for $5. Write an equation that models total ticket revenue $R$ if $m$ main floor seats and $b$ balcony seats are sold.

**7.** A furniture company makes a variety of wooden bookcases. The height of each shelf space is 13 inches. The top and bottom pieces are each 2 inches thick, and the pieces separating the shelf spaces are each $\frac{3}{4}$-inch thick. Write an equation that models the total height $h$ of a bookcase that contains $n$ shelf spaces.

**8 a.** Draw an arrow diagram that models the solution of $-3y - 8 = 13$.

    **b.** Solve the equation for $y$.

**9.** Which expressions are *not* like terms?

    **A.** $-5xy$ and $4xy$     **B.** $-4a^2$ and $-4a$

    **C.** $7xy$ and $9yx$     **D.** $-3r$ and $5r$

**3.** 17

**4a.** the amount deposited each month

**4b.** the original gift from her grandmother

**5.** D

**6.** $R = 8m + 5b$

**7.** $h = 13n + \frac{3}{4}(n - 1) + 2(2)$

**8a.**

Multiply by –3      Subtract 8

$y$      $-3y$      13

Divide by –3      Add 8

**8b.** $y = -7$

**9.** B

**10.** $3x + 4y$

**11.** $8ab + 9a - 1$

**12.** $h = 1$

**13.** $x = -12$

**14.** $n = \dfrac{4}{13}$

**15.** $r = -100$

**16.** $t = 9$

**17.** $t = 9$

**18.** $k < 0$ or $k > 2$

**19.** $d < -\dfrac{3}{2}$

**20.** $r \geq 17$

**21.** $-2 < m < -\dfrac{4}{5}$

**For Exercises 10–11, combine like terms.**

**10.** $4x - 2y - x + 6y$

**11.** $3ab + 9a + 5ba - 1$

**For Exercises 12–15, solve, then check.**

**12.** $5h - 3(h - 2) = 8$

**13.** $6(x + 3) = 4(x - 1) - 2$

**14.** $\dfrac{6n - 3}{5} = 1 - 4n$

**15.** $0.12r + 3 = 0.04r - 5$

**For Exercises 16–17, use the equation $10 - (t - 6) = 2(4t - 1) - 7t$.**

**16.** Use a table to solve the equation for $t$.

**17.** Solve the equation algebraically.

**18.** Write an inequality for the following statement. Then graph it.

$k$ is either less than 0 or greater than 2.

**For Exercises 19–21, solve for the variable.**

**19.** $2(d - 6) > 10d$

**20.** $3r \leq 5(r - 7) + 1$

**21.** $-2 < 5m + 8 < 4$

# Chapter 4
# Measurement: Perimeter, Area, and Volume

## Mathematical Overview

Learning to identify a variety of two- and three-dimensional figures as well as calculating the sums of angles, perimeters, circumferences, surface areas, and volumes are fundamental topics in geometry. In this chapter, students use geometric concepts to create a mathematical model for an efficient package design. They learn to solve literal equations for specified variables and use area and volume formulas to evaluate the efficiency of the designs. Students also draw nets for solids, recognize solid figures from their nets, and find the surface areas of solids. In the last lesson of this chapter, students use ratios to solve problems that involve similar solids. Solving equations is a skill emphasized throughout this chapter.

## Lesson Summaries

### Lesson 4.1   *Polygons*

In this lesson, students refresh their memories of the names and attributes of polygons. The review also includes regular, equilateral, and equiangular polygons, as well as how to mark figures to indicate equal sides and angle measures, right angles, and parallel sides. A detailed look at classifying five different quadrilaterals by their attributes leads students into solving problems related to the lengths of sides and the measures of angles in polygons. By the end of this lesson, students should be able to identify a polygon, classify a quadrilateral, and find the sum of the interior angles in a polygon.

### Lesson 4.2   *Investigation: Formulas and Literal Equations*

In this lesson, students extend their knowledge of equations with only one variable to formulas and literal equations. Through an Investigation and the use of arrow diagrams, students conceptualize how to solve for any one of the variables in a literal equation or formula. This lesson concludes with a review of the perimeter (circumference) formulas for polygons and circles.

### Lessons 4.3   *Activity: Area and Package Design and*
### 4.4   *Investigation: Volumes of Solid Figures*

In these lessons, students design non-traditional soft drink packages and consider ways to evaluate the efficiency of their designs. First, students consider two-dimensional models of three-dimensional packages. Area formulas are reviewed for quadrilaterals, triangles, and circles. Then in Lesson 4.4, students examine three-dimensional models and use their volumes to determine the efficiencies of packages. The formulas for the volumes of rectangular prisms, cubes, cylinders, pyramids, cones, and spheres are reviewed.

### Lesson 4.5   *R.A.P.*

In this lesson, students **R**eview **A**nd **P**ractice solving problems that require the use of skills and concepts taught in previous math levels. The skills reviewed in this lesson are skills that are needed as a basis for solving problems throughout this course.

### Lesson 4.6   *Activity: Surface Area*

In this Activity, students use nets to determine the amount of material needed to make a package for a six-pack of soft drinks. They apply what they know about area and volume to compare the surface area and volume of a standard six-pack package to that of a similar package in which the dimensions have been doubled. They discover, by comparing the volumes of the packages, that the new package is eight times the volume of the standard six-pack.

### Lesson 4.7   *Investigation: Similar Figures–Perimeter, Area, and Volume*

In this Investigation, students explore two similar solids and the relationships that exist between the scale factor and the ratios of the surface areas, lateral surface areas, and the volumes of the solids.

### Chapter 4   *Extension: Constructing the Net of a Cone*

In this Extension, students discover how to construct a net for a cone.

## Lesson Guide

| Lesson/Objectives | Materials | |
|---|---|---|
| **Chapter 4 Opener: Why Is Package Design Important?**<br>• recognize that package design is important and requires a broad understanding of mathematics. | | *Optional:*<br>• Toblerone candy package |
| **4.1 Polygons**<br>• classify polygons by their sides.<br>• classify quadrilaterals by their attributes.<br>• find the sum of the angle measures in a polygon. | | *Optional:*<br>• large paper polygon (not a triangle)<br>• scissors |
| **4.2 Investigation: Formulas and Literal Equations**<br>• solve a literal equation for a specific variable.<br>• find the perimeter of a polygon.<br>• find the circumference of a circle. | | |
| **4.3 Activity: Area and Package Design**<br>• create a mathematical model for an efficient package design.<br>• use area formulas to find the areas of various polygons.<br>• use areas of polygons to evaluate the efficiency of a package design. | *Per group:*<br>• centimeter ruler<br>• scissors<br>• Handout 4A (several copies) | *Optional:*<br>• apple, orange, or cake cut in half |
| **4.4 Investigation: Volumes of Solid Figures**<br>• use formulas to find the volumes of right prisms, cylinders, cones, pyramids, and spheres.<br>• use volumes of solids to evaluate the efficiency of a package design. | *Per group:*<br>• answers from Lesson 4.3 Question 6 | *Optional:*<br>• 3-D models |
| **4.5 R.A.P.**<br>• solve problems that require previously learned concepts and skills. | | |
| **4.6 Activity: Surface Area**<br>• draw a net for a solid figure.<br>• recognize solid figures from their nets.<br>• find the surface area of a solid. | *Per group:*<br>• centimeter ruler<br>• scissors<br>• tape<br>• Handout 4B (one per student) | *Optional:*<br>• a can with lateral area covered with paper<br>• 9 cubes |
| **4.7 Investigation: Similar Figures–Perimeter, Area, and Volume**<br>• determine the relationship that exists between the scale factor and the ratio of the surface areas of two similar solids.<br>• determine the relationship that exists between the scale factor and the ratio of the volumes of two similar solids. | | *Optional:*<br>• 1-inch cubes for building models of rectangular solids<br>• TRM table shell for Questions 1–9. |
| **Chapter 4 Extension: Constructing the Net of a Cone**<br>• construct a net for a cone with a given radius and slant height. | *Per student:*<br>• protractor<br>• compass<br>• scissors<br>• tape | *Optional:*<br>• grid paper |

## Pacing Guide

| | Day 1 | Day 2 | Day 3 | Day 4 | Day 5 | Day 6 | Day 7 | Day 8 | Day 9 | Day 10 |
|---|---|---|---|---|---|---|---|---|---|---|
| **Basic** | p. 96, 4.1 | 4.2 | 4.3 | 4.3, 4.4 | 4.4, 4.5 | 4.5, 4.6 | 4.6, 4.7 | 4.7, project | project, review | review |
| **Standard** | p. 96, 4.1 | 4.2 | 4.3 | 4.3, 4.4 | 4.4, 4.5 | 4.5, 4.6 | 4.6, 4.7 | 4.7, project | project, review | extension |
| **Block** | p. 96, 4.1, 4.2 | 4.3 | 4.4, 4.5 | 4.5, 4.6 | 4.6, 4.7 | 4.7, project | review, extension | | | |

### Supplement Support

See the Book Companion Website at www.highschool.bfwpub.com/ModelingwithMathematics and the Teacher's Resource Materials (TRM) for additional resources.

# Measurement: Perimeter, Area, and Volume

## CONTENTS

**5e** Engage

## Lesson Objective

- recognize that package design is important and requires a broad understanding of mathematics.

## Vocabulary

## Description

This reading helps students relate the importance of packaging to their lives. They should begin to recognize that mathematics plays an important part in packaging design.

### TEACHING TIP

After students have read the introduction to this chapter, lead a whole-class discussion asking students to give examples of packaging that "grabs" their attention. Then talk about why they remember the package.

If possible, bring a Toblerone candy package to class. Talk about its shape (triangular prism) and ask students why they think the shape of the package was chosen by the designer.

## Why Is Package Design Important?

A day rarely passes in which we do not use some sort of packaging. Packages that contain the food we eat keep the food from spoiling. The packaging also keeps the food clean and even protects the food from insects and disease.

The way any consumer product is packaged can have a great effect on its sales. An attractive package adds to the appeal of the product. The size of the package is important as well.

- A manufacturer can charge less for a smaller package. Lower prices can increase demand.
- Stores can display more items in a fixed space on a shelf if the items are small.
- Larger packages may mean volume discounts. For example, cereal may cost less per ounce if it is purchased in a larger box.

Packages are geometric. The design of efficient packages requires knowledge of both geometry and algebra. A good understanding of measurement is also important. Packages are three-dimensional with two-dimensional sides, so both volume and area play a role in package design.

In order to use mathematics to create a package and evaluate its efficiency, it is important to review the concepts, skills, and vocabulary of geometry. In this lesson, you will classify quadrilaterals and other polygons by their attributes. You will also explore the angle measures of polygons.

### CLASSIFYING POLYGONS

Packages come in many different shapes and sizes. Look around. You will see that the sides of some packages are circles, and others are in the shapes of polygons such as rectangles, triangles, and even trapezoids!

Recall that a **polygon** is a closed plane figure that is bounded by three or more line segments. The names of some common polygons are listed in the following table.

| Number of Sides | Name of Polygon |
|---|---|
| 3 | **triangle** |
| 4 | **quadrilateral** |
| 5 | **pentagon** |
| 6 | **hexagon** |
| 7 | **heptagon** |
| 8 | **octagon** |
| 9 | **nonagon** |
| 10 | **decagon** |
| 12 | **dodecagon** |
| $n$ | **$n$-gon** |

**Recall**

The slashes on the sides of a polygon are called *tick marks*. They are used to indicate the sides of the figure that are equal in length. The small arcs indicate angles that have the same measure.

Some polygons are called **regular** polygons. A regular polygon is both **equilateral** (all sides are the same length) and **equiangular** (all angles have the same measure). Both of the polygons below are hexagons. But only the one on the right is a regular hexagon.

POLYGONS **Lesson 4.1** 97

---

### Lesson Objectives
- classify polygons by their sides.
- classify quadrilaterals by their attributes.
- find the sum of the angle measures in a polygon.

### Vocabulary
- decagon
- dodecagon
- equiangular polygon
- equilateral polygon
- heptagon
- hexagon
- $n$-gon
- nonagon
- octagon
- parallelogram
- pentagon
- polygon
- quadrilateral
- rectangle
- regular polygon
- rhombus
- right angle
- square
- trapezoid
- triangle

### Description
In this lesson students investigate the names and attributes of polygons. They look more in depth into the attributes of five special quadrilaterals: parallelograms, rhombuses, rectangles, squares, and trapezoids. They also learn to calculate the sum of the interior angles of any polygon.

### TEACHING TIP

Ask students to give examples of other words that begin with the prefixes *tri-*, *quad-*, *hex-*, and *oct-*. Suggest that relating these words to the number of sides in a polygon might help them remember the names of the most common polygons.

---

### TEACHING TIP

Vocabulary organizers, such as the one below, are particularly helpful for this chapter.

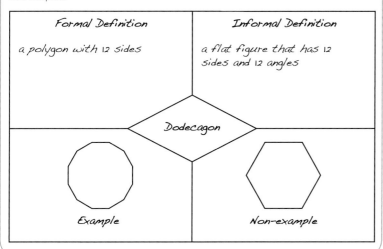

# LESSON 4.1

## TEACHING TIP

Ask students to look around them and give examples of quadrilaterals they see in the classroom.

**Recall**

The little square symbols in the corners of figures indicate **right angles**, which are angles whose measure is 90°. The arrows on the sides of figures indicate parallel line segments.

## CLASSIFYING QUADRILATERALS

Some quadrilaterals have special names. Listed below are the names, definitions, and descriptions of five special quadrilaterals.

- **Parallelogram**

A parallelogram is a quadrilateral with both pairs of opposite sides parallel.

Opposite sides are equal in length, and opposite angles are equal in measure.

- **Rhombus**

A rhombus is a parallelogram with four congruent sides.

Opposite angles are equal in measure.

- **Rectangle**

A rectangle is a parallelogram with four right angles.

Opposite sides are equal in length.

- **Square**

A square is a parallelogram with four congruent sides and four right angles.

Note that all squares are rectangles, but not all rectangles are squares.

- **Trapezoid**

A trapezoid is a quadrilateral with exactly one pair of parallel sides.

The Venn diagram below models the relationships among these five special quadrilaterals.

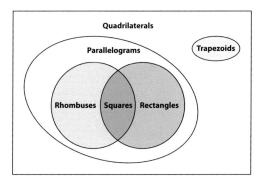

**TEACHING TIP**

The Venn diagram on Page 99 is a powerful model that relates the most common quadrilaterals. Take time to discuss this diagram with students. Ask why "Squares" are placed where they are. Also ask why "Trapezoids" are placed outside the "Parallelograms" oval.

# LESSON 4.1

## ADDITIONAL EXAMPLE

Quadrilateral *ABCD* is a parallelogram. Find the value of *x*.

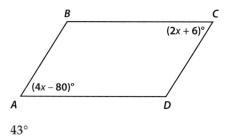

43°

---

### TEACHING TIP

To demonstrate that the sum of the measures of the angles of any given polygon is 180(*n* − 2) degrees, cut any polygon into triangles along the diagonal(s) from one vertex of the figure. Have students count the number of triangles and then use the fact that the sum of the angle measures in a triangle is 180° to calculate the sum of the angle measures in the polygon. (See Exercise 16 on page 102.)

## ADDITIONAL EXAMPLE

Find the sum of the angle measures in a dodecagon. 1,800°

---

Quadrilateral *ABCD* is a rhombus. Find the value of *x*.

**Solution:**

Since *ABCD* is a rhombus, it has four congruent sides. So, $AB = BC$.

| | |
|---|---|
| All sides of a rhombus are congruent. | $AB = BC$ |
| Substitute. | $5x - 6 = 2(x + 9)$ |
| Distributive Property | $5x - 6 = 2x + 18$ |
| Subtract 2*x* from both sides. | $3x - 6 = 18$ |
| Add 6 to both sides. | $3x = 24$ |
| Divide both sides by 3. | $x = 8$ |

### ANGLE MEASURES IN A POLYGON

The sum of the angle measures of a polygon with *n* sides is $180°(n - 2)$.

Find the sum of the angle measures in any parallelogram.

**Solution:**

A parallelogram has four sides, so $n = 4$.

$$180°(n - 2) = 180°(4 - 2)$$
$$= 360°$$

So, the sum of the measures of the angles in any parallelogram is 360°.

## Practice for Lesson 4.1

**For Exercises 1–2, choose the correct answer.**

1. Which is the most specific name for the figure below?

   **A.** quadrilateral **B.** rectangle **C.** square **D.** trapezoid

2. Which is the most specific name for the figure below?

   **A.** parallelogram **B.** rectangle **C.** square **D.** trapezoid

**For Exercises 3–8, state whether the figure is a polygon. If it is a polygon, give its name, and also state whether it is regular. If it is not a polygon, explain why.**

3.

4.

5.

6.

7.

8.

### COMMON ERROR

**Exercises 3–10** Some students may answer the questions based on how the figure looks. Remind them that they cannot make assumptions about lengths or angle measures based on how a diagram "looks."

## Practice For Lesson 4.1 Answers

1. A
2. D
3. yes, triangle, not regular
4. yes, regular octagon
5. no, not closed
6. yes, not regular, quadrilateral
7. no, sides are not all line segments
8. yes, parallelogram, not regular

**For Exercises 9–10, identify the special quadrilateral. Then find the value of $x$.**

9.

10.

11. Find the sum of the angle measures in an octagon.

12. Find the measure of one angle in a regular hexagon.

13. The expressions $4x + 7$ and $10x - 59$ represent the lengths, in feet, of two sides of a regular hexagon. Find the length of one side of the hexagon.

14. The expressions $(0.5x + 60)°$ and $(x + 40)°$ represent the measures of two angles of a decagon that are equal in measure. Find the measure of one of these angles.

15. It was stated in this lesson that all squares are rectangles, but not all rectangles are squares. Explain why this is true.

16. The sum of the angles of a triangle is 180°. You can use this fact to find the sum of the angle measures in any polygon.

To find the sum of the angle measures of a polygon,

- draw the figure,
- choose one vertex and draw all of the diagonal lines from that vertex to all of the other vertices,
- determine the number of triangles formed, and then
- calculate the sum of the angle measures in these triangles.

  a. Find the sum of the angle measures in a pentagon.
  b. Find the sum of the angle measures in a decagon.

9. parallelogram; $x = 60°$
10. rectangle; $x = 7.5$
11. 1,080°
12. 120°
13. $x = 11$; So, the length of one side is 51 feet.
14. $x = 40$; So, the measure of either of the angles is 80°.
15. Sample answer: A square has four right angles. So, it is a rectangle. But squares must have all four sides equal, and many rectangles do not.
16a. 540°
16b. 1,440°

In previous chapters, you used equations to model many different situations. If an equation states a rule for the relationship between two or more real-world quantities, it is often referred to as a **formula**. A formula is an example of a special type of equation called a literal equation. In this lesson, you will learn how to solve literal equations for specific values. You will also use formulas to find the perimeter of various figures.

## SOLVING LITERAL EQUATIONS

A **literal equation** is an equation that has more than one variable. For example, all of the following equations can be referred to as *literal equations* because each equation has more than one variable.

$$3m - 4n = 16 \qquad I = Prt \qquad V = lwh$$

The second and third equations can also be thought of as *formulas* because they state relationships between two or more real-world quantities. The formula $I = Prt$ relates simple interest $I$ to the principal $P$, the annual rate of interest $r$, and time in years $t$. The formula $V = lwh$ relates the volume of a rectangular solid $V$ to its length $l$, width $w$, and height $h$.

It is possible to solve a literal equation for any one of its variables. Look at the formula $V = lwh$. As it is written here, it is solved for the variable $V$. However, there are times when it might be helpful to solve it for one of the other variables.

Solve the formula for the volume of a rectangular solid $V = lwh$ for $w$.

**Solution:**

If you want to solve $V = lwh$ for $w$, it might be helpful to examine this arrow diagram.

This diagram shows that if you want to solve for $w$, you undo multiplying by $h$ and $l$ by dividing by $h$ and $l$. Algebraically, the solution looks like this:

| | |
|---|---|
| Original equation | $V = lwh$ |
| Divide both sides by $l$ and $h$. | $\dfrac{V}{lh} = \dfrac{lwh}{lh}$ |
| Simplify. | $\dfrac{V}{lh} = w$ or $w = \dfrac{V}{lh}$ |

Multiply by *l*    Multiply by *h*

*w* → → *V*

Divide by *l*    Divide by *h*

If you want to find the width $w$ of a rectangular solid when you know the volume $V$, length $l$, and height $h$, you can use the formula $w = \dfrac{V}{lh}$.

FORMULAS AND LITERAL EQUATIONS    **Lesson 4.2**    **103**

## Lesson Objectives
- solve a literal equation for a specific variable.
- find the perimeter of a polygon.
- find the circumference of a circle.

## Vocabulary
- circumference
- formula
- literal equation
- perimeter

## Materials List

## Description

This lesson is designed as a whole class/small group investigation (2–4 students). Have students read the information on the first page about formulas and literal equations. As a class, talk about Example 1.

In groups, have students work through **Questions 1–5**. Once all groups have completed the Investigation, have them share the formulas they remember. Keep track of the different formulas by writing them on the board or overhead projector.

*Wrapping Up the Investigation:*

Ask students if they have encountered formulas in other courses. If so, then ask why people other than mathematicians might need to use formulas.

Ask the students what they remember about perimeter and circumference. Note the formulas shown.

## ADDITIONAL EXAMPLE
Solve the literal equation $2x + 7y = 12$ for $y$.
$$y = \frac{12 - 2x}{7}$$

## ADDITIONAL EXAMPLE

The Pentagon, in Alexandria, Virginia, occupies a ground space that is a regular pentagon with side walls that are 921 feet in length. Find the perimeter of the Pentagon. 4,605 feet

## Lesson 4.2 Investigation Answers

1. $C = 10 + 1.4H$

2.

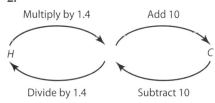

Multiply by 1.4     Add 10

$H$                                          $C$

Divide by 1.4     Subtract 10

To solve $C = 10 + 1.4H$ for $H$, subtract 10 from each side of the equation, then divide both sides by 1.4.

---

**Connection**

The *therm* is a unit of heat energy. One therm is the energy equivalent of about 29.3 kilowatt-hours of electrical energy or burning about 100 cubic feet of natural gas.

In the equation $C = 10 + 0.3H + 1.1H$, $C$ represents a homeowner's monthly natural gas cost in terms of the number of *therms* of heat $H$ used.

1. Before drawing an arrow diagram to represent this formula, notice that there are like terms on the right side of the equation. Simplify the formula by combining the like terms.

2. Now draw an arrow diagram and use it to explain how to solve your equation from Question 1 for $H$.

3. Solve $C = 10 + 0.3H + 1.1H$ for $H$ algebraically.

4. Write down as many formulas as you can from other contexts and explain the relationship that each represents.

5. Choose one of your formulas from Question 4 and explain why you might want to solve it for another variable.

**Recall**

Recall these perimeter formulas:

Square: $P = 4s$
Rectangle: $P = 2l + 2w$
Circle: $C = \pi d$ or $C = 2\pi r$

### PERIMETER AND CIRCUMFERENCE

The **perimeter** of a figure is the distance around the figure. It can be found by adding the lengths of all of the sides. In a polygon, it can also be found by using a formula that reflects the special properties of the given figure. Perimeter is measured in linear units such as feet, inches, or meters. The distance around a circle is called the **circumference** of the circle.

E X A M P L E ②

The Tevatron at Fermilab in Batavia, Illinois, is one of the highest-energy particle accelerators in the world. It has a circular shape with a radius of about 0.62 miles. What is the circumference of the Tevatron? (Round to the nearest tenth.)

0.62 mi

Solution:

$$C = 2\pi r$$
$$= 2\pi(0.62)$$
$$= 3.8955 \ldots$$
$$\approx 3.9 \text{ miles}$$

---

3. Original equation $\qquad$ $C = 10 + 0.3H + 1.1H$

   Combine like terms. $\qquad$ $C = 10 + 1.4H$

   Subtract 10 from both sides. $\qquad$ $C - 10 = 10 + 1.4H - 10$

   Simplify. $\qquad$ $C - 10 = 1.4H$

   Divide both sides by 1.4. $\qquad$ $\dfrac{C - 10}{1.4} = \dfrac{1.4H}{1.4}$

   Simplify. $\qquad$ $\dfrac{C - 10}{1.4} = H$

4. Sample answers: $A = \pi r^2$, $C = \pi d$, $V = lwh$, $d = rt$, etc. In the formula $A = \pi r^2$, $A$ represents the area of a circle expressed in terms of the constant $\pi$ and radius of the circle.

5. Sample answer: In the formula $A = \pi r^2$, you may need to know the radius of a circle but are only given its area.

**For Exercises 1–2, choose the correct answer.**

1. To solve the literal equation $5x = 7t + 6$ for $t$, what would you do first?
   **A.** Divide by 5   **B.** Subtract 7   **C.** Subtract 6   **D.** Multiply by 7

2. Which term cannot be used to describe $C = \pi d$?
   **A.** expression   **B.** equation   **C.** formula   **D.** literal equation

3. Consider the equation $2m - 7n = 24$.
   **a.** Solve the equation for $m$.
   **b.** Solve the equation for $n$.

4. Consider the equation $2(x + 3y) = 25$.
   **a.** Solve the equation for $x$.
   **b.** Solve the equation for $y$.

**For Exercises 5–6, solve the formula for the variable in red.**

5. $P = 2l + 2w$

6. $C = 2\pi r$

7. The equation $S = 180(n - 2)$ is a formula that is used to find the sum of the measures of the angles of a polygon with $n$ sides. Solve the equation for $n$.

8. The equation $A = P(1 + rt)$ is a formula that is used to find the amount of money available when an amount of money $P$ is deposited at a simple interest rate $r$ for $t$ years. Solve the equation for $r$.

**For Exercises 9–12, find the perimeter of each polygon.**

9.

10.

11. a square with sides of 7 centimeters
12. a regular octagon with sides of 2 inches

FORMULAS AND LITERAL EQUATIONS    **Lesson 4.2**    **105**

## Practice for Lesson 4.2 Answers

1. C
2. A
3a. $m = \dfrac{24 + 7n}{2}$
3b. $n = \dfrac{24 - 2m}{-7}$   or   $n = \dfrac{2m - 24}{7}$
4a. $x = \dfrac{25 - 6y}{2}$   or   $\dfrac{25}{2} - 3y$
4b. $y = \dfrac{25 - 2x}{6}$
5. $l = \dfrac{P - 2w}{2}$
6. $r = \dfrac{C}{2\pi}$
7. $n = \dfrac{S + 360}{180}$
8. $r = \dfrac{A - P}{Pt}$
9. $2(9 \text{ in.}) + 2(4 \text{ in.}) = 26 \text{ in.}$
10. $5 \text{ cm} + 6 \text{ cm} + 4 \text{ cm} + 7 \text{ cm} + 4 \text{ cm} = 26 \text{ cm}$
11. $4(7 \text{ cm}) = 28 \text{ cm}$
12. $8(2 \text{ in.}) = 16 \text{ in.}$

13. $C = \pi(22 \text{ ft}) \approx 69.12 \text{ ft}$
14. $2(12 \text{ ft}) + 2(9 \text{ ft}) = 42 \text{ ft}$
15. $2(6 \text{ cm}) + 2(2 \text{ cm}) = 16 \text{ cm}$
16. $2(94 \text{ ft}) + 2(50 \text{ ft}) = 288 \text{ ft}$
17. $2(4 \text{ in.}) + 2(3 \text{ in.}) = 14 \text{ in.}$
18a. yes, $30 \text{ in.} + 2(20 \text{ in.}) + 2(8 \text{ in.}) = 86 \text{ in.}$
18b. no, $42 \text{ in.} + 2(12 \text{ in.}) + 2(7 \text{ in.}) = 80 \text{ in.}$

13. Find the circumference of a circle with a radius of 11 feet.
14. How many feet of floor molding are needed to go around the floor of a 9 ft by 12 ft rectangular room?
15. Find the perimeter of the rectangular metal bracket in the figure below.

16. A basketball court is 94 feet long and 50 feet wide. After practice, team members run around the edge of the court. How far do they run in one trip around the court?

17. A stack of 4-inch-wide envelopes is 3 inches thick. How many inches must a rubber band be able to stretch in order to go around the stack?

18. The U.S. Postal Service considers a package "oversize" if the sum of its length and girth is more than 84 inches. (The girth of the package is the perimeter of a rectangle whose sides are equal to the two shorter dimensions. See the figure below.)

Girth          Length

Determine whether each rectangular package is oversize.
a. Dimensions: 30 in. × 20 in. × 8 in.
b. Dimensions: 42 in. × 12 in. × 7 in.

When efficient packaging is designed, many criteria are examined. The packaging must be economical. Conservation of both space and materials must be considered. In this lesson, you will design a soft-drink package and examine ways to evaluate the efficiency of your design.

The efficiency of a particular packaging design depends on the standards chosen to define efficiency. Not all people have the same criteria in mind. For example, manufacturers and sellers of soft drinks may be concerned about saving space in factories, delivery trucks, and stores. Public officials and conservationists, however, may be concerned with minimizing the amount of packaging material in landfills.

The top figure to the right shows a standard packaging for six cans of soft drink. Below it is a two-dimensional model that represents the bottom of the standard package. Notice the arrangement of the cans in this design.

Now it is your turn to design your own soft-drink package.

1. To simplify your first attempt at designing the package, work with a *two-dimensional* model of the problem. Handout 4A has six circles that are the same size as the base of a standard soda can. Cut these out and arrange them according to your design. Then draw line segments around your arrangement of cans to represent the package.

   In your design, you are free to vary the following:

   - the number of cans,
   - the shape of the package, and
   - the arrangement of the cans within the package.

   The only restriction is that your design must be different from the standard design shown.

AREA AND PACKAGE DESIGN    Lesson 4.3    **107**

## Lesson Objectives

- create a mathematical model for an efficient package design.
- use area formulas to find the areas of various polygons.
- use areas of polygons to evaluate the efficiency of a package design.

## Vocabulary

- area

## Materials List

*Per group:*
- centimeter ruler
- scissors
- several copies of Handout 4A

## Description

*Preparation:*

Have students work in groups of 2–4 students. Provide each group with several copies of Handout 4A, a centimeter ruler, and scissors.

*During the Activity:*

Have students read the introductory paragraphs of the lesson and then discuss why different people might have different criteria for package efficiency.

Talk about the standard soda six-pack design shown in the activity. Point out that groups can use any package design they want as long as it is not the "standard" design shown in the lesson.

*Closing the Activity:*

Have each group of students present their designs and their efficiencies to the class. Compare the efficiencies of the groups and see if any designs improve on the efficiency of the standard design. Tell students to keep their answers to **Question 6**, as they will need them in Lesson 4.4.

**COMMON ERROR**

Students who do not read carefully may not understand that they are to simplify their task by designing a *two-dimensional* model. In later lessons, they will refine this two-dimensional model and examine what happens when the height of the package is taken into account.

**TEACHING TIP**

**Question 1** If students struggle when thinking of a design, point out that their package can be any shape; for example, it could be circular, hexagonal, triangular, or even rectangular.

## Lesson 4.3 Activity Answers

1. Check students' designs.

**TEACHING TIP**

Some teachers have used this Activity as a graded task in which students or groups of students create either a computer designed presentation or a poster of their design.

2. Check students' measurements.

3a. Answers will vary with students' designs.

3b. Answers will vary with students' designs.

## Recall

**Area** is a measure of the amount of surface covered by a figure. It is measured in square units, such as square inches (in.²) or square meters (m²).

2. To evaluate your design, you will need to use a metric ruler to make several measurements. You will then use those measurements to calculate areas. The six figures below show some of the more common geometric figures. The given formulas can be used to help you make your calculations.

### • Parallelogram

The area of a parallelogram is the product of its base $b$ and height $h$:

$$A = bh$$

### • Rectangle

The area of a rectangle is the product of its length $l$ and width $w$:

$$A = lw$$

### • Square

The area of a square is the square of the length of one side $s$:

$$A = s^2$$

### • Triangle

The area of a triangle is one-half the product of its base $b$ and height $h$:

$$A = \frac{1}{2}bh$$

### • Trapezoid

The area of a trapezoid is one-half the product of its height $h$ and the sum of the bases $b_1$ and $b_2$:

$$A = \frac{1}{2}h(b_1 + b_2)$$

### • Circle

The area of a circle is the product of $\pi$ and the square of its radius $r$:

$$A = \pi r^2$$

3. To help you determine the efficiency of your two-dimensional design, calculate each of the following. Round to the nearest tenth.

   a. the total area of your two-dimensional package model

   b. the total area of the bottoms of the cans

**4** **a.** What percent of the area of the package is the total area of the cans?

    **b.** To increase the efficiency of a package, do you want to maximize or minimize this percent? Explain.

**5** **a.** Calculate the amount of package area per can.

    **b.** To increase the efficiency of a package, do you want to maximize or minimize the amount of package area per can? Explain.

**6.** To determine how the efficiency of your design compares with the efficiency of the standard rectangular six-pack package, find the following:

    **a.** The radius of an actual can in a two-dimensional model of a standard six-pack package is 3.3 cm. Calculate the area of the bottom of a single can and the area of the bottom of the package. Round to the nearest tenth.

    **b.** Find the efficiency of the standard package if the criterion is to maximize the percent of the package area used by the cans.

    **c.** Find the efficiency of the standard package if the criterion is to minimize the amount of package area per can.

    **d.** How do the efficiencies of the standard package compare with your design?

---

### Practice for Lesson 4.3

**For Exercises 1–6, find the area of each figure.**

**1.**

**2.**

**3.**

**Practice for Lesson 4.3 Answers**

1. 120 ft$^2$
2. A = $\pi(4.8)^2$ = 72.3822... ≈ 72.38 cm$^2$
3. 90 in.$^2$

---

**TEACHING TIP**

**Question 6** If students have trouble finding the area of the standard six-pack model, have them draw a picture that shows the six cans and the rectangle. Then suggest that they label the diameter of each circle (6.6 cm) and use that information to determine the length and the width of the rectangle. They should discover that the rectangle is 13.2 cm × 19.8 cm.

**TEACHING TIP**

Throughout this text, all calculations involving $\pi$ have been calculated using the $\pi$ key on a calculator and rounded to the nearest hundredth, unless specified otherwise in the student directions.

**4a.** Answers will vary with students' designs.

**4b.** Maximize the percent. Sample answer: You want the base of the cans to take up as much area of the base of the package as possible.

**5a.** Answers will vary with students' designs.

**5b.** Minimize. Sample answer: You want the amount of the base of the package taken up by one can to be as close to the area of the can as possible.

**6a.** Based on a radius of 3.3 cm, the area of the circle is about 34.2 cm$^2$; the area of the bottom of the six-pack package is about 261.4 cm$^2$.

**6b.** $\frac{6(34.2)}{261.4} \approx 79\%$. The cans use about 79% of the package's area.

**6c.** $\frac{261.4}{6} \approx 43.6$ cm$^2$; about 43.6 cm$^2$ of the package is used per can.

**6d.** Answers will vary with students' designs.

**4.**

**5.**

**6.**

4. $\frac{1}{2}\left(3\frac{1}{2}\right)\left(2\frac{1}{2}\right) = \frac{35}{8}$ or $4\frac{3}{8}$ ft$^2$

5. 169 square miles

6. $\frac{1}{2}\left(6\frac{1}{2}\right)(8 + 20) = 91$ ft$^2$

7. $A = \pi(1.5)^2 \approx 7.1$ in.$^2$

8. $11\frac{1}{4}$ ft$^2$

9. Yes. Sample explanation: If you round up both the length and the width, you get an area of $(10)(20) = 200$ square yards. So, the area is actually smaller than the carpeting available.

10a. $C = \pi d = \pi(5) = 15.7079\ldots \approx$ 15.7 in.

10b. $A = \pi r^2 = \pi(2.5)^2 = 19.6349\ldots \approx$ 19.6 in.$^2$

11. $A_{\text{total}} = (7\,\text{m})(7\,\text{m}) + (10\,\text{m})(6\,\text{m}) + (8\,\text{m})(10\,\text{m}) = 189\,\text{m}^2$

7. The National Hockey League (NHL) rulebook states that hockey pucks must be one inch thick and three inches in diameter. To the nearest tenth of a square inch, what is the area of one circular face of a hockey puck?

8. Some ski areas have developed techniques for making snow during the summer. This allows them to stay open all year. Tenney Mountain in New Hampshire begins its snow-making process by flash-freezing water into thin sheets. Each sheet is a $4\frac{1}{2}$-ft by $2\frac{1}{2}$-ft rectangle. Find the area of one sheet of ice.

9. A company needs to carpet a large space in its new office complex. Will 200 square yards of carpeting be enough to cover a floor that is 9 yards by 18 yards? Explain.

10. Find (a) the circumference and (b) the area of the circle below. Round to the nearest tenth.

11. Find the area of the figure below.

**12.** An octagonal window has sides of length 19 inches. The distance from the midpoint of a side to the center of the window is 23 inches. What is the area of the pane of glass in the window? (Hint: How many of the triangles shown in the figure will fit in the octagon?)

**13.** Is it possible for two rectangles to have the same perimeter but different areas? Explain. Draw figures if necessary.

**14.** Find the cross-sectional area of the steel beam shown in the figure below. (Note: all angles are right angles.)

**12.** There are 8 triangles, each with area $\frac{1}{2}(19)(23) = \frac{437}{2}$ in.² Total area is $8\left(\frac{437}{2}\right) = 1{,}748$ in.²

**13.** Yes. Sample explanation: Consider a rectangle that is 4 units by 6 units and another that is 3 units by 7 units. They both have a perimeter of 20 units, but the first has an area of 24 square units while the second has an area of 21 square units.

---

**TEACHING TIP**

**Exercise 14** Some students may not know what a cross section of an object is. Point out that it is a section of the object formed by a plane cutting through the object. Give them everyday examples, such as cutting through an apple, orange, or cake.

---

**14.** $A_{\text{total}} = 2(45 \text{ cm})(13 \text{ cm}) + (32 \text{ cm})(8 \text{ cm}) = 1{,}426 \text{ cm}^2$

# LESSON 4.4

## Lesson Objectives

- use formulas to find the volumes of right prisms, cylinders, cones, pyramids, and spheres.
- use volumes of solids to evaluate the efficiency of a package design.

## Vocabulary

- cone
- cube
- cylinder
- edges of a solid
- faces of a solid
- pyramid
- rectangular solid
- right prism
- solid
- sphere
- vertices of a solid
- volume

## Materials List

- answers from Lesson 4.3 Question 6

## Description

This lesson is designed as a small group investigation (2–4 students). Have students read the information on the first page about volume and then work through **Questions 1–5**. Once all groups have completed the Investigation, have them share their results.

*Wrapping Up the Investigation:*

Ask students what they learned from this Investigation. Be sure that they understand that the ability to model a three-dimensional object with a drawing of its two-dimensional base is dependent on the situation and the criteria being examined.

## Lesson 4.4 Investigation Answers

1. Based on the area of the base being 261.4 cm², the volume of the package is approximately 3,136.8 cm³.

---

**Lesson 4.4**  **INVESTIGATION: Volumes of Solid Figures**

In the previous lesson, the packaging efficiency problem was made simpler by using a two-dimensional model of a three-dimensional package. In this lesson, you will examine three-dimensional models and use their volumes to determine the efficiencies of packages.

### VOLUME

A **solid** is a three-dimensional figure that encloses a part of space. The **volume** of a solid is the measure of the amount of space that is enclosed. To find the volume, you need a unit that can fill the space that the solid occupies. The most convenient shape that can fill a space without gaps or overlaps is the cube. While area is measured in squares, one unit on each side, volume is measured in cubes, one unit on each side.

**Note**

In any geometric solid, the flat surfaces of the object are referred to as **faces**. The lines formed when two faces meet are called **edges**, and the points where the edges meet are called **vertices**.

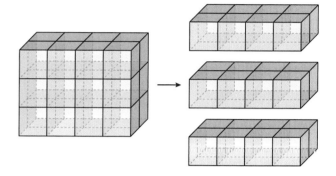

The mathematical modeling process often involves simplification. Modelers usually begin this way because it makes the problem easier to solve.

In the previous lesson, you modeled a three-dimensional standard six-pack package (usually called a **rectangular solid**) with a two-dimensional rectangle. If you multiply the area of that two-dimensional model by the height of its three-dimensional package, you will have its volume.

The cans in a standard six-pack are three-dimensional shapes called cylinders. A **cylinder** is a three-dimensional solid with a circular top and bottom. Its side surface is a rectangle when laid flat.

1. A standard six-pack is about 12 cm high. Use this height to find the volume of a standard six-pack package. (Recall that the radius of the base of one can is about 3.3 cm.)

**2.** Find the volume of one of the cans.

**3.** What percent of the volume of the package is used by the six cans?

**4.** What is the package volume per can?

**5.** Return to Question 6 from the Investigation in Lesson 4.3. Compare your results from that question to your answers to Questions 3 and 4 in this lesson.

   **a.** What effect does simplifying the problem to two dimensions have on this efficiency criterion: percent of the package space used by the cans?

   **b.** What effect does simplifying the problem to two dimensions have on this efficiency criterion: the amount of package space used per can?

## VOLUME FORMULAS

The following formulas are useful when calculating volumes:

- **Rectangular Solid**

The volume $V$ of a rectangular solid is the product of its length $l$, width $w$, and height $h$:

$$V = lwh$$

- **Cube**

The volume $V$ of a cube is the cube of the length of one edge $e$:

$$V = e^3$$

- **Right Prism**

The volume $V$ of a right prism is the product of the area of its base $B$ and its height $h$:

$$V = Bh$$

- **Cylinder**

The volume $V$ of a cylinder is the product of the area of its base ($\pi r^2$) and its height $h$:

$$V = \pi r^2 h$$

### TEACHING TIP

**Question 5** Students can see these effects by comparing their answers to **Questions 3 and 4** of this Investigation with **Questions 6b and 6c** of the Investigation in Lesson 4.3. Since the volume of the package is the area of its two-dimensional counterpart multiplied by 12 (the height of the package), the volume per can is the base area of each can multiplied by 12. Although there is an effect on the package space used per can criterion, the effect has no consequence for design selection since can height is constant.

### TEACHING TIP

It is always helpful to have three-dimensional models on hand for students who struggle visualizing a solid from its diagram.

**2.** Based on the area of the base of one can being 34.2 cm$^2$, the volume of one can is approximately 410.4 cm$^3$.

**3.** $\dfrac{6(410.4)}{3,136.8} \approx 79\%$; the cans use about 79% of the package's volume.

**4.** $\dfrac{3,136.8}{6} = 522.8$ cm$^3$; about 523 cm$^3$ of the package's volume is used per can.

**5a.** The percent of the space used by the cans is unaffected.

**5b.** Although there is an effect on the package space used per can, the effect has no consequence for design selection since can height is constant.

## Practice for Lesson 4.4 Answers

1. B
2. C
3. 343 cm³
4. 480 in.³

- **Pyramid**

The volume $V$ of a pyramid is one-third the product of the area of its base $B$ and its height $h$:

$$V = \frac{1}{3}Bh$$

- **Cone**

The volume $V$ of a cone is one-third the product of the area of its base ($\pi r^2$) and its height $h$:

$$V = \frac{1}{3}\pi r^2 h$$

- **Sphere**

The volume $V$ of a sphere is four-thirds the product of $\pi$ and the cube of its radius $r$:

$$V = \frac{4}{3}\pi r^3$$

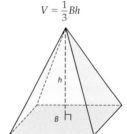

## Practice for Lesson 4.4

**For Exercises 1–2, choose the correct answer.**

1. In terms of $\pi$, the volume of a cylinder with a radius of 3 ft and a height of 8 ft is
   A. $48\pi$ cubic feet.
   B. $72\pi$ cubic feet.
   C. $192\pi$ cubic feet.
   D. $216\pi$ cubic feet.

2. In terms of $\pi$, the volume of a sphere with a radius of 3 ft is
   A. $12\pi$ cubic feet.
   B. $27\pi$ cubic feet.
   C. $36\pi$ cubic feet.
   D. $216\pi$ cubic feet.

**For Exercises 3–4, find the volume of each rectangular solid. Round answers to the nearest whole number.**

3.

7 cm
7 cm
7 cm

4.

5 in.
8 in.
12 in.

For Exercises 5–12, find the volume of each solid. Round answers to the nearest whole number.

5.

6.

7.

8. Right Prism

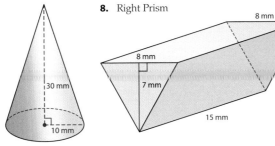

9. A rectangular solid with a base that is 5 cm by 4 cm and a height of 15 cm

10. A cube with an edge of 6 ft

11. A prism with a base area of 34 m² and a height of 6 m

12. A sphere with a diameter of 10 in.

13. Find the missing measure of the rectangular solid to the right if its volume is 672 cm³.

14. A supplier sells two toolboxes. Each toolbox is in the shape of a rectangular solid.

Box A is 30 in. by 14 in. by 8 in.
Box B is 24 in. by 18 in. by 8 in.

a. Which box has the greater volume?
b. How much greater is the volume of the larger box?

LESSON 4.4

5. About 113 m³
6. About 785 in.³
7. About 3,142 mm³
8. 420 mm³
9. 300 cm³
10. 216 ft³
11. 204 m³
12. About 524 in.³
13. 14 cm
14a. Box A: 3,360 in.³; Box B: 3,456 in.³; Box B has the greater volume.
14b. 3,456 in.³ − 3,360 in.³ = 96 in.³

**15.** Volume = (50 ft)(250 ft)(1,000 ft) = 12,500,000 ft³

**16.** $V = \frac{1}{3}\pi r^2 h = \frac{1}{3}(\pi)(38)^2(40) \approx$ 60,000 in.³

**17.** $V = \frac{1}{3}Bh = \frac{1}{3}(48)^2(260) =$ 199,680 m³

**18.** Volume = (2)(2)(8) + (2)(2)(4) + (2)(2)(6) = 32 + 16 + 24 = 72 in.³

**19.** $V = \frac{4}{3}\pi r^3 = \frac{4}{3}\pi(17.5)^3 =$ 22,449.2975 ≈ 22,000 in.³

**20.** $(14 \text{ ft})\left(\frac{12 \text{ in.}}{1 \text{ ft}}\right) = 168$ in.; $V = \pi r^2 h = \pi(0.5)^2(168) \approx$ 132 in.³

**15.** As part of the "Big Dig" harbor reconstruction project in Boston, a *casting basin* in the shape of a rectangular solid had to be created. The average dimensions of the concrete box were 50 ft deep, 250 ft wide, and 1,000 ft long. What is the volume of the casting basin?

**16.** A type of sand found in Alberta, Canada, has become a new source of oil. A two-ton pile of oil sand is in the shape of a cone 40 inches high and 6 feet 4 inches in diameter. Find the volume of the pile, to the nearest thousand cubic inches.

**17.** The Transamerica Building in San Francisco is about 260 meters high, with a square base measuring 48 meters on a side. Find the volume of a pyramid with these dimensions.

**18.** Find the volume of the solid shown in the figure below. All measurements are in inches.

**19.** Mike Carmichael of Alexandria, Indiana, began painting a baseball in 1977. The ball is now covered with more than 18,000 layers of paint. It is 35 inches in diameter and weighs 1,300 pounds. To the nearest thousand cubic inches, what is the volume of the painted ball?

**20.** Find the volume of water that can be contained in a 14-foot-long cylindrical pipe that has an inside diameter of 1.0 inch. Round your answer to the nearest cubic inch. (Hint: Change 14 feet to inches.)

**Fill in the blank.**

1. Terms whose variable parts are exactly the same are called
   _____ terms.

2. A figure that is both equilateral and equiangular is called a(n)
   _____ polygon.

**Choose the correct answer.**

3. Which figure is *not* a polygon?

   **A.** An equilateral triangle    **B.** A square

   **C.** A circle    **D.** A rhombus

4. The sum of the measures of the angles of a pentagon is
   _____ degrees.

   **A.** 180    **B.** 108    **C.** 360    **D.** 540

**Multiply or divide.**

5. $14.2 \times 0.4$    6. $0.05 \times 1.4$    7. $170.4 \div 8$

8. $28 \div 0.8$    9. $0.696 \div 5.8$    10. $7.77 \div 0.37$

**Add, subtract, multiply or divide.**

11. $0.8 + (-0.3)$    12. $-1.2 - 4.6$    13. $-0.3(4.1)$

14. $-5 - 5$    15. $-8 \div (-0.4)$    16. $5 \times (-0.5)$

**Solve.**

17. What is 5% of 34?    18. What is 120% of 22?

19. What is 0.5% of 18?    20. What is 3.2% of 8?

21. What is 0.02% of 1,500?    22. What is 14% of 3.5?

**5e** Evaluate

## Lesson Objective

- solve problems that require previously learned concepts and skills.

## Exercise Reference

Exercise 1: Lesson 3.5

Exercises 2–4: Lesson 4.1

Exercises 5–10: Appendix B

Exercises 11–16: Appendix I

Exercises 17–22: Appendix F

Exercises 23–26: Lesson 3.5

Exercises 27–30: Appendix M

Exercise 31: Lesson 1.2

Exercise 32: Lesson 4.3

## Lesson 4.5
## R.A.P. Answers

1. like
2. regular
3. C
4. D
5. 5.68
6. 0.07
7. 21.3
8. 35
9. 0.12
10. 21
11. 0.5
12. −5.8
13. −1.23
14. −10
15. 20
16. −2.5
17. 1.7
18. 26.4
19. 0.09
20. 0.256
21. 0.3
22. 0.49

23. $-4$
24. $\dfrac{2}{3}$
25. $3$
26. $6$
27. $2\sqrt{3}$
28. $3\sqrt{5}$
29. $4\sqrt{6}$
30. $10\sqrt{2}$
31. $3.90
32a. 78.84 in.
32b. 231.48 in.$^2$

**Solve and check.**

23. $4x - 8 = 6x$

24. $2(8m + 3) = 22 - 8m$

25. $5(a + 2) - 3 = 22$

26. $\dfrac{y}{2} = \dfrac{y + 3}{3}$

**Simplify.**

27. $\sqrt{12}$

28. $\sqrt{45}$

29. $\sqrt{96}$

30. $\sqrt{200}$

31. If 12 notebooks cost $9.36, what is the cost of 5 notebooks?

32. Find (a) the perimeter and (b) the area of the figure below. Use 3.14 for $\pi$.

24 in.

12 in.

In previous lessons, you examined many features that make a package the best package. In this lesson, you will explore how to determine the amount of material that is needed to make a package.

Most cartons are shaped like prisms. They start as a flat piece of material. Then they are folded into the shape of the prism. In this Activity, you will calculate the number of square centimeters of paperboard in a carton shaped like a prism. You will also explore how the flat version of the prism folds into a three-dimensional container.

The figure below shows a reduced version of Handout 4B. This two-dimensional version of a solid figure is called a **net**. This net folds into a triangular prism.

### Recall

A prism has two congruent parallel surfaces that are polygons. These two surfaces are sometimes called the *bases* of the prism. All of the other surfaces are rectangles.

Prisms are usually named for their bases.

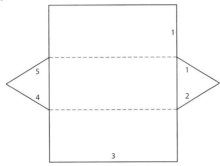

1. Cut out the net in Handout 4B.

2. Use area formulas to find the total number of square centimeters of paperboard in the prism's surface. You will need to do the following:

   • Draw in the heights on the triangles.
   • Use a ruler to measure the lengths of the edges and heights to the nearest tenth of a centimeter.
   • Write all measurements on your cut-out net.
   • Find the area of each rectangle or triangle and write it on your cut-out net.

3. Find the total area of your net.

4. In the figure above, some of the edges are numbered. Notice that two edges are numbered 1. When your net is folded into a triangular prism, the two edges numbered 1 will meet. Find and label the edge that meets each of the edges labeled 2, 3, 4, and 5.

SURFACE AREA    **Lesson 4.6**    **119**

## Lesson Objectives

• draw a net for a solid figure.
• recognize solid figures from their nets.
• find the surface area of a solid.

## Vocabulary

• net
• surface area

## Materials List

*Per group:*
• centimeter ruler
• scissors
• Handout 4B (one copy per student)
• tape

## Description

*Preparation:*

Have students work in groups of 2–4 students. Provide each student in each group with a copy of Handout 4B. Have members of the groups share rulers, scissors, and tape.

*During the Activity:*

Have students read the introductory paragraph and then begin assembling their triangular prisms. Point out that they should measure prior to folding and taping the edges together.

For **Questions 5 –7**, it might be helpful to have a rectangular prism available for students who are having trouble visualizing all six of the rectangular surfaces of the solid.

## Lesson 4.6 Activity Answers

3. Sample answer: Each triangular base has an area of about 11.2 cm². Each rectangular face has an area of about 64.5 cm². The total surface area is 2 × 11.2 + 3 × 64.5 or about 215.9 or approximately 216 cm².

4.

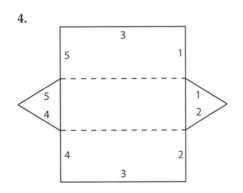

*Closing the Activity:*

Since the results to **Question 8b and 8c** may be surprising to some students, take time to discuss them.

5. Check students' prisms.
6. $SA = 2(19.8)(13.2) + 2(19.8)(12) + 2(13.2)(12) \approx 1{,}315 \text{ cm}^2$
7. $\dfrac{1{,}315}{6} \approx 219 \text{ cm}^2$
8a. 48 cans
8b. Surface area of the standard package: about 1,315 cm². Surface area of the new package: about 5,259 cm². The surface area of the new package is about 4 times the surface area of the standard package.
8c. Yes. Sample explanation: The standard package uses about 219 cm² per can, and the new package uses about 110 cm² per can. The new package uses about half the package material per can as that of the standard package. So, it is more efficient.

## Practice for Lesson 4.6 Answers

1. B
2. D
3. $SA = 150 \text{ ft}^2$

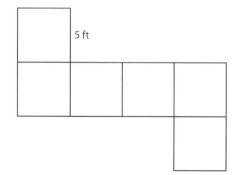

5 ft

4. $SA = 48\pi \approx 151 \text{ m}^2$

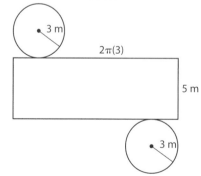

3 m

$2\pi(3)$

5 m

3 m

---

5. Use the numbers on your handout to help you fold your cut-out net into a prism. Use tape to hold the edges together. The total area that you found in Question 3 is known as the **surface area** of the triangular prism.

6. Find the surface area in square centimeters of a standard six-pack package whose length is 19.8 cm, width is 13.2 cm, and height is 12 cm.

7. What is the package surface area per can?

8. Suppose that you doubled the length, width, and height of a standard six-pack.
   a. How many cans would it hold?
   b. The surface area of the new package is about how many times greater than the surface area of the standard six-pack package?
   c. If the criterion for efficiency is surface area per can, is this new package more efficient? Explain.

### Practice for Lesson 4.6

**For Exercises 1–2, choose the correct answer.**

1. A cube has an edge of 6 feet. The surface area of the cube is measured in
   **A.** feet.          **B.** square feet.
   **C.** cubic feet.    **D.** It has no units.

2. What is the surface area of the prism at the right?
   **A.** 25 in.          **B.** 196 in.²
   **C.** 480 in.³        **D.** 392 in.²

5 in.
8 in.
12 in.

**For Exercises 3–4, sketch a net of the figure shown and label it. Then calculate the surface area of the figure to the nearest square unit.**

3. Cube

5 ft

4. Cylinder

3 m
5 m

**5.** The net shown below consists of four congruent triangles and one square. Name the three-dimensional figure whose net is shown. Then find its surface area.

6 m

8 cm

**6.** The edge of a cube is 7 mm long. Find the surface area of the cube.

**7.** How much newspaper will it take to cover a cube whose side length is 11 inches?

**8.** The label on a can of paint states that the paint will cover 400 ft² of surface. How many cans of paint are needed to paint a room (walls and ceiling only) that is 15 feet long, 20 feet wide, and 10 feet tall?

**9.** The soup can to the left is in the shape of a cylinder. The label surrounds the can without overlapping. Find the area of the label. Round to the nearest tenth of a square inch.

4.5 in.

3.0 in.

**10.** Find the surface area of the solid below if each cube has an edge of 3 cm.

**11.** The formula $SA = 4\pi r^2$ is used to find the surface area $SA$ of a sphere, where $r$ is the radius of the sphere. Find the surface area of a sphere with a radius of 4 inches. Round to the nearest square inch.

r

SURFACE AREA    Lesson 4.6    121

**5.** square pyramid; 160 cm²

**6.** 294 mm²

**7.** 726 in.²

**8.** $SA = 2(15)(10) + 2(20)(10) + 15(20) = 1,000$ ft²; 1,000 ft² ÷ 400 ft²/can = $2\frac{1}{2}$. So, 3 cans of paint are needed.

**9.** 42.4 in.²

**10.** 342 cm²

**11.** 201 in.²

**TEACHING TIP**

If students have trouble visualizing what the label of a can in **Exercise 9** looks like, bring a can to class, cover the lateral area with paper, then unwrap the paper. Students can then see that the desired area is in the shape of a rectangle. Point out how the length and width of the rectangle relate to the circumference and height of the can.

**COMMON ERROR**

**Exercise 10** Some students will fail to count the exposed surfaces correctly. Provide students with nine cubes. Have them build the model shown in the figure and then count the exposed surfaces. Remind them not to forget the surfaces on the bottom.

# LESSON 4.7

**5e** Explore

## Lesson Objectives

- determine the relationship that exists between the scale factor and the ratio of the surface areas of two similar solids.
- determine the relationship that exists between the scale factor and the ratio of the volumes of two similar solids.

## Vocabulary

- similar solids
- lateral surface area

## Materials List

## Description

This lesson is designed as a small group investigation (2–4 students). Have groups work through **Questions 1–9**. Encourage each group to keep track of the relationships between the scale factor of the smaller prism to the larger prism and the ratios asked for in the questions.

*Wrapping Up the Investigation:*

Use **Question 10** to wrap up this Investigation. As you are going over the ratios, remind students of the definition of lateral area.

---

## Lesson 4.7

### INVESTIGATION: Similar Figures—Perimeter, Area, and Volume

In Lesson 4.6, you examined two similar packages, the standard six-pack soda package and a new package in which the dimensions were doubled. You compared their surface areas and found that the surface area of the new package was four times the surface area of the standard package. In this lesson, you will examine two similar solids and explore the relationships that exist between the scale factor and the ratios of the surface areas and the volumes of the two similar solids.

### SIMILAR SOLIDS

Two three-dimensional figures are called **similar solids** if they have the same shape and the ratios of their corresponding *linear measurements* are equal. This ratio is the scale factor of the two similar solids.

1. The figure above shows two prisms. Is the smaller prism similar to the larger prism? Explain how you know.
2. Find the scale factor of the smaller prism to the larger one.
3. Find the ratio of the perimeter of the square base of the smaller prism to the perimeter of the square base of the larger prism. How does this ratio relate to the scale factor of the smaller prism to the larger one?
4. Find the ratio of the area of the square base of the smaller prism to the area of the square base of the larger prism. How does this ratio relate to the scale factor of the smaller prism to the larger one?
5. Find the surface area of each prism.

---

**Questions 1–9** For students who are having difficulty understanding the relationships in this Investigation, give them cubes and have them build physical models of each of the rectangular solids shown in the Investigation.

You may wish to provide students with this chart from the Teacher's Resource Materials to help organize students' answers.

| | Smaller Prism | Larger Prism | Ratio of Smaller to Larger Prism |
|---|---|---|---|
| Length of corresponding linear measurements | | | scale factor = |
| Perimeter of base | | | |
| Area of base | | | |
| Surface area | | | |
| Lateral surface area | | | |
| Volume | | | |

## Lesson 4.7 Investigation Answers

**1.–5.** See answers on page 123.

**122**

**Recall**

The **lateral surface area** of a three-dimensional figure is the surface area of the figure excluding the area of its bases. For example, the lateral surface area of a cylinder is the area of the curved surface.

Lateral Surface

**6.** Find the ratio of the surface area of the smaller prism to the surface area of the larger prism. How does this ratio relate to the scale factor of the smaller prism to the larger one?

**7.** Find the lateral surface area of each prism.

**8.** Find the ratio of the lateral surface area of the smaller prism to the lateral surface area of the larger prism. How does this ratio relate to the scale factor of the smaller prism to the larger one?

**9.** Calculate the volume of each solid and find the ratio of the volume of the smaller prism to the volume of the larger prism. How does this ratio relate to the scale factor of the smaller prism to the larger one?

**10.** In general, the results of your investigations in Questions 1–9 are true for all pairs of similar solids. Complete the following to summarize your results:

If the ratio of two corresponding sides of two similar solids is $a : b$, then
**a.** the ratio of the corresponding perimeters is _____.
**b.** the ratios of the base areas, the lateral surface areas, and the total surface areas are _____.
**c.** the ratio of the volumes is _____.

## E X A M P L E

Suppose that the scale factor of two similar cylinders is 2 : 7. Find each of the following:

**a.** the ratio of the heights of the cylinders
**b.** the ratio of the circumferences of their bases
**c.** the ratio of their base areas
**d.** the ratio of their surface areas
**e.** the ratio of their volumes

**Solution:**

**a.** The ratio of the heights of the cylinders is $\frac{2}{7}$.
**b.** The ratio of the circumferences of their bases is $\frac{2}{7}$.
**c.** The ratio of their base areas is $\left(\frac{2}{7}\right)^2 = \frac{4}{49}$.
**d.** The ratio of their surface areas is $\left(\frac{2}{7}\right)^2 = \frac{4}{49}$.
**e.** The ratio of their volumes is $\left(\frac{2}{7}\right)^3 = \frac{8}{343}$.

SIMILAR FIGURES—PERIMETER, AREA, AND VOLUME    **Lesson 4.7**    **123**

**6.** The ratio is $\frac{56}{126} = \frac{4}{9}$, which is equal to the square of the scale factor $\left(\frac{2}{3}\right)^2$.

**7.** The lateral surface area of the smaller prism is 48 cm². The lateral surface area of the larger prism is 108 cm².

**8.** The ratio is $\frac{48}{108} = \frac{4}{9}$, which is equal to the square of the scale factor $\left(\frac{2}{3}\right)^2$.

**9.** The volume of the smaller prism is 24 cm³. The volume of the larger prism is 81 cm³. The ratio is $\frac{24}{81} = \frac{8}{27}$, which is equal to the cube of the scale factor $\left(\frac{2}{3}\right)^3$.

**10a.** $a : b$
**10b.** $a^2 : b^2$
**10c.** $a^3 : b^3$

### ADDITIONAL EXAMPLE

Suppose the scale factor of two similar pyramids is 5 : 2. Find each of the following:

**a.** the ratio of the perimeters of the bases
**a.** 5 : 2

**b.** the ratio of the areas of the bases
**b.** 25 : 4

**c.** the ratio of the volumes of the pyramids
**c.** 125 : 8

**1.** Yes, both figures are rectangular prisms and the ratios of the corresponding linear measurements are equal. $\frac{2}{3} = \frac{6}{9}$

**2.** 2 : 3

**3.** The perimeter of the base of the smaller prism is 8 cm. The perimeter of the base of the larger prism is 12 cm. The ratio is $\frac{8}{12} = \frac{2}{3}$, which is the same as the scale factor.

**4.** The area of the base of the smaller prism is 4 cm². The area of the base of the larger prism is 9 cm². The ratio is $\frac{4}{9}$, which is equal to the square of the scale factor $\left(\frac{2}{3}\right)^2$.

**5.** The surface area of the smaller prism is 56 cm². The surface of the larger prism is 126 cm².

# LESSON 4.7

## Practice for Lesson 4.7

1. A
2. A
3a. 5 : 8
3b. $\left(\frac{5}{8}\right)^3 = \frac{125}{512}$
4. 3 : 7
5. 15 m³
6a. 3 : 4
6b. $\left(\frac{3}{4}\right)^2 = \frac{9}{16}$
6c. $\left(\frac{3}{4}\right)^3 = \frac{27}{64}$
6d. Sample answer: The larger ball contains $\left(\frac{4}{3}\right)^3$, or about 2.37 times as much string as the smaller ball, at 3.00 ÷ 1.50, or 2 times the cost. The larger ball is a better buy.

**Practice** for Lesson 4.7

**For Exercises 1–2, choose the correct answer.**

1. If the ratio of the volumes of two similar solids is 8 : 27, what is the ratio of the lengths of two corresponding edges?
   A. 2 : 3　　　　　　　　B. 8 : 27
   C. 16 : 54　　　　　　　D. 64 : 729

2. The scale factor of two similar solids is 2 : 5. The volume of the larger solid is 400 in³. What is the volume of the smaller solid?
   A. 25.6 in.³　　　　　　B. 64 in.³
   C. 125 in.³　　　　　　D. 160 in.³

3. The face of a small cube has an area of 25 m² and the face of a larger cube has an area of 64 m².
   a. Find the scale factor of the smaller cube to the larger one.
   b. Find the ratio of the volume of the smaller cube to the volume of the larger one.

4. The surface area of the smaller of two similar spheres is $18\pi$ ft³ and the surface area of the larger sphere is $98\pi$ ft³. Find the scale factor of the smaller to the larger solid.

5. The scale factor of the container shown below to one that is similar to it is 5 : 1. The volume of the container shown is 1,875 m³. Find the volume of the container that is similar to it.

6. Kite string is sold in two different sizes.
   a. If one ball of kite string has a diameter of 3 inches and the other ball has a diameter of 4 inches, find the ratio of the radius of the smaller ball to the radius of the larger ball.
   b. Find the ratio of the surface area of the smaller ball to the surface area of the larger ball.
   c. Find the ratio of the volume of the smaller ball to the volume of the larger ball.
   d. If the smaller ball of string costs $1.50 and the larger ball costs $3.00, which is the better buy? Explain.

**7.** A cylinder has a volume of 54 cubic inches. If the height and radius are changed so that they are $\frac{1}{3}$ their original size, what will be the volume of the new cylinder?

**8.** The two triangles in the figure are equilateral.

Find the ratio of the area of the smaller triangle to the area of the larger triangle.

**9  a.** Find the lateral surface area of the cylinder shown here.

**b.** Find the lateral surface area of a larger similar cylinder if the two cylinders have a scale factor of 1 : 2.

**10.** The diameters of two soup bowls with similar shape are 5 inches and 7 inches. The smaller bowl holds 10 fluid ounces. How much does the larger bowl hold?

**TEACHING TIP**

In **Exercise 8**, point out that the actual areas of the triangles are not needed. The only relationship needed is the scale factor.

**7.** 2 in.$^3$

**8.** $\left(\frac{2}{10}\right)^2 = \frac{4}{100}$ or $\frac{1}{25}$

**9a.** $LA = 2\pi rh = 2(\pi)(2)(3) \approx 37.7 \text{ m}^2$

**9b.** The ratio of the lateral areas is 1 : 4, so the lateral area of the larger cylinder is about 150.8 m$^2$.

**10.** 27.44 fluid ounces

## Materials List

- rectangular cardstock or light cardboard
- scissors
- tape
- rulers

## Description

In this project students use a rectangular piece of cardstock to design a closed top, rectangular, box-shaped container. Once designed, they build the physical model and discuss uses and other considerations for their shapes. This project works best when students work with a partner or in small groups.

## Sample Answers

Answers will vary based on the considerations the students chose to incorporate into their models. Written reports should demonstrate an understanding of measurement, calculations of area and volume, and their considerations for the box designs.

CHAPTER
# 4

# Modeling Project

## Building a Better Box

### Modeling Task

Your task in this modeling project is to use one piece of cardstock to design and create a closed-top container that is in the shape of a rectangular prism.

### Considerations

As you are designing your box, take into account the following considerations:

- the number of cuts needed
- the amount of waste material
- the purpose of the box (what it is to be used for)
- the material the box will be made from (wood, metal, etc.)
- how the box will be held together.

### Report

Once you have designed and created an actual covered box, write a report that includes the following:

- the dimensions and area of the unfolded cardstock you used to create your box,
- the volume of your box,
- the surface area of your box, and
- the features of your box. Be sure to discuss the considerations that you incorporated into your design.

MEASUREMENT: PERIMETER, AREA, AND VOLUME

# Chapter 4 Review

## You Should Be Able to:

### Lesson 4.1

- classify polygons by their sides.
- classify quadrilaterals by their attributes.
- find the sum of the angle measures in a polygon.

### Lesson 4.2

- solve a literal equation for a specific variable.
- find the perimeter of a polygon.
- find the circumference of a circle.

### Lesson 4.3

- create a mathematical model for an efficient package design.
- use area formulas to find the areas of various polygons.
- use areas of polygons to evaluate the efficiency of a package design.

### Lesson 4.4

- use formulas to find the volumes of right prisms, cylinders, cones, pyramids, and spheres.
- use volumes of solids to evaluate the efficiency of a package design.

### Lesson 4.5

- solve problems that require previously learned concepts and skills.

### Lesson 4.6

- draw a net for a solid figure.
- recognize solid figures from their nets.
- find the surface area of a solid.

### Lesson 4.7

- determine the relationship that exists between the scale factor and the ratio of the surface areas of two similar solids.
- determine the relationship that exists between the scale factor and the ratio of the volumes of two similar solids.

## Key Vocabulary

polygon (p. 97)

triangle (p. 97)

quadrilateral (p. 97)

pentagon (p. 97)

hexagon (p. 97)

heptagon (p. 97)

octagon (p. 97)

nonagon (p. 97)

decagon (p. 97)

dodecagon (p. 97)

$n$-gon (p. 97)

regular polygon (p. 97)

equilateral polygon (p. 97)

equiangular polygon (p. 97 )

## Chapter 4 Test Review Answers

1. It is not a polygon. Not all of its sides are line segments.
2. Sometimes; Sample explanation: If the rhombus is a square, then it is a regular polygon because all sides are equal in measure and all angles are equal in measure. If the rhombus is not a square, then it is not a regular polygon because not all of its angles are equal in measure.
3. 106 inches
4. 900°
5. $s = \dfrac{P}{4}$
6. $T = \dfrac{PV}{nR}$
7. $4(6 \text{ m}) = 24 \text{ m}$

## Chapter 4  Test Review

1. Is the figure below a polygon? Explain why or why not.

2. Is a rhombus a regular polygon? Explain why or why not.
3. The expressions $2(n + 30)$ inches and $(5n - 9)$ inches represent the measures of two sides of a regular pentagon. Find the length of one side of the pentagon.
4. Find the sum of the angle measures in any heptagon.
5. Solve $P = 4s$ for $s$.
6. The formula $PV = nRT$ shows the relationship among the pressure, volume, and temperature for an ideal gas. Solve the formula for $T$.
7. Find the perimeter of the figure shown below.

6 m

**8.** Find the perimeter of a parallelogram with sides of 10 inches and 5 inches.

**9.** Find the perimeter of a regular pentagon with sides of 7 centimeters.

**10.** The NHL rulebook states that hockey pucks must be one inch thick and three inches in diameter. To the nearest tenth of an inch, what is the circumference of the puck?

**11.** Find the area of a triangle with a base of 12.5 meters and a height of 9.8 meters.

**12.** Find the cross-sectional area of the concrete T–section shown in the figure.

**13.** Two popular fruit drinks are sold in different-sized containers.

Container A is a cylinder that has a circular base with an area of 7 in.² and a height of 4 inches.

Container B is a right prism that has a square base with an edge of 2 inches and a height of 6 inches.

**a.** Which container holds more?
**b.** How much more does the larger container hold?

**14.** Find the surface area of the solid in the figure below if each cube has an edge of 3 cm.

**15.** A grain storage silo is in the shape of a cylinder. It has a diameter of 26 feet and a height of 40 feet. What is the lateral area of the cylinder? Round to the nearest square foot.

**8.** $2(10 \text{ in.}) + 2(5 \text{ in.}) = 30$ in.

**9.** $5(7 \text{ cm}) = 35$ cm

**10.** $C = \pi(3) \approx 9.4$ in.

**11.** $A = \frac{1}{2}(bh) = \frac{1}{2}(12.5)(9.8) = 61.25 \text{ m}^2$

**12.** $A = (62.0 \text{ cm})(10.0 \text{ cm}) + (52.0 \text{ cm})(10.0 \text{ cm}) = 1{,}140 \text{ cm}^2$

**13a.** Container A: $(7 \text{ in.}^2)(4 \text{ in.}) = 28 \text{ in.}^3$; Container 2: $(2 \text{ in.})(2 \text{ in.})(6 \text{ in.}) = 24 \text{ in.}^3$; Container A holds more.

**13b.** $28 \text{ in.}^3 - 24 \text{ in.}^3 = 4 \text{ in.}^3$

**14.** $42(9 \text{ cm}^2) = 378 \text{ cm}^2$

**15.** $A = \pi dh = \pi(26)(40) \approx 3{,}267$ square feet

**16a.** triangular prism

**16b.** $30 + 2(1.7) = 33.4 \text{ cm}^2$

**16c.** $30 \text{ cm}^2$

**17.** $V = \frac{4}{3}\pi(1.05 \text{ m})^3 \approx 4.8 \text{ m}^3$

**18.** Volume of four balls:

$$V = 4\left(\frac{4}{3}\pi(3.3)^3\right) \approx 602.1 \text{ cm}^3$$

Volume of container:

$$V = \pi(3.3)^2(26.4) \approx 903.2 \text{ cm}^3$$

Percent of container that is filled

with balls $= \frac{602.1}{903.2} \approx 67\%$

**19.** $V = \frac{1}{3}Bh = \frac{1}{3}\left(\frac{1}{2} \cdot 4 \cdot 5\right)(7) = \frac{70}{3} \text{ cm}^3$

or $23\frac{1}{3} \text{ cm}^3$

**20.** $A = (9.5)(16)^2 = 2{,}432 \text{ in.}^2$ or

about $16.9 \text{ ft}^2$

---

**16 a.** Name the solid that can be made by folding the net in the figure shown below.

**b.** Find the surface area of the solid.

**c.** Find the lateral area of the solid.

**17.** The Ledyard Bridge across the Connecticut River in Hanover, New Hampshire is decorated with massive concrete balls. The largest ball has a diameter of about 2.1 meters. Find its volume to the nearest tenth of a cubic meter.

**18.** Each of the four balls in the container in the figure has a diameter of 6.6 cm. What percent of the container is filled with balls?

**19.** A pyramid has a base in the shape of a right triangle with legs of 5 cm and 4 cm. The height of the pyramid is 7 cm. Find its volume.

**20.** The scale factor of a model B757-200 Freighter to the actual aircraft is 1 : 16. Find the area of the lower aft door of the actual aircraft if the area of the lower aft door of the model is 9.5 square inches.

**21.** The dimensions of a standard six-pack of soda are about
19.8 cm × 13.2 cm × 12 cm.
- **a.** What is the volume of the standard six-pack? Round to the nearest cubic centimeter.
- **b.** Suppose that you double the dimensions of the standard package. What is the volume of the new package? Round to the nearest cubic centimeter.
- **c.** The volume of the new package is about how many times greater than the volume of the standard six-pack package?
- **d.** If the criterion for efficiency is the percent of the volume of the package that is used by the cans, is this new package more efficient than the standard six-pack? (Recall from Lesson 4.4 that the volume of one can is about 410.4 cm³ and the percent of the volume of the package that is used by the cans for a standard six-pack is about 79%.)

**22.** Package T is a trapezoidal prism and Package R is a rectangular prism.

- **a.** What is the volume of Package T?
- **b.** If both packages have the same volume, find the height of Package R.

**21a.** $V = (19.8)(13.2)(12) \approx 3{,}136$ cm³
**21b.** $V = (39.6)(26.4)(24) = 25{,}091$ cm³
**21c.** The volume of the standard package is about 3,136 cm³. The volume of the new package is about 25,091 cm³. The volume of the new package is about 8 times the volume of the standard package.
**21d.** No, the percent of the volume of the package that is used by the cans in the new package is about 79%, the same as in the standard package.

$$\frac{48(410.4 \text{ cm}^3)}{25{,}091 \text{ cm}^3} \approx 79\%$$

**22a.** 2,880 cm³
**22b.** 16 cm

## Lesson Objective

- construct the net of a cone with a given radius and slant height

## Vocabulary

- arc of a circle
- central angle of a circle
- height of a cone
- right cone
- sector of a circle
- slant height
- vertex of a cone

## Materials List

*Per group:*
- protractor
- compass
- scissors
- tape

## Description

In this lesson students use their knowledge of cones, nets, and circles to create a net of a right cone.

### TEACHING TIP

Point out to students that they must choose a radius (radius of the circular base) and slant height (radius of the sector of the circle) that will fit on their paper.

---

# Chapter Extension
## Constructing the Net of a Cone

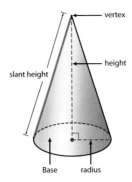

As a young child, did you ever wonder why you could take a paper circle or piece of circular lunchmeat and pinch and fold it until it suddenly became a cone-shaped figure? If so, read on and discover how to construct a net for a cone.

## CONES

A cone has a circular base. It also has a **vertex**, a point that is not in the plane that contains the base. If the **height**, a segment joining the vertex and the center of the base, is perpendicular to the base, the cone is a **right cone**. The **slant height** of a right cone is the distance from the vertex to any point on the base edge.

## THE NET OF A CONE

When you cut along a slant height and the base edge of a cone and then lay it flat, you get a net of the cone. The net consists of two parts:

- a circle that gives the base of the cone, and
- a sector of a circle that gives the lateral surface. (See the figure below.)

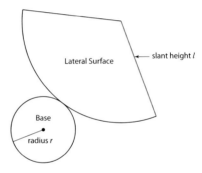

### Recall

- A **central angle** of a circle is an angle formed by any two radii in the circle. Its vertex is the center of the circle.
- An **arc** of a circle is a part of the circle. It consists of two endpoints and all the points on the circle between these endpoints.
- A **sector** of a circle is a region bounded by two radii and their intercepted arc.

central angle ∠AOB

MEASUREMENT: PERIMETER, AREA, AND VOLUME

## CONSTRUCTING THE NET

1. Choose a radius *r* for the base and a slant height *l* for your cone. Note that the slant height of your cone must be greater than the radius.

2. Using your radius, calculate the circumference of the base of the cone. (Leave your answer in terms of $\pi$.) This length is also the length of the arc in the sector of your net.

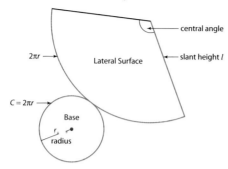

3. Now, consider *only* the lateral surface area part of the net. (See the figure below.) Notice that the lateral surface is a sector of a circle, and the slant height is actually the radius of that circle.

Use the following proportion to find the measure of the central angle of the sector:

$$\frac{\text{central angle of sector } \theta}{360°} = \frac{\text{length of arc of the sector}}{\text{circumference of entire circle}}$$

$$\frac{\theta}{360°} = \frac{2\pi r}{2\pi l}$$

$$\frac{\theta}{360°} = \frac{r}{l}$$

## Chapter 4 Extension Answers

1. Sample answer: radius $r = 14$ cm; slant height $l = 21$ cm

2. Sample answer: If the radius is 14 cm, then $C = 2\pi r = 2\pi(14) = 28\pi$ cm.

3. Sample answer: If $r = 14$ cm and $l = 21$ cm, $\frac{\theta}{360°} = \frac{r}{l}$; $\theta = \frac{360r}{l}$; $\theta = 240°$

5. Lateral area: $\left(\frac{270}{360}\right)\pi(20)^2 =$ 942.48 in.$^2$

Surface area: $942.48 + 706.86 = 1,649.34$ in.$^2$

4. You are now ready to construct the net for your cone.
   a. First construct the sector. Begin by using a protractor to draw an angle the size of your central angle from Question 3. Use a compass and a radius equal in measure to your slant height to construct the arc of your sector.
   b. Now use the radius of the base of your cone to construct a circle tangent to the sector. (See the figure in Question 2.)
   c. To test your calculations and measurements, cut out your net and fold it to see if it is indeed a cone with your chosen radius and slant height.

5. Consider a right cone with a radius of 15 inches and a slant height of 20 inches. Find the lateral area and the surface area of the cone. Round all answers to two decimal places.

# Chapter 5
## Functions and Their Representations

## Mathematical Overview

Throughout this chapter, students learn to use more than one representation to model given situations, know the reasons why they might need to do this, and select the representation that is most appropriate for their needs. As they progress through the chapter they learn to graph a linear equation using a table of values, using the slope-intercept form of the equation and using just the intercepts. Likewise, given the slope and *y*-intercept of a line, or a point and a line either parallel or perpendicular to the line, students write an equation of the line.

## Lesson Summaries

### Lesson 5.1    *Investigation: Representing Functions*

In this lesson, students investigate various types of representations that can be used to describe and represent functions. They use many of these representations during the Investigation to describe a function that could help a business determine the price of a product. As students progress through the lesson and practice items, they move from one form of representation to another.

### Lesson 5.2    *Activity: Linear Relationships*

In this Activity, students collect data and use what they know about direct variation, slope, and rate of change to analyze the data. During the Activity students identify independent and dependent variables, linear relationships, and the difference between discrete and continuous variables. This lesson concludes with students using a graph, table, or equation to make a prediction.

### Lesson 5.3    *Investigation: Identifying Linear Functions*

In this lesson, students focus on one particular type of function, the linear function. They examine the characteristics of linear functions and learn to identify them by examining equations, graphs, and tables. The Investigation focuses on depreciation of the value of a computer used for business purposes. Students determine that the depreciation function is a linear function.

### Lesson 5.4    *R.A.P.*

In this lesson, students **R**eview **A**nd **P**ractice solving problems that require the use of skills and concepts taught in previous math levels. The skills reviewed in this lesson are skills that are needed as a basis for solving problems throughout this course.

### Lessons 5.5    *Graphing Linear Equations and*
### 5.6    *Investigation: Writing Equations of Lines*

In Lesson 5.5, students use their knowledge of slope and plotting points to graph linear equations to get a visual summary of the relationship that exists between the two variables. They graph equations using the slope and the *y*-intercept, using the *x*- and *y*-intercepts, and using a graphing calculator. Then, in Lesson 5.6, the Investigation provides students with a graph from which they must describe what the slope and intercepts tell them about the relationship between the two variables. Finally, students learn to write an equation of a line when they do not have a graph, but are given two points on the line or one point and the slope of the line.

### Lesson 5.7    *Slopes of Parallel and Perpendicular Lines*

In this lesson, students investigate the slopes of parallel and perpendicular lines and use the information to find the equations of lines parallel (or perpendicular) to a given line.

### Chapter 5    *Extension: Special Functions*

In this Extension, students graph absolute value functions, a subset of piece-wise functions. Students also examine one example of a step function, the greatest integer function, $y = [\![x]\!]$. Given a table of values and a graph of the function, students determine the domain and range, evaluate the function for several given values, and then use the function to model a given situation.

# Lesson Guide

| Lesson/Objectives | Materials | |
|---|---|---|
| **Chapter 5 Opener: How Can You Find the Value of an Unknown Quantity?**<br>• recognize that equations can be used to predict the value of an unknown quantity from a value of a known quantity. | | |
| **5.1 Investigation: Representing Functions**<br>• represent functions in multiple ways.<br>• identify the domain and range of a function.<br>• identify the problem domain of a situation. | | *Optional:*<br>• grid paper<br>• TRM table shell for Question 3.<br>• TRM table shell for Exercise 14. |
| **5.2 Activity: Linear Relationships**<br>• collect and analyze data that have a constant rate of change. | *Per group:*<br>• scale (grams or tenths of an ounce)<br>• 10 objects, uniform in weight, weighing 0.2–0.4 oz (marbles, miniature candy bars, large metal washers, and 10-penny nails)<br>• container weighing between 3 and 6 ounces that is large enough to hold the 10 objects | *Optional:*<br>• grid paper<br>• 100-cm rope<br>• ruler<br>• TRM table shell for Question 2. |
| **5.3 Investigation: Identifying Linear Functions**<br>• identify linear functions from tables, graphs, and equations. | | *Optional:*<br>• grid paper<br>• Slinky®<br>• yardstick or meter stick<br>• small paper cup<br>• paper clips<br>• marbles<br>• TRM table shell for Question 1. |
| **5.4 R.A.P.**<br>• solve problems that require previously learned concepts and skills. | | |
| **5.5 Graphing Linear Equations**<br>• graph a linear equation using a table.<br>• graph a linear equation in slope-intercept form.<br>• graph a linear equation using the intercepts. | | *Optional:*<br>• grid paper |
| **5.6 Investigation: Writing Equations of Lines**<br>• write an equation of a line given its slope and *y*-intercept.<br>• use the definition of slope to write an equation of a line. | | *Optional:*<br>• grid paper |
| **5.7 Slopes of Parallel and Perpendicular Lines**<br>• write an equation of a line that passes through a given point and is parallel to a given line.<br>• write an equation of a line that passes through a given point and is perpendicular to a given line. | | *Optional:*<br>• grid paper |
| **Chapter 5 Extension: Special Functions**<br>• graph absolute value functions.<br>• graph piecewise-defined functions.<br>• graph step functions. | | *Optional:*<br>• grid paper |

See page 135 for the *Pacing Guide* and *Supplement Support*.

# Functions and Their Representations

## CONTENTS

## Pacing Guide

|            | Day 1        | Day 2      | Day 3    | Day 4    | Day 5            | Day 6               | Day 7    | Day 8           | Day 9             | Day 10    |
|------------|--------------|------------|----------|----------|------------------|---------------------|----------|-----------------|-------------------|-----------|
| **Basic**  | p. 136, 5.1  | 5.1        | 5.2      | 5.3      | 5.4              | 5.5                 | 5.6      | 5.7             | project           | review    |
| **Standard** | p. 136, 5.1 | 5.1, 5.2  | 5.2, 5.3 | 5.3, 5.4 | 5.4, 5.5         | 5.5, 5.6            | 5.6, 5.7 | 5.7, project    | project, review   | extension |
| **Block**  | p. 136, 5.1  | 5.2, 5.3   | 5.3, 5.4 | 5.5, 5.6 | 5.7, project     | review, extension   |          |                 |                   |           |

**Supplement Support**

See the Book Companion Website at www.highschool.bfwpub.com/ModelingwithMathematics and the Teacher's Resource Materials (TRM) for additional resources.

## Lesson Objective

- recognize that equations can be used to predict the value of an unknown quantity from the value of a known quantity.

## Vocabulary

## Description

This reading helps students see that mathematics is used in their everyday lives.

---

### TEACHING TIP

After students have read the Chapter Opener, lead a whole-class discussion asking students to name some pairs of measurable quantities that are related to each other in such a way that if you know the value of one quantity, you can determine the value of the other.

Sample answers might include *geometric relationships*, such as finding the area of a circle given its radius, *monetary relationships*, such as calculating cost given time and resources used, and *forecasting*, such as predicting future demand for a product based on past trends.

---

# How Can You Find the Value of an Unknown Quantity?

You may be familiar with Chuck E. Cheese's®, a chain of family entertainment centers headquartered in Irving, Texas. These centers provide arcade games, rides, prizes, food, and entertainment. As patrons win games, they receive tickets that can then be redeemed for prizes. During a single visit, a child might receive hundreds of these tickets.

In the early years of the company, there were no ticket-counting machines as there are today. Rather than count the hundreds of tickets one by one, an employee placed them on a scale. The scale was used to indirectly determine the number of tickets. How did a scale tell the employee how many tickets there were?

It was the connection between the weight of the tickets and the number of tickets that allowed the coupons to be "counted" indirectly. Once the weight of the tickets was found, the employee used a table, looked up the weight in a table, and found the number of tickets associated with that weight.

In this chapter, you explore many different input/output relationships and see how they can be used to predict the value of an *unknown* quantity from the value of a *known* quantity.

**INVESTIGATION: Representing Functions**

In Chapter 2, you explored quantities that varied directly. You found that two quantities are directly proportional if the ratio of the two quantities is constant. You used tables, graphs, and simple equations to describe these proportional relationships. In this lesson, you will investigate various representations that can be used to describe functions.

## TYPES OF REPRESENTATIONS

As you have seen in previous chapters, functions can be represented in several ways.

- by verbal descriptions
- by symbolic rules
- by diagrams, such as arrow diagrams
- by tables
- by graphs
- by manipulatives

In this Investigation, you will use many of these representations to describe a function that could help a business determine the price of a product.

Many businesses involve selling products. The total dollar amount received from product sales is called *revenue*. The revenue from a single product depends on its selling price. So, it is sometimes possible to express revenue as a function of price.

1. Suppose you decide to start a small business selling T-shirts in a resort town. On the first day, you decide to charge $10 for each shirt. If no one buys a shirt for $10, what is your total revenue?

2. Now suppose that on the next day, you reduce the selling price to $9. Ten people buy shirts at this price. What is your total revenue for that day?

3. To decide on the best price, you might use a table to see how different prices affect your total revenue. Suppose that reducing the price to $8 results in 20 sales and reducing the price to $7 results in 30 sales. Assume this pattern continues. Complete the table on the next page to show how the total revenue $R$ depends on the selling price $p$.

> **Recall**
> When two variables are related in such a way that for each *input* value there is exactly one *output* value, the relationship is called a *function*.

REPRESENTING FUNCTIONS    Lesson 5.1    **137**

---

## Lesson 5.1 Investigation Answers

1. $0
2. $90

3.

| Selling Price ($) | Number of Sales | Total Revenue ($) |
|---|---|---|
| 10 | 0 | 0 |
| 9 | 10 | 90 |
| 8 | 20 | 160 |
| 7 | 30 | 210 |
| 6 | 40 | 240 |
| 5 | 50 | 250 |
| 4 | 60 | 240 |
| 3 | 70 | 210 |
| 2 | 80 | 160 |
| 1 | 90 | 90 |
| 0 | 100 | 0 |

---

**5e** Explore

## Lesson Objectives
- represent functions in multiple ways.
- identify the domain and range of a function.
- identify the problem domain of a situation.

## Vocabulary
- domain
- intercept
- problem domain
- range

## Materials List
none

## Description

This Investigation works best if students work in pairs. Before beginning, review the definition of *function* in the **Recall** on the first page.

Have students work through the Investigation and the additional reading material after **Question 10.** Make sure that students pay particular attention to the new vocabulary that is introduced in this lesson.

*Wrapping Up the Investigation:*

Once all groups have completed the Investigation, debrief their results by asking what different types of representations they used or observed in the lesson.

Make sure that all students understand the difference between the (mathematical) *domain* of a function and the *problem domain* that applies when a function is used to model a real-world situation.

**4.** Independent variable: selling price $p$; dependent variable: revenue $R$. The amount of revenue depends on the selling price of the shirt.

**5.** There is exactly one revenue amount for each price.

**6.**

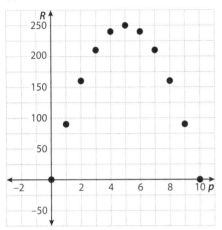

**7.** Sample answer: Price values for each of the points on the curve result in revenues that fit the pattern of the graph.

**8.** No, the graph should not extend to the left because negative prices make no sense in this context. The graph could be extended to the right, but no T-shirts would be sold at prices greater than $10, so the $R$-values would all be 0.

**9.** There are two $p$-intercepts at the points (0, 0) and (10, 0). There is only one $R$-intercept. Its coordinates are (0, 0). These intercepts mean that either a price of $0 or $10 will produce $0 in revenue.

**10.** $5; $250

| Selling Price ($) | Number of Sales | Total Revenue ($) |
|---|---|---|
| 10 | 0 | 0 |
| 9 | 10 | |
| 8 | 20 | |
| 7 | | |
| 6 | | |
| 5 | | |
| 4 | | |
| 3 | | |
| 2 | | |
| 1 | | |
| 0 | | |

**4.** Consider the variables selling price $p$ and revenue $R$ from your table. Which variable is the independent variable? Which is the dependent variable? Explain.

**5.** Explain why your table suggests that revenue is a *function* of selling price.

**6.** Using your values from Question 3, construct a scatter plot of revenue $R$ versus selling price $p$.

**7.** Connect the points in your graph with a smooth curve. Your curve now includes points for ordered pairs $(p, R)$ that were not in your table. What could these points mean?

**8.** For this situation, would it make sense to extend the graph to the left and right of the plotted points? Explain.

**9.** Any point where a graph touches or crosses either of the coordinate axes is called an **intercept**. An intercept is usually given the name of the appropriate variable. In this case, it is possible to have a $p$-intercept, an $R$-intercept, or both. What are the coordinates of the intercepts on your graph? Interpret the meaning of these intercepts.

**10.** For what price should you sell the T-shirts in order to produce maximum revenue? What is the maximum revenue?

**Note**

Not all tables represent functions. The table below shows the relationship between time worked and wages earned at a local store. At this store, some employees are paid overtime after working 40 hours, and others are not. Notice that the input value of 50 hours has two output values, $280 and $385. Hence, this table does not represent a function.

| Time Worked (hr) | Wages ($) |
|---|---|
| 20 | 140 |
| 30 | 210 |
| 40 | 280 |
| 50 | 280 |
| 50 | 385 |

## DOMAIN AND RANGE

The revenue function that you have been exploring can be written in symbolic form: $R = 100p - 10p^2$. This equation gives revenue $R$ as a function of price $p$.

You can verify that this equation models the situation by inserting price values from your table into the equation. For example, when $p = \$10$, $R = 100(10) - 10(10^2) = 0$. And when $p = \$7$, $R = 100(7) - 10(7^2) = 210$.

First consider this function without any real-life restrictions. Any input value can be substituted for $p$ in the function equation $R = 100p - 10p^2$ to produce a real output value. This includes all positive and negative numbers as well as 0. Hence, the domain of this function is unlimited. It includes all real numbers.

> The **domain** of a function is the set of all possible input values for which the function is defined.

As you saw from the graphs in Questions 6 and 7, there is a maximum value of 250 for $R$. So, the range of the function $R = 100p - 10p^2$ has an upper value of 250. But it has no lower limit. Negative values for $R$ can result from certain input values such as $p = 12$, for which $R = 100(12) - 10(12^2) = -240$.

> The **range** of a function is the set of all possible output values that the function generates from its domain.

Examine the graph of the function $R = 100p - 10p^2$. Since the domain of the function includes all real numbers, the graph would extend indefinitely to the left and to the right.

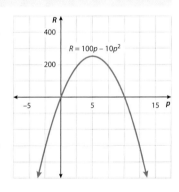

If you reexamine this function as it applies to a real-world situation, you may find that input values that make sense for the independent variable may be only a portion of the domain of the function. This restricted domain is often called the **problem domain**. The problem domain of a function includes only numbers that

- are actually reasonable values for the independent variable and
- will produce reasonable values for the dependent variable.

**TEACHING TIP**

Throughout this text, the domain of a function will sometimes be referred to as the *mathematical domain* in order to distinguish it from the problem domain of the function.

REPRESENTING FUNCTIONS    **Lesson 5.1**    **139**

## ADDITIONAL EXAMPLE

Consider the function
$I = 0.04P$.

**a.** Determine the domain for the function.

**b.** Determine the problem domain for the function if $P$ represents the principal invested at a local bank and $I$ represents the total interest earned in one year.

**a.** The domain of the function is all real numbers.

**b.** The problem domain in this situation consists of all real numbers greater than or equal to 0. (There is no largest reasonable value for the independent variable.)

> ### TEACHING TIP
>
> Point out to students that not all functions have problem domains. It is only when a function represents a real-world situation that these restrictions on the domain of the function need to be considered.

> ### COMMON ERROR
>
> **Exercise 2** If students confuse the independent and dependent variables, have them ask themselves which of the variables affects the outcome of the other. That variable is the independent variable. Also, remind them that the **in**put of the function is the **in**dependent variable.

## Practice for Lesson 5.1 Answers

1. Sample answer: One advantage of graphs and tables over verbal descriptions, equations, and arrow diagrams is that both graphs and tables display many input-output pairs at the same time. This makes important properties of the function more visible.

**2a.** variables: time and grade; independent variable: time; dependent variable: grade

In the function $R = 100p - 10p^2$, it is mathematically possible to substitute any real number for $p$. But in the T-shirt revenue context, the selling price $p$ only makes sense for 0, 10, and numbers between 0 and 10 that represent dollars and cents.

So the mathematical domain is all real numbers, but the problem domain is restricted to numbers between 0 and 10 inclusive.

Consider the function $A = 6.28r^2$.

**a.** Determine the domain for the function.

**b.** Determine the problem domain for the function if $r$ represents the radius of a circular object and $A$ represents the total area of these two circular objects.

**Solution:**

**a.** Any number can be substituted for $r$ in the function, so the domain is all real numbers, including 0 and negative numbers.

**b.** The problem domain in this situation consists of all real numbers greater than 0. There is no largest reasonable value for the independent variable.

As you investigate different types of functions, you will be using several types of representations. For example, it is possible to represent a situation with a table and then represent the situation with a graph, as you did in the Investigation. Or, you can begin with an equation or graph and move to other representations, as you will see in later lessons in this chapter.

## Practice for Lesson 5.1

1. Why might graphs and tables be preferred over other ways of representing a function?

2. For each situation, identify the two quantities that vary. Which is the independent variable? Which is the dependent variable?
   **a.** the amount of time spent studying and the grade earned on the test

**b.** the daily high temperatures in Texas for the month of August

**c.** the number of car accidents on a given interstate highway and the maximum speed limit

**For Exercises 3–5, state whether the table represents a function. Then explain why or why not.**

**3.**

| Day | Time Spent Hiking (hours) |
|-----|---------------------------|
| 1 | 3 |
| 2 | 1 |
| 3 | 2 |
| 4 | 3 |
| 5 | 2 |

**4.**

| x | y |
|----|----|
| 1 | 7 |
| −2 | 4 |
| 3 | 9 |
| −4 | −6 |
| 1 | 0 |

**5.**

| x | y |
|----|----|
| 2 | 3 |
| 4 | 4 |
| 6 | 4 |
| 8 | 5 |
| 10 | 6 |

**6.** The *vertical line test* can be used to determine whether a graph represents a function. This simple test states that if no vertical line can be drawn that intersects the graph more than once, the graph is a function. If such a vertical line can be drawn, the graph does not represent a function.

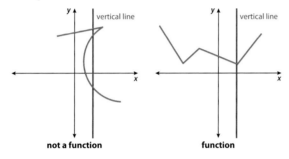

not a function          function

**2b.** variables: date and temperature; independent variable: date; dependent variable: temperature

**2c.** variables: number of accidents and speed limit; independent variable: speed limit; dependent variable: number of accidents

**3.** Yes; for each day (input value), there is exactly one amount of time spent hiking (output value).

**4.** No; the $x$-value of 1 has two different $y$ values, 7 and 0

**5.** Yes; for each input value $x$, there is exactly one output value $y$.

**TEACHING TIP**

**Exercise 6** Be sure to assign this problem as it explains how to use the vertical line test as a way to look at a graph and determine whether it is a graph of a function.

REPRESENTING FUNCTIONS     **Lesson 5.1**     **141**

**6a.** function; No vertical line can be drawn that intersects the graph in 2 or more points.

**6b.** function; No vertical line can be drawn that intersects the graph in 2 or more points.

**6c.** not a function; Any vertical line that intersects the graph will intersect in two points (except for a vertical line drawn through the point at the left end of the graph).

**6d.** not a function; The graph is a vertical line, so any vertical line intersecting the graph intersects it in two or more points.

**7.** Yes, for each input value (time), there is exactly one output value (speed).

**8.** All real numbers from 0 seconds to 17 seconds inclusive.

**9.** All real numbers from 0 meters per second to about 3.5 meters per second inclusive.

**10.** A, B, and D

**11.** Yes; (0, 0), all points from about (8.7, 0) through about (9.9, 0), and (17, 0)

For Parts (a–d), determine whether the graph represents a function. Explain why or why not.

**a.**

**b.**

**c.**

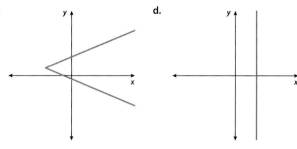

**d.**

For Exercises 7–11, use the graph below that shows the speed of a person as she walks up a hill and then sleds down.

**7.** Does this graph represent a function? Explain.

**8.** What is the domain of the function?

**9.** What is the range of the function?

**10.** Which of these points are on the graph?
   **A.** (1, 1)   **B.** (3, 2)   **C.** (2, 11)   **D.** (5, 2)

**11.** Does the graph have any intercepts? If so, identify them and estimate their coordinates.

**12.** Examine the verbal description, the table, and the graph shown below.

**Verbal Description**

On Thursday, a student studied 2 hours. On Friday and Saturday, he did not study. On Sunday through Thursday, he studied 1.5, 2.5, 1.0, 2.5, and 3.0 hours, respectively.

**Table**

| Day | Time (hr) |
|-----|-----------|
| 1 | 2.0 |
| 2 | 0 |
| 3 | 0 |
| 4 | 1.5 |
| 5 | 2.5 |
| 6 | 1.0 |
| 7 | 2.5 |
| 8 | 3.0 |

**Graph**

a. Does the table represent a function? Explain why or why not.
b. State the domain and range of the function shown in the graph.
c. Do all three of these representations represent the same function? Explain.

**13.** Consider the function $y = \frac{1}{x}$.
a. Is the point $(2, -2)$ on the graph of the function?
b. Determine the value of $y$ when $x = 4$.
c. What is the domain of this function?

**14.** An electric company charges $15 per month plus 10 cents for each kilowatt-hour (kWh) of electricity used.
a. Use the verbal description of this function to complete the table below.

| Electricity Used (kWh) | 0 | 100 | 200 | 300 | 400 | 500 | 600 | 700 | 800 | 900 | 1,000 |
|------------------------|---|-----|-----|-----|-----|-----|-----|-----|-----|-----|-------|
| Total Cost (dollars) | | | | | | | | | | | |

b. In this situation, identify the independent and the dependent variables.
c. Use your table to sketch a graph of this function.
d. Use the graph of the function to find the value of the independent variable when the dependent variable is $80.
e. Is the point $(0, 0)$ on the graph of the function?
f. What is a reasonable problem domain for this function? Explain.
g. Is this a direct variation function? Why or why not?

**12a.** Yes; for each day (input value), there is exactly one time (output value).
**12b.** domain: {1, 2, 3, 4, 5, 6, 7, 8}; range: {0, 1.0, 1.5, 2.0, 2.5, 3.0}
**12c.** Yes; all three represent the same relationship between the values in the domain and the range.
**13a.** No
**13b.** $y = \frac{1}{4}$
**13c.** All real numbers except 0

**14a.**

| Electricity Used (kWh) | 0 | 100 | 200 | 300 | 400 | 500 | 600 | 700 | 800 | 900 | 1,000 |
|------------------------|---|-----|-----|-----|-----|-----|-----|-----|-----|-----|-------|
| Total Cost (dollars) | 15 | 25 | 35 | 45 | 55 | 65 | 75 | 85 | 95 | 105 | 115 |

**14b.** Independent variable: amount of electricity used; dependent variable: total cost
**14c.**

**14d.** 650 kilowatt-hours
**14e.** no
**14f.** Sample answer: All numbers greater than or equal to 0 and less than 5,000 kWh or any other upper limit to the domain that seems reasonable.
**14g.** Sample answer: No, the ratio of total cost to electricity used is not constant. Also, the graph of the function does not pass through the origin.

**5e** Engage

## Lesson Objective

- collect and analyze data that have a constant rate of change.

## Vocabulary

- continuous
- discrete
- linear relationship

## Materials List

*Per group:*

- a scale that measures in grams or tenths of an ounce
- a container such as a small glass bowl that weighs between 3 and 6 ounces and is large enough to hold 10 objects
- ten or more objects that are uniform in weight and each weigh between 0.2 and 0.4 ounces. For example, marbles, miniature candy bars, large metal washers, or 10-penny nails work well in this Activity.

## Description

*Preparation:*

Have students work in groups of 2–4 students. Provide each group with a scale and at least 10 objects that are uniform in weight.

Teaching Option: The data collection portion of this lesson can be done as a demonstration where the teacher or a student collects the data in front of the class and records it in a table for the class to use.

*During the Activity:*

Before starting the data collection portion of this Activity, have students answer **Question 1**. You may want to discuss their answers before the weighing begins.

Have students carefully collect the desired data by first weighing the container without any objects.

## Lesson 5.2 Activity Answers

**1–7.** See answers beginning on page 621.

---

**Lesson 5.2**  **ACTIVITY:  Linear Relationships**

In Lesson 5.1, you learned that functions can be described in many different ways. In this lesson, you will collect data and use what you know about direct variation, slope, and rate of change to analyze the data.

In this Activity, you will be given a container and several objects. You will first weigh the container with no objects in it and record its weight in a table. Then you will place objects in the container, one at a time, and record the new weight.

1. What is the independent variable in this data collection activity? What is the dependent variable? Explain.
2. Weigh the container with no objects in it.
   a. How much does it weigh? Record this weight in a table like the one below.

| Number of Objects | 0 | 1 | 2 | 3 | 4 | 5 | 6 | 7 | 8 | 9 | 10 |
|---|---|---|---|---|---|---|---|---|---|---|---|
| Weight (oz) | | | | | | | | | | | |

   b. Place one object in the container. Check the weight and record it in your table.
   c. Add a second object to the container and record the weight in your table. Repeat until the table is complete.
3. Use the data in your table to create a scatter plot of weight $w$ versus the number of objects $n$ in the container.
4. When the points in a scatter plot lie along a straight line, the relationship between the two variables is called a **linear relationship**. Is the relationship between the total weight of the container with objects and the number of objects linear? Why or why not?
5. What are the domain and range for this situation? Why?
6. Is the relationship between the total weight and the number of objects a proportional relationship? Explain.
7. Is this relationship a function? Explain.

---

*Closing the Activity:*

After students have completed the Activity, have them discuss what they know about the relationship between the number of objects and the total weight of the container and objects. Make note of their vocabulary by making a list of the words used. Terms used should include words such as independent variable, dependent variable, linear relationship, proportional relationship, range, domain, function, intercept, discrete variable, and continuous variable.

### TEACHING TIP

**Question 6** provides the opportunity to compare and contrast proportional relationships and linear relationships. Point out to students that all proportional relationships are linear, but not all linear relationships are proportional. Take time to look at a table and graph of this function as well as a table and graph of a direct proportion (**Exercise 12 , page 147**). Examine the ratios of the dependent variable to the independent variable as well as the ratios of $y$-change to $x$-change between any two points, pointing out what each ratio tells you about the function.

8. Two quantities have a *positive relationship* when the dependent variable increases as the independent variable increases. If one quantity decreases when the other increases, the quantities have a *negative relationship*.

Do you think this relationship is better described as a "positive relationship" or as a "negative relationship"? Explain.

Some variables in data sets are **discrete**, which means that only certain values (often integers) are possible for the data. For example, the independent variable in your table may be discrete because it can only take on whole number values because fractional parts of one of your objects may make no sense in this situation. However, if it makes sense for a variable to take on any real-number value, then the variable is **continuous**. This means that the actual values could include any real number up to the maximum number of objects in your data.

If your independent variable is discrete, then your scatter plot should show distinct points. If it is continuous, it makes sense to connect the points with a line.

9. Is your independent variable continuous or discrete? Explain.

There are times that it is helpful to connect the points in a scatter plot even when the variables are discrete, especially if you plan to use your data to make predictions. However, you should be aware that doing so changes the domain shown in the graph from *some* values to *all* values.

10. To make it easier to examine the relationship between the number of objects $n$ and the weight $w$, draw a line through the points on your scatter plot. Describe your graph.

11. Find the slope of your graph in Question 10. Then write a sentence that interprets the slope as a rate of change.

12. What are the coordinates of the $w$-intercept of your graph? What is the meaning of the $w$-intercept in this situation?

13. Write an equation that models the weight $w$ of the objects and container after $n$ objects have been placed in the container.

14. Use your graph, table, or equation to predict the weight when there are twenty objects in the container.

LINEAR RELATIONSHIPS    Lesson 5.2    145

**TEACHING TIP**

The answer to **Question 9** depends on the objects used in the Activity. If the objects used are items such as mini-candy bars that can be cut into pieces, it may make sense to talk about a fractional part of an object. In other cases such as marbles, nails, and washers, it may not make sense.

**TEACHING TIP**

In **Question 13**, if students have difficulty writing an equation, remind them of the work they did in **Lesson 3.2**. Point out that it might be helpful for them to first write a sentence expressing the relationship between weight and the number of objects.

8. Positive relationship; As the independent variable increases in value, the dependent variable increases in value.

9. Answers will vary. If it makes sense to talk about fractional parts of an object (*e.g.*, small candy bars), the variable is continuous. If not (*e.g.*, marbles), the variable is discrete.

10. Sample answer: The graph appears to be linear with a $w$-intercept of 6.3 (the weight of the container). The graph increases from left to right as the number of objects increases.

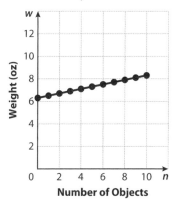

11. Sample answer: For the pairs (2, 6.7) and (3, 6.9):
$$\frac{\Delta w}{\Delta n} = \frac{6.9 - 6.7}{3 - 2} = \frac{0.2}{1} = 0.2 \text{ ounces}$$
per object; the weight on the scale increases at a rate of 0.2 ounces each time an object is added.

12. The coordinates of the $w$-intercept are (0, 6.3). This is the value of the dependent variable (weight) when there are 0 objects in the container.

13. Sample answer: $w = 0.2n + 6.3$

14. Sample answer: About 10.3 oz

# LESSON 5.2

## TEACHING TIP

**Exercises 1–11** Rather than using the data given in the exercises, provide groups of students with rope. Have them measure the original length of their rope with no knots and record the length in a table. Then have them tie knots, one at a time, and record the new length.

Once the data set is complete, have them answer **Exercises 1–11.**

## TEACHING TIP

In **Exercises 1–11**, students apply and extend what they have learned about modeling data that have a linear pattern. Having worked with linear data whose model passes through the origin and with linear data whose model has a non-zero y-intercept, students now work with linear data whose model has a non-zero y-intercept and a decreasing rate of change, or negative slope.

## Practice for Lesson 5.2 Answers

1. Independent variable: the number of knots; dependent variable: the length of the rope; Since the number of knots in the rope explains the length of the rope, it is the independent variable.
2. discrete; It makes no sense to talk about a fractional part of a knot.
3. whole numbers 0 to 5 (the number of knots tied)
4. Range: the lengths of the rope (60, 68, 76, 84, 92, and 100 cm)
5. Sample answer: The graph appears to be linear with an l-intercept of 100.

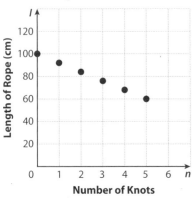

**For Exercises 1–11, use the following information.**

The length of a rope was measured and recorded in the table below. Knots were tied in the rope, one at a time. After each knot was added, the length of the rope was measured and recorded. A total of five knots were tied.

| Number of Knots | Length of Rope (cm) |
|---|---|
| 0 | 100 |
| 1 | 92 |
| 2 | 84 |
| 3 | 76 |
| 4 | 68 |
| 5 | 60 |

1. What is the independent variable in this situation? What is the dependent variable? Explain.
2. Is the independent variable discrete or continuous? Explain.
3. What is the domain for this situation?
4. What is the range for this situation?
5. Create a scatter plot of the length l of the rope versus the number of knots n tied in the rope. Describe your graph.
6. Is this a proportional relationship? Explain.
7. Is this relationship a function? How do you know?
8. Do you think this relationship is better described as a "positive relationship" or as a "negative relationship"? Explain.
9. What are the coordinates of the l-intercept of your graph? What is the meaning of the l-intercept in this situation?
10. Find the rate of change for any two pairs of values in your table.
11. In symbolic form, this function can be written as $l = -8n + 100$.
    a. Use this equation to predict the length of the rope when 11 knots are tied in it.
    b. Use this equation to predict how many knots will have to be tied in the rope so that its length is 44 cm.

6. Sample answer: This is not a proportional relationship even though the graph is linear because the ratio of the length of the rope to the number of knots is not constant, for example $\frac{92}{1} \neq \frac{84}{2} \neq \frac{76}{3}$. Also, the graph does not pass through the origin (0, 0).
7. Yes, for each input value, there is exactly one output value.
8. Negative relationship; As the independent variable increases in value, the dependent variable decreases in value.

9. The l-intercept has coordinates (0, 100). This is the value of the dependent variable (length of the rope) when there are 0 knots in the rope.
10. Sample answer: For the pairs (2, 84) and (3, 76):
    $$\frac{\Delta l}{\Delta n} = \frac{84 - 76}{2 - 3} = \frac{8}{-1} = -8 \text{ cm/knot}$$
**11a.** 12 cm
**11b.** 7 knots

**2 a.** Label the third column of your table "Depreciation per Year" as shown below. This column shows the average rate of change of the value of the computer with respect to age during each year.

| Age (years) | Computer Value (dollars) | Depreciation per Year (dollars/year) |
|---|---|---|
| 0 | 3,600 | — |
| 1 | 2,880 | $\dfrac{2,880 - 3,600}{1 - 0} = -720$ |
| 2 | | |
| 3 | | |
| 4 | | |
| 5 | | |

  **b.** Complete the table.
  **c.** What do you notice about the rate of change of this function?
**3.** What is the domain of the function $v = -720t + 3,600$?
**4.** What is the problem domain of the function $v = -720t + 3,600$?
**5.** Construct a scatter plot of the data in your table.
**6.** Is this relationship a linear relationship? If so, draw a line through the points on your scatter plot.
**7.** Give the coordinates and interpret the meaning of any intercepts on your graph.
**8.** Determine the slope of your graph.
**9.** Compare and contrast all of your different representations of the function $v = -720t + 3,600$. What do you notice?

Any function whose equation can be written in the form $y = mx + b$, where $m$ and $b$ are real numbers, is a **linear function**. This form of the equation of a linear function is called **slope-intercept form**. It expresses the dependent variable $y$ in terms of the independent variable $x$, the slope of the line $m$, and the $y$-intercept of the line whose coordinates are $(0, b)$.

**10.** Is the depreciation function $v = -720t + 3,600$ a linear function? Explain.

You now have three criteria that can be used to identify linear functions.

> Linear functions are characterized by the following:
> * equations of the form $y = mx + b$, where $m$ and $b$ are real numbers
> * graphs that are non-vertical straight lines
> * rates of change that are constant

**Recall**
The **y-intercept** of a graph is the $y$-value of the point where the graph intersects the $y$-axis.

The **x-intercept** of a graph is the $x$-value of the point where the graph intersects the $x$-axis.

---

# LESSON 5.3

**TEACHING TIP**

**Question 2** The numerator in the third column of this table is found by subtracting the previous year's value from the current year's value. Since the value decreases, the depreciation is negative.

**2a.** Check students' tables.
**2b.**

| Computer Value (dollars) | Depreciation per Year (dollars/year) |
|---|---|
| 3,600 | — |
| 2,880 | $\dfrac{2,880 - 3,600}{1 - 0} = -720$ |
| 2,160 | $\dfrac{2,160 - 2,880}{2 - 1} = -720$ |
| 1,440 | $\dfrac{1,440 - 2,160}{3 - 2} = -720$ |
| 720 | $\dfrac{720 - 1,440}{4 - 3} = -720$ |
| 0 | $\dfrac{0 - 720}{5 - 4} = -720$ |

**2c.** The rate of change, the ratio of $\dfrac{\text{change in value}}{\text{change in age}}$ between any 2 consecutive years, is constant and equal to –720.
**3.** All real numbers, because any number can be used as an input for the function.
**4.** In the context of this problem, only the numbers 0, 1, 2, 3, 4, and 5 are meaningful.
**5.**

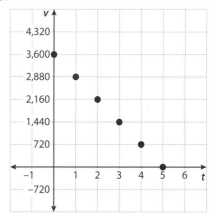

---

**6.** Yes, it is a linear relationship.

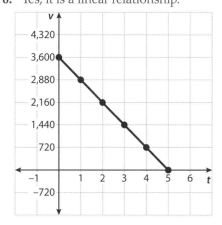

**7.** The $v$-intercept is the point $(0, 3,600)$, and the $t$-intercept is the point $(5, 0)$. The $v$-intercept indicates the value of the computer ($3,600) at time zero. The $t$-intercept indicates that at the end of 5 years, the value of the computer is $0.
**8.** The slope is –720 dollars per year.
**9–10.** See answers on page 148.

## Practice for Lesson 5.3 Answers

1. Yes, this represents a linear function because the rates of change are constant. $\frac{\Delta y}{\Delta x} = 2$

2. No, this does not represent a linear function because the rates of change are not constant.

3. Yes, this graph represents a linear function because the graph of this function is a non-vertical line.

4. No, this graph does not represent a linear function because the graph of this relationship is a vertical line where the input value has more than one output.

5. Yes, this equation represents a linear function because the equation is written in the form $y = mx + b$, where the slope ($m$) is equal to 4 and the $y$-intercept ($b$) is equal to 7.

6. Yes, this equation represents a linear function because this equation can be written in the form $y = mx + b$ ($y = 2x - 4$), where the slope ($m$) is equal to 2 and the $y$-intercept ($b$) is equal to $-4$.

7. No, this equation does not represent a linear function because it cannot be written in the form $y = mx + b$.

**For Exercises 1–8, state whether the table, graph, or equation represents a linear function. Explain why or why not.**

1.

| $x$ | $-1$ | 0 | 1 | 2 | 3 |
|---|---|---|---|---|---|
| $y$ | $-3$ | $-1$ | 1 | 3 | 5 |

2.

| $x$ | $-3$ | $-1$ | 1 | 3 | 5 |
|---|---|---|---|---|---|
| $y$ | 9 | 1 | 1 | 3 | 25 |

3.

4.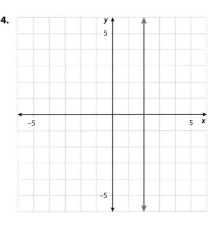

5. $y = 4x + 7$

6. $6x - 3y = 12$

7. $x = 12$

8. $y = 2x^2 + 4$

**For Exercises 9–12, choose the equation that best represents the linear function described in the given table or graph.**

9.

| $x$ | $y$ |
|---|---|
| $-4$ | 0 |
| 0 | 8 |
| 4 | 16 |

A. $y = -2x + 8$
B. $y = 2x + 4$
C. $y = 2x + 8$
D. $y = -2x + 4$

10.

| $x$ | $y$ |
|---|---|
| 0 | 6 |
| 2 | 4 |
| 4 | 2 |

A. $y = 2x + 6$
B. $y = -x + 6$
C. $y = x + 6$
D. $y = -2x + 6$

8. No, this equation does not represent a linear function because it cannot be written in the form $y = mx + b$.

9. C

10. B

**11.**

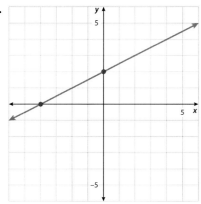

A. $y = \frac{1}{2}x + 2$

B. $y = 2x + 2$

C. $y = \frac{1}{2}x - 4$

D. $y = 2x - 4$

**12.**

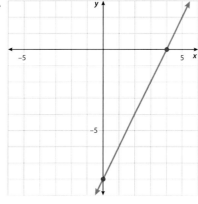

A. $y = 2x + 8$

B. $y = -2x - 8$

C. $y = 2x + 4$

D. $y = 2x - 8$

**13.** In Lesson 5.2, you answered questions about the table on the right, which shows the relationship between the weight $w$ of the tickets given out at a family arcade center and the number of tickets $t$.

a. Is the number of tickets a linear function of the weight of the tickets? Explain why or why not.

b. What is the slope of the line that could be used to describe this function?

c. Give the coordinates and interpret the meaning of any intercepts of the line that could be used to describe this function.

d. Write an equation that represents the linear function described in the table.

e. If a person turns in a pile of tickets that weighs 135 grams, about how many tickets are there?

| Weight (grams) | Number of Tickets |
|---|---|
| 0 | 0 |
| 10 | 46 |
| 20 | 92 |
| 30 | 138 |
| 40 | 184 |
| 50 | 230 |

**11.** A

**12.** D

**13a.** Yes, this represents a linear function as the rates of change are constant. $\frac{\Delta t}{\Delta w} = 4.6$ tickets per gram

**13b.** 4.6 tickets per gram

**13c.** Sample answer: The intercept on the vertical axis is the origin $(0, 0)$. This intercept indicates that when there is no weight, there are no tickets.

**13d.** $t = 4.6w$

**13e.** about 621 tickets

**14a.** The number of marbles placed in the cup is the independent variable and the distance from the bottom of the table to the top of the cup is the dependent variable.

**14b.** Yes, the rates of change are approximately constant.

**14c.** 2 cm per marble

**14d.** The intercept on the vertical axis is the point (0, 17.2). The intercept on the horizontal axis is not in the problem domain of the function. The intercept on the vertical axis indicates the distance from the bottom of the table to the top of the cup when there are no marbles in the cup.

**14e.** Sample answer: $y = 2x + 17.2$

**14.** A small Slinky with a cup attached at the bottom is suspended from the edge of a table. Marbles are added to the cup, one at a time, and the distance from the bottom of the table to the top of the cup is measured.

Distance from bottom of table to top of cup

The data collected are shown in the table below.

| Number of Marbles | Distance from Bottom of Table to Top of Cup (cm) |
|---|---|
| 0 | 17.2 |
| 1 | 19.2 |
| 2 | 21.1 |
| 3 | 23.3 |
| 4 | 25.2 |
| 5 | 27.1 |

**a.** What is the independent variable in this relationship? What is the dependent variable?

**b.** Is this relationship a linear function? Explain.

**c.** What is the slope of the line that could be used to describe this function?

**d.** Give the coordinates and interpret the meaning of any intercepts of the line that could be used to describe this function.

**e.** Write an equation that represents the linear function described in the table.

**Fill in the blank.**

1. The set of all possible input values for the independent variable of a function is called the _____ of the function.

2. Any function that can be written in the form $y = mx + b$ is called a(n) _____ function.

3. The _____ surface area of a three-dimensional figure is the surface area of the figure, excluding the area of the bases.

**Choose the correct answer.**

4. If the ratio of the corresponding sides of a rectangular solid is 3 : 4, what is the ratio of the corresponding surface areas?

   **A.** $\frac{3}{4}$  **B.** $\frac{4}{3}$  **C.** $\frac{9}{16}$  **D.** $\frac{27}{64}$

5. Which solid can be folded from the net shown on the left?
   **A.** triangle
   **B.** triangular prism
   **C.** triangular pyramid
   **D.** quadrilateral

6. What is the sum of the measures of the angles of any pentagon?
   **A.** 5°  **B.** 108°  **C.** 540°  **D.** 900°

7. In which quadrant of the coordinate plane does the point $(-2, 1)$ lie?
   **A.** I  **B.** II  **C.** III  **D.** IV

**Write the decimal as a percent.**

8. 0.015  9. 0.6  10. 1.8  11. 5.0

**Write the percent as a decimal.**

12. 6%  13. 65%  14. 128%  15. 0.7%

## Lesson Objective

• solve problems that require previously learned concepts and skills.

## Exercise Reference

Exercise 1: Lesson 5.1
Exercise 2: Lesson 5.3
Exercises 3–4: Lesson 4.7
Exercise 5: Lesson 4.6
Exercise 6: Lesson 4.1
Exercise 7: Appendix O
Exercises 8–15: Appendix E
Exercises 16–18: Appendix J
Exercises 19–20: Appendix F
Exercises 21–22: Lesson 3.6
Exercise 23: Lesson 5.1
Exercise 24: Lesson 4.2
Exercises 25–26: Lesson 2.5
Exercise 27: Lesson 2.3
Exercises 28–29: Lesson 4.4
Exercise 30: Lesson 4.6
Exercise 31: Appendix N

## Lesson 5.4 R.A.P. Answers

1. domain
2. linear
3. lateral
4. C
5. C
6. C
7. B
8. 1.5%
9. 60%
10. 180%
11. 500%
12. 0.06
13. 0.65
14. 1.28
15. 0.007

**16.** Distributive Property
**17.** Commutative Property of Multiplication
**18.** Zero Property of Multiplication
**19.** 20%
**20.** 600%
**21.** $t \geq 3$

**22.** $x < -2$

**23.** Yes, for each value in the domain, there is exactly one value in the range.
**24.** $n = \dfrac{4 - m}{2}$ or $n = 2 - \dfrac{m}{2}$
**25.** 2
**26.** undefined
**27.** $n = \dfrac{2}{3}m$
**28.** a cylinder
**29.** $V = Bh = \pi r^2 h = \pi(16)(8) \approx 402.1 \text{ cm}^3$
**30.** $SA \approx 301.6 \text{ cm}^2$
**31.** mean: 9.2 s; median: 7.5 s; range: 15 s

**Identify the property illustrated by the equation.**

**16.** $8(4 + 2) = 8(4) + 8(2)$

**17.** $5 \times 6 = 6 \times 5$

**18.** $0 \cdot a = 0$

**Solve.**

**19.** What percent of 45 is 9?     **20.** What percent of 12 is 72?

**Solve for the variable. Check your solution and graph it on a number line.**

**21.** $t + 1 \geq 4$          **22.** $8 - 3x > 14$

**23.** Is the relationship shown in the table a function? Explain.

| $x$ | $-2$ | $-1$ | 0 | 1 | 2 |
|---|---|---|---|---|---|
| $y$ | 4 | 1 | 0 | 1 | 4 |

**24.** Solve the equation $16 = 4(2n + m)$ for $n$.

**25.** Find the slope of the line that passes through the points $(3, 8)$ and $(-1, 0)$.

**26.** Find the slope of the line that passes through the points $(-4, 5)$ and $(-4, -2)$.

**27.** The variable $n$ is directly proportional to $m$. If $n = 10$ when $m = 15$, then write an equation that gives $n$ as a function of $m$.

**For Exercises 28–30, use the solid figure shown on the left.**

**28.** Identify the figure.

**29.** Find the volume of the figure.

**30.** Find the surface area of the figure.

**31.** Find the mean, median, and range of the times shown in the table.

4 cm

8 cm

| Trial Number | 1 | 2 | 3 | 4 | 5 | 6 | 7 | 8 | 9 | 10 |
|---|---|---|---|---|---|---|---|---|---|---|
| Time (s) | 8 | 14 | 5 | 3 | 18 | 6 | 7 | 15 | 10 | 6 |

A graph of a function can provide a quick visual summary of the relationship that exists between two variables. In this lesson, you will use your knowledge of plotting points and slope to graph linear equations.

A **linear equation** is an equation of a line. When looking at a graph of a linear equation, it is important to remember this very important fact.

> Every point on the graph represents a solution to the linear equation, and every solution to the equation can be represented by a point on the graph.

## GRAPH AN EQUATION USING A TABLE

The linear equation $C = 20 + 55t$ can be used to represent the relationship between the cost $C$ in dollars of renting a jet ski and the rental time $t$ in hours.

One way to sketch the graph of this linear equation is to create a table of values in the domain of the relationship. Then plot the ordered pairs and connect the points.

| $t$ | $20 + 55t$ | $C$ | Ordered Pair $(t, C)$ |
|---|---|---|---|
| 0 | $20 + 55(0)$ | 20 | $(0, 20)$ |
| 2 | $20 + 55(2)$ | 130 | $(2, 130)$ |
| 4 | $20 + 55(4)$ | 240 | $(4, 240)$ |

This graph shows the three points from the table and a line drawn through them. Notice that the line has not been extended to the left of the vertical axis since it is meaningless to talk about time being less than zero in this real-world context.

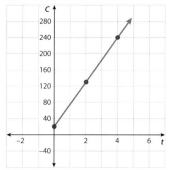

**Note**

Since you know that this relationship is linear, you need only two points to determine the line. However, it is a good idea to have a third point to help you avoid mistakes.

## Lesson Objectives

- graph a linear equation using a table.
- graph a linear equation in slope-intercept form.
- graph a linear equation using the intercepts.

## Vocabulary

- linear equation

## Description

In this lesson students use what they know about the slope of a line and plotting points to graph an equation. Three techniques are introduced in this lesson:

- creating a table of ordered pairs and plotting the points
- using slope-intercept form of a linear equation
- using the $x$- and $y$-intercepts

> **TEACHING TIP**
>
> Make sure students fully understand the blue-highlighted statement on page 155 of this lesson. The importance of being able to connect the points on a graph with the solutions to an equation should be stressed.

> **TEACHING TIP**
>
> Explain that the graph of $C = 20 + 55t$ does not extend to the left of the $y$-axis because negative values for $t$ are not in the problem domain; that is, they make no sense in this problem. In other words, you cannot rent a jet ski for a negative amount of time.

**ADDITIONAL EXAMPLE**

Determine the intercepts of $2x + 5y = 12$. Then use them to graph the equation.
$x$-intercept: 6; $y$-intercept: $2\frac{2}{5}$

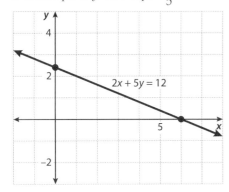

## GRAPH AN EQUATION IN SLOPE-INTERCEPT FORM

When a linear equation is in slope-intercept form, a graph can be quickly made. For example, to sketch the graph of $y = \frac{1}{3}x + 2$, identify the slope and the $y$-intercept. The slope is equal to $\frac{1}{3}$. The $y$-intercept is 2, so the point (0, 2) is on the graph.

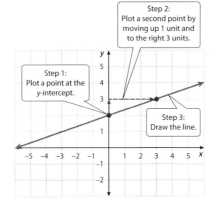

Step 2:
Plot a second point by moving up 1 unit and to the right 3 units.

Step 1:
Plot a point at the $y$-intercept.

Step 3:
Draw the line.

To graph the equation:

- Plot the point (0, 2).
- From the point at the $y$-intercept, use the slope of $\frac{1}{3}$ to identify another point. Move up 1 unit and to the right 3 units. Then plot a point.
- Draw a line through the two points.

## GRAPH AN EQUATION USING INTERCEPTS

Another quick way to graph a linear equation is to use the $x$- and $y$-intercepts.

- First find the two intercepts. (To find the $x$-intercept, let $y = 0$ in the equation. To find the $y$-intercept, let $x = 0$.)
- Plot a point at each intercept.
- Draw a line through the two points.

**E X A M P L E**

Determine the intercepts of $2x - 3y = 9$. Then use them to graph the equation.

**Solution:**

To find the $x$-intercept, let $y = 0$.

$$2x - 3y = 9$$
$$2x - 3(0) = 9$$
$$2x = 9$$
$$x = 4.5$$

To find the $y$-intercept, let $x = 0$.

$$2x - 3y = 9$$
$$2(0) - 3y = 9$$
$$-3y = 9$$
$$y = -3$$

9. $y = 3x - 2$; slope = 3; $y$-intercept = $-2$

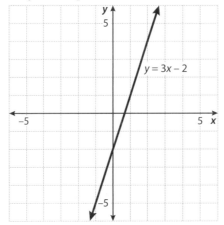

$y = 3x - 2$

10. $y = -2$; slope = 0; $y$-intercept = $-2$

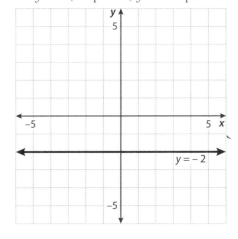

$y = -2$

Now plot points at the intercepts and draw a line through the two points.

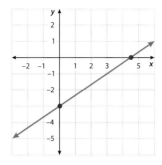

**Exercises 1 and 2** require the use of a graphing calculator. In **Exercise 1,** students explore how changing the value of $m$ in the equation $y = mx + b$ affects the graphs of the lines. In **Exercise 2,** students explore how changing the value of $b$ affects the graphs.

TEACHING TIP

**Exercises 1 and 2** refer to an "appropriate" viewing window. Encourage students to consider the functions and select a window that shows the important features of the graphs, such as intercepts and possible intersections of the functions. In these two exercises, a $[-10, 10] \times [-10, 10]$ screen with an Xscl and a Yscl of 1 is appropriate.

**Practice** for Lesson 5.5

1. Use a graphing calculator. Enter the equations $y = x + 2$, $y = -2x + 2$, and $y = \frac{1}{2}x + 2$ in the $\boxed{Y=}$ list on the function screen. Then graph them in an appropriate viewing window that shows the important features of each graph. Write a description of what you see. How are these graphs the same? How are they different?

2. Use a graphing calculator. Enter the equations $y = 2x$, $y = 2x + 1$, and $y = 2x - 3$ in the $\boxed{Y=}$ list on the function screen. Then graph them in an appropriate viewing window. Write a description of what you see. How are these graphs the same? How are they different?

**For Exercises 3–6, write the equation in slope-intercept form. Then identify the slope and $y$-intercept.**

3. $2x - 3y = 12$       4. $2x + 4y = 4$

5. $6 - 2y = 0$       6. $2x - y = 8$

**For Exercises 7–8, make a table of values and graph the equation.**

7. $y - 3x = -4$       8. $x + 2y = 1$

**For Exercises 9–10, write the equation in slope-intercept form, identify the slope and $y$-intercept, and graph the equation.**

9. $3x - y = 2$       10. $2y + 4 = 0$

GRAPHING LINEAR EQUATIONS    **Lesson 5.5**    **157**

COMMON ERROR

**Exercises 3–6, 9–10** Some students may forget to write the equation in slope-intercept form before trying to identify the slope and $y$-intercept.

**Practice for Lesson 5.5 Answers**

1. Sample answer: All three graphs have the same $y$-intercept. The slopes are different. The graph of the line with the negative slope slants down from left to right. The two lines with positive slopes slant up from left to right. The greater the absolute value of the slope is, the steeper the line is.

2. Sample answer: All three graphs have the same slope. The $y$-intercepts are different. The graph of $y = 2x + 1$ is the same as the graph of $y = 2x$, but shifted up 1 unit. The graph of $y = 2x - 3$ is the same as the graph of $y = 2x$, but shifted down 3 units. All three lines are parallel.

3. $y = \frac{2}{3}x - 4$; slope $= \frac{2}{3}$; $y$-intercept $= -4$

4. $y = -\frac{1}{2}x + 1$; slope $= -\frac{1}{2}$; $y$-intercept $= 1$

5. $y = 3$; slope $= 0$; $y$-intercept $= 3$

6. $y = 2x - 8$; slope $= 2$; $y$-intercept $= -8$

7. Tables will vary.

8. Tables will vary.

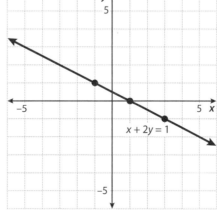

9–10. See answers can on page 156.

# LESSON 5.5

## TEACHING TIP

**Exercise 13** Take this opportunity to review the terms *continuous* and *discrete* variables. In this situation, *n* is discrete, so the graph is actually a set of points. Remind students that the points can be connected with a line if they feel that it helps to show the general trend of the context.

**For Exercises 11–12, identify the intercepts and graph the equation.**

**11.** $12x - 3y = 6$      **12.** $\frac{1}{2}y + 3x = 3$

**13.** The equation $C = 40 + 5n$ can be used to represent the relationship between the yearly cost $C$ in dollars for a student who has a membership to the Museum of Nature and Science in Dallas, Texas and the number of times $n$ the student attends the IMAX® Theater at the museum.
   **a.** Graph the equation.
   **b.** Use your graph to determine the cost of a student attending the theater four times.

**14.** A cable television company charges a monthly fee of $10, plus $4 for each movie rented for their movie plan.
   **a.** Write an equation that gives the total monthly cost $C$ for $n$ movie rentals.
   **b.** Graph the equation.
   **c.** Use your graph to determine the cost for a month if 8 movies are rented.

**15.** Explain the statement "Not all linear equations represent linear functions."

**11.** $x$-intercept: $\frac{1}{2}$; $y$-intercept: $-2$

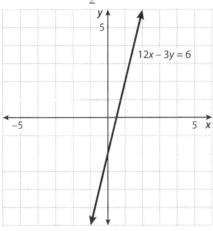

**12.** $x$-intercept: 1; $y$-intercept: 6

**13a.**

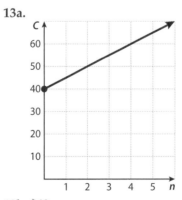

**13b.** $60
**14a.** $C = 10 + 4n$

**14b.**

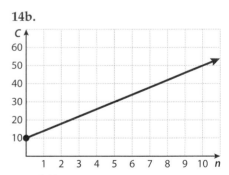

**14c.** $42
**15.** Sample answer: A vertical line can be represented with an equation of the form $x = a$, where $a$ is a real number. This line is not a function because there is more than one output for each input value.

## INVESTIGATION: Writing Equations of Lines

In Lesson 5.5, you learned to graph linear equations. In this lesson, you will learn to find an equation of a line given information such as two points on the line or a point on the line and the slope.

**Note**

A *rule of thumb* can be thought of as a useful principle or method that is not intended to be strictly accurate or reliable in every situation.

People are concerned about good nutrition and exercise as they strive to lead a healthier life. In their attempts to change their lifestyles, they often encounter graphs that relate weights and heights. The graph below reflects an old and outdated *rule of thumb* that was used in the past for finding an ideal weight from a given height.

1. Use your prior knowledge to describe the graph and the relationships represented.
2. According to the graph, what was considered an ideal weight for a person who was 6′ 8″ tall? Explain how you found your answer.
3. Find what was considered to be an ideal weight for a person who was 5′ 8″, for a person who was 5′ 3.5″, and for a person who was 7′ 4″. Explain any problems you encountered in finding these weights.

The problems that you encountered in Question 3 can be resolved if you find an equation for the line. You can do this by finding the slope of the line and the *y*-intercept.

4. a. Find the slope of the line.
   b. What does the slope of the line tell you about the relationship between a person's height and his or her ideal weight?
5. The *y*-intercept of this graph is −200. For this context, what does the *y*-intercept tell you?
6. Now that you have found the slope of the line and the *y*-intercept, find an equation of the line.
7. Use your equation from Question 6 to predict the ideal weight for each of the given heights.
   a. 5′ 6.5″          b. 4′ 10″          c. 7′ 7″

WRITING EQUATIONS OF LINES     **Lesson 5.6**     **159**

## Lesson Objectives

- write an equation of a line given its slope and *y*-intercept.
- use the definition of *slope* to write an equation of a line.

## Vocabulary

- point-slope form

## Materials List

## Description

Before beginning this Investigation, have students read the first paragraph. Ask them if anyone knows of any "rules of thumb." As an example, one rule says that when an adult's arms are stretched out straight to the side, the distance from his or her nose to the tips of his or her fingers is about one yard.

Have students look at the graph. Make sure that students understand that this graph represents an old and outdated rule of thumb that is no longer used and should not be used to predict their ideal weights. Doctors today take into account many variables and use several different measures to decide on a range of weights for individual people.

**Question 1** can be used as a class discussion before groups of students begin the Investigation. This question provides a way to do an extensive review of what students should know about linear functions. Creating a list of all of these concepts will help students realize how much they actually know. As you discuss this question, you may need to ask students leading questions such as "Which variable is the independent variable? How do you know?" or "Is this a positive or negative relationship?"

**TEACHING TIP**

If students struggle finding an equation for **Question 6**, it might be helpful to remind them about the slope-intercept form of an equation.

## Lesson 5.6 Investigation Answers

1. Sample answers: This graph represents a function that is linear. It shows a positive relationship. The slope of the line is positive. The graph is continuous. The problem domain is from 60 inches to about 83 inches. It is not a direct variation function. No intercepts are shown on the graph.
2. First convert the height into inches: 80″; Find 80″ along the horizontal axis, and then move up to find the point on the graph. The ideal weight is the *y*-coordinate of that point, 200 lb.
3. The approximate ideal weights were: 5′8″ (140 lb); 5′3.5″ (118 lb); 7′4″ (240 lb). The problems encountered involve accuracy and the limitations of the graph.
4a. $m = 5$
4b. A slope of 5 means that for every 1-inch change in height, there is a corresponding 5-pound change in weight.
5. A person with a height of 0 inches should have a weight of −200 pounds. Of course, this makes no sense in this context.
6. $y = 5x − 200$
7a. 132.5 lb
7b. 90 lb
7c. 255 lb

*Wrapping Up the Investigation:*

Once all groups have completed the Investigation, use **Question 8** to debrief them. As you talk about whether the graph is a good model, point out that the rule of thumb that was used to create the graph did not take into account things such as a person's sex, age, or frame size. This model is particularly poor for very tall or very short people.

**8.** Answers will vary. Sample answer: This is not a good model because it does not take into account the sex, age, bone structure, or frame size of a person. For tall people, the ideal weight seems to be too low.

## TEACHING TIP

The point-slope form of the equation of a line is written as $y - k = m(x - h)$ for two reasons. One is to avoid the use of subscripts that are confusing to some students. The other reason is in the hope that once students begin to think in terms of translations (Chapter 9), they will see that this is simply a translation of the graph $y = mx$, a line with a slope of $m$ that passes through the origin.

If you prefer to use the more traditional equation, $y - y_1 = m(x - x_1)$, feel free to introduce it here.

## ADDITIONAL EXAMPLE

Find an equation for a line that passes through the point (–1, 4) and has a slope of 2. $y = 2x + 6$

**8.** Do you think that the line in the graph provides a good model for predicting ideal weight from any given height? Explain.

## WRITING AN EQUATION GIVEN THE SLOPE AND A POINT

One of the challenges of the Investigation was to accurately find the $y$-intercept of the graph so that you could find the equation for the line. There are times that you will need to find the equation of a line and do not have a graph, the slope of the line, or the $y$-intercept. But you may have other information, such as points on the line.

> A linear equation in the form $y - k = m(x - h)$, where $m$ is the slope of the line and $(h, k)$ is a point on the line, is written in **point-slope form**.

This equation can be derived from the definition for slope, $m = \dfrac{y_2 - y_1}{x_2 - x_1}$. If you replace the point $(x_1, y_1)$ with the coordinates of the point on the line $(h, k)$ and $(x_2, y_2)$ with any point on the line $(x, y)$, you get $m = \dfrac{y - k}{x - h}$ or $y - k = m(x - h)$.

Find an equation for a line that passes through the point (1, 5) and has a slope of $-2$.

**Solution:**

Use the point-slope form.

| | |
|---|---|
| Point-slope form | $y - k = m(x - h)$ |
| Substitute (1, 5) for $(h, k)$ and $-2$ for $m$. | $y - 5 = -2(x - 1)$ |
| Simplify. | $y = -2x + 7$ |

## WRITING AN EQUATION GIVEN TWO POINTS

To find the equation of a line when given two points on the line

- find the slope of the line.
- Then use either one of the two points and the slope in the point-slope form.

## Slopes of Parallel and Perpendicular Lines

If two lines are parallel, what do you know about their slopes? If two lines are perpendicular, what do you know about their slopes? In this lesson, you will investigate the slopes of parallel and perpendicular lines and use that information to find the equations of lines parallel (or perpendicular) to a given line.

### PARALLEL LINES

Recall that **parallel lines** are lines in a plane that do not intersect.

> Two distinct, non-vertical lines are parallel if and only if they have the same slope. All vertical lines are parallel.

### E X A M P L E ❶

Find an equation for a line that is parallel to the line $y = -3x + 5$ and passes through the point $(2, -4)$.

#### Solution:

The slope of the given line is $-3$, so any line parallel to it will have a slope of $-3$.

Use the point-slope form and the point $(2, -4)$ to find an equation.

| | |
|---|---|
| Point-slope form | $y - k = m(x - h)$ |
| Substitute $(2, -4)$ for $(h, k)$ and $-3$ for $m$. | $y - (-4) = -3(x - 2)$ |
| Simplify. | $y = -3x + 2$ |

p. 161 problems: 1

#12: Incorrect. Find out correct
✓ your error via close
reading of problem.

---

## Lesson Objectives

- write an equation of a line that passes through a given point and is parallel to a given line.
- write an equation of a line that passes through a given point and is perpendicular to a given line.

## Vocabulary

- parallel lines
- perpendicular lines

## Description

This lesson provides students an opportunity to use what they learned in Chapter 4 and to work with geometry and algebraic concepts in the same lesson.

> **TEACHING TIP**
>
> Remind students that the phrase "if and only if" provides a way to write two converse statements as a single statement. So, the "if and only if" statement about parallel lines means:
> - If two distinct, non-vertical lines are parallel, then they have the same slope.
> - If two distinct, non-vertical lines have the same slope, then they are parallel.

> **TEACHING TIP**
>
> There are other ways to find an equation for **Example 1**. For instance, an equation can be found by using the slope-intercept form of a linear equation, $y = mx + b$, substituting 2 for $x$ and $-4$ for $y$, then solving for $b$. Feel free to share alternative methods with students.

## ADDITIONAL EXAMPLE ❶

Find an equation for a line that is parallel to the line $y = 5x - 2$ and passes through the point $(-1, 4)$.
$y = 5x + 9$

## PERPENDICULAR LINES

Recall that two lines are **perpendicular** if they meet to form right angles (90°).

> Two distinct, non-vertical lines are perpendicular if and only if their slopes are negative reciprocals of each other. Vertical and horizontal lines are also perpendicular.

For example, a line with a slope of 2 and a line with a slope of $-\frac{1}{2}$ are perpendicular because 2 and $-\frac{1}{2}$ are negative reciprocals of each other.

**Note**

In order for two numbers to be *negative reciprocals* of each other, they must be opposite in sign *and* reciprocals of each other. The product of two numbers that are negative reciprocals is $-1$. For example, $\frac{2}{3}$ and $-\frac{3}{2}$ are negative reciprocals, so $\frac{2}{3}\left(-\frac{3}{2}\right) = -1$.

**ADDITIONAL EXAMPLE 2**

Find an equation for a line that is perpendicular to the line $y = \frac{2}{3}x - 2$ and passes through the point (2, –4).

$$y = -\frac{3}{2}x - 1$$

### E X A M P L E 2

Find an equation for a line that is perpendicular to the line $y = -3x + 5$ and passes through the point (2, −1).

**Solution:**

The slope of the given line is −3, so any line perpendicular to it will have a slope of $\frac{1}{3}$.

Use the point-slope form.

Point-slope form $\qquad\qquad\qquad\qquad y - k = m(x - h)$

Substitute $(2, -1)$ for $(h, k)$ and $\frac{1}{3}$ for $m$.   $y - (-1) = \frac{1}{3}(x - 2)$

Simplify. $\qquad\qquad\qquad\qquad\qquad\qquad y = \frac{1}{3}x - \frac{5}{3}$

**ADDITIONAL EXAMPLE 3**

Consider the points $D(1, 4)$, $E(2, 2)$, and $F(6, 0)$. Are lines $DE$ and $EF$ parallel, perpendicular, or neither? Explain.

Neither; these two lines share the same point $E(2, 2)$, so they cannot be parallel. Since the two lines both have negative slopes, they cannot be perpendicular.

### E X A M P L E 3

Consider the points $A(2, 3)$, $B(4, 5)$, and $C(6, 3)$. Are lines $AB$ and $BC$ parallel, perpendicular, or neither?

**Solution:**

The slope of line $AB = \frac{3 - 5}{2 - 4} = \frac{-2}{-2}$ or 1.

The slope of line $BC = \frac{5 - 3}{4 - 6} = \frac{2}{-2}$ or −1.

The slopes are negative reciprocals of each other, so $\overleftrightarrow{AB} \perp \overleftrightarrow{BC}$.

For Exercises 1–2, find an equation for the line that passes through the given point and is parallel to the graph of the given line.

**1.** $(3, -1); y = 2x - 4$

**2.** $(4, -2); x - y = 3$

For Exercises 3–4, find an equation for the line that passes through the given point and is perpendicular to the given line.

**3.** $(-4, 2); y = \frac{2}{3}x + 1$

**4.** $(2, -5); x + 5y = 1$

For Exercises 5–6, determine whether the two lines are parallel, perpendicular, or neither.

**5.** Line 1: $2x - 5y = -8$
Line 2: $4y + 10x = 7$

**6.** Line 1: contains the points $(1, 1)$ and $(-1, -5)$
Line 2: has a slope of 3 and a $y$-intercept of $-6$

**7.** Write an equation for the line that passes through the point $(-4, 2)$ and is parallel to the line shown in the graph.

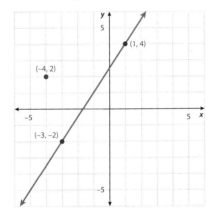

**8.** Write an equation of the line that is perpendicular to the graph of $y = 5x + 15$ and passes through the origin.

**COMMON ERROR**

**Exercises 3–4** Students may think that the negative reciprocal of a number must be negative. Remind them that it means "opposite in sign."

## Practice for Lesson 5.7 Answers

**1.** $y = 2x - 7$

**2.** $y = x - 6$

**3.** $y = -\frac{3}{2}x - 4$

**4.** $y = 5x - 15$

**5.** perpendicular

**6.** parallel

**7.** $y = \frac{3}{2}x + 8$

**8.** $y = -\frac{1}{5}x$

9. Write an equation of the line that has an *x*-intercept of 4 and is parallel to the line that passes through (5, 0) and (4, 3).

10. Determine whether *ABCD* is a parallelogram. Explain your reasoning.

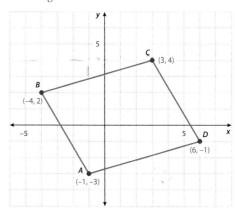

11. Square *ABCD* has vertices at $A(2, 4)$, $B(4, -2)$, $C(-2, -4)$, and $D(-4, 2)$.
    a. Find the slopes of the diagonals of the square.
    b. What is the relationship between the two diagonals?

12. You know that vertical and horizontal lines are perpendicular. Explain why the product of their slopes is not equal to $-1$.

13 a. Find an equation of the line that is perpendicular to the line $y = 4$ and passes through the point $(5, -1)$.
    b. Are the slopes of these lines negative reciprocals of each other?

9. $y = -3x + 12$
10. Yes, $\overline{AB}$ and $\overline{CD}$ have the same slope $\left(-\frac{5}{3}\right)$, so they are parallel. $\overline{BC}$ and $\overline{AD}$ have the same slope $\left(\frac{2}{7}\right)$, so they are parallel. Since both pairs of opposite sides of quadrilateral *ABCD* are parallel, it is a parallelogram.
11a. slope of $\overline{AC} = 2$; slope of $\overline{BD} = -\frac{1}{2}$
11b. They are perpendicular.
12. Sample answer: The slope of a horizontal line is 0 and the slope of a vertical line is undefined. So, there is no product of the two slopes.
13a. $x = 5$
13b. No, one of the lines is horizontal with a slope of 0 and the other is a vertical line with an undefined slope. Vertical and horizontal lines are perpendicular.

#10: Richer detail of explanation required. See textbook.

✓⊞ 11A: Draw a diagram first. Incorrect What line segments are its diagonals? Calculate the slope.

✓⊞ 11b: Incorrect because #11a incorrect.

✓ #12: Skipped.

✓ #13a and b mislabeled as 12a and b.
✓ 13a: Correct. No work shown. How did you solve?
13b: not explanation needed. Correct.

## It's in the News

Look on the Internet, in newspapers, and in magazines for at least two graphs of lines. Based on what you know, write a report on what you found. Be sure to include copies of the graphs you found, the equations of the lines, and interpretations of the slopes of the lines as well as the $y$-intercepts. Be sure to show your work.

Graphs can be drawn in such a way that they are misleading or deceptive. Look for possible deceptive graphs. If you find one, indicate what makes the graph deceptive. Discuss whether you think that the deception is intentional or not.

As you write your report, do not forget to identify where you found your graphs. If any of them come from a website, include the URL of the site.

# MODELING PROJECT

**5e**  Elaborate

## Materials List

- newspapers
- magazines
- Internet

## Description

Students are asked to search magazines, newspapers, and the Internet for graphs of lines. Once they have found a graph, they find the equation of the line and interpret the slope and $y$-intercept. Each report should include at least two lines. This project works best when students work individually.

## Sample Answers

Answers will vary depending on the lines students find. Student answers should show the calculations used to determine the equations of the lines. Answers should also reflect the contexts shown in the graphs.

# Chapter 5  Review

## You Should Be Able to:

### Lesson 5.1

- represent functions in multiple ways.
- identify the domain and range of a function.
- identify the problem domain of a situation.

### Lesson 5.2

- collect and analyze data that have a constant rate of change.

### Lesson 5.3

- identify linear functions from tables, graphs, and equations.

### Lesson 5.4

- solve problems that require previously learned concepts and skills.

### Lesson 5.5

- graph a linear equation using a table.
- graph a linear equation in slope-intercept form.
- graph a linear equation using the intercepts.

### Lesson 5.6

- write an equation of a line given its slope and $y$-intercept.
- use the definition of slope to write an equation of a line.

### Lesson 5.7

- write an equation of a line that passes through a given point and is parallel to a given line.
- write an equation of a line that passes through a given point and is perpendicular to a given line.

## Key Vocabulary

intercept (p. 138)

domain (p. 139)

range (p. 139)

problem domain (p. 139)

linear relationship (p. 144)

discrete variables (p. 145)

continuous variables (p. 145)

linear function (p. 149)

slope-intercept form (p. 149)

$y$-intercept (p. 149)

$x$-intercept (p. 149)

linear equation (p. 155)

point-slope form (p. 160)

parallel lines (p. 163)

perpendicular lines (p. 164)

**7a.** (2, –2), (1, –1), (–2, 0)

**7b.** $y = -\dfrac{1}{5}$

**7c.** All real numbers except 4.

**8.** Yes, the rates of change are constant. $\dfrac{\Delta y}{\Delta x} = 2$

**9.** No; this graph is a vertical line where the input value has more than one output value.

**10.** Yes; this equation, written in the form $y = mx + b$, is $y = 0x + 6$, where the slope $m$ is equal to 0 and the $y$-intercept $b$ is equal to 6.

**11.** Graphs 1 and 2 have the greatest $y$-intercepts, and both have negative slopes. Graph 1 is steeper, so it has the equation $y = -1.4x + 10$. Graph 2 has the equation $y = -0.5x + 10$. Graphs 3 and 4 have positive $y$-intercepts that are less than 10. The slope of graph 3 is less than the slope of graph 4, so graph 3 has the equation $y = 0.8x + 5$. Graph 4 has the equation $y = 1.2x + 5$. Graph 5 is the only one with a negative $y$-intercept, so its equation is $y = 2.3x - 5$.

---

**7.** Consider the function $y = \dfrac{x + 2}{x - 4}$.

   **a.** Which of the following points are on the graph of the function?

     (2, −2)     (1, −1)     (−4, 0)     (−2, 0)

   **b.** Determine the value of $y$ when $x = -1$.

   **c.** What is the domain of this function?

**For Exercises 8–10, state whether the table, graph, or equation represents $y$ as a linear function of $x$. Explain why or why not.**

**8.**

| x | −4 | −2 | 0 | 2 | 3 |
|---|----|----|---|---|---|
| y | 6 | 10 | 14 | 18 | 20 |

**9.**

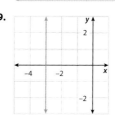

**10.** $y = 6$

**11.** The following functions were graphed with a computer drawing program: $y = 1.2x + 5$, $y = 0.8x + 5$, $y = 2.3x - 5$, $y = -0.5x + 10$, and $y = -1.4x + 10$.

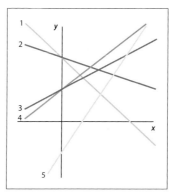

The order in which the lines were drawn is unknown, and the axes do not show a scale. Explain how you can identify the graph of each equation.

## Chapter 5  Test Review

For Exercises 1–5, determine whether the relationship is a function.
Explain why or why not.

1.
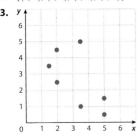

| x | −2 | 4 | 7 | 11 | 15 |
|---|----|---|---|----|----|
| y | 1 | −2 | 11 | 5 | 0 |

2. $\{(1, 6), (2, 6), (3, 6), (4, 6)\}$

3.

4. $y = -3$

5. $x = -3$

6. The graph below represents the relationship between the distance $d$ a car travels and the amount of gasoline $g$ it uses.

a. Use the graph to complete the table.

| Amount of Gas (gal) | 0 | 2 | 4 | 6 | 8 |
|---------------------|---|---|---|---|---|
| Distance Traveled (mi) | | | | | |

b. Is the relationship between the amount of gas used and the distance traveled a function? Explain.

c. What is the independent variable in this situation?

d. Write an equation to find the distance a car travels $d$ for any amount of gas used $g$.

## CHAPTER REVIEW

### Chapter 5 Test Review Answers

1. Yes; each $x$-value has only one $y$-value.
2. Yes; each $x$-value has only one $y$-value.
3. No; the $x$-value of 2 has two different $y$-values (as do two other $x$-values).
4. Yes; the equation represents a horizontal line, and each $x$-value has exactly one $y$-value.
5. No; the equation represents a vertical line, and the $x$-value of −3 has an infinite number of different $y$-values.

6a.

| Amount of Gas (gal) | 0 | 2 | 4 | 6 | 8 |
|---------------------|---|---|---|---|---|
| Distance Traveled (mi) | 0 | 50 | 100 | 150 | 200 |

6b. Yes; For each amount of gas $g$, the distance traveled $d$ is different.

6c. In this case, either variable could be considered to be the independent variable. The graph shows the amount of gas as the independent variable.

6d. $d = 25g$

---

Chapter 5 Review (pp. 169–171)

#3: Specify what points are wrong.

~~Correct~~

#4: More depth "because the equation _____."

~~And)~~ ~~Correct, but...~~

#5: $x = -3$ → vertical line → infinitely many y-values for single x-value of −3.

#6a: Put variables' names in box, ~~Correct~~ Need units

#6d: Define your variables, then ~~Correct~~ use them in slope calc. and construction of equation.

**For Exercises 12–14, graph the equation.**

**12.** $y + 4x = 8$

**13.** $5y - 2x = 10$

**14.** $x + 2 = 0$

**For Exercises 15–19, write an equation for the line with the given properties.**

**15.** Slope of $-\dfrac{5}{2}$ and passes through the point $(8, 4)$

**16.** Passes through the point $(5, 1)$ and is parallel to the graph of $y = -x + 7$

**17.** Passes through the points $(-4, 12)$ and $(2, 3)$

**18.** Perpendicular to the graph of $y = \dfrac{1}{4}x - 3$ and has a $y$-intercept of 1

**19.** $x$-intercept of $-5$ and a $y$-intercept of 10

**20.** Suppose that a popular country-western singer can sell out the Cotton Bowl, which has 25,704 seats, when the ticket price is set at \$50. If the ticket price is raised to \$80, only 16,000 are estimated to attend. Assume that the relationship between ticket sales and price is linear. Write an equation to model the relationship.

**12.**

**13.**

**14.**

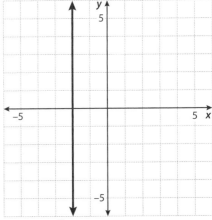

**15.** $y = -\dfrac{5}{2}x + 24$

**16.** $y = -x + 6$

**17.** $y = -\dfrac{3}{2}x + 6$

**18.** $y = -4x + 1$

**19.** $y = 2x + 10$

**20.** Sample answer:
$y = -323.5x + 41{,}879$

## Lesson Objectives

- graph absolute value functions.
- graph piecewise-defined functions.
- graph step functions.

## Vocabulary

- absolute value function
- greatest integer function
- piecewise-defined function
- step function

## Description

In this Extension, piecewise-defined functions are defined. Then absolute value functions are defined as a subset of the piecewise-defined functions. Students are shown how to graph $y = |x|$ and then are asked questions relating to the function.

> ### TEACHING TIP
>
> If necessary, remind students that the quantity $|x|$ equals either $x$ or $-x$, depending on whether $x$ is positive or negative. Show examples of $x$ values that are negative and $-x$ values that are positive. Students often think $-x$ always represents a negative number.

The **absolute value function**, $y = |x|$, is actually a **piecewise-defined function**. That is, it is made up of pieces of different functions. Its domain is split into smaller intervals. Over each interval, the function has the characteristics of the piece defined for that interval.

The function $y = |x|$ can be defined piecewise by the following equation:

$$y = \begin{cases} x & \text{if } x \geq 0 \\ -x & \text{if } x < 0 \end{cases}$$

Since the absolute value function is a combination of two functions, it takes on the characteristics of each of them for the two different intervals.

- When $x \geq 0$, the function is defined by the direct variation function $y = x$. Recall that the graph of this function is a straight line with a slope of 1.

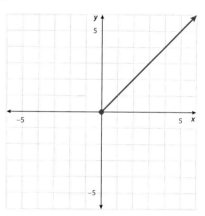

- When $x < 0$, the function is defined by the linear function $y = -x$. This function is a decreasing function whose graph is a straight line with a slope of $-1$.

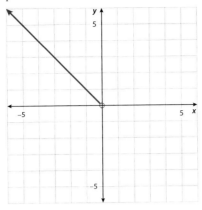

The graph of $y = |x|$ includes all the points on these two graphs.

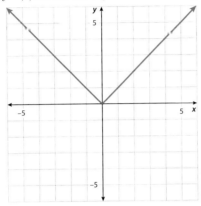

1. Look at the graph of $y = |x|$. Explain how you know that it is the graph of a function.

2  a. When $x > 0$, is the graph increasing or decreasing?
   b. When $x < 0$, is the graph increasing or decreasing?

3  a. What happens to the graph as $x$ increases without bound? (Hint: to answer this question, look at the graph to see what happens to it as you move farther and farther to the right along the horizontal axis.)

## Chapter 5 Extension Answers

1. Sample answer: For each input value $x$, there is exactly one output value $y$. It passes the vertical line test.
2a. increasing
2b. decreasing
3a. The graph increases.

**TEACHING TIP**

**Questions 2–3** are included here because they foreshadow what you want students to observe as they begin to explore the end behaviors of functions that are not linear. This may be confusing to students at first, but it is worth the time to have students look at these characteristics and behaviors of different functions.

**TEACHING TIP**

In **Question 2b,** some students may not understand how the graph can be *decreasing* when $x < 0$ and yet in **Question 3b,** be *increasing* as $x$ decreases without bound. To explain this, have students look at the graph of $y = |x|$ when $x < 0$. In **Question 2b**, students should be looking at the *slope* of the line in the piece of the graph that is to the left of the origin. In **Question 3b**, they should be looking at the *end behavior* of the function as $x$ decreases. It may help to ask students what would happen to the graph when $x$ goes from $-100$ to $-200$. They should see that the graph increases.

# CHAPTER 5
# EXTENSION

**3b.** The graph increases.

**4.**

**5.**

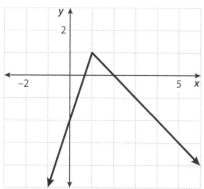

**6a.** the set of integers

**6b.** 3

**6c.** −4

**6d.** 3

**7.**

**b.** What happens to the graph as $x$ decreases without bound? (Hint: to answer this question, look at the graph to see what happens to it as you move farther and farther to the left along the horizontal axis.)

**4.** Graph the function $y = -|x|$.

**5.** Graph the piecewise-defined function:

$$y = \begin{cases} 2 - x & \text{if } x \geq 1 \\ 3x - 2 & \text{if } x < 1 \end{cases}$$

**6.** A **step function** is another special type of function that is made up of line segments or rays. The **greatest integer function**, written as $y = [\![x]\!]$, is one example of a step function. For all real numbers $x$, this function returns the greatest integer that is less than or equal to $x$. Examine the following table and the graph of $y = [\![x]\!]$.

| $y = [\![x]\!]$ | |
|---|---|
| $x$ | $y$ |
| −1 | −1 |
| −0.5 | −1 |
| 0 | 0 |
| 0.25 | 0 |
| 0.75 | 0 |
| 1 | 1 |
| 1.3 | 1 |
| 1.8 | 1 |
| 2 | 2 |
| 2.1 | 2 |

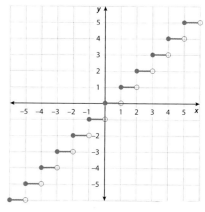

**a.** The domain of the greatest integer function is the set of all real numbers. What is the range?

**b.** Evaluate $y = [\![x]\!]$ for $x = 3.5$.

**c.** Evaluate $y = [\![x]\!]$ for $x = -3.5$.

**d.** Evaluate $y = [\![2x]\!]$ for $x = 1.6$.

**7.** A babysitter charges $10 per hour or any fraction of an hour. Draw a graph of this situation.

**174**    **Chapter 5**    FUNCTIONS AND THEIR REPRESENTATIONS

# Chapter 6
## Describing Data

## Mathematical Overview

The mathematical science used to analyze surveys and other data is known as *statistics.* It is important for statisticians to reduce collected data into easily understood and usable summaries. This can often be achieved by describing the data graphically as well as numerically. The graphical methods presented in this chapter include line graphs, circle graphs, bar graphs, pictographs, and histograms. The numerical measures for summarizing data presented in this chapter are the mean, median, mode, range, quartiles, and standard deviation. Students explore combining the numerical summaries with two types of graphical displays, stem-and-leaf plots and box plots. And finally, students examine the methods by which data are collected and how the method chosen, as well as the size of the sample, may influence the result of a survey.

## Lesson Summaries

### Lesson 6.1    *Investigation: Graphs of Data*

In this Investigation, students interpret information from a line graph (used to show trends over time), a circle graph (used to show parts of a whole), a bar graph (uses bar length to compare data), and a pictograph (uses symbols to compare data), and draw conclusions from the data. Students use many of these representations to identify important subsets and trends in the data. As students progress through the lesson and Practice items, they evaluate each of these types of graphs, which are often used for formal presentations or published work.

### Lesson 6.2    *Activity: The Center of a Data Set*

In this lesson, students consider ways to describe a data set with a single number. During the Activity, each group of students collects five different sets of data from the members of their group and then combines these data with the data collected from other groups in the class to form whole-class data sets. Students create dot plots or bar graphs of each whole-class data set and determine the measure of center (mean, median, or mode) that most accurately describes the data set. This lesson concludes with students using graphing calculators to find the mean and median of a set of data.

### Lesson 6.3    *Stem-and-Leaf Diagrams and Box Plots*

In this lesson, students construct and interpret two types of data displays (stem-and-leaf diagrams and box plots) that combine graphical methods with numerical summaries of data. They examine gaps in the distribution, outliers, extremes, and quartiles. This section concludes with students using a graphing calculator to make a box plot of a set of data.

### Lesson 6.4    *R.A.P.*

In this lesson, students **R**eview **A**nd **P**ractice solving problems that require the use of skills and concepts taught in previous math levels. The skills reviewed in this lesson are skills that are needed as a basis for solving problems throughout this course.

### Lesson 6.5    *Activity: Sampling*

In this Activity, students identify the types of sampling methods used to collect data and examine how each type of method influences the result of a survey. The types of samples investigated in this lesson are convenience sample, biased sample, simple random sample, stratified random sample, and interval sample.

### Chapter 6    *Extension: Frequency Tables and Histograms*

In this Extension, students use grouped frequencies to construct a histogram. A list of guidelines for histogram construction is presented in detail.

# Lesson Guide

| Lesson/Objectives | Materials | |
|---|---|---|
| **Chapter 6 Opener: How Does the Census Help Us Understand Our Country?**<br>• recognize that the mathematical science called statistics is used in analyzing surveys and other data. | | |
| **6.1 Investigation: Graphs of Data**<br>• read and interpret bar graphs, pictographs, circle graphs, and line graphs. | • graphing calculators | *Optional:*<br>• TRM circle graph template for Exercises 1 and 2<br>• TRM pictograph shell for Exercises 1 and 2<br>• computer spreadsheet program such as Microsoft® Excel®<br>• grid paper |
| **6.2 Activity: The Center of a Data Set**<br>• choose appropriate measures of center for a data set. | *Per group:*<br>• centimeter ruler | *Optional:*<br>• TRM table shell for Questions 1 (a–e) |
| **6.3 Stem-and-Leaf Diagrams ad Box Plots**<br>• use, construct, and interpret stem-and-leaf diagrams to organize and display data.<br>• use extremes, quartiles, and standard deviation to describe a set of data.<br>• use, construct, and interpret box plots to display and compare data. | • graphing calculators | *Optional:*<br>• TRM stem-and-leaf diagram shells<br>• computer spreadsheet program such as Microsoft Excel |
| **6.4 R.A.P.**<br>• solve problems that require previously learned concepts and skills. | | *Optional:*<br>• grid paper |
| **6.5 Activity: Sampling**<br>• use a sample mean to estimate the mean of a population.<br>• identify types of sampling methods.<br>• indicate when a sampling method is biased. | • names of students in the class written on individual pieces of paper<br>• container to hold the pieces of paper | |
| **Chapter 6 Extension: Frequency Tables and Histograms**<br>• construct a grouped frequency histogram from data. | | *Optional:*<br>• computer spreadsheet program (Excel)<br>• grid paper<br>• graphing calculator |

# Pacing Guide

| | Day 1 | Day 2 | Day 3 | Day 4 | Day 5 | Day 6 | Day 7 | Day 8 | Day 9 | Day 10 |
|---|---|---|---|---|---|---|---|---|---|---|
| **Basic** | p. 176, 6.1 | 6.1, 6.2 | 6.2, 6.3 | 6.3, 6.4 | 6.4, 6.5 | 6.5 | project | project, review | review | |
| **Standard** | p. 176, 6.1 | 6.1, 6.2 | 6.2, 6.3 | 6.3, 6.4 | 6.4, 6.5 | 6.5 | project | project, review | review | extension |
| **Block** | p. 176, 6.1 | 6.2, 6.3 | 6.3, 6.4 | 6.4, 6.5 | project | review, extension | | | | |

**Supplement Support**

See the Book Companion Website at www.highschool.bfwpub.com/ModelingwithMathematics and the Teacher's Resource Materials (TRM) for additional resources.

# Describing Data

## CONTENTS

## Lesson Objective

- recognize that the mathematical science called *statistics* is used in analyzing surveys and other data.

## Vocabulary

- statistics

## Description

This reading gives an overview of the U.S. Census and its importance. It points out that mathematics–based statistics is important to understanding and using the information gathered in a census.

---

### TEACHING TIP

Point out to students that a large amount of census information, for the U.S. and for individual states, is available on the Internet. For example, information can be found at http://2010.census.gov and at http://factfinder2.census.gov.

---

## How Does the Census Help Us Understand Our Country?

Every 10 years since 1790, the U.S. government has conducted a census to count the population of the country. The census is required by the U.S. Constitution, which states

> The actual Enumeration shall be made within three Years after the first Meeting of the Congress of the United States, and within every subsequent Term of ten Years, in such Manner as they shall by Law direct.

To begin the 2010 census, Robert Groves, the director of the Census Bureau, traveled by dogsled to the Eskimo village of Noorvik, Alaska to count its 650 residents.

The U.S. population has grown from about 2 million in 1790 to over 300 million in 2010. The Census Bureau tries to actually count every person living in the United States and its territories. But only about 72% of the 134 million census forms are returned. To increase response rates in 2010, a huge advertising campaign was used. Guides printed in 59 different languages helped people understand the forms. A "Census in Schools" campaign increased the participation of immigrant families whose children learned about the census.

The census is used to determine the number of representatives each state has in the U.S. Congress. More than $400 billion of federal funds are distributed according to the census. For this reason, the census is important to communities for support of hospitals, schools, job training centers, bridges, and other projects.

A huge amount of information is provided by the census and related surveys, such as people's occupations, education levels, ancestries, and incomes. Summarizing and analyzing this information involves a mathematical science called **statistics**. Pictures, graphs, and charts used to display data can help you understand information more clearly.

Clifton Jackson, the oldest resident of Noorvik, Alaska, was the first person counted for the 2010 census.

A visual display, such as a graph, helps a reader to see and understand an entire data set at a glance. It can make it easier to identify important subsets and trends in the data. In this lesson, you will examine several types of graphs and evaluate their usefulness.

You are probably familiar with the following types of graphs:

- bar graphs
- pictographs
- circle graphs
- line graphs

Each type of graph is useful for certain kinds of data. Sometimes more than one type of graph can be appropriate for a single data set.

### TYPES OF GRAPHS

A **line graph** is often used to show trends over time. The line graph below shows the changes in the U.S. population from 1790 to 2010. Line segments connect the points on the graph even though data are not available for non-census years. This is often done for line graphs in order to help show trends more clearly.

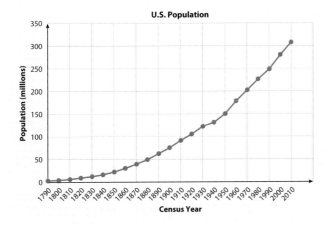

**U.S. Population**

1. Describe the overall trend in the U.S. population between 1790 and 2010.
2. What would the slope of one of the line segments tell you?
3. During what 10-year period did the population grow the least?
4. When was the population about half of its value in 2010?

GRAPHS OF DATA     **Lesson 6.1**     **177**

**5e**   Explore

## Lesson Objective

- read and interpret bar graphs, pictographs, circle graphs, and line graphs.

## Vocabulary

- bar graph
- circle graph
- line graph
- pictograph

## Materials List

## Description

This lesson is designed as a small group investigation (2–4 students). Students should work through **Questions 1–13** to analyze and interpret information contained in various types of graphs. The focus of this lesson is on interpreting graphs, not constructing them, although students are asked to make graphs in **Exercises 1(a) and 2**.

If your students have created graphs using Microsoft Excel or a similar spreadsheet program, point out that graphs are usually referred to as "charts" by such programs.

*Wrapping Up the Investigation:*

Conduct a whole-class discussion and ask students what types of graphs they think are particularly good for displaying various kinds of information, and why.

### TEACHING TIP

Point out to students that line graphs are drawn with line segments connecting data points, but that intermediate points on each segment cannot be assumed to have meaning in connection with the data.

### TEACHING TIP

In **Question 2**, point out to students that they are not asked to find the slope of a line segment, only to explain its meaning.

## Lesson 6.4 Investigation Answers

1. Sample answer: The population has increased steadily, with a greater rate of change in later years compared to earlier years.
2. Sample answer: The slope would be equal to the average rate of change of the population between any two census years.
3. Sample answer: The population appears to have grown the least from 1790–1800, although 1930–1940 was also a very slow growth period.
4. Sample answer: about 1950

### TEACHING TIP

Remind students that a line graph is not the same thing as the graph of a line, which they studied in **Chapter 5**.

**177**

5. High School Graduate
6. Sample answer: Reverse the axes and use horizontal bars.

A **bar graph** can be used to compare amounts in different categories. The table shows the highest education level reached by people in the United States who were at least 25 years old in 2008.

| Education Level | Number of People | Percent of Total Population |
|---|---|---|
| No high school diploma | 30,068,765 | 15 |
| High school graduate | 57,032,214 | 29 |
| Some college | 42,565,378 | 21 |
| Associate's degree | 15,006,479 | 8 |
| Bachelor's degree | 35,003,071 | 17 |
| Graduate/professional degree | 20,354,111 | 10 |

SOURCE: AMERICAN COMMUNITY SURVEY 2008

This vertical bar graph (sometimes called a *column graph*) allows you to quickly see the relative numbers of people in each educational category.

5. What was the most common education level for people in the United States who were over 25 in 2008?
6. Describe another way to display the data in a bar graph.

The bar graph above shows the number of people who have reached each education level. But the categories taken together make up the whole population of people in the United States who were at least 25 years old.

When the categories in a bar graph are parts of a whole, it is more common to show the amount in each category as a percent of the whole as shown in the graph below.

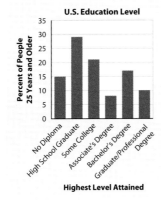

U.S. Education Level

A **circle graph** or *pie chart* is also frequently used to show parts of a whole.

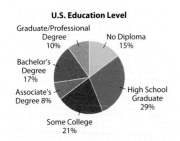

U.S. Education Level

7. What percent of people had some kind of college degree?

8. What percent of people had completed high school but did not have a college degree?

9. Must the percents in a circle graph always add to exactly 100%? Explain.

**Pictographs** are often used in newspapers and magazines to emphasize the kind of data that are being displayed. This graph shows the actual numbers of college graduates in the various regions of the United States.

College Degrees by Region

10. Which region has the most residents with college degrees? How do you know?

11. Which region has the fewest residents with college degrees?

12. Can you tell from the graph what percent of people in the Midwest have college degrees? Explain.

13. About how many people in the West have college degrees?

TEACHING TIP

Point out that "circle graph" is the name usually used for this type of graph in school textbooks. In the workplace these types of graphs are frequently called "pie charts."

TEACHING TIP

Emphasize the fact, as pointed out in **Question 9**, that if a circle graph displays data as percents, they should always add to 100% unless rounding of individual values causes a *slight* deviation from 100%.

TEACHING TIP

You may need to point out that the data displayed in the pictograph, *College Degrees by Region*, are not the same data examined previously for the bar and circle graphs.

TEACHING TIP

Remind students that both bar graphs and pictographs may be oriented either vertically or horizontally.

12. No; you would need to know how many people live in the Midwest to be able to determine the percent of the people with college degrees.

13. Sample answer: between 15 and 20 million; about 17 million

7. 35%

8. 50%

9. Sample answer: They should add to 100% in most cases because the categories form parts of a whole, but this may vary slightly due to rounding errors.

10. South; it is represented by the greatest number of caps.

11. Northeast

## LESSON 6.1

### ADDITIONAL EXAMPLE

The graph below shows the percent of people living in various regions of the country who were *not* born in the United States of America.

**Not Born in the U. S.**

**a.** What percent of people living in the West were born in the U.S.? about 79%

**b.** Can you tell from the graph how many people in the Midwest were born in the U.S.? no

**c.** Why do the percents not add to 100%? The percents are not parts of the whole country, but parts of the separate regions.

## EXAMPLE

The bar graph shows the percent of people 25 years of age or older in various regions of the United States who have earned at least one type of college degree.

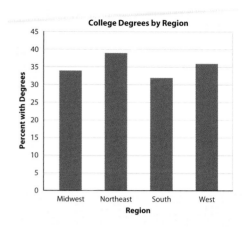

**College Degrees by Region**

**a.** The pictograph in the Investigation showed that the South had more people with college degrees. However, the bar in this graph is tallest for the Northeast. Explain.

**b.** Explain why the percents for all the bars do not add up to 100%.

**c.** Would a circle graph be appropriate for these data? Explain.

### Solution:

**a.** The bars show a percent of the population having a college degree in each region. The South has more people with degrees, but that number is a smaller percent of the total number of people who live in the South.

**b.** The graph shows the percent with degrees for each region. The bars as a group do not represent one whole population.

**c.** Since the bars do not represent parts of a whole, a circle graph is not appropriate.

**1b.** Sample answer: Since the categories are parts of a whole, a circle graph shows the relative portions of the population doing each kind of work.

**2.** Sample answer:

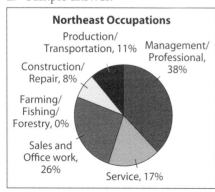

**Northeast Occupations**

Production/ Transportation, 11%
Management/ Professional, 38%
Construction/ Repair, 8%
Farming/ Fishing/ Forestry, 0%
Sales and Office work, 26%
Service, 17%

**3.** Sample answer: A smaller portion of the population in the Northeast is involved in Production/ Transportation, Construction/ Repair, and Farming/Fishing/ Forestry than in the U.S. as a whole. A slightly greater portion is involved in Management/ Professional and in Sales and Office Work.

**4.** Sample answer: A bar graph or a pictograph would be appropriate. Since all people in the graph are in the same category, a pictograph illustrating that occupation (using, for example, a hammer or hard hat) provides a good visual cue.

**5.** Sample answer: A line graph would show the trend over time. A bar graph, or even a pictograph, might also work.

## Practice for Lesson 6.1

**For Exercises 1–5, use the information shown in the table below.**

| | Occupations by Region (millions of people) | | | | |
|---|---|---|---|---|---|
| Region | Midwest | Northeast | South | West | Total U.S. |
| Management/Professional | 11.19 | 10.31 | 17.7 | 11.85 | 51.1 |
| Service | 5.48 | 4.75 | 8.84 | 5.99 | 25.1 |
| Sales and Office Work | 8.29 | 6.98 | 13.39 | 8.55 | 37.2 |
| Farming/Fishing/Forestry | 0.20 | 0.08 | 0.31 | 0.40 | 0.99 |
| Construction/Repair | 2.77 | 2.15 | 5.49 | 3.20 | 13.6 |
| Production/Transportation | 5.05 | 3.00 | 6.54 | 3.67 | 18.3 |
| Total for the Region | 33.0 | 27.3 | 52.3 | 33.7 | 146.3 |

SOURCE: AMERICAN COMMUNITY SURVEY 2008

1. This table shows the number of people who are in various occupations for the four main geographic regions of the United States. The data are given as millions of people age 16 years or older.
   a. Make a graph that compares the different occupational groups for the entire United States. Choose one of the four types—line graph, circle graph, bar graph, or pictograph—if appropriate. Remember to title and label your graph. Give a key for a pictograph.
   b. Explain your choice of graph.

**Note**
You may wish to use a computer spreadsheet to make your graph, if one is available, especially if you are making a circle graph.

2. Make the same kind of graph to compare the occupational groups for the region where you live.

3. Describe what your graphs from Exercises 1 and 2 tell you about your region as compared to the whole nation.

4. What types of graphs could be used to compare the number of people involved in Construction/Repair groups for the different regions?

5. If you had data showing the number of people in the United States engaged in production and transportation in each of the last 10 years, explain what kind of graph might be appropriate to show this information.

## Practice for Lesson 6.1 Answers

**1a.** Note: students should create either a circle graph, bar graph, or a pictograph (a line graph is not appropriate for these data). Sample answer:

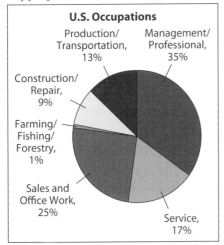

**U.S. Occupations**

- Production/Transportation, 13%
- Management/Professional, 35%
- Construction/Repair, 9%
- Farming/Fishing/Forestry, 1%
- Sales and Office Work, 25%
- Service, 17%

**1b–5.** See answers on page 180.

**Exercises 6–9** If students are curious, point out that recent rule changes prohibit NBA teams from drafting students directly from high school.

6. eight
7. The overall trend was toward drafting greater numbers of high school students.
8. The number increased by 7 students (8 – 1).
9. There were fewer high school students drafted in 2002 than in 2001.

**For Exercises 6–9, use the following information.**

The line graph shows the number of high school students that were selected in the National Basketball Association (NBA) draft's first round from 1995 to 2004.

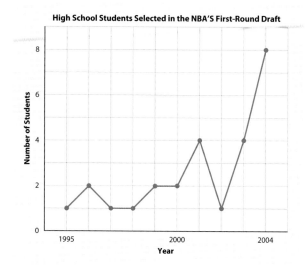

High School Students Selected in the NBA'S First-Round Draft

6. How many students were chosen in the first round of the draft in 2004?
7. What does the graph tell you about the trend in drafting high school students?
8. By how much did the number of students increase from 2002 to 2004?
9. Between 2001 and 2002, the line slants downward. What does this indicate?

**For Exercises 10–12, use the following information.**

The bar graph shown on the next page describes the amount of caffeine in several popular drinks.

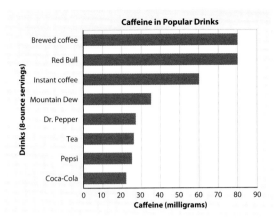

Caffeine in Popular Drinks

10. about 25 mg
11. An 8-ounce cup of brewed coffee contains twenty more milligrams of caffeine than an 8-ounce cup of instant coffee.
12. The total amount of caffeine in the two drinks is equivalent to the caffeine in one 8-ounce serving of instant coffee.

10. How much caffeine is in an 8-ounce serving of Pepsi?

11. How does the amount of caffeine in one 8-ounce cup of brewed coffee compare to that in one 8-ounce cup of instant coffee?

12. The total amount of caffeine in one 8-ounce Pepsi and one 8-ounce Mountain Dew is equivalent to the caffeine in one 8-ounce serving of which drink?

**For Exercises 13–19, use the following information.**

The pictograph shown below shows the number of Calories burned by a 150-pound person during 30 minutes of the activity listed.

Calories Burned in 30 Minutes

Key: = 30 Calories.

GRAPHS OF DATA     **Lesson 6.1**     **183**

183

**13.** $30 \div 2 = 15$ Calories

**14.** walking up stairs;
$9(30) = 270$ Calories

**15.** $2(30) + 15 = 75$ Calories

**16.** walking up stairs

**17.** chopping wood

**18.** Sample answer: Yes; the lengths of the bars would be proportional to the number of Calories burned by each activity.

**19.** Sample answer: No; the categories are not parts of a whole.

**20.** silver

**21.** silver, white, blue, black

**22.** Sample answer: Silver is about three times as popular, since the area of the silver sector is about 3 times as large as the area of the blue sector.

---

**TEACHING TIP**

You may wish to have students use a computer spreadsheet to do **Exercise 23**.

---

**13.** If ![fire icon] represents 30 Calories, what does ![icon] represent?

**14.** During which activity are the most Calories burned? How many Calories are burned in 30 minutes of doing this activity?

**15.** How many Calories are burned during 30 minutes of ironing?

**16.** Which activity burns twice as many Calories as raking leaves?

**17.** Which activity burns more than 135 Calories, but less than 270 Calories, in 30 minutes?

**18.** Would a bar graph be appropriate for displaying this information? Why or why not?

**19.** Would a circle graph be appropriate for displaying this information? Why or why not?

**For Exercises 20–22, use the following information.**

The circle graph shows the most popular color choices for vehicles in 2005.

**Most Popular Vehicle Colors**

Other 25% · Silver 37% · Black 11% · Blue 13% · White 14%

**20.** What color was most popular in 2005?

**21.** List the colors in order of popularity from greatest to least (not including "other").

**22.** About how many times more popular is silver than blue? Explain.

**23.** Most graphing calculators have several types of plots available for displaying data. The one that is similar to a line graph is called an *xyLine* plot. An xyLine plot displays the data as points. Then it connects the points in the order of their appearance in the **Xlist** and **Ylist**. Use the data in the table to create an xyLine plot.

| Day | 1 | 2 | 3 | 4 | 5 | 6 | 7 | 8 | 9 | 10 |
|---|---|---|---|---|---|---|---|---|---|---|
| °F | 83 | 88 | 89 | 95 | 95 | 98 | 77 | 85 | 85 | 88 |

To make an xyLine plot of these data, follow these steps:

**Step 1**   Store the data in two or more lists.

**Step 2**   Define the **STAT PLOT**. (Hint: Do not forget to deselect the **Y=** functions.)

**Step 3**   Define the viewing window. (Note: It is important that the window be defined correctly in order to see all the data. For these data, a scale from 0 to 11 on the horizontal axis and a scale of 0 to 100 on the vertical axis will allow all of the data to be viewed.)

**Step 4**   Display the plot.

$[0, 11] \times [0, 100]$

**a.** Use the graph from Step 4 to describe any trends you might see.

**23a.** Sample answer: The temperature rose for the first several days, then dropped, but rose again. Generally, the temperatures were in the 80s and 90s.

**23b.** Sample graph:

[0, 8] × [0, 100]

**b.** The table below shows the numbers of multiple births of at least five babies in the United States from 1997–2003.

| Year | 1997 | 1998 | 1999 | 2000 | 2001 | 2002 | 2003 |
|---|---|---|---|---|---|---|---|
| Number of Multiple Births | 79 | 79 | 67 | 77 | 85 | 69 | 85 |

Use a graphing calculator to create a line graph of the data. (Hint: As you enter these data into the calculator, you may want to use 1 for 1997, the first year. Then use 2 for 1998, the second year, and so on. By doing so, your viewing window will consist of smaller numbers.)

Data can be summarized in various ways. A graph shows how data are distributed. There are also numerical measures for summarizing data. In this lesson, you will consider ways to describe a data set with a single number.

"The average age of passenger cars in the U.S. rose . . . to 9.4 years old" in 2009, according to *Car Blog* on consumerreports.org. What do you think the word "average" stands for in this sentence?

As you may already know, the average value of data can be measured in more than one way. Commonly used *measures of center* of a data set are the mean, the median, and the mode. (See Appendix N.)

| Measure of Center | When It Is Used |
|---|---|
| The **mean** of a data set is found by dividing the sum of all the data values by the number of values in the set. | The mean provides a good description for a data set that is clustered, with few values that are much greater or less than the rest of the data. |
| The **median** of a data set is the middle value in an ordered list if there is an odd number of data values. For a data set that contains an even number of values, the median is the mean of the two middle values. | The median is a good way to describe a data set when there are values that are much larger or smaller than most of the data. |
| The **mode** of a data set is the most frequently occurring data value or values in the data set. A data set can have one mode or more than one mode. If every data value in a data set occurs exactly the same number of times, or if all data values are different, there is no mode. | The mode may be used when many of the data have the same value, or when the data are not numerical. |

The word "average" is usually used to describe the mean of a data set. But the average mentioned in the *Car Blog* quote actually refers to the median age of cars. To avoid misunderstanding, it is best to specify which measure of center is being used.

## Lesson Objective

- choose appropriate measures of center for a data set.

## Vocabulary

- dot plot
- mean
- median
- mode
- outlier

## Materials List

- centimeter rulers

## Description

*Preparation:*

Have students work in groups of 3 students. Each student can then perform data analysis for 1 or 2 of the 5 questions in **Questions 1(a–e)** in the survey.

*During the Activity:*

You may wish to accumulate responses to each question on the board, perhaps by creating a column for each question. Group members could then add their data to each column. You may want to separate the shoe size data into subsets for girls and boys, since girls' and boys' shoes are measured differently.

*Closing the Activity:*

Conduct a class discussion of answers to **Questions 8–10** to make sure students see the advantages of each of the three measures of center. Point out that the objective is to find a single number to describe a set of data. Both the context of the situation and the distribution of numerical values help determine which measure or measures are most appropriate in any particular case.

**TEACHING TIP**

Point out that measures of center are also referred to more formally as "measures of central tendency."

**TEACHING TIP**

If students ask about the reference to "data values" in the definition of mode, point out that for non-numerical data sets (e.g., colors of cars, team names, etc.) "data values" is used for both numerical and non-numerical data.

# LESSON 6.2

**TEACHING TIP**

Students may need a review of how to make a dot plot. If necessary, make a dot plot of one of the data sets to use as a model, or use a student-created dot plot.

**TEACHING TIP**

Point out to students that a dot plot provides a quick look at the distribution of a data set, and allows identification of outliers. It serves a similar, although more informal, purpose as a histogram, which is discussed in the Extension to this chapter. While usually used to graph quantitative data, dot plots can also be used with qualitative data for the purpose of visualizing a distribution.

**TEACHING TIP**

Dot plots are sometimes referred to as "line plots" or "number line plots." Instead of dots, X's are occasionally used, as seen in **Exercises 29–33** in **Lesson 3.4**.

**TEACHING TIP**

For **Question 5**, you may want to have students use a calculator to find the means.

**TEACHING TIP**

For **Question 7**, point out that hand span is a continuous variable. Data sets for continuous variables frequently have no mode.

**Recall**

A **dot plot** is a simple plot that consists of a group of data points plotted on a number line. For example, this dot plot shows the number of times members of a group of college freshmen wash their hair in a week.

1. Record the responses of each member of your group to each of the following questions.
   a. How many letters are in your first name?
   b. What is your favorite color?
   c. What is your age in months?
   d. What is your shoe size?
   e. What is the length of your hand-span, measured to the nearest tenth of a centimeter?

2. At your teacher's direction, combine your results for Question 1, Parts (a–e), with those of the rest of the class to generate five whole-class data sets.

3. Make a dot plot or bar graph of the class data for each of the five parts. Split the work among the members of your group so that each student makes one or two dot plots or bar graphs.

4. Identify any data sets that contain outliers. (Recall that an **outlier** is any value that is much greater or much less than the rest of the data.)

5. Calculate the mean, median, and mode for each set when possible.

6. Explain how a dot plot is useful for finding each of the three measures of center.

7. Identify any of the five data sets for which one or more of the measures of center do not exist. Explain.

8. For which data sets, if any, does the mode provide the best measure of center? Justify your answer.

9. For which data sets, if any, does the median provide the best measure of center? Justify your answer.

10. For which data sets, if any, does the mean provide the best measure of center? Justify your answer.

## Practice for Lesson 6.2

**For Exercises 1–4, fill in the blank.**

1. The _____ is the middle value of an ordered data set.

2. The _____ is the value(s) of a data set that occur(s) most often.

3. The _____ can be strongly affected by outliers.

4. A data set can have more than one _____.

## Lesson 6.2 Activity Answers

**1–5.** Answers will vary.

**6.** Sample answers: The *mode* is obvious from the dot plot, since it has the largest collection of dots. The dot plot orders the data, making the *median* easier to find. The dot plot shows the frequency of each value, so the *mean* can be calculated more efficiently.

**7.** There is no mean or median for favorite color, since the data are not numeric. There will be no mode for a data set that consists of all different values, such as possibly the hand span measurements.

**8.** Sample answers: favorite color, since the mean and median do not exist; shoe size, in a situation in which a large number of students wear the same size

**9.** Any sets except favorite color may be mentioned here. In particular, hand span is a possibility if there are outliers.

**10.** Any sets except favorite color may be mentioned, especially any in which data are clustered, with no outliers.

## Practice for Lesson 6.2 Answers

1. median
2. mode
3. mean
4. mode

**For Exercises 5–6, find the mean, median, and mode.**

5. Use the dot plot of daily high temperatures in Boston during January 2007.

**Daily High Temperature (°F)**

6. The Army Corps of Engineers helps to counteract the erosion of beaches by pumping in sand. The table shows the amounts of sand used by the Corps of Engineers to maintain beaches in various Florida counties since the 1970s.

| County | Amount of Sand (millions of cubic yards) |
| --- | --- |
| Miami-Dade | 18.9 |
| Brevard | 10.8 |
| Palm Beach | 8.1 |
| Bay | 7.9 |
| Broward | 7.7 |
| Pinellas | 7.5 |
| Duval | 6.2 |
| St. Johns | 3.7 |
| Lee | 3.2 |
| Martin | 2.4 |
| Manatee | 2.2 |
| St. Lucie | 2.0 |
| Sarasota | 1.3 |

SOURCE: THE NEW YORK TIMES

7. According to the American Community Survey (ACS), the median age of the U.S. population in 2008 was 36.9 years. What does this statistic tell you about the ages of people in the United States?

5. mean: 34.2°F; median: 34°F; modes: 27°F and 40°F
6. mean: 6.3 million yd$^3$; median: 6.2 million yd$^3$; no mode
7. Half the population was older than 36.9 years and half the population was younger than 36.9 years.

THE CENTER OF A DATA SET    **Lesson 6.2**    **189**

# LESSON 6.2

**8a.** mean: 5.5 days; median: 2.5 days; mode: 2 days

**8b.** Sample answer: The mean is not a good representation, as it would indicate that it takes over 5 days for the typical letter to be delivered. The mode or the median describes the data best.

**8c.** The new mean is about 2.9 days, the new median is 2 days, and the mode is still 2 days.

**8d.** the mean

**9.** Sample answer: 4, 5, 6, 14, 16

**10.** 5

**11.** 2

**12.** Sample answer: The manager might use the mode in order to decide which shoe size to keep more of in stock.

**13.** Sample answer: The mean is most affected by outliers, so it should change the most. The median will typically only be slightly affected, and the mode will not change.

---

**8.** Ten letters were mailed from Missouri to Florida. The numbers of days that it took for the letters to be delivered are shown in the list below.

$$1, 2, 2, 2, 2, 3, 4, 5, 5, 29$$

   **a.** Find the mean, median, and mode for the data set.
   **b.** Which measure of center best describes the data set? Explain.
   **c.** What happens to the three measures of center if you remove the outlier from the data set?
   **d.** Which measure of center is most affected by the outlier?

**9.** Create a data set of five numbers that will give a median of 6 and a mean of 9.

**10.** The median of four numbers is 8. If three of the numbers are 2, 11, and 12, what is the other number?

**11.** The mean of four numbers is 8. If three of the numbers are 6, 8, and 16, what is the other number? (Hint: Write a formula for calculating the mean of four numbers.)

**12.** For your class survey in Question 1, Part (d) from the Investigation, in which measure of center would the manager of a shoe store be most interested?

**13.** Suppose a new student comes into your class who is much taller than everyone else. Which of the three measures of center for class height do you expect to change the most due to the addition of the new student? Explain.

**14.** Many graphing calculators make it easy to find the mean and median of a set of data. The table below shows the high temperatures for the last 10 days of October in Phoenix, Arizona.

| Day | 1 | 2 | 3 | 4 | 5 | 6 | 7 | 8 | 9 | 10 |
|---|---|---|---|---|---|---|---|---|---|---|
| Temperature (F°) | 86 | 84 | 85 | 84 | 83 | 80 | 85 | 86 | 86 | 81 |

**Step 1:** To find the mean temperature, enter the data into a list, such as **L1**, in the calculator.

**Step 2:** Display the **[LIST] MATH** menu. Choose **mean** from the menu. Then enter **L1** as the data list.

Similar steps can be followed to find the median of a data set.

For Parts (a) and (b), use a graphing calculator to find the mean and median of each set of numbers.

**a.** 12,743; 42,987; 14,965; 8,123; 18,854; 17,102

**b.** 1.023; 4.1; 8.75; 14.123; 0.0125; 8.2398; 12.0427; 17.349; 6

**c.** The table below shows the sizes in acres of some of the world's largest amusement parks.

| Park | Walt Disney World Resort (USA) | Six Flags Great Adventure (USA) | Cedar Point (USA) | Busch Gardens (USA) | Tokyo Disney Resort (Japan) |
|---|---|---|---|---|---|
| Size (acres) | 30,000 | 2,200 | 364 | 335 | 114 |

SOURCE: WIKIPEDIA.ORG

Find the mean, median, and mode of the data.

**d.** For Part (c), which measure of center best describes the data set? Explain.

**14a.** mean: 19,129; median: 16,033.5

**14b.** mean: 7.96; median: 8.2398

**14c.** mean: 6,602.6 acres; median: 364 acres; no mode

**14d.** Sample answer: The median is a better measure of the typical size of the large amusement parks. The mean is strongly affected by the largest value of 30,000 acres.

# LESSON 6.3

## Lesson Objectives

- use, construct, and interpret stem-and-leaf diagrams to organize and display data.
- use extremes, quartiles, and standard deviation to describe a set of data.
- use, construct, and interpret box plots to display and compare data.

## Vocabulary

- box plot
- interquartile range
- lower extreme
- lower quartile
- range
- standard deviation
- stem-and-leaf diagram
- upper extreme
- upper quartile

## Description

This lesson introduces two methods of displaying data that are less formal than the graphs discussed in **Lesson 6.1**. Stem-and-leaf diagrams and box plots are often used for preliminary data analysis, but less frequently for formal presentations or published work.

---

## Lesson 6.3 | Stem-and-Leaf Diagrams and Box Plots

Graphs and measures of center both provide useful information about a data set. In this lesson, you will examine two types of data displays that combine graphical methods with numerical summaries of data.

### STEM-AND-LEAF DIAGRAMS

**Note**

A stem-and-leaf diagram is sometimes called a *stem-and-leaf plot* or just a *stemplot*.

A **stem-and-leaf diagram** is a graph that uses the digits of each number in the data set. It provides a visual display that groups the data but also shows all the numerical values.

In a stem-and-leaf diagram, each data value is separated into a *stem* and a *leaf*. Stems may have as many digits as needed. Each leaf usually contains only the rightmost digit of each number. All leaves must have the same place value.

For example, suppose that a cell phone manufacturer tests batteries to find out how long they hold a charge. The total talk times in hours for 18 batteries are:

$$6.4, 4.9, 6.2, 7.0, 5.9, 3.9, 7.3, 5.5, 6.4,$$
$$5.8, 9.2, 4.6, 6.1, 6.8, 6.5, 7.6, 6.4, 5.1$$

To create a stem-and-leaf diagram for these data:

- Write the data in order. In this case, the data are listed in order from least to greatest.

$$3.9, 4.6, 4.9, 5.1, 5.5, 5.8, 5.9, 6.1, 6.2,$$
$$6.4, 6.4, 6.4, 6.5, 6.8, 7.0, 7.3, 7.6, 9.2$$

- Since the data range from 3.9 to 9.2, let the stems represent the ones digits from 3 to 9. Let the leaves represent the tenths digits. Write the ones digits vertically from least to greatest. Then draw a vertical line to the right of these numbers.

**Talk Time (hours)**

| | |
|---|---|
| 3 | |
| 4 | |
| 5 | |
| 6 | |
| 7 | |
| 8 | |
| 9 | |

---

- Separate each number in the ordered data set into a stem and a leaf (ones digits and tenths digits). Write each leaf to the right of its stem. Stem values are listed only once, but each leaf is listed separately. So, there can be many leaves with the same value. Make sure that the leaves are listed in order, from least to greatest.

**Talk Time (hours)**

| | |
|---|---|
| 3 | 9 |
| 4 | 6 9 |
| 5 | 1 5 8 9 |
| 6 | 1 2 4 4 4 5 8 |
| 7 | 0 3 6 |
| 8 | |
| 9 | 2 |

- Provide a key to your plot that explains how to read the stems and leaves.

**Talk Time (hours)**

| | |
|---|---|
| 3 | 9 |
| 4 | 6 9 |
| 5 | 1 5 8 9 |
| 6 | 1 2 4 4 4 5 8 |
| 7 | 0 3 6 |
| 8 | |
| 9 | 2 |

Key: 3 | 9 represents 3.9 hours.

Notice these features of a stem-and-leaf diagram:

1. You can locate the median of the data easily by counting in from either end of the leaves until you find the middle number or numbers. In this example, the median is 6.3 hours (the mean of 6.2 and 6.4).

2. Stem-and-leaf diagrams can help you locate gaps in the distribution. They can also help you identify outliers. Notice that the measurement of 9.2 hours stands apart from the other data values. When this happens, you may be able to find an explanation for the outlier.

3. A stem-and-leaf diagram has the visual appearance of a bar graph. This allows you to see any pattern that may be present in the data distribution.

### MEASURES OF VARIATION

When summarizing data, you not only have to know something about the center of the data, but you often need to know how spread out the data are. One way to do this is to find the **lower** and **upper extremes** (the least and the greatest data values, also called *minimum* and *maximum*), the range, the median, and the quartiles.

**TEACHING TIP**

Make sure students see that the stems are the numbers to the left of the vertical line in a stem-and-leaf diagram, while the leaves are the numbers to the right of the line, and that all leaves are one digit and must have the same place value.

**TEACHING TIP**

If students use a calculator or computer spreadsheet, you may want to point out that data can be sorted automatically in either ascending or descending order.

**TEACHING TIP**

Point out to students that the 0 in this stem-and-leaf diagram represents the value 7.0. A blank row, like the one to the right of the "8" stem, indicates that there are no data having that stem.

Point out to students that the upper and lower extremes, median, and upper and lower quartiles are sometimes referred to as the "5-number summary" or "5-value summary" of a data set.

## ADDITIONAL EXAMPLE 1

The table shows the percent of health club memberships sold by month in the U.S.

| Month | % Sold |
|-------|--------|
| Jan | 12.4 |
| Feb | 9.5 |
| Mar | 8.7 |
| Apr | 6.9 |
| May | 7.8 |
| June | 7.6 |
| July | 6.8 |
| Aug | 7.6 |
| Sept | 8.4 |
| Oct | 8.6 |
| Nov | 7.7 |
| Dec | 7.8 |

SOURCE: INT'L HEALTH, RACQUET & SPORTSCLUB ASSN.

Find the upper and lower extremes, the range, the median, and the upper and lower quartiles for the data.
lower extreme = 6.8, upper extreme = 12.4, range = 5.6, median = 7.8, $Q_1 = 7.6$, $Q_3 = 8.65$

The **range** is the difference between the upper and lower extremes. To calculate the quartiles:

- Arrange the data in order from least to greatest.
- Locate the median of the data.
- The **lower quartile** (or *first quartile*), $Q_1$, is the median of the data values that are *below* the median of the entire data set.
- The **upper quartile** (or *third quartile*), $Q_3$, is the median of the data values that are *above* the median of the entire data set.

When there is an odd number of values, the rule for computing quartiles excludes the median of the data set.

$$3 \quad 3 \quad \underset{Q_1}{\underline{5}} \quad 7 \quad 9 \quad \underset{median = 9}{\underline{9}} \quad 14 \quad 17 \quad \underset{Q_3}{\underline{21}} \quad 23 \quad 23$$

For these data, the lower quartile, $Q_1$, is 5, the median of the five values below the median of the entire data set. The upper quartile, $Q_3$, is 21, the median of the five values above the median of the entire data set. The range is $(23 - 3) = 20$.

When there is an even number of data values, the two middle values are included in calculations of the upper and lower quartiles.

$$4 \quad 4 \quad \underset{Q_1 = 6.5}{\underline{6 \quad 7}} \quad 7 \quad \underset{median = 9}{\underline{8 \quad 10}} \quad 11 \quad \underset{Q_3 = 14}{\underline{14 \quad 14}} \quad 18 \quad 19$$

For these data, the lower quartile, $Q_1$, is the median of the data values below 9. The median of these six values is the mean of 6 and 7, which is 6.5. And the upper quartile, $Q_3$, is the median of the data values above 9. The median of these six values is the mean of 14 and 14, which is 14.

## E X A M P L E 1

A class of twenty-one students earned the following scores on a test:

47, 56, 59, 65, 74, 76, 78, 78, 78, 80, 82, 83, 83, 85, 87, 87, 88, 90, 91, 94, 98

Find the upper and lower extremes, the range, the median, and the upper and lower quartiles.

**Solution:**

Since the data are listed in order, you can see that 47 is the lower extreme and 98 is the upper extreme. The range is $(98 - 47) = 51$.

The median is the middle number 82.

To calculate $Q_1$, look at the data values below the median. The median of these ten data values is the mean of 74 and 76. The lower quartile is $\frac{74 + 76}{2} = 75$. $Q_3$ is the median of the ten data values above the median. $Q_3 = \frac{87 + 88}{2} = 87.5$.

Another measure of variation is the **interquartile range**. It is the difference between the upper quartile and the lower quartile.

Find the interquartile range for the test score data in Example 1.

**Solution:**

From Example 1, the upper quartile is 87.5 and the lower quartile is 75. So, the interquartile range is $87.5 - 75 = 12.5$.

Still another measure of variation is the **standard deviation**, symbolized by a lowercase sigma, $\sigma$. The standard deviation is somewhat tedious to compute by hand, but a calculator can provide it for any data set. On a TI-83/84 calculator, the standard deviation is part of one-variable statistics (**1-Var Stats**) on the $\boxed{\text{STAT}}$ **CALC** menu.

```
EDIT CALC TESTS
1 1-Var Stats
2:2-Var Stats
3:Med-Med
4:LinReg(ax+b)
5:QuadReg
6:CubicReg
7↓QuartReg
```

Usually, more than half of a data set should be contained within one standard deviation of the mean of the data set.

**ADDITIONAL EXAMPLE 2**

Find the interquartile range for the table of data in the Additional Example 1 on the previous page. $8.65 - 7.6 = 1.05$

**TEACHING TIP**

You may want to point out that the standard deviation discussed here is the *population standard deviation* $\sigma$, which is only used when *all* members of a population being studied have been included in the data set. It is calculated

using the formula $\sigma = \sqrt{\dfrac{\sum\limits_{i=1}^{n}(X_i - \mu)^2}{n}}$,

where $n$ is the number of values $X$ in the population and $\mu$ is the *population mean*. In words, the population standard deviation is the square root of the mean of the squared deviations from the mean of the population.

When a *sample* from a population is used, the *sample standard deviation* $s$ is calculated using the formula

$s = \sqrt{\dfrac{\sum\limits_{i=1}^{n}(X_i - \overline{X})^2}{n - 1}}$, where $\overline{X}$ is the

*sample mean*. The sample standard deviation is used to estimate the true population standard deviation from data that constitute only a sample of the population. The sample standard deviation is not discussed in this text.

# LESSON 6.3

## ADDITIONAL EXAMPLE ③

**a.** For the table of data in the Additional Example 1 on page 194, determine the interval from one standard deviation below the mean to one standard deviation above the mean.

$\sigma \approx 1.43$ and the mean is 8.32; Interval is 6.89 to 9.75.

**b.** What percent of the data values is contained in the interval found in Part (a)? $\frac{10}{12} \approx 83\%$

The test score data from Example 1 are repeated below.

47, 56, 59, 65, 74, 76, 78, 78, 78, 80, 82, 83, 83, 85, 87, 87, 88, 90, 91, 94, 98

**a.** Determine the interval from one standard deviation below the mean to one standard deviation above the mean.

**b.** What percent of the data values is contained in the interval found in Part (a)?

**Solution:**

**a.** Enter the test score data in calculator list **L1**. Find the lists for data entry by choosing **EDIT** on the **STAT** menu.

Then calculate one-variable statistics for the list.

The standard deviation $\sigma_x$ is about 12.6. The mean ($\bar{x}$) of 79 is also computed. One standard deviation below the mean is $79 - 12.6 = 66.4$, and one standard deviation above the mean is $79 + 12.6 = 91.6$. The required interval is from 66.4 to 91.6.

**b.** Fifteen of the twenty-one test scores, or about 71%, are between 66.4 and 91.6.

## BOX PLOTS

**Box plots**, also called *box-and-whisker plots,* use the upper and lower extremes, the median, and the upper and lower quartiles to provide a visual representation of the distribution of a set of data.

To create a box plot of the cell phone talk time measurements:

- Write the data in order from least to greatest. Identify the lower extreme, the upper extreme, the median, the lower quartile, and the upper quartile.

$$3.9, 4.6, 4.9, 5.1, 5.5, 5.8, 5.9, 6.1, 6.2, 6.4, 6.4, 6.4,$$
$$6.5, 6.8, 7.0, 7.3, 7.6, 9.2$$

Lower extreme = 3.9          Upper extreme = 9.2

$$\text{Median} = \frac{6.2 + 6.4}{2} = 6.3$$

Lower quartile $Q_1$ (median of the nine data values below 6.3) = 5.5
Upper quartile $Q_3$ (median of the nine data values above 6.3) = 6.8

- Draw a number line that includes the extremes.

- Plot the lower extreme, the lower quartile, the median, the upper quartile, and the upper extreme above the number line.

- Draw a box from the lower quartile to the upper quartile. Divide the box with a vertical line drawn through the median. Then draw the "whiskers," a horizontal line from the lower extreme to the lower quartile and another from the upper quartile to the upper extreme.

- Title the plot.

**Cell Phone Talk Time (hours)**

**TEACHING TIP**

You may wish to tell students that outliers can be shown in a *modified box plot* as unconnected dots lying outside the ends of the whiskers. An outlier is often defined as a point that is more than 1.5 times the interquartile range $(Q_3 - Q_1)$ below $Q_1$ or above $Q_3$.

## ADDITIONAL EXAMPLE ④

Make a box plot of the data from the Additional Example 1 on page 194. Sample answer:

**Health Club Memberships (per Month)**

## Practice for Lesson 6.3 Answers

**1.**

**Total Scores**

```
1 | 9
2 | 3  6  6  8
3 | 1  6  6
4 | 0  4  8  9
5 | 4  5
6 | 2
7 | 2
```

Key: 1|9 represents scores that total 19.

---

Notice that the median and overall range of the data can be observed easily in a box plot. But unlike stem-and-leaf diagrams, box plots do not show individual data values. So it is not possible to observe gaps or outliers in a box plot.

## E X A M P L E ④

Make a box plot of the test score data from Example 1.

47, 56, 59, 65, 74, 76, 78, 78, 78, 80, 82, 83, 83, 85, 87, 87, 88, 90, 91, 94, 98

**Solution:**

Identify the five values from Example 1 needed to create the plot.

Lower extreme = 47          Upper extreme = 98

Median = 82

Lower quartile $Q_1$ (median of the ten data values below 82) = 75

Upper quartile $Q_3$ (median of the ten data values above 82) = 87.5

Draw a number line that includes the extremes.

Plot the five values above the number line.

Draw the "box" and the "whiskers," and then title the plot.

**Test Scores**

## Practice for Lesson 6.3

**1.** The total scores (for both teams) in each of the National Football League (NFL) games during the first week of the 2009 season were 23, 31, 26, 72, 55, 26, 48, 54, 19, 62, 36, 40, 28, 36, 49, and 44. Make a stem-and-leaf diagram of the data. (Hint: Use the ones digits for the leaves.)

**2.** A lab group for a biology experiment measured the heights of 16 plants after a week of growth. The heights of the plants (in centimeters) are given below.

12.7, 15.1, 16.5, 13.3, 14.8, 17.0, 15.9, 14.6, 11.7, 13.4, 15.3, 12.8, 15.3, 13.6, 14.2, 16.7

Make a stem-and-leaf diagram for the data.

**3.** Name the five values needed to make any box plot.

**4.** The data below show the number of hours spent studying last week by ten classmates.

8, 15, 9, 5, 8, 10, 3, 6, 3, 5

**a.** Calculate the median of the data.
**b.** Identify the lower and upper extremes.
**c.** Identify the lower and upper quartiles.

**5.** A researcher gathered data on the number of gray hairs on the heads of 25-year-olds. The stem-and-leaf diagram displays the data that she gathered from 40 people who were each 25 years old.

**Number of Gray Hairs on the Heads of 25-Year-Olds**

```
0 | 0 0 0 0 1 2 2 4 4 5 6 6 7 8 9
1 | 0 1 2 3 3 5 5 6 7
2 | 2 3 3 5 7
3 | 1 3 4 4 4 8
4 | 0 4 5
5 | 6
6 | 7
```
Key: 4|5 represents 45 gray hairs.

**a.** What is the median number of gray hairs for these 40 people? Show or explain how to determine the median.
**b.** What is the range of the number of gray hairs for these people? Show or explain how you obtained your answer.
**c.** What are the lower quartile and the upper quartile? Explain how to determine these values.
**d.** Make a box plot that displays the same data as in the stem-and-leaf diagram.

STEM-AND-LEAF DIAGRAMS AND BOX PLOTS    Lesson 6.3    **199**

**2. Plant Height (cm)**
```
11 | 7
12 | 7 8
13 | 3 4 6
14 | 2 6 8
15 | 1 3 3 9
16 | 5 7
17 | 0
```
Key: 12|8 represents 12.8 cm.

**3.** median, lower extreme, upper extreme, lower quartile, upper quartile

**4a.** Arrange the data in order, from the least to the greatest, (3, 3, 5, 5, 6, 8, 8, 9, 10, 15). Since there is an even number of data values, calculate the mean of the two middle numbers. median $= \frac{6+8}{2} = 7$

**4b.** lower extreme $= 3$; upper extreme $= 15$

**4c.** $Q_1$ is the median of the five values below the median (7) of the entire data set. The lower quartile is 5. The upper quartile $Q_3$ is the median of the five numbers above the median (7) of the entire data set. The upper quartile is 9.

**COMMON ERROR**

**Exercise 5(d)** Some students may think that quartiles divide the box plot into four equal parts. Point out that quartiles divide the number of data values into four equal parts and not the plot itself. So, one-fourth of the number of data values lies in each of the four sections of the plot.

**5d.**

**Number of Gray Hairs on the Heads of 25-Year-Olds**

**5a.** 14; Find the 20th and 21st numbers from the bottom, counting in the leaves digits only. The mean of the two middle data values (13 and 15) is the median.

**5b.** 67; Subtract the lower extreme (0) from the upper extreme (67).

**5c.** $Q_1 = 5.5$, $Q_3 = 32$; The lower quartile is the median of the 20 values below the overall median of 14. The upper quartile is the median of the 20 values above the overall median.

**6.** lower extreme = 110, upper extreme = 250, median = 155, $Q_1 = 130$, $Q_3 = 210$

**Calories in Cereal (per serving)**

**7.** Sample answer: You can find the mean from a stem-and-leaf diagram, because all of the data values are included. You cannot find the mean from a box plot, because only summary values are seen in a box plot.

**8.** Sample answer: A stem-and-leaf diagram is similar to both a dot plot and a bar graph, since it shows how all the data values are distributed. But a bar graph can also be used for categories that are not numerical; a stem-and-leaf diagram cannot be used for non-numerical data. A box plot uses a numerical scale like a dot plot, but it does not display all the data values.

**9a.** No, a box plot does not provide information about the mean.

**9b.** Yes, the median is 15.

**9c.** No, there could be more than one value at the upper extreme.

**9d.** Yes, the lower quartile contains one-fourth of the data.

**9e.** Yes, half of the data are contained within the lower and upper quartiles.

**9f.** No, the range is $(21 - 9) = 12$.

**10a.** Sample answer: The box plot for July is much further to the right on the number line.

**10b.** Yes. The upper extreme for January's daily temperatures is slightly further to the right than the lower extreme for July.

**6.** Ten brands of cereal contain the following numbers of Calories per serving: 230, 110, 160, 250, 150, 210, 160, 130, 115, and 130. Make a box plot of the data.

**7.** Is it possible to use a stem-and-leaf diagram or a box plot to find the mean of a data set? Explain.

**8.** Compare the use of stem-and-leaf diagrams and box plots with dot plots and bar graphs for displaying data.

**9.** A box plot of the 30 top per-game point scorers in a women's basketball league is shown below.

Based on the data in the box plot, indicate whether each of the following statements *must* be true. Explain your reasoning for each statement.

**a.** The mean number of points scored in a game is 15 points.

**b.** Half of the top 30 per-game point scorers scored at least 15 points.

**c.** Only one woman scored 21 points in a game.

**d.** Twenty-five percent of the top per-game point scorers scored between 9 and 12 points per game.

**e.** Half of the 30 top per-game point scorers scored between 12 and about 17.7 points per game.

**f.** The range of the points scored per game in this group of players is 14.

**10.** *Double box plots* can be used to compare data sets. The one below summarizes daily high temperatures (measured in degrees Fahrenheit) in one northern city for the months of January and July 2011.

**Daily High Temperature (°F) in 2011**

**a.** Describe how the double box plot shows that July was generally hotter than January in 2011.

**b.** Were any January days hotter than any July days? Explain how you know by looking at the double box plot.

**c.** Which month had a greater range of daily high temperatures? Explain.

**d.** What is the difference between the two median temperatures?

**10c.** The length of the box plot is greater for January, so there was a greater difference between the lower and upper extreme temperatures in January than in July.

**10d.** Sample answer: $81 - 33 = 48$ degrees

**For Exercises 11–12, use the following information.**

Professional sports teams do a lot of traveling during a season. The table below shows the total scheduled air miles for each National Football League team during one recent season (including preseason games).

| Team | Total Miles | Team | Total Miles |
|---|---|---|---|
| Oakland Raiders | 30,702 | Cleveland Browns | 14,856 |
| Seattle Seahawks | 30,298 | Detroit Lions | 14,852 |
| San Francisco 49ers | 25,752 | Tennessee Titans | 14,838 |
| San Diego Chargers | 25,344 | New Orleans Saints | 14,402 |
| Arizona Cardinals | 24,108 | Tampa Bay Buccaneers | 14,204 |
| St. Louis Rams | 21,530 | Chicago Bears | 13,872 |
| Houston Oilers | 20,314 | New York Jets | 13,784 |
| Dallas Cowboys | 20,124 | Baltimore Ravens | 13,574 |
| Miami Dolphins | 19,422 | Indianapolis Colts | 13,178 |
| Denver Broncos | 19,410 | New York Giants | 13,148 |
| Kansas City Chiefs | 18,244 | Washington Redskins | 12,422 |
| Minnesota Vikings | 17,802 | Jacksonville Jaguars | 12,390 |
| Green Bay Packers | 17,024 | Buffalo Bills | 10,574 |
| Pittsburgh Steelers | 16,984 | Atlanta Falcons | 9,550 |
| Philadelphia Eagles | 15,672 | Cincinnati Bengals | 9,240 |
| New England Patriots | 15,200 | Carolina Panthers | 8,966 |

SOURCE: THE BOSTON GLOBE

**11.** Many graphing calculators are able to make box plots. All that is needed is a list of data. The calculator will automatically determine the five numbers needed to draw the box plot. Consider the following situation:

    **a.** Enter the travel data into list **L1** in your calculator.
    **b.** Turn on one of the data plots. Choose the box plot icon. Enter **L1** as the data list.
    **c.** Set an appropriate window. Only the $x$-variable range is important. Make sure that it includes the lower extreme and the upper extreme of the data.
    **d.** Instruct the calculator to create the graph by pressing the **GRAPH** key.

STEM-AND-LEAF DIAGRAMS AND BOX PLOTS   **Lesson 6.3**   **201**

**11a.** Sample answer: Data are entered into **L1**.

**11b.** Sample plot menu screen:

**11c.** Sample window:

**11d.** Sample graph:

**11e.** lower extreme = 8,966;
upper extreme = 30,702;
lower quartile = 13,376;
upper quartile = 19,773;
median = 15,028

```
1-Var Stats
↑n=32
 minX=8966
 Q₁=13376
 Med=15028
 Q₃=19773
 maxX=30702
■
```

**12a.** The mean is about 16,931 miles and the standard deviation is about 5,519 miles. One standard deviation below the mean is 16,931 − 5,519 = 11,412 miles, and one standard deviation above the mean is 16,931 + 5,519 = 22,450 miles.

**12b.** Twenty-three of the thirty-two values, or about 72%, are within one standard deviation of the mean.

**12c.** 19,773 − 13,376 = 6,397 miles

**12d.** Sixteen of the thirty-two values, or 50%, are between the lower and upper quartiles. Since about one-fourth of a data set should usually be below the lower quartile, and one-fourth should be above the upper quartile, about one-half should be between the quartiles.

**e.** The five values used to form the box plot are computed by the **1-Var Stats** command on the ⎡STAT⎤ **CALC** menu. After entering the command, you must scroll down to see these values. Use a calculator to find the lower and upper extremes, the lower and upper quartiles, and the median of the data in **L1**.

**12.** Repeat the calculation from Exercise 11, Part (e) to see the mean and standard deviation of the travel data.

   **a.** Determine the interval from one standard deviation below the mean to one standard deviation above the mean. Round to the nearest whole number.

   **b.** What percent of the data values is contained in the interval found in Part (a) above?

   **c.** Find the interquartile range for the data.

   **d.** What percent of the data values is contained between the lower and upper quartiles? Is this what you would expect? Explain.

**Fill in the blank.**

1. The set of _____ _____ consists of the counting numbers, their opposites, and zero.

2. A _____ number can be expressed as a ratio $\frac{a}{b}$, where $a$ and $b$ are integers and $b \neq 0$.

**Choose the correct answer.**

3. Which equation illustrates the Identity Property of Multiplication?

   **A.** $6(0) = 0$  **B.** $6(1) = 6$  **C.** $6 + 0 = 6$  **D.** $6 + (-6) = 0$

4. Which expression is equivalent to $2n - 3(n - 5)$?

   **A.** $-n - 15$  **B.** $n + 15$  **C.** $15 - n$  **D.** $-n + 5$

**Add, subtract, multiply, or divide.**

5. $1\frac{3}{5} + 2\frac{17}{20}$  
6. $8\frac{1}{5} - 2\frac{3}{4}$  
7. $5 - 1\frac{3}{5}$  
8. $2\frac{1}{2} \times 1\frac{3}{4}$  
9. $4 \div 1\frac{3}{4}$  
10. $1\frac{3}{4} \div 4$

**Write each fraction as a percent to the nearest tenth of a percent.**

11. $\frac{3}{20}$  
12. $\frac{1}{8}$  
13. $\frac{3}{11}$

**Write each percent as a fraction.**

14. $18\%$  
15. $0.5\%$  
16. $120\%$

**Find the value of each expression.**

17. $-14 - (-3)$  
18. $0 - (-2) + 6$  
19. $-8 - 8 + 5$  
20. $-3(7)\left(-\frac{1}{3}\right)$  
21. $\frac{-2 - 8}{-4}$  
22. $-6(3) + 2(-3)$

**Solve.**

23. 15 is 50% of what number?

24. 6 is 100% of what number?

25. 130% of what number is 52?

26. Solve $3x - 7y = 42$ for $y$.

**5e** Evaluate

## Lesson Objective

- solve problems that require previously learned concepts and skills.

## Exercise Reference

Exercises 1–3: Appendix J

Exercise 4: Lesson 3.5

Exercises 5–10: Appendix A

Exercises 11–16: Appendix E

Exercises 17–22: Appendix I

Exercises 23–25: Appendix F

Exercise 26: Lesson 4.2

Exercise 27: Lesson 5.6

Exercise 28: Lesson 2.3

Exercises 29–30: Lesson 5.5

Exercise 31: Lesson 4.2

Exercise 32: Lesson 4.3

## Lesson 6.4 R.A.P. Answers

1. integers
2. rational
3. B
4. C
5. $4\frac{9}{20}$
6. $5\frac{9}{20}$
7. $3\frac{2}{5}$
8. $\frac{35}{8}$ or $4\frac{3}{8}$
9. $\frac{16}{7}$ or $2\frac{2}{7}$
10. $\frac{7}{16}$
11. $15\%$
12. $12.5\%$
13. $27.3\%$
14. $\frac{9}{50}$
15. $\frac{1}{200}$
16. $\frac{6}{5}$ or $1\frac{1}{5}$
17. $-11$
18. 8
19. $-11$
20. 7
21. $\frac{5}{2}$ or $2\frac{1}{2}$
22. $-24$
23. 30
24. 6
25. 40
26. $y = \frac{3x - 42}{7}$ or $y = \frac{3}{7}x - 6$

**203**

**27.** $y = 2x$

**28.** This is a direct variation. The ratio of distance traveled $d$ to time $t$ is always 0.05. An equation is $d = 0.05t$.

**29.**

**30.**

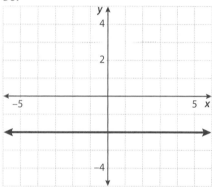

**31.** $C = 2\pi r \approx 26.4$ m

**32.** $A = \pi r^2 \approx 201.1$ in.$^2$

**27.** Write an equation of a line that passes through the points (3, 6) and (2, 4).

**28.** The table shows walking time $t$ in minutes and distance traveled $d$ in miles.

| Time Walked (min) | Distance Traveled (mi) |
| --- | --- |
| 10 | 0.5 |
| 20 | 1.0 |
| 30 | 1.5 |
| 40 | 2.0 |
| 50 | 2.5 |

State whether the relationship is a direct variation. If it is, explain how you know and write an equation relating the variables.

**29.** Graph $y = -4x - 1$.

**30.** Graph $y = -2$.

**31.** The radius of a circle is 4.2 meters. Find its circumference.

**32.** The diameter of a circle is 16 inches. Find its area.

Before data can be analyzed, they must be collected. The method used to collect data can affect the usefulness of the data. In this lesson, you will examine how the sampling method influences the result of a survey.

If you want to find out information about a population, you can conduct a survey. A **survey** consists of asking a group of people to answer one or more questions and recording their responses. If all members of a population you want to study are surveyed, the survey is called a **census**. A census of the entire population of the United States is very expensive. (The 2010 U.S. census cost over $10 billion.) Even so, the U.S. census usually misses about one-fourth of the population.

During non-census years, the U.S. government conducts the American Community Survey (ACS). The ACS is not a census, because it surveys only part of the population. The group that is surveyed is called a **sample**. If that sample is representative of the population, its results will be very close to the results of a complete census, but it requires much less time and expense.

### ESTIMATING COMMUTING TIME

The 2008 ACS survey found that the average commuting time from home to work for Americans is about 25 minutes. You can conduct your own survey to estimate the average commuting time to school for students in your class.

1. Record the time it takes for each member of your group to get to school from his or her home on a typical day. Then find the mean commuting time for members of your group. This value is called the **sample mean**.

2. You could use your answer to Question 1 to estimate the average commuting time for the population consisting of your entire class. But since your data came only from your group, your sample is a **convenience sample**. That is, it was the easiest sample to collect. Depending on how groups were formed, this sample may be biased. A **biased sample** is one that is not representative of an entire population. It favors one or more parts of the population.

   In a **random sample**, every individual in the population has the same chance of being included. Determine a method for choosing

## Lesson Objectives

- use a sample mean to estimate the mean of a population.
- identify types of sampling methods.
- indicate when a sampling method is biased.

## Vocabulary

- biased sample
- census
- convenience sample
- interval sample
- margin of error
- population mean
- random sample
- sample
- sample mean
- simple random sample
- stratified random sample
- survey

## Materials List

- names of students in the class written on individual pieces of paper
- container to hold the pieces of paper

## Description

*Preparation:*

Have students work in groups of 4 if possible. Since their first sample is within their own group, this will allow comparison with a random sample of size 4 in **Question 3**.

*During the Activity:*

You may wish to accumulate responses to **Question 5** on the board, so each group can copy the data.

Discuss with students how each group is or is not representative of the entire class population. Do the members of one group all get to school by bus? Are another group's members more of a mixture of walkers, drivers, and bus riders?

*Closing the Activity:*

Again in **Question 7**, the sample means for random samples of size 4 and 10 should be listed on the board. If the students have worked in self-selected groups, then the random samples should in general give better results (closer to the true class mean) than the convenience sample. Emphasize that the "mean of sample means" should also be closer to the true overall mean for larger sample sizes. (This is an elementary version of the Central Limit Theorem of statistics.)

### TEACHING TIP

For **Question 2**, you may want to suggest the use of a calculator to generate random numbers for selection, with students listed alphabetically and assigned a number. An alternative is to hand out a printed random number table or list. Each group should continue to generate random numbers until four unique numbers are found.

### Lesson 6.5 Activity Answers

1. Answers will vary.
2. Sample answer: Write everyone's name on a piece of paper. Mix the pieces of paper together in a container and draw 4 names.

3. Answers will vary.
4. Answers will vary.
5. Sample answer: 20 minutes
6. Sample answer: The estimate for the size 10 sample is closer to the true mean than the estimates for the smaller samples.
7. Answers will vary.
8. Results will vary somewhat, but the larger the sample, the closer the estimate should be to the true population mean.

### TEACHING TIP

Point out to students that an estimate based on a sample always involves sampling error. Sampling error is not a mistake, but is the error associated with using a sample to estimate characteristics of a population. Statisticians typically measure sampling error by calculating an estimate's margin of error. The margin of error gives a good idea of how close the estimate is to the corresponding value of the population. The margin of error is dependent on the size of the sample.

---

a random sample of 4 students (a sample of size 4) from the population of students in your class.

3. Determine a random sample of 4 students in your class, and ask those students to tell you their commuting times. Find the sample mean.

4. Enlarge your sample to 10 students by randomly choosing 6 more students from the class. Determine the mean commuting time for your sample of size 10.

5. You have three estimates for the mean commuting time of students in your class. One is based on a convenience sample, and two are based on random samples of different sizes.

   Now, as a class, list everyone's commuting time and find the true mean for the class. This is called the **population mean**.

6. Describe how your three estimates compare to the true mean commuting time for the class.

7. Finally, list the sample means for all of the random samples of size 4 from all the different groups. Find the overall mean of those sample means. Then do the same for all of the samples of size 10.

8. Compare the two values for the "mean of the sample means" from Question 7 with the true population mean. What can you conclude about the relationship between sample size and accuracy?

### ESTIMATION AND SAMPLE SIZE

Of course, in actual practice a sample is usually collected in order to estimate the value of some unknown quantity. As you saw in the Activity, larger samples will, in most cases, provide an estimate that is closer to the true value for the population under study. For example, the yearly American Community Survey sends questionnaires to about 3 million addresses. That is about $2\frac{1}{2}\%$ of the total number of households in the United States. When a sample mean is used to estimate the value of a population mean, the estimate is almost never exactly correct. Even when no mistakes are made in collecting the sample data, there is a **margin of error** that is a measure of the accuracy of the estimate. Using a larger sample size reduces the margin of error.

In your survey, you used a **simple random sample**. Not only were all students equally likely to be included, every *sample* of a given size had the same chance of being chosen. In a simple random sample, members of the sample are selected by chance from the entire population.

There are sometimes good reasons to use other sampling methods.

- In a **stratified random sample**, a population is separated into well-defined groups. Then each of those groups is randomly sampled. For example, splitting a population into geographic regions and sampling each region can ensure that each region is represented in a survey.

- An **interval sample** (also called a *systematic sample*) involves a "system" for selecting sample members. Instead of pure chance, the population to be sampled could be arranged in a list. Then, for example, every 10th member on the list could be chosen. Or every 5th person entering a concert could be surveyed.

## Practice for Lesson 6.5

**For Exercises 1–4, fill in the blank.**

1. To estimate a quantity that describes a population, you can collect data on a(n) _____.

2. A survey that is conducted on all members of a population being studied is called a(n) _____.

3. If every individual in a population has the same chance of being included in a sample, the sample is a(n) _____ sample.

4. A sample that is chosen based on ease of collection is called a(n) _____ sample.

5. The margin of error in a poll can be reduced by _____ the size of the sample.

6. Indicate whether each sampling method produces a *convenience sample*, a *simple random sample*, a *stratified random sample*, or an *interval sample*.
   a. To find out what the preferred ice cream flavor is, wait outside an ice cream parlor and ask every 4th person leaving the store to name his or her favorite flavor until you get 25 responses.
   b. To study the amount of time students spend doing homework each day, use a random number generator to select 25 students from the student enrollment database to survey.
   c. To study the amount of time students spend doing homework each day, use a random number generator to select 25 freshmen, 25 sophomores, 25 juniors, and 25 seniors to survey.
   d. To determine people's favorite websites, go to an Internet cafe. Ask the first 20 people who enter to name their favorite website.
   e. To determine the most popular type of cake, ask all the members of your family at a birthday party.

7. Suppose the method of Exercise 6, Part (a) were used to find out people's favorite type of dessert. Explain why the sample might not be a representative sample.

## Practice for Lesson 6.5 Answers

1. sample
2. census
3. random
4. convenience
5. increasing
6a. interval sample
6b. simple random sample
6c. stratified random sample
6d. convenience sample
6e. convenience sample
7. Sample answer: People who go to an ice cream parlor are more likely to prefer ice cream to other kinds of desserts, so the sample could be biased.

8. C; Only for sample C does every student in the school (the population being studied) have the same chance of being selected. In particular, sample B is biased because students on the basketball team are more likely to pick basketball as their favorite professional sport.

8. A student wants to determine the favorite professional sport of students in her high school. Which of the following samples is most likely to give her a representative sample? Explain your answer.
   A. a random sample of the students in the art honor society
   B. a random sample of students on the basketball team
   C. a random sample of students on the official school enrollment roster
   D. a random sample of students in the library during lunch

9. The school librarian wants to determine how many students use the library on a regular basis. What type of sampling method (*convenience sample*, *simple random sample*, *stratified random sample*, or *interval sample*) would he use if he chose to do each of the following:
   a. Select every 3rd student who enters the library on Tuesday.
   b. Use a random number generator to randomly select 50 students from the school's attendance roster.
   c. Randomly select 20 students in the cafeteria during each of the three lunch periods on Monday.

10. Each of the following surveys has some sort of bias. Explain why the type of sampling that was chosen for the survey might lead to biased results.
    a. A doctor wants to survey her patients to determine what kind of food they like so that she may better understand their dietary habits. She decides to ask the next 50 patients that she sees about what kind of foods they like to eat.
    b. A teacher decided to survey his students about the amount of crime in their neighborhoods. He numbered his students consecutively and then used a random number generator to randomly select 15 students to speak with a uniformed police officer about the crimes that they witness in their neighborhoods.
    c. Another teacher decided to ask each of her students how they felt about the homework she was assigning. She decided to mail a survey home to each of her students' parents. Many of the surveys came back in the mail as "undeliverable."

11. A *voluntary response sample* is a sample that depends on people returning a printed survey, responding to an Internet preference poll, or phoning or texting a message. For example, during a televised National Football League game, viewers are asked to send a text message about whether they approve of a new overtime rule. Explain why such a sample might be biased.

12. Explain why the convenience sample from Question 1 of the Activity might be biased.

9a. convenience sample or interval sample
9b. simple random sample
9c. stratified random sample
10a. Sample answer: Patients may claim to have a healthier diet than they really have. They may be unwilling to tell their doctor about junk foods that they eat. The kinds of foods they like may not be the kinds that they usually eat. Also, the next 50 patients may not be representative of all her patients.
10b. Sample answer: Students may be unwilling to speak candidly about crime to a police officer.
10c. Sample answer: All students may not be equally likely to be included in the sample, depending on the reasons for the undeliverable surveys.
11. Sample answer: People with a strong interest in a question are more likely to respond, so the sample may not be representative of all football fans. Also, responding depends on having a cellphone.
12. Sample answer: If a group includes friends who live within walking distance of school, the estimated commute time could be low compared to the class average.

## What a State You're In!

In Lesson 6.1 you looked at some of the kinds of information contained in the U.S. Census. Data on a large variety of social, economic, housing, and other characteristics are available.

Investigate some characteristics of your own state or community. You can find information by doing an Internet search using this phrase "U.S. Census Bureau Fact Sheet." Just enter the appropriate information where it says "Get a Fact Sheet for your community."

Prepare a report that summarizes some types of data about your state or community.

- Include at least two different data sets.
- Include three of the types of graphical displays you studied in this chapter. They could be based on different data sets, or you may find that more than one type of display could be used for the same data set.
- Include numerical information, such as measures of center and range.
- After analyzing the data, write a summary paragraph explaining what you learned about your state or community.

# MODELING PROJECT

5e Elaborate

## Materials List

## Description

In this project students are asked to investigate the United States Census to locate and report on information related to their state or community. They should be encouraged to explore the available information and find topics that interest them. This project should be done individually

## Sample Answers

Students' reports will vary, depending on the data they choose to investigate. For instance, they could choose to focus on local aspects of the kinds of characteristics they examined in **Lesson 6.1**. Or they may find topics of particular relevance to their own lives. Some possibilities include occupational data, ethnicity, ancestry, language spoken at home, and age breakdown of the population being studied. For example, a Hispanic student might want to examine the lineage of a state's Hispanic population (Mexican, Puerto Rican, Cuban, etc.).

Categorical data could be displayed in bar graphs, circle graphs, or pictographs. Historical data could be shown in a line graph if it is numerical. Household income levels could be shown in a bar graph, and measures of center could be found. Mean values for most numerical categories are available, and medians and modes can be determined from the given distributions.

# Chapter 6  Review

## You Should Be Able to:

### Lesson 6.1

- read and interpret bar graphs, pictographs, circle graphs, and line graphs.

### Lesson 6.2

- choose appropriate measures of center for a data set.

### Lesson 6.3

- use, construct, and interpret stem-and-leaf diagrams to organize and display data.
- use extremes, quartiles, and standard deviation to describe a set of data.

- use, construct, and interpret box plots to display and compare data.

### Lesson 6.4

- solve problems that require previously learned concepts and skills.

### Lesson 6.5

- use a sample mean to estimate the mean of a population.
- identify types of sampling methods.
- indicate when a sampling method is biased.

## Key Vocabulary

line graph (p. 177)

bar graph (p. 178)

circle graph (p. 179)

pictograph (p. 179)

mean (p. 187)

median (p. 187)

mode (p. 187)

dot plot (p. 188)

outlier (p. 188)

stem-and-leaf diagram (p. 192)

lower extreme (p. 193)

upper extreme (p. 193)

range (p. 194)

lower quartile (p. 194)

upper quartile (p. 194)

interquartile range (p. 195)

standard deviation (p. 195)

box plot (p. 197)

survey (p. 205)

census (p. 205)

sample (p. 205)

sample mean (p. 205)

convenience sample (p. 205)

biased sample (p. 205)

random sample (p. 205)

population mean (p. 206)

margin of error (p. 206)

simple random sample (p. 206)

stratified random sample (p. 206)

interval sample (p. 207)

## Chapter 6  Test Review

**For Exercises 1–5, fill in the blank.**

1. A(n) _____ graph can *only* be used to display parts of a whole.

2. A measure of center that can be used to describe non-numerical data is the _____.

3. A(n) _____ is constructed using five values that summarize a data set.

4. In a(n) _____ sample, all members of a population are equally likely to be included.

5. The bar graph below shows the age distribution of people in the United States in 2008, out of a total population of 304 million.

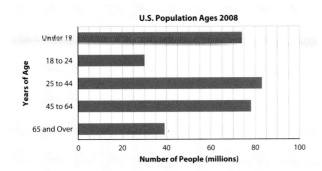

**U.S. Population Ages 2008**

a. Which of the categories contains the most people?
b. Approximately how many people were 18 years or older in 2008?
c. Approximately what percent of the population was under 18 years in 2008?
d. Could a circle graph be used to display these data? Explain.

## Chapter 6 Test Review Answers

1. circle
2. mode
3. box plot
4. random
5a. ages 25–44
5b. about 230 million
5c. about 24%
5d. Yes, the categories are parts of a whole.

**6a.** Drive (car, truck, van) Alone

**6b.** U.S.: Carpool; San Francisco: Public Transit

**6c.** 76% + 11% = 87%

**6d.** equally likely

**6e.** more likely

**6f.** Sample answer: A resident of San Francisco is 3 times as likely to walk to work.

**7.** mean: 16.2; median: 17; mode: 17 and 18

**8.** Sample answer: 3, 6, 7, 10, 14

**9.** The mean will become smaller, but the median and mode will stay the same.

---

**6.** The circle graphs below show commuting patterns for workers age 16 years and over.

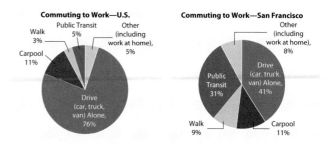

**a.** What is the most common way that people get to work in the United States as a whole, and also in San Francisco?

**b.** What is the second most common way that people get to work in the United States as a whole, and also in San Francisco?

**c.** What percent of the U.S. population drives or rides in a car, truck, or van to get to work?

**d.** Is a resident of San Francisco more likely, less likely, or equally likely to carpool to work, compared to people in the United States as a whole?

**e.** Is a resident of San Francisco more likely, less likely, or equally likely to take public transit to work, compared to people in the United States as a whole?

**f.** How does the likelihood of a person walking to work compare in San Francisco and the United States as a whole?

**7.** Find the mean, median, and mode for the following data set. (Round the mean to the nearest tenth.)

18, 15, 17, 18, 12, 17

**8.** Create a data set of five values that will give a median of 7 and a mean of 8.

**9.** The youngest teacher in a school leaves and is replaced by an even younger teacher. What do you expect will happen to the mean, median, and mode of teacher ages?

**10.** The diameters (in inches) of 20 Ponderosa pine trees in Yosemite National Park are 36, 28, 28, 41, 19, 32, 22, 38, 25, 17, 31, 20, 25, 19, 39, 33, 17, 37, 23, and 39.

Make a stem-and-leaf diagram of the data. (Hint: Use the ones digits for the leaves.)

**11.** Find each of the following for the data in Exercise 10.
  **a.** the lower extreme
  **b.** the upper extreme
  **c.** the median
  **d.** the lower quartile
  **e.** the upper quartile

**12.** Use the summary numbers from Exercise 11 to make a box plot of the diameter data.

**13.** The school music club wants to survey a sample of students to find out which musical performers students in the school prefer. What type of sample (*convenience sample, simple random sample, stratified random sample,* or *interval sample*) would be collected in each of the following situations?
  **a.** Five students are randomly selected from each homeroom in the school.
  **b.** The first 30 students who enter the band room after school are surveyed.
  **c.** From a numbered alphabetical list of all students in the school, every 15ᵗʰ student is selected.
  **d.** From a numbered alphabetical list of all students in the school, a random number generator is used to select 50 students.

**14.** Suppose you want to find out where students in your school shop for their clothes. Why might it *not* be a representative sample if you surveyed only members of the girls' or boys' basketball teams?

## CHAPTER REVIEW

**10.** **Tree Diameters (inches)**

```
1 | 7  7  9  9
2 | 0  2  3  5  5  8  8
3 | 1  2  3  6  7  8  9  9
4 | 1
```
Key: 1|7 represents 17 inches.

**11a.** 17
**11b.** 41
**11c.** 28
**11d.** 21
**11e.** 36.5

**12.**

**Tree Diameters (inches)**

**13a.** stratified random sample
**13b.** convenience sample
**13c.** interval sample
**13d.** simple random sample
**14.** Sample answer: Basketball players might tend to be taller than the general student population, which could influence where they shop.

# CHAPTER 6 EXTENSION

**5e** Elaborate

## Lesson Objective

- construct a grouped frequency histogram from data.

## Vocabulary

- class
- class width
- grouped frequency table
- histogram

## Materials List

## Description

In this lesson, students learn to group large data sets into classes and construct grouped frequency tables and histograms.

CHAPTER

# 6 Chapter Extension
## Frequency Tables and Histograms

Very large data sets may not be easily pictured with simple graphs like those in Lesson 6.1. In such cases, grouping of the data is often used. In this lesson, you will use grouped frequencies to construct a histogram, which is similar to a bar graph.

The table below shows data on major worldwide earthquakes of the 20th century. For each year, of the one hundred years from 1900 to 1999, the total number of major earthquakes having a Richter magnitude of 7.0 or greater was recorded. The total for each year is listed below.

| | | | | | | | | | |
|---|---|---|---|---|---|---|---|---|---|
| 13 | 14 | 8 | 10 | 17 | 26 | 32 | 27 | 18 | 32 |
| 36 | 34 | 32 | 33 | 32 | 18 | 26 | 21 | 21 | 14 |
| 8 | 11 | 14 | 23 | 18 | 17 | 19 | 20 | 22 | 19 |
| 13 | 26 | 13 | 14 | 22 | 24 | 21 | 22 | 26 | 21 |
| 23 | 24 | 27 | 41 | 31 | 27 | 35 | 26 | 28 | 36 |
| 39 | 21 | 17 | 22 | 17 | 19 | 15 | 34 | 10 | 15 |
| 22 | 18 | 15 | 20 | 15 | 22 | 19 | 16 | 30 | 27 |
| 29 | 23 | 20 | 16 | 21 | 21 | 25 | 16 | 18 | 15 |
| 18 | 14 | 10 | 15 | 8 | 15 | 6 | 11 | 8 | 7 |
| 13 | 10 | 23 | 16 | 15 | 25 | 22 | 20 | 16 | 11 |

SOURCE: U.S. GEOLOGICAL SURVEY

The mean or median would summarize the data with a single number, and a box plot would provide more detail. But in order to present the data so that patterns in the data distribution can be more easily seen, we can first group the data into **classes**. Each class should contain a range, or width, of earthquake counts. For example, classes with a width of 5 would be from 0 to 4 major earthquakes per year, from 5 to 9 major earthquakes per year, etc. A **grouped frequency table** for these data, using this range of counts, would look like the table on the next page.

**214** Chapter 6 DESCRIBING DATA

| Number of Major Earthquakes per Year | Frequency |
|---|---|
| 0–4 | 0 |
| 5–9 | 6 |
| 10–14 | 16 |
| 15–19 | 27 |
| 20–24 | 24 |
| 25–29 | 13 |
| 30–34 | 9 |
| 35–39 | 4 |
| 40–44 | 1 |

The table reveals some information that cannot be easily seen in the data list. For example, many years have around 20 or so major earthquakes. But we also see that it is relatively rare for either fewer than 10 or more than 34 major quakes to occur in a single year.

## A GROUPED FREQUENCY HISTOGRAM

The figure below is a **histogram** of the grouped frequency data. It shows each class as a bar. In this histogram, the bars are vertical, but some histograms have horizontal bars. Since the class width is 5, the width of the bar is equal to 5. The length or height of the bar is measured on a scale that shows the frequency of the number of values in each class.

It would be difficult to look at the original data list and make any real sense of it. The histogram provides a visual summary of the entire data set. One disadvantage of this approach is that by sorting the data into classes, there is a loss of the individual values. This disadvantage, however, is usually far outweighed by the added clarity and the ease of finding patterns in the data.

Much of the information contained in the original data list can be found by reading the histogram. For example:

- The total number of years of data involved can be determined by adding the heights of all the bars.

- In most years there have been from 10 to 29 major earthquakes.

- The number of years in which there have been fewer than 15 major earthquakes can be found by adding the heights of the first two bars, for a total of 22 years.

However, it is not possible, for example, to determine the exact number of years in which there were more than 32 earthquakes. This is because a single bar includes 30, 31, 32, 33, and 34 earthquakes per year, and you cannot distinguish the frequencies of individual values. It *is* possible to determine that there were 14 years with *at least* 30 major earthquakes. Just total the heights of the last three bars ($9 + 4 + 1 = 14$ years).

It is also not possible to determine the fewest and the greatest number of major earthquakes that occurred in any single year just by reading the graph. The grouping into classes has eliminated the individual data values.

## GUIDELINES FOR HISTOGRAM CONSTRUCTION

The purpose of a histogram usually is to convey a maximum amount of information about the distribution of a set of measurements with a minimum of numerical detail. For this to occur, these guidelines should be followed:

- Most histograms should contain from 5 to 20 classes, depending on the size of the data set. If there are too few classes, any pattern in the data will be lost. But using too many classes leads to excess fluctuation in bar height. This would defeat the purpose of the graph.

- A rule of thumb that is often used sets the number of classes at approximately the value of the square root of the number of values in the data set, excluding outliers. So, for example, if there are 36 data values in a set, with no outliers, 6 classes would be a good choice.

- The **class width** (that is, the range of values contained in the group) should be the same for all classes. Otherwise, the pictorial information is distorted.

- Labeling the classes on the graph should make it clear where each bar of the histogram starts and stops. In the example on major earthquakes, it is clear that the 30–34 class does not overlap the 35–39 class. However, some people might have labeled this histogram differently. For example, the labeling in the graph below simplifies the data scale and makes it less cluttered. But it is not clear which class contains a value of exactly 40, since it is at the boundary of two different classes. It appears that 40 is the upper limit of one class and the lower limit of another.

**Major Earthquakes 1900–1999**

- When histograms are labeled this way, it is a good idea to include a note of explanation, such as "Lower limits are included in each class." The labeling of histograms created with computer spreadsheets or calculators is often done automatically. It may not be clear exactly how the labeling is related to the group data. Caution should be exercised when interpreting such graphs.

The table on the next page shows the number of pizza restaurants in all 50 states.

You may want to have students use a graphing calculator to create a histogram of the data in the table on page 218. A histogram can be created on a calculator by first entering data from the grouped frequency table into calculator lists. Only the lower class limits are entered into list **L1**, and the corresponding frequencies are entered into list **L2**.

Then a **STAT PLOT** is produced based on those lists.

Using the trace feature on the histogram allows direct examination of both the frequency and the class width. Notice that the calculator clearly distinguishes the exact data interval contained in the selected bar.

## Chapter 6 Extension Answers

1. Sample answer: There are 48 values in the data set without the outliers. The square root of 48 is about 7. So, there should be about 7 classes in the range from 108 to 3,047. One possibility is to use a class width of 400. This results in 8 classes, not including the outliers, but it uses a nice round number for class width.

| Number of Pizza Restaurants | Frequency |
|---|---|
| 1–400 | 13 |
| 401–800 | 10 |
| 801–1,200 | 12 |
| 1,201–1,600 | 4 |
| 1,601–2,000 | 5 |
| 2,001–2,400 | 1 |
| 2,401–2,800 | 2 |
| 2,801–3,200 | 1 |
| 3,201–3,600 | 0 |
| 3,601–4,000 | 0 |
| 4,001–4,400 | 0 |
| 4,401–4,800 | 0 |
| 4,801–5,200 | 1 |
| 5,201–5,600 | 0 |
| 5,601–6,000 | 0 |
| 6,001–6,400 | 0 |
| 6,401–6,800 | 1 |

| State | Number of Pizza Restaurants | State | Number of Pizza Restaurants |
|---|---|---|---|
| Alabama | 1,071 | Montana | 236 |
| Alaska | 149 | Nebraska | 471 |
| Arizona | 919 | Nevada | 406 |
| Arkansas | 776 | New Hampshire | 119 |
| California | 6,524 | New Jersey | 1,182 |
| Colorado | 929 | New Mexico | 454 |
| Connecticut | 732 | New York | 2,574 |
| Delaware | 133 | North Carolina | 1,673 |
| Florida | 2,505 | North Dakota | 165 |
| Georgia | 1,515 | Ohio | 2,387 |
| Hawaii | 217 | Oklahoma | 1,034 |
| Idaho | 298 | Oregon | 806 |
| Illinois | 3,047 | Pennsylvania | 1,682 |
| Indiana | 1,394 | Rhode Island | 136 |
| Iowa | 838 | South Carolina | 1,011 |
| Kansas | 708 | South Dakota | 158 |
| Kentucky | 879 | Tennessee | 1,652 |
| Louisiana | 952 | Texas | 5,200 |
| Maine | 212 | Utah | 469 |
| Maryland | 721 | Vermont | 128 |
| Massachusetts | 620 | Virginia | 1,701 |
| Michigan | 1,838 | Washington | 1,357 |
| Minnesota | 933 | West Virginia | 314 |
| Mississippi | 685 | Wisconsin | 1,286 |
| Missouri | 1,195 | Wyoming | 108 |

SOURCE: U.S. DEPARTMENT OF COMMERCE, U.S. CENSUS BUREAU

1. Organize the data in a grouped frequency table. Use an appropriate number of classes. Notice that California and Texas are outliers. To allow more detail for the remaining 48 states, determine class width by considering the range of the remaining 48 states, which is from 108 to 3,047. (However, be sure to include California and Texas in the histogram.)

2. Make a histogram of the data in your grouped frequency table.

2. Sample answer:

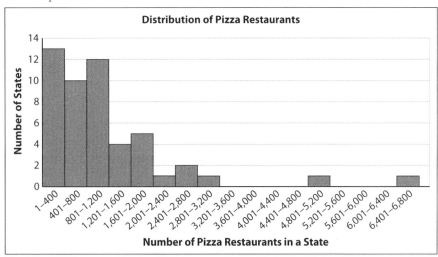

# Chapter 7
## Linear Models from Data

## Mathematical Overview

In this chapter, students measure the lengths of their classmates' forearms, as well as their heights. They investigate patterns in the data by making scatter plots of height versus the length of the bone in the forearm. Students learn to examine ways to compare different models for their data and to judge their effectiveness. When there is a linear trend to the data, they model that trend with a line that describes the data well. Students use graphing calculators to find residuals and to find the least-squares line using linear regression. They also learn to judge the appropriateness of a linear model, to compare models, and to draw reasonable conclusions. When necessary, they revise their models in order to make better predictions.

## Lesson Summaries

### Lesson 7.1    Activity: Bones and Height

In this Activity, students work in groups to collect data about the length of their forearms and their heights. Then they use those data to create scatter plots and explore possible relationships between bone length and height. They examine their scatter plots for patterns such as positive or negative relationships, strong or weak linear relationships, and nonlinear relationships. They also look for possible outliers. The same groups formed for this lesson, as well as the scatter plots they made, will be used again throughout this chapter.

### Lessons 7.2    Investigation: Fitting Lines to Data and 7.3    Investigation: Residuals and Judging the Quality of Fit

In these Investigations, students revisit their scatter plots from Lesson 7.1. Through the Investigation in Lesson 7.2, each group of students fits a line to their scatter plot and uses it to create a linear model (equation) for the data. They use their equation to make a prediction about the height of a person given his/her forearm length. Students end this lesson by making a scatter plot, finding a line that appears to model the data well, and then writing an equation for that line. In Lesson 7.3, the criteria for determining a line that models the data well are changed and students examine methods for comparing the quality of fit for different lines. Students use graphing calculators to find residuals. They also make and use a residual plot to decide whether a model is a good one.

### Lesson 7.4    Investigation: Predicting from Linear Models

In this Investigation, students once again revisit their scatter plots from Lesson 7.1 and use their linear models to make predictions about values that were not part of their data. Students learn about interpolation and extrapolation.

### Lesson 7.5    R.A.P.

In this lesson, students **R**eview **A**nd **P**ractice solving problems that require the use of skills and concepts taught in previous math levels. The skills reviewed in this lesson are skills that are needed as a basis for solving problems throughout this course.

### Lesson 7.6    Activity: Linear Regression

In this Activity, students are given a set of data regarding the number of registered powerboats and the number of manatees killed in Florida. Students use graphing calculators to make scatter plots of the data. They then use a process called *linear regression* to find the best-fitting linear model based on the least-squares criterion. The last exercise in this lesson asks students to use linear regression to find a least-squares model for their class height vs forearm length data from Lesson 7.1 and compare it to the model they found in Lesson 7.2.

### Lesson 7.7    Comparing Models

In this lesson, students examine a variety of different linear models to investigate a data set and judge the effectiveness of the models to decide which model is most useful. Students learn the difference between data-driven models and theory-driven models.

### Chapter 7    Extension: Correlation

In this Extension, students expand upon what they learned about residuals in Lesson 7.3 to include another way to measure the strength of a model, the correlation of a data set. They examine both positively and negatively correlated data, and they use the quadrant count ratio (QCR) as a method to measure and describe the correlation of the two variables in their data. Students also take a look at the correlation coefficient as another means for getting a specific description of the linear correlation of a data set.

219a

## Lesson Guide

| Lesson/Objectives | Materials | |
|---|---|---|
| **Chapter 7 Opener: What Happened to Amelia Earhart?**<br>• recognize that mathematical models can be used to help determine the identity of skeletal remains. | | *Optional:*<br>• historical articles or documentaries about Amelia Earhart<br>• newspaper articles related to the discovery of ancient skeletal remains |
| **7.1 Activity: Bones and Height**<br>• use scatter plots to identify patterns in data. | *Per group:*<br>• measuring tape with a centimeter scale<br>• ruler<br>• grid paper | *Optional:*<br>• TRM table shells for Questions 3 and 4<br>• masking tape<br>• computer spreadsheet program such as Microsoft® Excel® |
| **7.2 Investigation: Fitting Lines to Data**<br>• draw a line that represents a linear trend on a scatter plot and find a linear model for the data. | *Per group:*<br>• scatter plot from the Activity in Lesson 7.1<br>• several pieces of uncooked spaghetti<br>• graphing calculator<br>• ruler | *Optional:*<br>• computer spreadsheet program (Excel)<br>• grid paper |
| **7.3 Investigation: Residuals and Judging the Quality of Fit**<br>• find the residuals for a linear model.<br>• use residuals to compare models. | *Per group:*<br>• data from the Activity in Lesson 7.1<br>• graph from the Investigation in Lesson 7.2<br>• graphing calculator | *Optional:*<br>• computer spreadsheet program such as Excel<br>• grid paper |
| **7.4 Investigation: Predicting from Linear Models**<br>• use a linear model to make predictions.<br>• decide when the use of a model is appropriate. | *Per group:*<br>• data and model from the Activity in Lesson 7.1 | *Optional:*<br>• grid paper |
| **7.5 R.A.P.**<br>• solve problems that require previously learned concepts and skills. | | |
| **7.6 Activity: Linear Regression**<br>• use linear regression to fit a least-squares model to data. | *Per student:*<br>• graphing calculator | *Optional:*<br>• computer spreadsheet program such as Excel<br>• video clip about manatees, available on YouTube. |
| **7.7 Comparing Models**<br>• evaluate the appropriateness of different linear models for a set of data.<br>• use a subset of a data set to create a model and make predictions. | *Per student:*<br>• graphing calculator | *Optional:*<br>• grid paper |
| **Chapter 7 Extension: Correlation**<br>• use quantitative measures of correlation to evaluate a model. | *Per student:*<br>• graphing calculator | *Optional:*<br>• computer spreadsheet program such as Excel<br>• grid paper |

## Pacing Guide

| | Day 1 | Day 2 | Day 3 | Day 4 | Day 5 | Day 6 | Day 7 | Day 8 | Day 9 | Day 10 | Day 11 |
|---|---|---|---|---|---|---|---|---|---|---|---|
| **Basic** | p. 220, 7.1 | 7.1, 7.2 | 7.2 | 7.3 | 7.4 | 7.5 | 7.6 | 7.7 | project | review | |
| **Standard** | p. 220, 7.1 | 7.1, 7.2 | 7.2 | 7.3 | 7.4 | 7.5 | 7.6 | 7.7 | project | review | extension |
| **Block** | p. 220, 7.1 | 7.2, | 7.3, 7.4 | 7.4, 7.5 | 7.6, 7.7 | 7.7, project | project, review | review, extension | | | |

**Supplement Support**

See the Book Companion Website at www.highschool.bfwpub.com/ModelingwithMathematics and the Teacher's Resource Materials (TRM) for additional resources.

# CHAPTER

# 7

# Linear Models from Data

## CONTENTS

# CHAPTER 7 OPENER

**5e** Engage

## Lesson Objective

- recognize that mathematical models can be used to help determine the identity of skeletal remains.

## Vocabulary

## Description

This reading is intended to make connections between the chapter's focus on modeling and situations students may be familiar with, either from watching television crime shows, learning about Amelia Earhart in a history class, or reading historical articles about Amelia Earhart.

### TEACHING TIP

Ask students about scientific and mathematical methods they may have seen used during episodes of television shows. If any students have seen a movie or documentary about Amelia Earhart, ask them to share any additional information they have beyond what is in the reading.

### CONNECTION

This may be an opportunity to collaborate with a teacher of American history and show students a connection between mathematics and a historical subject.

### TEACHING TIP

Use a model or your own arms and legs to point out where to find the humerus, tibia, and radius bones. Have students agree that the radius is the shortest of the three bones.

### TEACHING TIP

You may want to look for and share with students newspaper articles related to the discovery of ancient skeletal remains, for example during excavations, or the identification of remains after natural disasters such as tornadoes or earthquakes. An Internet search for "bones discovered" may provide other ideas.

## What Happened to Amelia Earhart?

Amelia Earhart is one of the most famous pilots of all time. She was the first woman to fly solo across the Atlantic Ocean and later the Pacific Ocean. On June 1, 1937 she set off on a flight around the world along with her navigator. On July 2, their plane vanished between New Guinea and Howland Island. The U.S. Navy searched but did not find a trace of them. To this day their fate is unknown.

Sixty years later, a group trying to solve this mystery heard about bones that were found on a Pacific Island in 1940. A report filed at that time included some measurements of the bones.

Scientists known as *forensic anthropologists* can use mathematical models to predict such things as height, gender, and ethnic background from bone measurements. These models are sometimes used to help solve crimes, in real life as well as those depicted on popular television shows such as *CSI* and *Bones*. They are also frequently used to help identify the remains of military service people who may have been previously listed as missing in action (MIA).

| Bone | Length (cm) |
|---|---|
| Humerus (upper arm) | 32.4 |
| Tibia (lower leg) | 37.2 |
| Radius (forearm) | 24.5 |

SOURCE: BURNS, KAREN R, PH.D. ET AL. "AMELIA EARHART'S BONES AND SHOES?", 1998 ANNUAL CONVENTION OF THE AMERICAN ANTHROPOLOIGICAL ASSOCIATION, PHILADELPHIA

In this chapter you will be asked to think like a forensic anthropologist. You will collect data, build mathematical models, and use your models to predict a person's height.

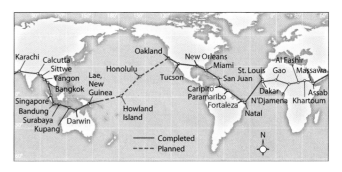

In Chapter 2 and again in Chapter 5, you examined data that showed linear patterns. But data involving two variables are sometimes too spread out for the patterns to be obvious. In this lesson, you will gather data to explore a possible relationship between bone length and height.

Do you think taller people have longer bones? It seems reasonable that a person's height is related to the lengths of his or her bones. In order to develop forensic models that can be used to predict height, scientists examine large quantities of data on bone measurements for people whose heights are known. You can collect similar data for the students in your class.

Height    Forearm

1. The lengths of long bones are more likely to be good predictors of height than short bones. One of the bones in your forearm is relatively easy to measure. Decide on a method for measuring your height in centimeters and the length of the *ulna*, the forearm bone that runs from your elbow to your wrist. The accuracy of your model will depend on the quality of the data collected.

2. Have two different students use your method to measure both the forearm length and height of the same student. Measure forearm length to the nearest half-centimeter (0.5 cm) and measure height to the nearest centimeter.

   Are the measurements from both students approximately the same in each case? If not, modify your method and test again. When there is only a small amount of variation in the results, discuss your method with other groups. Then select one method that the entire class will use to collect data.

3. Measure both the length of the forearm bone and the height of each member of your group. Record your results in a table.

| Name | Forearm Length (cm) | Height (cm) |
|---|---|---|
| | | |
| | | |
| | | |

4. Share your data with the rest of the class. Extend your table to include forearm length and height measurements for each member of your class.

---

## TEACHING TIP

For **Question 1**, to ensure accuracy in measuring heights, you may want to have masking tape available so students can temporarily mark spots on the wall.

## TEACHING TIP

For **Question 2**, the variation in forearm length and height measurements should be no more than about 1 centimeter.

## TEACHING TIP

Beginning with **Question 4**, an alternative for data analysis is to have students use a computer spreadsheet program. This makes it especially easy to save their work for further analysis.

## Lesson 7.1 Activity Answers

1. Sample answer:
   For forearm length: Place your elbow on a flat surface with forearm sticking straight up. Have someone measure the length from the surface to the depression between the two bones in the wrist.

   For height: Stand with no shoes on with your back against a wall. Have someone place a ruler horizontally on your head and measure how high it is from the floor.

2. The method selected will vary with different classes.

3. See table in answer for Question 4 on page 222.

---

## Lesson Objective

- use scatter plots to identify patterns in data.

## Vocabulary

- linear form
- strong linear relationship
- weak linear relationship

## Materials List

- measuring tape with a centimeter scale
- ruler
- grid paper

## Description

*Preparation:*

Have students work in groups of 3 or 4. If necessary, explain to students that measuring to the nearest half-centimeter means distinguishing between, for example, 24.0 cm and 24.5⁶ cm.

*During the Activity:*

After students have completed **Questions 1 and 2**, lead a discussion of methods for measuring the forearm bone. The class should agree on a single method, so that data will be comparable for all groups.

*Closing the Activity:*

Have students share their judgments regarding patterns in their scatter plots. They will most likely exhibit a weak positive linear relationship, but there should be a general consensus about the trends they observe. This is an opportunity to discuss with students how a scientist might approach this situation: make a conjecture or hypothesis that the relationship is positive, then collect and analyze data to confirm or reject the hypothesis.

Be sure to tell students to save their class data and scatter plots, as they will further analyze the data in Lessons 7.2 and 7.3.

# LESSON 7.1

**TEACHING TIP**

For **Question 5**, point out that there could be a situation involving forearm length and height for which the roles of independent and dependent variables are reversed. But for the forensic science context in this Activity, forearm length will be used to estimate height, so forearm length is the independent variable.

**TEACHING TIP**

**Question 6** Make sure that students' graphs use the entire sheet of grid paper to allow for accurate plotting.

4. Sample data:

| Forearm Length (cm) | Height (cm) |
|---|---|
| 24.0 | 157 |
| 24.5 | 166 |
| 27.0 | 164 |
| 24.0 | 164 |
| 23.0 | 161 |
| 27.5 | 164 |
| 27.0 | 167 |
| 26.0 | 162 |
| 26.0 | 175 |
| 28.5 | 166 |
| 26.5 | 172 |
| 25.5 | 176 |
| 26.5 | 173 |
| 27.0 | 177 |
| 27.0 | 174 |
| 31.0 | 192 |
| 28.0 | 172 |
| 29.0 | 180 |
| 27.0 | 174 |
| 28.0 | 175 |
| 32.0 | 185 |
| 30.0 | 185 |
| 30.0 | 178 |

5. On a sheet of grid paper, draw two axes. Identify the independent and dependent variables. Then label each axis with one of the variables and establish a scale that includes all of the values in your data set.

6. Make a scatter plot of your forearm/height data. Plot each point as accurately as possible.

7. Describe any patterns or trends that you see in your scatter plot.

When you examine a scatter plot, take note of a few properties that will help you analyze the data.

• Do the points appear to be scattered on either side of a straight line? If so, the scatter plot has a **linear form**, and it would make sense to describe it with a linear equation (a member of the $y = mx + b$ family).

• Does the pattern made by the points drift upward as you look from left to right? If so, the two variables are positively related (as one variable increases, the other tends to increase). If the pattern drifts downward, then the two variables are negatively related (as one variable increases, the other tends to decrease).

• Do the points fall very close to a line? If so, the variables have a **strong linear relationship**. If the data are more scattered away from a line, the variables have a **weak linear relationship**.

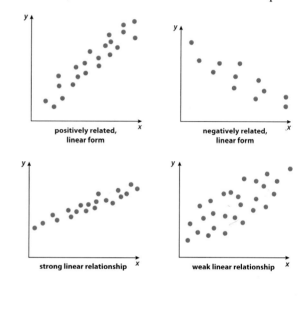

5. Sample answer: The independent variable is forearm length and the dependent variable is height.

6. Sample scatter plot:

**Class Forearm/Height Data**

7. Sample answer: The points are widely scattered, but they are generally higher on the right.

The variables in the scatter plot to the right are positively related but the form of the scatter plot is not linear.

8. Does your scatter plot have a linear form? Explain.

9. Are forearm length and height positively or negatively related? Explain.

10. If your scatter plot has a linear form, do the variables have a strong or weak linear relationship?

11. Does your scatter plot reveal any outliers in the data? Explain.

Save your data table and scatter plot for use in later lessons in this chapter.

**positively related, nonlinear form**

## Practice for Lesson 7.1

For Exercises 1–4, examine the scatter plot and state whether it appears to contain a pattern. If it does, indicate whether it shows

   **a.** a positive relationship, a negative relationship, or neither.

   **b.** a strong linear relationship, a weak linear relationship, or a nonlinear relationship.

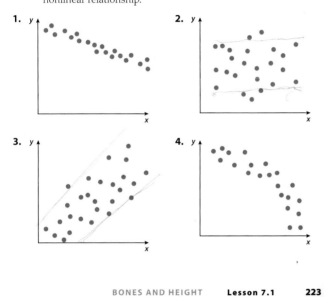

1.

2.

3.

4.

BONES AND HEIGHT    **Lesson 7.1**    **223**

8. Sample answer: Yes, a straight line could be drawn that would describe the overall pattern.

9. They are positively related, because as forearm length increases so does height.

10. Sample answer: The variables appear to have a somewhat weak linear relationship.

11. Answers will vary.

## Practice for Lesson 7.1 Answers

**1a.** negative relationship

**1b.** strong linear relationship

**2.** no pattern

**3a.** positive relationship

**3b.** weak linear relationship

**4a.** negative relationship

**4b.** nonlinear relationship

# LESSON 7.1

### COMMON ERROR

**Exercise 5** If students mistakenly identify "Number of Women" as the independent variable, point out that it would be incorrect to say that the number of women in the House of Representatives determines the term.

> dependent variables.

**5a.** The term is the independent variable and the number of women is the dependent variable.

**5b.** Sample scatter plot:

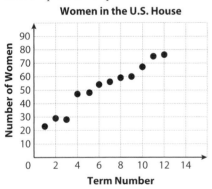

**Women in the U.S. House**

**5c.** Sample answer: The variables are positively related. There appears to be a strong linear relationship, at least from Term 4 on.

---

**5.** The table shows how the number of women elected to the U.S. House of Representatives has changed in recent years.

| Term | Number of Women |
|---|---|
| 1987–89 | 23 |
| 1989–91 | 29 |
| 1991–93 | 28 |
| 1993–95 | 47 |
| 1995–97 | 48 |
| 1997–99 | 54 |
| 1999–2001 | 56 |
| 2001–03 | 59 |
| 2003–05 | 60 |
| 2005–07 | 67 |
| 2007–09 | 75 |
| 2009–11 | 76 |

SOURCE: OFFICE OF THE CLERK, U.S. HOUSE OF REPRESENTATIVES

  **a.** Identify the independent and dependent variables.
  **b.** Make a scatter plot of the data. (Hint: Let the dates 1987–89 be Term 1, 1989–91 be Term 2, etc.)
  **c.** Describe any pattern you see in your scatter plot.

**For Exercises 6–7, do the following.**
  **a.** Identify the independent and dependent variables.
  **b.** State whether you think the relationship between the two variables is positive or negative, or neither. Explain your answer.

**6.** For twenty highways during one month, average car speeds and the numbers of fatal accidents are recorded.

**7.** For eight weeks in the summer, the amount of rainfall and the average number of cars in a beach parking lot are recorded.

**6a.** independent variable: car speed; dependent variable: number of fatal accidents

**6b.** Sample answer: The relationship could be positive, because high speeds are likely to cause more accidents.

**7a.** independent variable: rainfall; dependent variable: average number of cars in parking lot

**7b.** Sample answer: The relationship is negative because people are less likely to go to the beach when it rains.

**224**    **Chapter 7**    LINEAR MODELS FROM DATA

**INVESTIGATION:   Fitting Lines to Data**

In Chapter 5 you learned how to find an equation for a line when you are given points on the line. In this lesson you will fit a line to a scatter plot and use it to create a linear model for the data.

The scatter plot of your class's forearm length and height data is likely to be fairly spread out. But forensic scientists, conducting similar experiments, have found the data to have a positive linear form.

1. Would a direct variation function be a good model for your data? Explain.

2. To help you find a line that models the data in your scatter plot, use a piece of uncooked spaghetti. Place it on your scatter plot in such a way that it best describes the pattern in the data. Try moving the spaghetti up and down, and vary its slope. Decide what guidelines or rules can be used to help determine a line that best describes the trend in the data. This is sometimes called a *line of best fit.*

3. Suppose the rule chosen is, "Place the line so that half the points are above it and half below." Why is this rule not enough to specify a good line?

4. Discuss possible guidelines for finding a line that fits the data with other groups to see if there is any agreement.

5. When you have decided on a line that fits the data using your piece of spaghetti, *draw* a line in that position on your scatter plot.

6. Choose two points *on* your line, one near the left end of the line, and one near the right end of the line. They do not have to be data points. Use the coordinates of those points to find the slope of the line.

7. Explain why the chosen points should be far apart instead of close together.

8. Find an equation for your line of best fit that expresses height $h$ as a function of forearm length $f$. In other words, find an equation in slope-intercept form that models the data well.

9. Use your model to predict the height of a student with a forearm that is 22.5 centimeters long.

10. Explain the meaning of the slope in terms of forearms and heights.

11. Explain the meaning of the vertical intercept in terms of forearms and heights.

12. What is the mathematical domain of your function?

13. What is a reasonable problem domain for your equation when used to model the data relating height to forearm length?

## Lesson Objective

• draw a line that represents a linear trend on a scatter plot and find a linear model for the data.

## Vocabulary

## Materials List

• scatter plot from the Activity in Lesson 7.1
• uncooked spaghetti
• ruler

## Description

Students should work in the same groups they were in for Lesson 7.1's Activity to investigate drawing and interpreting a line that fits their scatter plot of the class data on height vs forearm length. The points are likely to show quite a bit of scatter, but will likely still show an upward trend.

*Wrapping Up the Investigation:*

Conduct a class discussion about **Questions 10 and 11**, so that all students see how to interpret slope and intercept in this context. Also make sure students understand the difference between the domain of a mathematical function and the problem domain of a mathematical model.

**TEACHING TIP**

For **Question 1**, you may need to remind students that for a direct variation function
• ratios of the variables are constant, and
• the graph of the function passes through the origin.

**TEACHING TIP**

For **Question 3**, use a piece of spaghetti to demonstrate that a nonvertical line with any slope can be found that has half of the points above it and half below. Point out that the distances of points from the line should also be considered.

## Lesson 7.2 Investigation Answers

**1–13.** See answers beginning on page 621.

**TEACHING TIP**

For **Question 4**, lead a class discussion about finding a good-fitting line. Encourage students to propose a variety of reasonable criteria, but steer the discussion toward finding a line that
• captures the trend in the data and
• lies in the middle of the field of points.

One possible strategy is to draw *two lines that enclose almost all the points* as shown below.

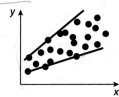

Then draw a line in between these two lines.

**TEACHING TIP**

**Question 6** Make sure students understand that they should use two points *on their line* to determine the slope of the line.

**TEACHING TIP**

**Question 8** Remind students that the variables in this model are forearm length and height. Encourage them to choose meaningful letters rather than just *x* and *y.*

## ADDITIONAL EXAMPLE

The table shows a salon worker's sales and tips for one afternoon.

| Sale Amount ($) | Tip Amount ($) |
|:---:|:---:|
| 10 | 2 |
| 15 | 3 |
| 20 | 2 |
| 25 | 4 |
| 30 | 4 |
| 35 | 6 |
| 40 | 5 |
| 45 | 7 |

**a.** Identify the independent and dependent variables.
independent: sale amount
dependent: tip amount

**b.** Make a scatter plot of the data.

**c.** Draw a line that fits the data well and find its equation.

Sample answer: $t = 0.16s - 0.30$

**d.** State the problem domain for your model.
$s \geq 0$

**e.** Explain the meaning of the slope.
There is an average increase in tip of $0.16 for each extra dollar of sales.

**f.** Predict the tip for a sale of $55.
$8.50

**g.** What sale amount should produce a tip of $3.50?
$23.75

---

### E X A M P L E

The table below shows the average outside temperature each month from September to May. The average amount of natural gas used per day of each month is also shown.

| Month | Sept | Oct | Nov | Dec | Jan | Feb | Mar | Apr | May |
|---|:---:|:---:|:---:|:---:|:---:|:---:|:---:|:---:|:---:|
| Outdoor Temperature (°F) | 48 | 46 | 38 | 29 | 26 | 28 | 49 | 57 | 65 |
| Gas Used per Day (ft³) | 510 | 490 | 600 | 890 | 880 | 850 | 440 | 250 | 110 |

**a.** Identify the independent and dependent variables. Explain your choice.

**b.** Make a scatter plot of the data.

**c.** Draw a line that appears to best describe the data. Find its equation.

**d.** State the problem domain for your model.

**e.** Explain the meaning of the slope for this context.

**f.** Predict average daily gas usage for a month with an average outdoor temperature of 60°F.

**g.** For what average outdoor temperature would the daily gas use average 720 cubic feet?

**Solution:**

**a.** The amount of gas used depends, for the most part, on the outside temperature. So temperature is the independent variable, and gas used is the dependent variable.

**b.** and **c.**

The equation will have the linear form $g = mt + b$, where $t$ is the outdoor temperature, in degrees Fahrenheit, and $g$ is the volume of gas used, in cubic feet. The data point (65, 110) appears to be on the line. So does the point (31, 800). The slope of the line is $m = \frac{800 - 110}{31 - 65} \approx -20.3$.

Using a slope of $-20.3$ and the point $(31, 800)$, solve for the intercept $b$.

$$800 = (-20.3)(31) + b$$
$$800 = -629.3 + b$$
$$b \approx 1{,}429$$

The equation is $g = -20.3t + 1{,}429$.

**d.** Negative amounts of gas used make no sense in this context. To find the temperature for which no gas would be used, solve the equation $-20.3t + 1{,}429 = 0$.

| | |
|---|---|
| Original equation | $-20.3t + 1{,}429 = 0$ |
| Subtract 1,429 from both sides. | $-20.3t = -1{,}429$ |
| Divide by $-20.3$. | $t \approx 70.4$ |

The problem domain is $t \leq 70.4$.

**e.** The slope, with units, is $-20.3 \frac{ft^3}{{}^\circ F}$. For each increase of 1 Fahrenheit degree in the average outdoor temperature, 20.3 cubic feet less of gas is used per day.

**f.** When $t = 60^\circ F$, $g = (-20.3)(60) + 1{,}429 = 211$. Gas usage would average 211 cubic feet per day.

**g.** Solve the equation $-20.3t + 1{,}429 = 720$.

| | |
|---|---|
| Original equation | $-20.3t + 1{,}429 = 720$ |
| Subtract 1,429 from both sides. | $-20.3t = -709$ |
| Divide by $-20.3$. | $t \approx 34.9$ |

So, the average outdoor temperature would be about $35^\circ F$.

## Practice for Lesson 7.2

**1.** Which of the graphs below show(s) a line that appears to model the given data well? Explain your reasoning.

**Graph A**

**Graph B**

**Graph C**

## Practice for Lesson 7.2 Answers

1. Sample answer: Graph B; Although the line in Graph A hits more points, a best-fit line should take into account the distance of each point from the line. The line in Graph B not only captures the trend in the scatter plot, it has been placed so that points are scattered on both sides of it.

# LESSON 7.2

**COMMON ERROR**

**Exercise 3** Some students may think that they have to choose lines that pass through two data points. Point out that this is not the case.

**COMMON ERRORS**

**Exercise 7** If students attempt to graph pounds of beads vs cost, ask them to explain how one variable depends on the other. The cost depends on the amount of beads needed by the jewelry maker. So, the amount of beads is the independent variable.

**Exercise 12** As an alternative to using a graphing calculator, have students use a computer spreadsheet program like Excel to make a scatter plot. They can insert a line on the "chart" by choosing a line from the "Insert Shape" menu.

**2.** See answer to Exercise 3.

**3.** Sample answer: $h = 5f + 15.5$

**4.** Sample answer: A person whose forearm is 1 inch longer than another person's forearm will be about 5 inches taller.

**5.** Sample answer: 63 inches

**6.** Sample answer: 10.5 inches

**7.** Sample answer:

---

For Exercises 2–6, use the following data that were collected from a group of adults.

| Forearm Length (in.) | 10.3 | 10.9 | 11.6 | 11.4 | 10.0 | 9.2 | 10.9 | 10.2 | 10.1 | 10.6 | 10.6 |
|---|---|---|---|---|---|---|---|---|---|---|---|
| Height (in.) | 69 | 72 | 74 | 71 | 63 | 64 | 70 | 69 | 64 | 64 | 69 |

**2.** Make a scatter plot of the data.

**3.** Draw a line that appears to model the trend in the data well. Find its equation.

**4.** Explain the meaning of the slope for this context.

**5.** Use your model to predict the height of a person with a forearm length of 9.5 inches.

**6.** Use your model to predict the forearm length of a person that is 68 inches tall.

| Pounds of Beads | Cost (dollars) |
|---|---|
| 1 | 1.00 |
| $1\frac{1}{4}$ | 1.50 |
| 2 | 2.10 |
| $2\frac{1}{4}$ | 2.40 |
| $2\frac{3}{4}$ | 3.05 |
| 3 | 3.50 |
| $3\frac{3}{4}$ | 4.00 |

For Exercises 7–11, use the data in the table to the left, which shows the cost of different amounts of bulk bead purchases by a maker of jewelry for two months.

**7.** Make a scatter plot and draw a line that appears to fit the data well.

**8.** Find an equation for your line.

**9.** Explain the meaning of the slope. Does it make sense for this context?

**10.** Explain the meaning of the vertical intercept. Does it make sense for this context?

**11.** How much does your model predict that 5 pounds of beads would cost?

**12.** Semester grades for 8 students in a geography class are shown in the table below. Use a graphing calculator to make a scatter plot and draw a line that fits the data well.

| 1st Semester Grade | 62 | 64 | 71 | 78 | 82 | 85 | 95 | 97 |
|---|---|---|---|---|---|---|---|---|
| 2nd Semester Grade | 54 | 64 | 65 | 70 | 77 | 72 | 88 | 88 |

**a.** Enter the data into the first two lists, **L1** and **L2** of your calculator.

**b.** Turn on one of the data plots. Choose the scatter plot icon. Enter **L1** as the **Xlist** and **L2** as the **Ylist**.

**c.** Choose an appropriate window so that all the data will show as points on the graph.

**d.** Create the graph by pressing the **GRAPH** key.

**e.** Display the **[DRAW]** menu. Then select **Line(** from the **DRAW** menu. Locate a starting point for your line near the left side of the screen and press **ENTER**. Then move the cursor to the right side to choose an end point and again press **ENTER**.

**f.** Use the coordinates of two points on your line to determine an equation for your line.

---

**8.** Sample answer: $C = 1.12p - 0.02$

**9.** For each additional pound of beads purchased, the cost increases by $1.12. This is the average cost per pound of beads, so it makes sense in this context.

**10.** It is the cost to buy 0 pounds of beads. The value of –0.02 is very close to 0, so it makes sense in this context.

**11.** Sample answer: $5.58, or approximately $5.60

**12a.** Sample answer: Data are entered into **L1** and **L2**.

**12b.** Sample plot menu screen:

**12c–12f.** See answers beginning on page 621.

## INVESTIGATION: Residuals and Judging the Quality of Fit

There are a number of different criteria for determining how well a line describes the pattern in a set of data. In this lesson, you will examine methods for comparing the quality of fit for different lines.

Your class may have come up with several different guidelines for finding a line that best fits the data. Most people would agree that a best-fit line should pass as close as possible to as many points as possible. But how can this goal be measured numerically so that different models can be compared objectively? The key to this judgment is a quantity called a **residual**.

When a prediction is made from data, the difference between the actual value of the dependent variable and the predicted value is called the **residual error**, or just the **residual**. For a dependent variable $y$,

$$residual = actual\ y - predicted\ y$$

Therefore, a residual is the difference between the height of a data point and the height of the graph for the same input value.

1. Look at the original forearm length and height measurements for members of your group from the Activity in Lesson 7.1. Locate the points on your graph of the class data from the Investigation in Lesson 7.2 that correspond to your group's data. On your graph, draw vertical lines that represent the residuals for members of your group.

2. State whether each residual is positive or negative. Explain how your answers are shown on the graph.

3. Pick one of your group's data points. Identify the forearm length. Use your linear model from Lesson 7.2 to predict the height of a person with this forearm length.

4. Calculate the residual for the point you chose in Question 3.

## Lesson Objectives

- find the residuals for a linear model.
- use residuals to compare models.

## Vocabulary

- least-squares criterion
- least-squares line
- residual
- residual error
- residual plot

## Materials List

- data from the Activity in Lesson 7.1
- graph from the Investigation in Lesson 7.2

## Description

Students should continue to work in the same groups they were in for the previous two lessons to investigate residuals for the class data on height vs forearm length. They examine criteria for comparing the usefulness of different linear models.

Tell students to continue to save their forearm/height data for use in **Exercise 6** of Lesson 7.6 and for the Extension to this chapter, if you decide to use it.

If students have used a computer spreadsheet for Lessons 7.1 and 7.2, they should continue to use the spreadsheet for this lesson rather than a graphing calculator.

*Wrapping Up the Investigation:*

For **Question 11**, have each group write the equation of their linear model on the board, along with the sum of the squares of their residuals, so that groups can compare their models with the rest of the class.

## Lesson 7.3 Investigation Answers

1. Sample answer: Points are (24.0, 157), (24.5, 166), (27.0, 164), and (24.0, 164).

**Class Forearm/Height Data**

2–4. See answers beginning on page 622.

**TEACHING TIP**

If necessary, review how to store data in lists on a graphing calculator. The instructions given in **Question 7** are for a TI-83/84 calculator. Point out to students that names of calculator lists (**L1**, **L2**, etc.) are entered into expressions (**Question 7**) by selecting appropriate keys such as **L1** on the calculator keyboard, not by separately typing **L** and then **1**. Suggest that one student inputs values while another reads the numbers to input. It is very easy to skip one or more of the numbers in long lists, and if this happens the residuals will not be computed correctly.

5. Sample answer: The model predicts a height of 171.6 cm, but the person's actual height is only 164 cm, so the prediction is too large by 7.6 cm.

6. For (24.0, 164), the predicted value is $3.33(24.0) + 81.7 \approx 161.6$ cm, and the residual is $164 - 161.6 = 2.4$ cm.
   For (24.5, 166), the predicted value is $3.33(24.5) + 81.7 \approx 163.3$ cm, and the residual is $166 - 163.3 = 2.7$ cm.
   For (24.0, 157), the predicted value is $3.33(24.0) + 81.7 \approx 161.6$ cm, and the residual is $157 - 161.6 = -4.6$ cm.

7. Sample results:

8. All the residuals would be 0.

9. No, the negative residuals will tend to cancel out the positive residuals.

10. Sample answer: 642.86

5. Explain in detail the meaning of your answer to Question 4.

6. Determine the residuals for the other members of your group.

7. Residuals for even a large data set can easily be found with the aid of a graphing calculator.

   - If you have not already done so, enter all of your class data for forearm length in the first list **L1** in the list editor. (Access the list editor with the **STAT** key.)
   - Enter the corresponding height values into the second list **L2**.
   - Enter your linear model from Lesson 7.2 as **Y1** on the function screen **Y=**.
   - In the third list **L3**, you will enter all the values predicted by the function. But this can be done with a single entry. With the cursor on the name of the list **L3**, press the **ENTER** key. The cursor jumps to the editing line at the bottom of the screen.

   - With the cursor on the editing line, go to the **VARS** **Y-VARS** menu and select **Function**. Select **Y1**. Then type **( [L1] )** and press **ENTER**. This tells the calculator to substitute each value from the **L1** list as an input to the function **Y1** to get the predicted value of the function for that input value.

   - Each residual is the difference between a number in **L2** and the corresponding number in **L3**, or (actual $y$ − predicted $y$). To compute all of the residuals in the fourth list **L4**, move the cursor to the editing line for **L4** and type **L2 − L3**. The list will fill with the values of the residuals.

8. Suppose that all the points in a scatter plot lie on the same line. If you find the equation of that line, what can you say about the residuals?

9. Each residual is a measure of part of the error in the linear model. Could you find a measure of the total error for the model by adding all the residuals? Why or why not?

10. The most commonly used criterion for judging goodness of fit is called the **least-squares criterion**. It involves finding the sum of the *squares* of the residuals. In this method, the model with the

*minimum sum for all the squares of the residuals* is the best-fitting model. You can use your calculator to find the sum of the squares of the residuals.

- Use the squaring key $\boxed{x^2}$ to enter the squares of the residuals from **L4** into the fifth list **L5**.

- To find the sum of the squares, display the **[LIST]** menu. Then select **sum(** from the **MATH** menu and enter **L5**.

| L3 | L4 | L3 | 5 |
|---|---|---|---|
| 161.62 | ⁻4.62 | ------ | |
| 163.29 | 2.715 | | |
| 171.61 | ⁻7.61 | | |
| 161.62 | 2.38 | | |
| 158.29 | 2.71 | | |
| 173.28 | ⁻9.275 | | |
| 171.61 | ⁻4.61 | | |

L5 =L₄²

Compute the sum of the squares of the residuals for your model.

**11.** Compare your result to those of other groups. Or try other linear models yourself by adjusting your original trend line. See if you can find a model for which the sum of the squares of the residuals is less than for your model.

## SQUARED RESIDUALS AND RESIDUAL PLOTS

Squaring the residual errors gives emphasis to values that deviate more from the overall pattern. The best-fitting line according to the least-squares criterion is the one for which the sum of the squares of the residuals is a minimum. This is equivalent to adjusting the line until the total area of the squares having sides equal to the residuals is minimized.

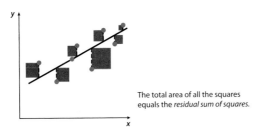

The total area of all the squares equals the *residual sum of squares.*

For this reason, the line for which the sum of the squares of the residuals is a minimum is often called the **least-squares line**. In Lesson 7.6 you will use technology to find this best-fitting line.

A **residual plot** can help you to judge whether a line is a good fit to data. A residual plot is a scatter plot of the residuals versus the independent variable. It allows a direct visual comparison of the sizes

**11.** Results will vary.

## Practice for Lesson 7.3 Answers

1. plot C; Plot B shows a definite pattern, so the residuals are not random. The residuals in plots A and C appear to be random, but they are generally smaller in plot C.

2a. Sample residual plot based on sample data from the Activity:

[20, 35] × [−12, 12]

2b. The residuals are small and random, so the model is a good one.

3. Sample scatter plot:

[0, 4] × [0, 50]

4. Sample graph:

[0, 4] × [0, 50]

---

of the residuals. If a linear equation is a good model for a data set, two requirements should be met.

- The residuals should be small relative to the data values.
- The points in the residual plot should be randomly scattered above and below the axis that represents a residual of 0.

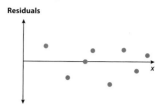

If the residual plot shows a clear pattern as in the figure below, the model is probably not a good one.

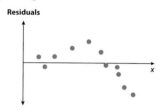

In a case like this, another type of model, such as a nonlinear model, should be used.

## Practice for Lesson 7.3

1. Residual plots for three different models of the same data set are shown.

If the scale on all three graphs is the same, which of the three is the best model for the data? Justify your answer.

---

5. Sample answer: The residuals (**L2** − **L3**) for each model are shown in **L4**.

| L2 | L3 | L4 | 4 |
|---|---|---|---|
| 13 | 3.5 | 9.5 | |
| 8 | 13.7 | -5.7 | |
| 24 | 17.1 | 6.9 | |
| 40 | 22.2 | 17.8 | |
| 33 | 34.1 | -1.1 | |
| 15 | 37.5 | -22.5 | |
| 45 | 46 | -1 | |

L4(1)=9.5

| L2 | L3 | L4 | 4 |
|---|---|---|---|
| 13 | 10.5 | 2.5 | |
| 8 | 17.1 | -9.1 | |
| 24 | 19.3 | 4.7 | |
| 40 | 22.6 | 17.4 | |
| 33 | 30.3 | 2.7 | |
| 15 | 32.5 | -17.5 | |
| 45 | 38 | 7 | |

L4(1)=2.5

6. First student: 1,543; Second student: 978; The second model is a better model because it has a lower residual sum of squares.

7a. Sample scatter plot:

2. Your class data should be stored in lists **L1** and **L2** as part of the Activity in this lesson. The residuals should be stored in list **L4**.
   a. Make a residual plot of residuals vs forearm length.
      - Use **[STAT PLOT]** to create a scatter plot with **L1** (the forearm lengths) as the **Xlist** and **L4** (the residuals) as the **Ylist**.
      - Choose an appropriate window for the plot. The **Ymin** and **Ymax** values should be chosen so that the values of all the residuals will be included on the graph.
   b. Does your residual plot suggest that your model is a good one?

**For Exercises 3–6, use the table below.**

| x | 0.5 | 1.1 | 1.3 | 1.6 | 2.3 | 2.5 | 3.0 | 3.2 |
|---|-----|-----|-----|-----|-----|-----|-----|-----|
| y | 13 | 8 | 24 | 40 | 33 | 15 | 45 | 26 |

3. Make a scatter plot of the data.
4. One student used the equation $y = 17x - 5$ to model the data. Another student used the equation $y = 11x + 5$. Graph both lines on your scatter plot.
5. Compute the residuals for each value of $x$ for both models.
6. Find the residual sum of squares for each model. Which is the better model for the data according to the least-squares criterion?

**For Exercises 7–8, do the following.**
   a. Make a scatter plot of the data.
   b. Draw a line that you think best models the pattern in the data.
   c. Find an equation for the line.
   d. Make a residual plot for your model.
   e. Use your residual plot to decide whether the model is a good one for the data.

7.

| x | 2.4 | 0.6 | 3.5 | 1.9 | 3.7 | 1.1 | 2.6 | 3.1 | 1.3 | 2.0 |
|---|-----|-----|-----|-----|-----|-----|-----|-----|-----|-----|
| y | 168 | 187 | 152 | 178 | 164 | 174 | 160 | 166 | 182 | 163 |

8.

| x | 39 | 27 | 42 | 20 | 48 | 30 | 38 | 35 | 24 | 43 | 32 | 46 | 26 | 36 |
|---|----|----|----|----|----|----|----|----|----|----|----|----|----|----|
| y | 26 | 14 | 21 | 0 | 37 | 10 | 27 | 16 | 7 | 25 | 9 | 33 | 12 | 21 |

**7b.** Sample answer:

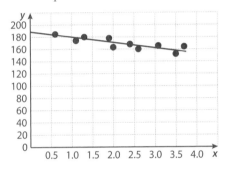

**7c.** Sample answer:
$y = -8.8x + 189$

**7d.** Sample residual plot:

$[0, 4] \times [-10, 10]$

**7e.** Sample answer: The residuals are relatively small compared to the data and randomly scattered, so the model appears to be a good one.

**8a.** Sample scatter plot:

**8b.** Sample answer:

**8c.** Sample answer: $y = 1.2x - 22$

**8d.** Sample residual plot:

$[15, 50] \times [-10, 10]$

**8e.** Although the residuals are small, they appear to have a repeating pattern, so the model may not be a good one.

# LESSON 7.4

**5e** Explore

## Lesson Objectives

- use a linear model to make predictions.
- decide when the use of a model is appropriate.

## Vocabulary

- extrapolation
- interpolation

## Materials List

*Per group:*

- data and model from the Activity in Lesson 7.1

## Description

Students should continue to work in the same groups they were in for the previous three lessons to make predictions from their model of height vs forearm length. In this lesson, they will revise their model to make it more useful in making predictions about females.

*Wrapping Up the Investigation:*

**Question 5** Lead a class discussion about flaws in the modeling process. You can also point out that the bone found in 1940 was a radius bone. The bone measured in the Lesson 7.1 Activity is the ulna bone, which is easier to measure and may be slightly longer than the radius.

This may be a good time to discuss modeling as a process. Whether a model is data-driven as in this chapter, or theory-driven as in many examples in Chapters 3 and 5, it should be tested against the facts and revised if need be.

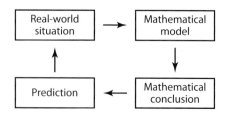

Some real-world situations must be simplified so that a mathematical model can be built. But if predictions from a simple model are not accurate, the model is revised by reexamining its assumptions. Sometimes several

234

## Lesson 7.4    INVESTIGATION: Predicting from Linear Models

Once you have a model that fits a data set well, you can use it to make predictions about values that were not part of the data. In this lesson, you will use linear models to make predictions.

The bones that were found in the Pacific in 1940 were analyzed at a medical school in Fiji. The conclusion was that the bones were from a male who was about 5 feet 5 inches tall. So it was thought that they could not have been Amelia Earhart's bones.

But later analysis of the report suggested that it was flawed. Even though the bones themselves were discarded, the data were still known. Forensic anthropologists Dr. Karen Burns and Dr. Richard Jantz analyzed the measurements. They built models from extensive data sets to predict height and gender, as well as ethnic origin. Their conclusion was that the bones were most likely from a white female of European background who was about 5 feet 7 inches tall. This description fits Amelia Earhart. While this result does not prove that the bones were hers, they have strengthened the resolve of some interested people to continue to look for additional evidence.

1. Recall from Chapter 6 that sample data can be used to predict population traits only if the sample is representative of the population as a whole. You now have a model that relates forearm length and height for a sample consisting of the students in your class. Is your sample representative of students your age? Explain.

2. The forearm bone found in the Pacific in 1940 was 24.5 centimeters long. Use the model that you developed in Lesson 7.2 to predict the height of a person with a forearm bone measuring 24.5 cm.

3. Does your model suggest that the bone could have come from Amelia Earhart's forearm? Explain.

4. Based on your model, how long would you expect the forearm of a 5 foot 7 inch person to be?

5. Discuss with your classmates reasons why your model might not be appropriate for answering questions about Amelia Earhart.

6. Explain how you might use your class data to find a model that is a better predictor of either female or male heights.

### INTERPOLATION AND EXTRAPOLATION

A model can usually be used to make reliable predictions only within the interval of values indicated by the problem domain. For example, suppose that a group of people whose forearms vary from 21 cm to 33 cm is used to create a model for predicting height. If the model is a

revisions, represented by trips around the modeling diagram, may be necessary. **Questions 6 and 7** provide an opportunity to discuss how students' models might be improved.

## Lesson 7.4 Investigation Answers

1. Answers will vary, but should take into account whether certain ethnic groups are present in numbers significantly different from those in the general population. Gender could also be taken into account.

2. Sample answer based on the model: $h = 3.33f + 81.7, h \approx 163$ cm

3. Sample answer: Possibly not; 163 cm is about 5 feet 4 inches, which is 3 inches shorter than Amelia's height.

4. Sample answer: 5 feet 7 inches is about 170 cm. Based on $3.33f + 81.7 = 170, f \approx 26.5$ cm.

5. Sample answer: The model is for teenagers, not adults.

6. Sample answer: Make separate scatter plots of the data for females only, or for males only, in order to find models to predict heights for a single gender.

good one, it can be used to predict height for a person with a forearm length such as 26 cm. Using a model to make predictions within the range of known data is called **interpolation**.

But what if someone has a 38-cm forearm? This is significantly beyond the problem domain of the model. So the model might not give a good prediction. Using a model based on data to make predictions outside the range of the data is called **extrapolation**. Extrapolating from data may not produce useful results.

## E X A M P L E

The table shows the approximate number of Native Americans in the U.S. Military over a period of six years.

| Year | 2001 | 2002 | 2003 | 2004 | 2005 | 2006 |
|------|------|------|------|------|------|------|
| Number of Native Americans | 720 | 825 | 910 | 1,080 | 1,125 | 1,300 |

SOURCE: U.S. ARMY RECRUITING COMMAND/*THE BOSTON GLOBE.*

The equation $N = 113.43Y - 226{,}261$ is a linear model for the data. In this model, $Y$ represents the calendar year and $N$ represents the number of Native Americans in the military.

**a.** Use the given model to estimate the number of Native Americans in the military for 2007 and also for 2011.

**b.** Which estimate is likely to be a more accurate predictor? Explain.

**Solution:**

**a.** For 2007,
$$N = 113.43Y - 226{,}261$$
$$= 113.43(2007) - 226{,}261$$
$$= 1{,}393.01$$
$$\approx 1{,}393 \text{ people}$$

For 2011,
$$N = 113.43Y - 226{,}261$$
$$= 113.43(2011) - 226{,}261$$
$$= 1{,}846.73$$
$$\approx 1{,}847 \text{ people}$$

**b.** Both estimates involve extrapolation, but 2007 is only one year beyond the data. Therefore, the prediction for 2007 is likely to be more accurate.

PREDICTING FROM LINEAR MODELS    **Lesson 7.4**    **235**

**b.** Which estimate is likely to be the more accurate predictor? Why?

The year 2009 is only 3 years beyond the known data, instead of 10 years beyond the known data, so the prediction for 2009 is likely to be more accurate.

---

## LESSON 7.4

**TEACHING TIP**

Make sure students understand that interpolation is usually fairly reliable, but that extrapolation can be risky, especially for values significantly beyond the known data.

**TEACHING TIP**

If students are curious about where the model in the example came from, you can tell them that it is based on linear regression, which will be studied in Lesson 7.6 of this chapter.

**TEACHING TIP**

Point out to students that there is nothing wrong with using calendar years as an independent variable for forecasting, but they need to be very careful if numbers from such a model are rounded.

## ADDITIONAL EXAMPLE

The table shows the percent of physicians in the United States who were women over a 36-year period.

| Year | Percent of Physicians Who Were Women |
|------|------|
| 1970 | 8 |
| 1975 | 9 |
| 1980 | 12 |
| 1985 | 15 |
| 1990 | 17 |
| 1995 | 21 |
| 2000 | 24 |
| 2006 | 28 |

SOURCE: AMERICAN MEDICAL ASSOCIATION, ST. LOUIS POST-DISPATCH

The equation $P = 0.5721Y - 1{,}120.4$ is a linear model for the data, where $P$ represents the percent of physicians who were women and $Y$ represents the calendar year.

**a.** Use the given model to estimate the percent of physicians expected to be women in 2009 and also in 2016.

29%, 33%

The example on the previous page uses a linear model for *forecasting* into the future. This is a very common application of modeling. For example, the U.S. Military may rely on forecasts like this to plan for future personnel needs. But forecasting always involves uncertainty. It assumes that conditions in the future will be similar to the conditions that produced the data. And predicting more than one or two time periods into the future can be especially unreliable.

Notice that the absolute value of the $N$-intercept for the equation in the example is very large. This is because the independent variable is the calendar year, measured in the thousands. This can lead to prediction errors due to rounding. For example, if the coefficient 113.43 were rounded to 113, the model would predict a value of $113(2007) - 226{,}261 = 530$. This corresponds to an error of over 60%.

A better choice would be to replace the calendar year data with time measured in years after 2000. The years 2001, 2002, and so on, become Year 1, Year 2, etc. A model using these time values is $N = 113.43t + 596.33$. This model predicts a value of 1,390 for the year 2007, where $t = 7$. But if 113.43 were rounded to 113, the prediction would be 1,387. The error is less than 1%.

## Practice for Lesson 7.4

For Exercises 1–7, use the table below, which shows data relating the length of men's femur (upper leg) bones and their heights.

| Femur Length (cm) | Height (cm) | Femur Length (cm) | Height (cm) |
|---|---|---|---|
| 45 | 165 | 42 | 160 |
| 53 | 190 | 47 | 178 |
| 46 | 168 | 40 | 160 |
| 38 | 150 | 55 | 195 |
| 54 | 188 | 50 | 175 |
| 52 | 185 | 43 | 165 |
| 39 | 155 | 48 | 175 |
| 51 | 186 | 44 | 166 |
| 41 | 157 | 49 | 178 |

1. Make a scatter plot of height vs femur length.

## Practice for Lesson 7.4 Answers

1. See answer for Exercise 2.
2. Sample answer: $h = 2.6F + 50$

**Height vs Femur Length**

**2.** Find a linear model that captures the trend in the data. Let $F$ represent femur length and $h$ represent height.

**3.** Suppose a 51.6-cm femur is found among some skeletal remains. Use your model to predict the height of the person to whom the femur belonged.

**4.** If a man is 178 cm (about 5 ft 10 in.) tall, what does your model predict for the length of his femur? If the sample data in the table came from a representative sample of men, do you think your answer is a good predictor? Explain.

**5.** If a man is 203 cm (about 6 ft 8 in.) tall, what does your model predict for the length of his femur? Do you think your answer is a good predictor? Explain.

**6.** If a woman is 160 cm (about 5 ft 3 in.) tall, what does your model predict for the length of her femur? Do you think your answer is a good predictor? Explain.

**7.** Femurs that belonged to two men are found. One femur is one centimeter longer than the other. Predict the difference in their heights. Explain how you were able to find your answer even though the lengths of the two bones were not given.

**For Exercises 8–11, use the table below, which shows how the percent of adults who smoke cigarettes in one state has changed over time.**

| Year | Percent of Adults Who Smoke |
| --- | --- |
| 1987 | 28 |
| 1992 | 24 |
| 1997 | 20 |
| 2002 | 19 |
| 2007 | 16 |

**8.** Replace the calendar year data with time measured in years after 1980. Make a scatter plot of the data.  $1980 = t \, 0$

**9.** Find a linear model that captures the trend in the data. Let $t$ represent time in years after 1980, and let $P$ represent the percent of adults who smoke.

**10.** Use your model to predict the percent of adults in this state who smoked in 2010. Do you expect this to be an accurate prediction?

**11.** According to your model, when will there be no adults in this state who smoke? Do you expect this to be an accurate prediction?

PREDICTING FROM LINEAR MODELS   **Lesson 7.4**   **237**

*handwritten notes (left column):*

p. 236
Have John explain explanations of #4, 5, 6, 7 in key and compare with his explanation ✓

#9: Key calculated slope, then derived linear equation via point-slope.
And #2: How did John do his?
→ Problem asks for "linear model"

#10: "years after 1980", so t = 30 in 2010

#11: Involves extrapolation 25 years beyond final data points 2007.

**LESSON 7.4**

**2.** See answer on page 236.

**3.** 184 cm

**4.** 49.2 cm; Yes, since this is within the domain of the model the prediction should be fairly accurate.

**5.** 58.8 cm; Possibly not, since this involves extrapolating beyond the known data, and the linear trend may not continue.

**6.** 42.3 cm; No, the data were taken from a sample of men. The relationship between femur length and height may be different for women.

**7.** Sample answer: The difference in predicted heights is 2.6 cm. The slope of 2.6 in the equation $h = 2.6 F + 50$ indicates that for every 1 cm difference in femur length, the predicted height changes by 2.6 cm.

**8.** See answer for Exercise 9.

**COMMON ERROR**

**Exercise 8** Remind students that using calendar years for building a forecasting model can lead to inaccuracies due to rounding. If students ask, point out that it is also correct to designate 1987 as Year 1 or Year 0, as an alternative to the strategy suggested in the text.

**9.** Sample answer: $P = -0.65t + 33.5$

*(graph: "Smoking Trend", x-axis "Years After 1980" from 0 to 35, y-axis "Percent of Adults Who Smoke" from 0 to 35)*

*(text partially obscured by handwritten notes):* ample answer: $-0.65t + 33.5 = 0$, o $t$ is about 52. Fifty-two years fter 1980 is 2032. This is probably ot reliable, since it involves xtrapolation 25 years beyond the ata. And it is unlikely that the umber of smokers will ever rop to 0.

**10.** Sample answer: $-0.65(30) + 33.5 = 14\%$; This is only 3 years beyond the data, so the prediction should be reasonably accurate.

**237**

**5e** Evaluate

## Lesson Objective

- solve problems that require previously learned concepts and skills.

## Exercise Reference

Exercises 1: Lesson 1.2

Exercises 2–4: Appendix O

Exercises 5–10: Appendix B

Exercises 11–14: Appendix D

Exercises 15–20: Appendix H

Exercises 21–23: Lesson 3.5

Exercises 24–26: Lesson 3.6

Exercise 27: Lesson 4.3

Exercise 28: Lesson 1.2

Exercises 29–32: Lesson 6.3

## Lesson 7.5 R.A.P. Answers

1. congruent
2. origin
3. B
4. C
5. 9.37
6. 14.55
7. 10.79
8. 20.2
9. 0.063
10. 120
11. 32
12. 3.9
13. 10
14. 6.7
15. 2
16. 20
17. $\frac{1}{3}$
18. 57
19. 11
20. 7
21. −18
22. 5
23. $3\frac{1}{2}$

24.
25.
26.

---

**Fill in the blank.**

1. Two figures that have the same shape and size are

   _____.

2. The point $(0, 0)$ on a graph is called the _____.

**Choose the correct answer.**

3. The point $(-3, 6)$ lies in which quadrant?
   - **A.** I
   - **B.** II
   - **C.** III
   - **D.** IV

4. Which point lies in quadrant IV?
   - **A.** $(2, 3)$
   - **B.** $(-2, -3)$
   - **C.** $(2, -3)$
   - **D.** $(-2, 3)$

**Add, subtract, multiply, or divide.**

5. $6.27 + 3.1$
6. $0.45 + 6.1 + 8$
7. $14 - 3.21$
8. $18.3 - 4.2 + 6.1$
9. $0.03 \times 2.1$
10. $6 \div 0.05$

**Solve. Round non-integer answers to the nearest tenth.**

11. $\frac{b}{6} = \frac{16}{3}$
12. $\frac{6}{7} = \frac{2a}{9}$
13. $\frac{14}{y} = \frac{7}{5}$
14. $\frac{9}{5} = \frac{12}{n}$

**Evaluate.**

15. $8 - 3 \times 2$
16. $2(4 + 6)$
17. $\frac{2(4) - 3}{15}$
18. $(7 + 2)^2 - 6 \times 4$
19. $4^2 - 3 \times 2 + 1$
20. $4^2 - 3 \times (2 + 1)$

**Solve.**

21. $4(m - 9) = 7(m + 2) + 4$
22. $20 - 3h = 5h - 20$
23. $13t - 28 = 3t + 7$

**Graph the inequality on a number line.**

24. $x < 1.5$
25. $-2 \geq x$
26. $-1 \leq x < 4$

**27.** What fraction of the rectangle is shaded?

**28.** A sculpture of an Asian Longhorned Beetle is 18 feet long. If the scale of this model is 12 feet to 1 inch, how long is the actual beetle?

**For Exercises 29–32, use the data shown in the stem-and-leaf diagram.**

**Test Scores**

| | |
|---|---|
| 4 | 8 |
| 5 | 5 |
| 6 | 3  7 |
| 7 | 1  3  3  8 |
| 8 | 1  1  2  8  8  8 |
| 9 | 0  3  3  7  8  8  9 |

Key: 7|3 represents a test score of 73.

**29.** How many people took the test?

**30.** What is the range of the data?

**31.** What is the mode?

**32.** What is the median?

**27.** $\frac{5}{7}$

**28.** 1.5 inches

**29.** 21

**30.** 51

**31.** 88

**32.** 82

**5e** Engage

## Lesson Objectives

- use linear regression to fit a least-squares model to data.

## Vocabulary

- linear regression

## Materials List

## Description

*Preparation:*

Have students work in groups of 2–4. If students have used a computer spreadsheet program for earlier lessons in this chapter, you may wish to have them use it to do this Activity. Regression options are found under Layout/Trendline when a graph is selected.

*During the Activity:*

Students should work through **Questions 1–7** to find a least-squares model for the given data and use a residual plot to help them decide if the model is appropriate.

*Closing the Activity:*

Each group should make a presentation based on the criteria listed in **Question 8**.

### CONNECTION

You may want to show students a video clip about manatees. There are a number of videos available on YouTube. A few of these discuss the contribution of powerboats to manatee injuries and deaths

---

**Lesson 7.6**  **ACTIVITY:  Linear Regression**

In previous lessons in this chapter, you learned how to find a linear model from data and to judge how well it fits the data. In this lesson, you will use technology to find what is considered to be the best-fitting model.

On the coast of Florida lives the manatee, a large and friendly marine mammal. However, this gentle Florida mammal does not live an easy life. It is one of the most endangered marine mammals in the United States. There are only a few thousand manatees left. One major threat to the manatee population is that many manatees are killed by powerboats each year.

Should the Florida Department of Environmental Protection limit the number of registered boats in order to protect the manatee population? Before they decide, they will have to present a convincing argument to the public.

In this Activity you must make a convincing case for whether or not to restrict powerboats. These are the main steps in building a good argument to present to the authorities:

- Find a model that describes the relationship between manatee deaths and powerboat registrations.
- Show that the model does a good job of describing the data.
- Use the model to make a prediction.

**1.** The table on the next page contains data on the number of powerboats registered in Florida (in thousands) and the number of manatees killed from 1977 through 1990.

| Year | Powerboat Registrations (in thousands) | Manatees Killed |
|---|---|---|
| 1977 | 447 | 13 |
| 1978 | 460 | 21 |
| 1979 | 481 | 24 |
| 1980 | 498 | 16 |
| 1981 | 513 | 24 |
| 1982 | 512 | 20 |
| 1983 | 526 | 15 |
| 1984 | 559 | 34 |
| 1985 | 585 | 33 |
| 1986 | 614 | 33 |
| 1987 | 645 | 39 |
| 1988 | 675 | 43 |
| 1989 | 711 | 50 |
| 1990 | 719 | 47 |

**Note**

The data are for pleasure boats only. Commercial boats are not included.

Does there appear to be a relationship between powerboat registrations in Florida and manatee deaths? Explain.

2. To make a recommendation about restricting the number of powerboat registrations, you must find a model that describes the relationship between manatee deaths and powerboat registrations. Which variable should be the independent variable and which should be the dependent variable? Explain your choice.

3. Use your graphing calculator to make a scatter plot of the data.

Recall from Lesson 7.3 that the least-squares line is commonly accepted as the best linear model for a data set that has a linear trend. To find this line, you could experiment with fitting lines to the data in your scatter plot and calculating the sum of the squares of the residuals for each line. The line with the minimum value for that sum would be the best-fitting line. Or you could use your calculator, which has a built-in program that automatically finds that best line using the least-squares criterion.

The process is called **linear regression**. You can find it under **LinReg(ax+b)** on the **STAT** **CALC** menu. (The calculator uses "a" to represent the slope of the line instead of *m*.) If your powerboat

LINEAR REGRESSION    **Lesson 7.6**    **241**

## Lesson 7.6 Activity Answers

1. Sample answer: Yes, they appear to be positively related. The number of manatee deaths generally increases as the number of powerboats increases.

2. Powerboat registrations should be the independent variable since it will be used to explain the increase in manatee deaths. Manatee deaths is the dependent variable since it appears to depend on the number of powerboats.

3. Sample graph:

[400, 800] × [0, 60]

**TEACHING TIP**

Students may notice that there are two different choices for linear regression on their calculator. If so, tell them that the **LinReg(a+bx)** form is often used in statistics courses. The one suggested here, **LinReg(ax+b)**, is similar to the $y = mx + b$ form used in this course.

**TEACHING TIP**

You can point out to students that including **Y1** in the linear regression command (**LinReg(ax+b) L1, L2, Y1**) will automatically paste the regression equation into the function **Y1**. The graph of the least-squares line will then appear on the scatter plot. However, there will be many extra decimal places, which might obscure the equation.

**TEACHING TIP**

Try to ensure that students' calculators have "Diagnostics" turned off. (Use the **Diagnostics Off** command from the **CATALOG**.) Otherwise the correlation coefficient **R** (called *r* in this text), as well as **R²**, will appear when they execute the **LinReg** command. Appearance of these values may distract students from concentrating on the parameters of the linear model. A new calculator will by default have diagnostics off, so this should not be an issue for most students unless they have previously used the regression features on their calculators.

**4.** $d = 0.125r - 41.4$

**5.** Sample answer: The slope tells you that when the number of powerboat registrations increases by 1 unit (1,000 boats), you can expect 0.125 additional manatee deaths. The value of the $d$-intercept is meaningless in this context. It would seem to give the number of manatee deaths when there are no powerboats registered. But 0 registrations is far outside the problem domain for this situation. In any case, a negative number of manatee deaths makes no sense.

---

**TEACHING TIP**

**Question 7** If students have forgotten how to find residuals, tell them to refer back to Lesson 7.3. You may wish to tell students that their calculator will automatically create a list of residuals whenever a regression command is executed. It can be found under the **LIST** **NAMES** menu, and is called **RESID**.

---

**COMMON ERROR**

**Exercises 1 and 2** Some students may get incorrect answers for these two exercises because they forget that the independent variable is expressed in units of "thousands of registrations."

---

**6.** Sample answer: There appear to be about as many points above the line as below the line. Most points are close to the line. So, the line appears to fit the data fairly well.

[400, 800] × [0, 60]

registration data are in list **L1** and manatee deaths in **L2**, enter the command like this.

**4.** Use your calculator to find the least-squares model for your data. Let $d$ represent the number of manatee deaths per year. Let $r$ represent the number of powerboat registrations. Round your slope and intercept values to three digits.

**5.** Explain what your slope and intercept tell you about boats and manatees.

**6.** Enter the equation of your model as **Y1**. Look again at your graph, which now includes your least-squares line. Does the line appear to fit the data well? Support your answer.

**7.** Make a residual plot for your model. Explain how it can help you decide if your model is a good one.

**8.** Present to the class a convincing case for whether or not to restrict powerboat registrations. Use your scatter plot and your linear regression model. Your argument should include the three main steps listed at the start of this lesson.

- Find a model that describes the relationship between manatee deaths and powerboat registrations.
- Show that the model does a good job of describing the data.
- Use the model to make a prediction.

### Practice for Lesson 7.6

**1.** Suppose that you want to reduce the number of manatee deaths to about 30 per year. How many powerboat registrations would you recommend? Explain how you found your answer.

**2.** What if, instead, you recommend a limit of 700,000 powerboat registrations? Predict the number of manatees that would be killed each year, on average, if this proposal were adopted.

**7.** Sample answer: The points are randomly scattered, and there is no pattern in the residual plot. The model seems to be a good one.

[400, 800] × [−10, 10]

**8.** Answers will vary. Students should back up their answers with predictions based on their linear regression model and scatter plot.

**Practice for Lesson 7.6 Answers**

**1.** Sample answer: About 571,000; Solve $30 = 0.125r - 41.4$ for $r$. Or look in the **TABLE** on the calculator and find 30 in the **Y1** list, assuming that the equation of the model is stored in **Y1**.

**2.** About 46 manatees would be killed each year.

**3.** Predict how many additional manatees, on average, would be killed by powerboats each time the number of boat registrations is raised by 50,000. Justify your answer.

**4.** In 2006, there were 989,000 powerboat registrations and 92 manatees killed by powerboats. Even though the least-squares model should only be used to predict the number of manatee deaths when the number of powerboat registrations is between 447,000 and 719,000, how well does the least-squares model predict the number of manatees killed in 2006?

**5.** The table below shows data for the years 1996 through 2007. Combine these with the data given in Question 1 on page 241.

| Year | Powerboat Registrations (in thousands) | Manatees Killed |
|------|------|------|
| 1996 | 751 | 60 |
| 1997 | 797 | 54 |
| 1998 | 806 | 66 |
| 1999 | 805 | 82 |
| 2000 | 841 | 78 |
| 2001 | 903 | 81 |
| 2002 | 923 | 95 |
| 2003 | 940 | 73 |
| 2004 | 946 | 69 |
| 2005 | 974 | 79 |
| 2006 | 989 | 92 |
| 2007 | 992 | 73 |

SOURCE: FLORIDA DEPARTMENT OF HIGHWAY SAFETY AND MOTOR VEHICLES

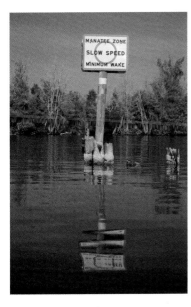

**a.** What is the equation of a new line of best fit?

**b.** Graph both the old and new lines of best fit on the calculator scatter plot.

**c.** What does the new slope tell you?

**d.** What is the predicted number of manatee deaths for 2006 with the new model? Is it closer to the actual number than the prediction from the old model?

**6.** Use linear regression to find a least-squares model for your class height vs forearm length data from Lesson 7.1. How does your model from Lesson 7.2 compare to the least-squares model?

**3.** Sample answer: six; Since the units for the powerboats are in thousands, a 50,000 increase in registrations corresponds to an increase of 50 units for the independent variable. The model predicts an increase of $(0.125)(50) = 6.25$, or about 6 additional deaths per year.

**4.** Sample answer: The predicted number of deaths using the model is 82. This is 10 fewer than the actual number killed. Since the model was extrapolated 15 years beyond the data, it is not expected to be accurate.

**5a.** $d = 0.134r - 45.5$

**5b.** Sample graph:

**[400, 1,000] × [0, 100]**

> **COMMON ERROR**
>
> **Exercise 5b** You may need to remind students that they need to resize their calculator windows when the more recent data are added to their lists.

**5c.** Sample answer: The new slope of 0.134 indicates that you can expect 0.134 additional manatee deaths each time the number of powerboats is increased by one unit (1,000 boats).

**5d.** 87; Yes, the new model gives a better prediction, with an error of only 5.

**6.** Sample answer based on sample data from Lesson 7.2: $h = 3.005f + 90.47$; The hand-drawn line had the equation $h = 3.33f + 81.7$. The slope of the least-squares line is a little less than the slope of the hand-drawn line, and the intercept is a little greater.

## Lesson Objectives

- evaluate the appropriateness of different linear models for a set of data.
- use a subset of a data set to create a model and make predictions.

## Vocabulary

- data-driven model
- theory-driven model

## Description

This lesson is the culmination of students' study of modeling throughout Chapter 7. They should be able to use a variety of linear models to investigate a data set and critically compare the usefulness of competing models.

### TEACHING TIP

The exercise set for this lesson may prove time intensive for many students, so you may want to assign **Exercises 1–5** as homework and then use the remaining exercises as in-class group work the following day.

### TEACHING TIP

Before beginning this lesson, take the time to remind students of the various guidelines for modeling data and evaluating models that they have studied in this chapter.

- Create a scatter plot of the data and examine it to see if it has a linear form.
- Model a linear trend with a line that describes that trend. Try to keep the residuals close to zero.
- Use linear regression to find the least-squares line or line of best fit.
- Use caution when extrapolating a model beyond the range of the data.

| Lesson 7.7 | Comparing Models |

In this chapter, you have seen a variety of models and methods for constructing and evaluating models. In this lesson, you will examine ways of comparing different models and judging their effectiveness.

### MODELS BASED ON DIFFERENT INDEPENDENT VARIABLES

Over the years, many kinds of models have been used to predict people's heights. You have already used a model based on a person's forearm length to predict height. Here are a few others:

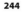

- Artists have found that the rule of thumb, "a 14-year-old is about 7 head-lengths tall," helps them draw teenagers with heads correctly proportioned to their bodies. This rule of thumb can be expressed by the equation $h = 7l$, where $l$ represents head length and $h$ represents height. For adults, the multiplier is changed to 7.5.

- Early models (from the late 1800s) that predicted height from the lengths of long bones were also based on ratios. For example, the ratio of height and femur (thigh-bone) length was given as 3.72. Using $F$ for femur length, the resulting equation is $h = 3.72F$.

- Archaeologists study ancient human life. They use general rules of proportions. For example, an archaeologist might use the rule of thumb that the forearm of a typical female teenager is 16% of her height. Using $f$ for forearm length and $h$ for height, the resulting equation is $f = 0.16h$.

- Dr. Mildred Trotter (1899–1991) was a physical anthropologist. She was well known for her work on height prediction based on the lengths of long bones. During World War II, the armed services sometimes had problems identifying the remains of dead soldiers. Dr. Trotter was asked to help. She refined earlier models by adding a constant, resulting in the familiar linear models of the form $y = mx + b$. Her model for height based on femur length is $h = 2.38F + 61.41$. (All measurements are in centimeters.)

- Another of Dr. Trotter's formulas predicts height from a known tibia (a lower leg bone) length. That model is $h = 2.52T + 78.62$.

- In still another formula, Dr. Trotter used *both* the tibia and the femur to predict height, $h = 1.30(F + T) + 63.29$.

When multiple models are available to predict the same quantity, you can use the methods you have learned in this chapter to help you decide which model to use.

- A good model should describe any trend that can be seen in a scatter plot of the data. It will account for an observed positive or negative relationship.
- Residual errors should be small relative to the size of the data values. A residual plot should reveal small and random residuals, with no obvious pattern.
- A common measure for goodness of fit is the sum of the squares of the residuals. This sum should be as small as possible for a good model. Linear regression finds the linear model that minimizes this sum.
- The true test of a model is whether it makes good predictions. If two models are used to predict measurements that are not included in the data set, the one that makes more accurate predictions is preferred.

### E X A M P L E

The data in the table were collected from a ninth-grade class. The asterisks (*) indicate missing values.

| Height (cm) | Stride Length (cm) | Forearm Length (cm) |
|---|---|---|
| 166.0 | 58.2 | 28.5 |
| 164.5 | 55.9 | 27.2 |
| 175.0 | 59.1 | 28.6 |
| 184.0 | 68.9 | 30.5 |
| 161.0 | 72.5 | 26.5 |
| 164.0 | * | 28.2 |
| 171.0 | * | 29.0 |

a. Find a linear model that predicts a ninth-grader's height from stride length.

b. Find a linear model that predicts a ninth-grader's height from forearm length.

c. Use both of your models to predict the height of a ninth-grader whose stride is 73 cm and whose forearm length is 27 cm.

d. Which of the two estimates is more reliable? Explain.

## ADDITIONAL EXAMPLE

The heights and head lengths of 6 people are shown in the table.

| Head Length (cm) | Height (cm) |
|---|---|
| 23.0 | 163.0 |
| 25.0 | 174.0 |
| 24.0 | 166.5 |
| 25.0 | 181.0 |
| 23.5 | 170.5 |
| 22.0 | 154.0 |

Use the models for adults ($h = 7.5l$) and for teenagers ($h = 7l$) to help you decide if the data in the table came from a group of teenagers or a group of adults.

They were probably teenagers, as residuals for the teenage model are small and random, for the adult model larger and all negative.

### TEACHING TIP

Point out to students that, even though the slope-intercept equation is commonly given as $y = mx + b$, and that calculators and computers typically use this form, a function used to model a real situation might be more useful if it is written with variables appropriate to the context.

**Solution:**

**a.** The least-squares model is $h = 0.168s + 160$.

**b.** The least-squares model is $h = 5.59f + 10.9$.

**c.** Using the model based on stride length, $h = 0.168(73) + 160 \approx 172$ cm.

Using the model based on forearm length, $h = 5.59(27) + 10.9 \approx 162$ cm.

**d.** Scatter plots of the data and the calculated models are shown below.

The model based on forearm length is more reliable, since the points appear more concentrated along the least-squares line. To reinforce this conclusion, look at the respective residual plots.

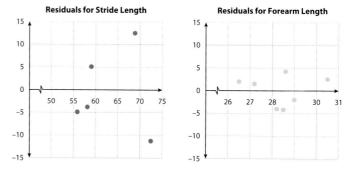

Residuals appear to be random in both plots, but the residuals for the forearm length plot are generally smaller than those for stride length.

## LINE FITTING WITH DOMAIN RESTRICTIONS

The table below shows a teenager's earnings from babysitting jobs for the past 9 months. She would like to use the data to forecast her possible earnings for the month of June.

| Month | Aug | Sept | Oct | Nov | Dec | Jan | Feb | Mar | Apr |
|---|---|---|---|---|---|---|---|---|---|
| Earnings ($) | 29 | 30 | 36 | 34 | 38 | 40 | 53 | 64 | 79 |

To the left is a scatter plot of the data, with August as Month 1.

Linear regression shown in the middle graph produces the model $E = 5.7m + 16.3$.

This model predicts an income for June (Month 11) of $5.7(11) + 16.3 = \$79$.

But the scatter plot shows that the earnings have increased more quickly over the last few months than they had before January. So, a model based only on the data from January through April may give a more accurate forecast for June, assuming the more recent trend continues.

If the problem domain is restricted to months from January through April, the resulting least-squares line has a greater slope.

The new model shown in the bottom graph is $E = 12.8m - 37$. The predicted income for June is $12.8(11) - 37 = 103.8$, or about $104.

Of course, as discussed in Lesson 7.4, extrapolating beyond the domain of a model is always somewhat risky. But basing a model on more recent trends in data often yields more accurate predictions.

COMPARING MODELS    **Lesson 7.7**    **247**

# LESSON 7.7

## Practice for Lesson 7.7 Answers

1. Sample answer: There are three femurs, and two are very close in length, probably belonging to the same person. So, these three bones probably belong to two people. It is possible that the bones actually belong to three people.

2. Using the first formula and the known tibia length predicts a height of $2.52(41.6) + 78.62 \approx 183$ cm. Substituting this height in the second formula and solving for $F$ gives a femur length of 51.1 cm. So, the tibia most likely came from the taller person, the one with the longer femur.

3. Sample answer: Assume that there are only two people. Then the two shorter femurs, the shorter ulna, and the radius probably came from the shorter person. The length of a person's radius should be similar to the length of the ulna, since they are both forearm bones. Using the artists' formula for adults, $h = 7.5(\text{head length}) = 7.5(23.0 \text{ cm}) = 172.5$ cm, so the skull could be from either person, since it suggests a height about halfway between the taller person (about 183 cm) and the shorter person (about 160 cm).

4. Sample answer: Yes, it is possible. Trotter's femur formula predicts a height of 160 cm for the shorter person. Since the adult head length formula predicts a height of 172.5 cm, it may not be from the shorter person if the shorter person is an adult. So, there could be a third adult with a height between the other two. But if the shorter person were a teenager, the head length model predicts

If data are widely scattered, it may not be clear whether a linear trend or some nonlinear trend is appropriate. In such cases, always examine a linear relationship first. Then see if other types of relationships provide better models for the data. As a general rule, "simpler is better."

All of the models discussed in this chapter are **data-driven models**. That is, they were evaluated based on how well they described data. But a good modeler always considers theory as well. A **theory-driven model** is constructed based on the modeler's prior knowledge of known connections between variables. Whenever possible, both theory and the analysis of experimental data are used to create the best models.

### Practice for Lesson 7.7

**For Exercises 1–5, use the following information.**

Bones are sometimes found in rugged areas. A hiker in Arizona's Superstition Mountains found a skull, eight long bones, and many bone fragments. Police investigated and recorded data similar to the table below.

| Bone Type | Number Found | Length (cm) |
|---|---|---|
| Femur | 3 | 41.5, 41.4, 50.8 |
| Tibia | 1 | 41.6 |
| Ulna | 2 | 22.9, 29.0 |
| Radius | 1 | 21.6 |
| Humerus | 1 | 35.6 |
| Skull (including jaw) | 1 | 23.0 |
| Fragments | More than 10 | From 3.0 to 5.0 cm |

1. The police report that the bones belong to at least two people. How do they know?

2. Dr. Trotter used formulas to predict height from tibia length ($h = 2.52T + 78.62$) and from femur length ($h = 2.38F + 61.41$). Explain how you can use these formulas to decide which of the leg bones came from the same person.

3. Which bones do you think belong to the same person? Explain your reasoning. (Hint: Information found at the beginning of this lesson may be useful.)

a height of $7(23.0 \text{ cm}) = 161$ cm, which is close to the height of the shorter person. So, if there are only two people, one is most likely a teenager.

5. Sample answer: For the taller person, Trotter's three formulas predict heights of 183 cm, 182 cm, and 183 cm, so the taller person is between 182 and 183 cm (about 6 feet) tall. For the shorter person, Trotter's femur formula gave 160 cm and the teenager's head length formula gave 161 cm. So, the second person could be a teenager between 160 and 161 cm (about 5 feet 3 inches) tall. Or, the skull could belong to an adult

who was about 172.5 cm (5 feet 8 inches) tall and there is a third and shortest person, who could be a shorter adult (possibly female).

**4.** Do you think it is possible that the bones could belong to at least three people? Explain.

**5.** Use all of the information you have to estimate the heights of the people whose bones were found.

**6.** The table below lists adult data on height vs forearm length. Compare your model based on your class data from Lesson 7.2 with the 16% rule mentioned in the third bullet on the first page of this lesson. Which model does a better job of describing the data in the table? Explain your reasoning.

| Forearm Length (cm) | 26.1 | 27.7 | 29.5 | 29.0 | 25.4 | 23.4 | 27.7 | 25.9 | 25.7 | 26.9 | 26.9 |
|---|---|---|---|---|---|---|---|---|---|---|---|
| Height (cm) | 175 | 183 | 188 | 180 | 160 | 163 | 178 | 175 | 163 | 163 | 175 |

**For Exercises 7–12, use the following scenario.**

A young swimmer's favorite stroke is the butterfly. Her times are listed in the table to the left.

| Race Number | 50-Yard Butterfly Time (seconds) |
|---|---|
| 1 | 60.81 |
| 2 | 66.11 |
| 3 | 47.32 |
| 4 | 42.69 |
| 5 | 43.40 |
| 6 | 44.82 |
| 7 | 42.67 |
| 8 | 45.17 |
| 9 | 41.20 |
| 10 | 43.68 |
| 11 | 42.47 |
| 12 | 41.74 |
| 13 | 40.40 |
| 14 | 42.90 |

**7.** Make a scatter plot of the data. Describe the nature of the relationship between time and race number. Are any outliers present? If so, describe them, and explain why you think they might have occurred.

**8.** Determine the least-squares line and make a residual plot. Does the linear model appear to describe the data well? Explain.

**9.** What effect do the outliers have on the least-squares line? How do you think the least-squares line would change if the two outliers were removed from the data? Explain your reasoning.

**10.** Remove the outliers from the data and find a new least-squares line and residual plot. Does the linear model appear to describe the remaining data well? Explain.

**11.** Use your revised model to predict the swimmer's time for her 15th race.

**12.** On average, by how much are her times decreasing from race to race? Can this pattern continue indefinitely? Explain.

**TEACHING TIP**

**Exercises 4 and 5** Students may want to know the "correct" answer. These questions are meant to be somewhat open-ended, so tell them that as long as they use the models appropriately, there may be more than one correct answer.

**TEACHING TIP**

**Exercise 6** You may need to remind students that they determined a model for predicting height from forearm length when they found an equation for their line of best fit in Question 8 on page 225 of the Investigation in Lesson 7.2.

**COMMON ERROR**

**Exercises 7 and 8** Students may need to be reminded that the scatter plot of the data and the residual plot are used for different purposes. It is not appropriate or useful to try to model the residual plot with a linear function, even though parts of their residual plot in **Exercise 8** may look linear.

**4–5.** See answers on page 248.

**6.** Sample answer: The line of best fit for the class data (Lesson 7.2) is $h = 3.33f + 81.7$. For the rule of thumb, if forearm length is 16% of height, then $f = 0.16h$, so $h = 6.25f$. The residual plots are shown below.

**[20, 30] × [−20, 20]**

**[20, 30] × [−20, 20]**

The class model (residual plot on the left) seems to fit the data better. The residuals are somewhat smaller in general and more scattered above and below 0.

Only one residual is significantly below 0 for the 16% rule model. Since both models are based on teenagers, it is possible that they both may have predicted shorter heights for adults.

**7.** Sample plot:

**[0, 15] × [35, 70]**

There are two outliers, for the first two times. She was new to the event at the beginning.

**8.** $t = -1.26n + 55.6$

**[0, 15] × [−15, 15]**

The model is only fair, and it is affected by the outliers.

**9.** Sample answer: The outliers pull the line up higher on the left end. Without the outliers, the slope should be closer to 0.

**10–12.** See answers beginning on page 622.

**13.** Independent variable: year; dependent variable: number of registrations. The slope indicates the increase in boat registrations per year.

**14.** Answers will vary. Sample answer: The pattern is a bit wavy, but it looks rather straight.

[0, 16] × [400, 750]

**15.** $r = 21.6t + 405.5$ (Numbers are rounded to the nearest tenth.)

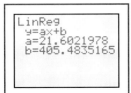

**TEACHING TIP**

**Exercise 19** Students may ask about creating a graph of the piecewise-defined function using their calculator or a computer spreadsheet. While this is possible with a calculator, it is not a simple process. Suggest that they produce separate least-squares lines using only a subset of the data, then draw them on grid paper along with the scatter plot.

**16.** The residuals do not look randomly scattered. Instead they form a strong V-pattern. This suggests that the least-squares equation is not a good model for predictions.

[0, 16] × [−40, 35]

**17.** 1983

**18.** Set 1: $r = 13.32t + 437.7$;
Set 2: $r = 28.32t + 332.5$

---

**For Exercises 13–21, use the data in the table to the left, from Lesson 7.6.**

| Year | Powerboat Registrations (in thousands) | Manatees Killed |
|------|------|------|
| 1977 | 447 | 13 |
| 1978 | 460 | 21 |
| 1979 | 481 | 24 |
| 1980 | 498 | 16 |
| 1981 | 513 | 24 |
| 1982 | 512 | 20 |
| 1983 | 526 | 15 |
| 1984 | 559 | 34 |
| 1985 | 585 | 33 |
| 1986 | 614 | 33 |
| 1987 | 645 | 39 |
| 1988 | 675 | 43 |
| 1989 | 711 | 50 |
| 1990 | 719 | 47 |

Your analysis of the manatee data strongly indicated that the number of manatees killed by powerboats increases as the number of registered boats increases. It seems natural to ask whether you could also use a linear model to predict the number of powerboat registrations in future years.

**13.** To determine how powerboat registrations are related to years, examine the first two columns of the table. Which is the independent variable, and which is the dependent variable? What will the slope mean if the data are linear?

**14.** Make a scatter plot of the data. Instead of entering the year data directly into your calculator (1977, 1978, etc.), renumber the years, letting 1977 be Year 1, 1978 be Year 2, and so forth. Does the scatter plot appear to have roughly a linear form?

**15.** Determine the least-squares line. Write its equation.

**16.** Use your calculator to make a residual plot for the least-squares line. From examining the residual plot, determine if the least-squares line is adequate to describe the pattern of these data. Explain why or why not.

**17.** Your residual plot in Exercise 16 should have appeared V-shaped. Trace along the points in the plot until you reach the point at the bottom of the V. What year is associated with this point?

**18.** Divide your data on powerboats and years into two sets. In the first set, use the data that corresponds to the year identified in Exercise 17 and earlier. In the second set, use the data after the identified year. Enter the data from Set 1 into Lists 1 and 2 of the calculator. Enter the data from Set 2 into Lists 3 and 4. Determine the least-squares line for each of these two sets of data. Write the equations.

**19.** Now plot the data and graph the lines. (Remember that the first line applies to the domain of the first data set, and the second line to the domain of the second data set.) Make a sketch of the scatter plot and the graphs of these lines.

**20.** Does the model consisting of the two half-lines pieced together appear to fit the data better than the single regression line? Make a residual plot for this pieced linear model. Based on the residual plot, does this model appear to describe the data adequately? Explain why or why not.

**21.** What would be your prediction for the number of powerboat registrations in 1991?

---

**19.**

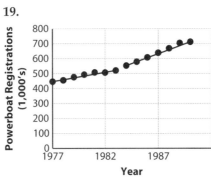

**20.** Yes. The points in the residual plot appear to be more randomly scattered above and below the line $y = 0$.

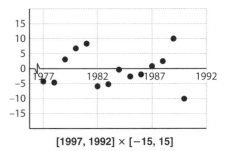

[1997, 1992] × [−15, 15]

**21.** For 1991, the value of $t$ is 15. Using the second model, based only on the years 1984–1990, the prediction is $28.32(15) + 332.5 = 757$ registrations.

## Who Am I?

You are an anthropologist that has found nine bones of two or more individuals. The table below contains information about these bones.

| Skeleton 1 (possibly a female) | Skeleton 2 (taller of the two) | Uncertain |
|---|---|---|
| Femur: 413, 414 | Femur: 508 | Skull: 230 |
| Ulna: 228 | Ulna: 290 | Humerus: 357 |
| | | Radius: 215 |
| | | Tibia: 416 |

**Note: All bone measurements are in millimeters.**

The table on the next page contains actual data from the Forensic Anthropology Data Bank (FDB) at the University of Tennessee. The FDB contains demographic and other kinds of data on skeletons from all over the United States. These individuals most likely are unidentified bodies that went to forensic anthropologists for analysis and identification.

Use the data in the FDB table to answer the following items. Present your findings in a formal report. All of your conclusions must be supported by statistical analysis of the data.

1. Use linear regression to find two different least-squares models that you can use to predict people's heights from the lengths of various long bones in their arms and legs. Explain which of these models you would prefer to use and why.

2. Based on these data, do you agree that Skeleton 1 is female? Do the data provide any information that would help you decide whether Skeleton 2 is male or female?

3. Find models for relationships between pairs of long bones that would help you decide whether the bones in the "Uncertain" column belong to Skeleton 1, Skeleton 2, or to some other person.

4. Predict the heights of Skeleton 1 and Skeleton 2. Explain why you chose the model that you used to make your decision.

## Materials List

## Description

In this project, students are asked to use actual data from the Forensic Anthropology Data Bank to make predictions as to the gender and height of the individuals to whom a set of bones belong. This project works well when students work together in small groups of two or three.

## Sample Answers

1. Answers will vary. A regression model based on the female data and femur length $f$ that could be used to predict height $h$ is $h = 0.262f + 47.4$.

2. Yes, because only three of the males have femur lengths close to 413 and 414 mm. Skeleton 2 is probably male as only one female femur length is over 500 mm.

3. The least-squares equations relating femur length $f$ and humerus length $H$ are:

   for males, $H = 0.5568f + 74.256$

   for females, $H = 0.4426f + 122.29$

   The 413.5 cm (average) femur length for Skeleton 1 (female) predicts a humerus of 297.0 cm. The 508 cm femur for Skeleton 2 (male) predicts a 357.1 cm humerus. So the humerus is from Skeleton 2. And since the tibia is always shorter than the femur, the tibia that was found must also be from Skeleton 2. The radius should be almost as long as the ulna, so the radius that was found must be from Skeleton 1.

4. Based on femur length $f$:
   Skeleton 1 (using female data):
   $h = 0.262f + 47.4$
   So, $h = 156$ mm.
   Skeleton 2 (using male data):

   $h = 0.211f + 76.3$
   So, $h = 183$ mm.

## Data from FDB

Key to Data: Gender (1 = female, 2 = male)
Height (cm), Humerus (mm), Radius (mm), Ulna (mm)
Femur (mm), Tibia (mm), Fibula (mm)

| Gender | Height | Humerus | Radius | Ulna | Femur | Tibia | Fibula |
|---|---|---|---|---|---|---|---|
| 1 | 168 | 307 | 240 | 258 | 448 | 384 | 368 |
| 1 | 178 | 336 | 247 | 261 | 463 | 404 | 390 |
| 1 | 161 | 294 | 213 | 227 | 413 | 335 | 322 |
| 1 | 155 | 324 | 262 | 279 | 465 | 395 | 375 |
| 1 | 165 | 314 | 243 | 258 | 432 | 364 | 364 |
| 1 | 168 | 303 | 223 | 244 | 441 | 355 | 342 |
| 1 | 165 | 311 | 231 | 254 | 436 | 362 | 360 |
| 1 | 173 | 312 | 248 | 266 | 483 | 405 | 401 |
| 1 | 165 | 322 | 229 | 246 | 448 | 368 | 352 |
| 1 | 163 | 298 | 221 | 245 | 443 | 355 | 361 |
| 1 | 153 | 280 | 218 | 234 | 410 | 345 | 344 |
| 1 | 165 | 294 | 220 | 235 | 448 | 354 | 353 |
| 1 | 170 | 311 | 235 | 253 | 440 | 360 | 347 |
| 1 | 160 | 316 | 214 | 226 | 437 | 356 | 348 |
| 1 | 159 | 292 | 223 | 233 | 419 | 346 | 336 |
| 1 | 163 | 315 | 228 | 251 | 438 | 356 | 347 |
| 1 | 165 | 303 | 237 | 249 | 451 | 356 | 348 |
| 1 | 165 | 308 | 234 | 248 | 439 | 348 | 344 |
| 1 | 165 | 315 | 227 | 240 | 448 | 363 | 353 |
| 1 | 175 | 316 | 244 | 260 | 473 | 390 | 374 |
| 1 | 180 | 333 | 256 | 278 | 475 | 391 | 381 |
| 1 | 168 | 321 | 230 | 248 | 450 | 365 | 362 |
| 1 | 163 | 299 | 219 | 236 | 435 | 357 | 339 |
| 1 | 165 | 304 | 246 | 264 | 467 | 392 | 383 |
| 1 | 160 | 309 | 236 | 248 | 432 | 364 | 358 |
| 1 | 158 | 319 | 246 | 268 | 442 | 371 | 364 |
| 1 | 165 | 325 | 242 | 250 | 448 | 378 | 365 |
| 1 | 170 | 335 | 248 | 263 | 474 | 400 | 382 |
| 1 | 182 | 334 | 254 | 273 | 514 | 420 | 407 |
| 1 | 165 | 307 | 230 | 248 | 452 | 363 | 355 |
| 1 | 163 | 297 | 240 | 260 | 435 | 356 | 356 |
| 1 | 143 | 282 | 216 | 233 | 398 | 334 | 318 |
| 1 | 154 | 297 | 228 | 248 | 423 | 344 | 334 |
| 1 | 171 | 342 | 272 | 290 | 485 | 418 | 407 |
| 1 | 162 | 303 | 237 | 262 | 433 | 367 | 364 |
| 1 | 150 | 308 | 220 | 247 | 383 | 352 | 341 |
| 1 | 157 | 288 | 201 | 215 | 429 | 363 | 350 |
| 1 | 158 | 314 | 239 | 263 | 432 | 371 | 358 |
| 1 | 162 | 306 | 250 | 268 | 444 | 355 | 352 |
| 1 | 159 | 310 | 238 | 255 | 449 | 362 | 352 |
| 2 | 169 | 337 | 254 | 273 | 460 | 396 | 385 |
| 2 | 153 | 296 | 223 | 243 | 407 | 337 | 338 |
| 2 | 175 | 339 | 256 | 271 | 470 | 390 | 381 |
| 2 | 179 | 343 | 242 | 263 | 464 | 378 | 371 |
| 2 | 179 | 352 | 253 | 269 | 484 | 407 | 397 |
| 2 | 198 | 354 | 263 | 292 | 508 | 417 | 412 |
| 2 | 173 | 327 | 256 | 276 | 463 | 383 | 387 |
| 2 | 180 | 357 | 268 | 278 | 494 | 401 | 390 |
| 2 | 178 | 344 | 254 | 269 | 464 | 371 | 366 |
| 2 | 175 | 339 | 245 | 272 | 456 | 374 | 366 |
| 2 | 177 | 343 | 250 | 266 | 483 | 361 | 365 |
| 2 | 180 | 353 | 260 | 281 | 490 | 420 | 415 |
| 2 | 170 | 303 | 235 | 249 | 435 | 366 | 361 |
| 2 | 191 | 364 | 263 | 278 | 511 | 430 | 417 |
| 2 | 188 | 349 | 269 | 288 | 498 | 427 | 423 |
| 2 | 179 | 323 | 256 | 276 | 486 | 398 | 400 |
| 2 | 180 | 350 | 263 | 280 | 480 | 419 | 418 |
| 2 | 181 | 350 | 263 | 282 | 488 | 391 | 381 |
| 2 | 178 | 337 | 272 | 272 | 475 | 393 | 390 |
| 2 | 172 | 344 | 255 | 281 | 470 | 400 | 393 |
| 2 | 188 | 360 | 269 | 283 | 510 | 422 | 416 |
| 2 | 189 | 347 | 272 | 283 | 547 | 432 | 445 |
| 2 | 177 | 330 | 246 | 262 | 462 | 386 | 370 |
| 2 | 166 | 322 | 242 | 258 | 442 | 373 | 374 |
| 2 | 186 | 332 | 267 | 283 | 478 | 391 | 388 |
| 2 | 177 | 322 | 245 | 265 | 457 | 397 | 395 |
| 2 | 176 | 332 | 259 | 274 | 458 | 382 | 378 |
| 2 | 180 | 323 | 251 | 275 | 448 | 390 | 387 |
| 2 | 173 | 335 | 253 | 273 | 497 | 404 | 389 |
| 2 | 175 | 330 | 253 | 274 | 470 | 384 | 382 |
| 2 | 169 | 313 | 252 | 265 | 472 | 391 | 385 |
| 2 | 175 | 336 | 256 | 274 | 464 | 388 | 377 |
| 2 | 181 | 390 | 284 | 303 | 521 | 440 | 435 |
| 2 | 193 | 356 | 297 | 318 | 522 | 451 | 433 |
| 2 | 182 | 362 | 275 | 293 | 499 | 424 | 405 |
| 2 | 169 | 322 | 249 | 266 | 426 | 366 | 356 |
| 2 | 180 | 337 | 265 | 281 | 482 | 412 | 399 |
| 2 | 185 | 363 | 286 | 302 | 520 | 429 | 420 |
| 2 | 180 | 355 | 274 | 292 | 490 | 422 | 424 |
| 2 | 170 | 378 | 272 | 291 | 512 | 404 | 390 |
| 2 | 180 | 370 | 278 | 292 | 523 | 429 | 420 |
| 2 | 175 | 333 | 260 | 273 | 484 | 398 | 386 |
| 2 | 168 | 342 | 262 | 280 | 484 | 404 | 385 |
| 2 | 170 | 347 | 269 | 291 | 476 | 396 | 393 |
| 2 | 166 | 315 | 240 | 260 | 456 | 377 | 362 |
| 2 | 185 | 363 | 295 | 309 | 524 | 446 | 427 |
| 2 | 191 | 382 | 299 | 316 | 537 | 479 | 466 |

# Chapter 7 Review

## You Should Be Able to:

### Lesson 7.1
- use scatter plots to identify patterns in data.

### Lesson 7.2
- draw a line that represents a linear trend on a scatter plot and find a linear model for the data.

### Lesson 7.3
- find the residuals for a linear model.
- use residuals to compare models.

### Lesson 7.4
- use a linear model to make predictions.

- decide when the use of a model is appropriate.

### Lesson 7.5
- solve problems that require previously learned concepts and skills.

### Lesson 7.6
- use linear regression to fit a least-squares model to data.

### Lesson 7.7
- evaluate the appropriateness of different linear models for a set of data.
- use a subset of a data set to create a model and make predictions.

## Key Vocabulary

linear form (p. 222)

strong linear relationship (p. 222)

weak linear relationship (p. 222)

residual (p. 229)

residual error (p. 229)

least-squares criterion (p. 230)

least-squares line (p. 231)

residual plot (p. 231)

interpolation (p. 235)

extrapolation (p. 235)

linear regression (p. 241)

data-driven model (p. 248)

theory-driven model (p. 248)

## Chapter 7  Test Review

**For Exercises 1–3, fill in the blank.**

1. The difference between an actual data value and a predicted value is called a(n) _____ error.

2. Using a model to make predictions beyond the range of the data is called _____.

3. The process that a calculator or computer uses to find a linear model for data for which the sum of the squares of the residuals is minimized is _____ _____.

## Chapter 7 Test Review Answers

1. residual
2. extrapolation
3. linear regression

4. Sample scatter plot:

5. Sample answer:
$S = 2.75y + 33.25$

6. The salary cap increases by 2.75 million dollars per year.

7. Sample answer: A residual plot shows the errors that are not explained by the model. If they are small and randomly scattered above and below 0, the model is a good one.

8.

[2, 9] × [−10, 10]

[2, 9] × [−10, 10]

Sample answer: The residuals are somewhat smaller for the second model, and they are almost all negative for the first model, again suggesting that the second model is better. There does appear to be a slight S-shaped pattern in both sets of residuals, though, so a

**For Exercises 4–6, use the following information.**

The table below shows changes in the National Basketball Association (NBA) salary cap over a 10-year period. A team whose payroll is above the salary cap must pay a "luxury tax" to the NBA.

| Year | 2000 | 2001 | 2002 | 2003 | 2004 | 2005 | 2006 | 2007 | 2008 | 2009 |
|---|---|---|---|---|---|---|---|---|---|---|
| Salary Cap ($millions) | 34 | 36 | 43 | 40 | 44 | 44 | 50 | 53 | 56 | 59 |

SOURCE: NATIONAL BASKETBALL ASSOCIATION

4. Make a scatter plot of the data.
5. Draw a line that appears to best describe the data. Find its equation.
6. Explain the meaning of the slope in this context.
7. Explain how a residual plot can be used to help you determine whether a model does a good job of describing data.
8. The table shows the total value of counterfeit goods sold on the Internet from 2003 to 2008.

| Year | 2003 | 2004 | 2005 | 2006 | 2007 | 2008 |
|---|---|---|---|---|---|---|
| Value of Counterfeit Sales ($billions) | 45.5 | 62.4 | 78.9 | 98.9 | 119.7 | 137.0 |

SOURCE: MARKMONITOR/*THE BOSTON GLOBE.*

Two people estimated linear models for forecasting the future value $V$ of counterfeit sales. The first model is $V_1 = 19t − 13$, and the second is $V_2 = 18.5t − 11$. (Time $t$ is measured in years after 2000.)

Make residual plots for the two models. Explain what they show about the models.

**For Exercises 9–13, use the following information.**

The table on the next page shows the winners of the Indianapolis 500 auto race and their average speed every four years, from 1912 to 1972. (No race was run in 1944 due to World War II.)

9. Make a scatter plot of the data and find the equation of a linear regression model. Let $S$ represent speed and $t$ the number of years since 1912 as the independent variable.
10. Explain the meaning of the slope and $S$-intercept.

nonlinear model might be better than both.

9. $S = 1.298t + 78.231$

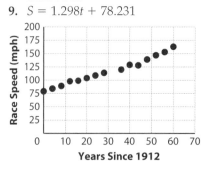

10. Every year the speed increases by 1.298 miles per hour. This is equivalent to about a 5 mph increase every 4 years. The $S$-intercept indicates that the model predicts a speed of 78.231 mph for 1912, very close to the actual speed for that year.

## Indianapolis 500 Auto Race Results

| Year | Number of Years Since 1912 | Winner | Winner's Average Race Speed (mph) |
|------|------|------|------|
| 1912 | 0 | Joe Dawson | 79 |
| 1916 | 4 | Dario Resta | 84 |
| 1920 | 8 | Gaston Cheverolet | 89 |
| 1924 | 12 | L. L. Corum & J. Boyer | 98 |
| 1928 | 16 | Louis Meyer | 99 |
| 1932 | 20 | Fred Frame | 104 |
| 1936 | 24 | Louis Meyer | 109 |
| 1940 | 28 | Wilbur Shaw | 114 |
| 1944 | 32 | — | — |
| 1948 | 36 | Mauri Rose | 120 |
| 1952 | 40 | Troy Ruttman | 129 |
| 1956 | 44 | Pat Flaherty | 128 |
| 1960 | 48 | Jim Rathmann | 139 |
| 1964 | 52 | A. J. Foyt | 147 |
| 1968 | 56 | Bobby Unser | 153 |
| 1972 | 60 | Mark Donohue | 163 |

SOURCE: WWW.INDIANAPOLISMOTORSPEEDWAY.COM

**11.** A. J. Foyt won the Indianapolis 500 in 1977 with an average speed of 161.3 mph. How well does the linear regression model predict this value?

**12.** For what year does the model predict that the average speed would be 200 mph?

**13.** Dario Franchitti won the 2010 race with an average speed of 161.6 mph. Is the model a good predictor for this year? Why or why not?

**11.** Sample answer: 1977 is Year 65 for the model. The model predicts $1.298(65) + 78.231 \approx 162.6$ mph, which is off by only 1.3 mph, an error of less than 1%. The prediction is extrapolated not far beyond the data, so it is fairly accurate.

**12.** Solving $1.298t + 78.231 = 200$ gives $t \approx 94$ years, or the year 2006.

**13.** Sample answer: The model predicts $1.298(98) + 78.231 = 205.4$ mph. The model is not a good predictor for this year. This involves extrapolation far beyond the data, so accuracy would not be expected. Since the 1980s, speeds have been reduced as a safety measure to help reduce the likelihood of serious accidents. Because of the new conditions, the model from prior years is no longer valid.

**14.** Sample plot:

**15.** Sample answer: There is a positive
relationship. Better golfers should
have lower scores for both practice
and competition.

**16.** Sample answer: $c = 0.410p + 50.0$

**17.** It is not possible to tell from the
given information whether the
player is good or poor.

**18.** Sample answer: $c = 0.754p + 20.5$

**19.** Sample answer: With outlier
included, $c = 0.410(95) + 50.0 \approx$
89; without the outlier, $0.754(95) +$
$20.5 \approx 92$. Assuming this golfer is
typical of most of the other team
members, the 92 prediction should
be more reliable. Residual plots
should support this conclusion.

**For Exercises 14–19, use the following information.**

The 11 members of a college women's golf team play a practice round, then
the next day they play a round in competition on the same course. Their
scores are shown in the table. (A golf score is the total number of strokes
required to complete the course, so low scores are better.)

| Player | 1 | 2 | 3 | 4 | 5 | 6 | 7 | 8 | 9 | 10 | 11 |
|---|---|---|---|---|---|---|---|---|---|---|---|
| Practice | 89 | 90 | 87 | 95 | 86 | 81 | 105 | 83 | 88 | 91 | 79 |
| Competition | 94 | 85 | 89 | 89 | 81 | 76 | 89 | 87 | 91 | 88 | 80 |

**14.** Make a scatter plot of competition score vs practice score.

**15.** Describe the relationship between practice and competition scores. Is
there a positive or negative relationship? Explain why you would expect
the scores to have a relationship like the one you observe.

**16.** Find a linear model for the relationship.

**17.** One point on the scatter plot is clearly an outlier. A good golfer can have
a bad round, or a weak golfer can have a good round. Can you tell from
the given data whether the unusual point is produced by a good player
or by a poor player?

**18.** Remove the outlier and find a new linear model for the remaining data.

**19.** Another golf team member shot a 95 in practice. Predict her score in
competition using each of your models. Which do you think is more
reliable?

# CHAPTER 7

## Chapter Extension
### Correlation

You learned in Lesson 7.3 how residuals can help you evaluate how well a linear model fits a data set. In this lesson, you will study another technique for evaluating a linear model.

Recall that the residual errors are the differences between the actual $y$-values in a data set and the $y$-values predicted by a model. The sum of the squares of those errors is a measure of the goodness of the model. The smaller the sum of the squares, the better the model. The process of linear regression produces the model with the least sum of squares.

Even the least-squares model is usually not perfect in explaining the variation in a data set. If it were, the residuals and the sum of the squares of the residuals would be 0. It is often helpful to have another way to measure the strength of a model, which is described by **correlation**. When the values of one variable are associated with the values of another variable, the variables are said to be correlated.

| Forearm Length (cm) | Height (cm) | Forearm Length (cm) | Height (cm) |
|---|---|---|---|
| 24.0 | 157 | 26.5 | 173 |
| 24.5 | 166 | 27.0 | 177 |
| 27.0 | 164 | 27.0 | 174 |
| 24.0 | 164 | 31.0 | 192 |
| 23.0 | 161 | 28.0 | 172 |
| 27.5 | 164 | 29.0 | 180 |
| 27.0 | 167 | 27.0 | 174 |
| 26.0 | 162 | 28.0 | 175 |
| 26.0 | 175 | 32.0 | 185 |
| 28.5 | 166 | 30.0 | 185 |
| 26.5 | 172 | 30.0 | 178 |
| 25.5 | 176 | | |

- Two variables are **positively correlated** if above-average values of the first variable tend to occur with above-average values of the second variable, and below-average values of the two variables also occur together.

- Two variables are **negatively correlated** if above-average values of the first variable tend to occur with below-average values of the second variable, and below-average values of the first variable occur with above-average values of the second variable.

To see how correlation can be measured, consider the data to the left on forearm length and height.

1. Make a scatter plot of the data. Find the mean of the forearm lengths and the mean of the heights. Then find the point whose coordinates are equal to the mean values of the two variables. Draw a horizontal line and a vertical line through that point.

CHAPTER EXTENSION    **Chapter 7**    **257**

## Lesson Objective
- use quantitative measures of correlation to evaluate a model.

## Vocabulary
- correlation
- correlation coefficient
- negatively correlated
- positively correlated
- quadrant count ratio

## Description

In this lesson, students examine two measures of correlation, the quadrant count ratio (QCR) and the more common correlation coefficient ($r$). Pearson's correlation coefficient $r$ is the traditional measure of correlation. The QCR was proposed by Peter Holmes in 2001 as a more intuitive introduction to the concept. The development found here was inspired by an article in *The Mathematics Teacher* [Vol. 102(4), November 2008] by Gary D. Kader and Christine A. Franklin.

> **TEACHING TIP**
>
> Suggest that students refer back to Lesson 7.3 and look at the graph on the first page of that lesson to review the meaning of residual errors.

> **TEACHING TIP**
>
> **Question 1** Students may notice that the table contains two data pairs that are identical (27.0, 174). Tell them that they are plotted at the same point, but the values are used twice for correlation.

## Chapter 7 Extension Answers

1. (27, 172)

**Class Forearm/Height Data**

2. upper right
3. lower left

2. The horizontal and vertical lines divide the graph into 4 quadrants: upper left, upper right, lower left, and lower right. Which quadrant has above-average values for both variables?

3. Which quadrant has below-average values for both variables?

4. Assign a numerical value to each point on the graph, as follows:

• If the point lies in one of the quadrants that you identified in Questions 2 and 3, its value is +1.

• If the point lies in one of the other two regions, its value is −1.

• If the point appears to lie exactly on either the horizontal or vertical line, its value is 0.

5. One measure of the correlation of the two variables is the **quadrant count ratio** (QCR). The QCR is found by counting the total number of points in each quadrant, adding these quadrant counts, and dividing by the total number of points on the graph.

$$\text{QCR} = \frac{\text{Sum of quadrant counts}}{\text{Total number of points}}$$

Determine the QCR for your data.

6. What is the largest possible value of the QCR for *any* data set? Explain.

7. What is the least possible value of the QCR for *any* data set? Explain.

The QCR can be used to describe the correlation of two variables.

• A positive value for the QCR suggests a positive relationship between the variables.

• A negative value for the QCR suggests a negative relationship between the variables.

• If the correlation between the variables is strong, the QCR will be close to 1 or −1.

• If the correlation between the variables is weak, the QCR will be close to 0.

8. What does the value of the QCR tell you about your data?

One weakness of the QCR is that all points have equal weight in its calculation. A more widely used measure of correlation is the **correlation coefficient**. This number, called $r$, gives greater weight to points that are farther from the lines that divide the graph into quadrants.

The calculation of $r$ is complicated. But many calculators and computer programs can compute $r$ for any data set. One advantage of using $r$ is that it specifically describes the *linear* correlation of a data set.

4. Sample answer: upper right quadrant—6 points, each with value +1; lower left quadrant—5 points, each with value +1; upper left quadrant—3 points, each with value −1; lower right quadrant—2 points, each with value −1; on a line—7 points (two of which are identical), each with value 0

5. Sample answer:
$$\frac{6(+1) + 5(+1) + 3(-1) + 2(-1) + 7(0)}{23}$$
$$\approx 0.26$$

6. If all points have a count of +1, the numerator will equal the denominator, and the QCR will be +1.

7. If all points have a count of −1, the numerator will be the negative of the denominator, and the QCR will be −1.

8. Since the QCR is positive, but closer to 0 than to +1, there is a weak positive relationship between forearm length and height for the class.

9. When you perform a linear regression on a calculator, it automatically stores the value of the correlation coefficient. To find it on a TI-83/84 calculator, select **Statistics** on the **VARS** menu. Find **r** under **EQ**.

Find the value of the correlation coefficient to two decimal places for your data.

10. The correlation coefficient shares the same properties listed in Question 7 for the QCR, but it applies strictly to linear relationships. It usually gives a better indication of the strength of such relationships, and it is more commonly used. An $r$-value close to $+1$ or $-1$ implies a strong linear relationship, while the $r$-value will be close to 0 if the linear relationship is weak. An $r$-value of exactly $+1$ or $-1$ means all points lie on a single line.

What does your $r$-value tell you about your data?

11. The correlation between deaths of manatees and the number of powerboat registrations in Florida was a major reason that restrictions were placed on powerboats. Enter the data into a calculator and use linear regression to find the least-squares line. Then find and interpret the value of the correlation coefficient for the data, shown below.

| Year | Powerboat Registrations (in thousands) | Manatees Killed |
|------|-----------------------------------------|-----------------|
| 1977 | 447 | 13 |
| 1978 | 460 | 21 |
| 1979 | 481 | 24 |
| 1980 | 498 | 16 |
| 1981 | 513 | 24 |
| 1982 | 512 | 20 |
| 1983 | 526 | 15 |
| 1984 | 559 | 34 |
| 1985 | 585 | 33 |
| 1986 | 614 | 33 |
| 1987 | 645 | 39 |
| 1988 | 675 | 43 |
| 1989 | 711 | 50 |
| 1990 | 719 | 47 |

9. Sample answer: 0.78
10. Sample answer: The $r$-value is closer to $+1$ than to 0, so there seems to be a fairly strong positive linear relationship.
11. $r = 0.94$; there is a strong positive linear relationship between powerboat registrations and manatee deaths.

12. Sample answer: As long as all points are in the upper left and lower right quadrants, the QCR is −1. But the points could be scattered randomly in those quadrants, rather than lying on the same line.

13a. The equation is a better model for Data Set A because the points in the scatter plot appear to have a positive linear relationship. In the scatter plot for Data Set B, the points follow an obvious curve.

13b. For Data Set A, the residuals would be random, some positive and some negative. For Data Set B, there would be an obvious pattern to the residuals. Those near the ends of the plot would all be negative, and those in the middle would all be positive.

12. For the scatter plot below, all points lie on the same line. Both the QCR and the correlation coefficient would be −1. This situation is called *perfect linear correlation*.

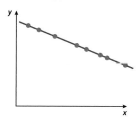

An $r$-value of $+1$ or $-1$ always implies perfect linear correlation. Explain how the QCR might be $-1$ without there being perfect linear correlation.

13. Scatter plots for two different data sets are shown below.

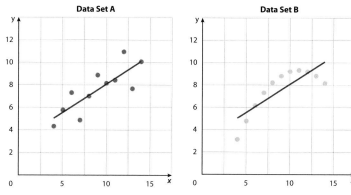

For each data set, the least-squares line is $y = 0.5x + 3$ and the correlation coefficient is 0.82.

a. For which data set is the equation $y = 0.5x + 3$ a better model? Explain.

b. How do you expect the residual plots for the two data sets to compare?

Both the QCR and the correlation coefficient can be useful in helping you to judge the strength of a linear model, although the correlation coefficient is usually preferred. Either one, the QCR or the correlation coefficient, can be greater than the other, depending on the shape of the scatter plot. But neither one should be used as the only measure of the appropriateness of a model. The scatter plot should always be examined first, and residuals provide a complementary measure of goodness of fit.

# Chapter 8
## Systems of Equations and Inequalities

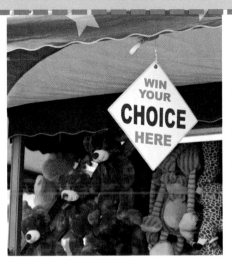

## Mathematical Overview

Learning to write and then solve a system of equations or inequalities is the foundation for solving real-world problems involving situations in which two or more quantities change at the same time. In this chapter, students focus on quantities that change linearly. Students explore writing and solving systems of equations that model real-world situations with no solution (inconsistent system), one solution (consistent, independent system), or unlimited solutions (consistent, dependent system) by graphing, by substitution, by elimination, or a combination of elimination and substitution. Students solve inequalities in two variables by graphing and then expand this skill to solve systems of two variable inequalities by graphing. This chapter concludes with students using what they have learned in the chapter, along with guidelines for linear programming, to optimize the profit or income from a business.

## Lesson Summaries

### Lesson 8.1 Investigation: Using Tables and Graphs to Compare Linear Models

In this Investigation, students, working in pairs, use tables and graphs to solve systems of two linear equations. The pairs work together to create a table of values for two linear functions and find an input value that makes the function values equal. They also use a graphing calculator to find a coordinate pair that is a solution to each of two equations in a system. In addition, they construct and use graphs to solve systems of equations. While completing the Practice for this lesson, students examine a system that has no solution, as well as a system that has unlimited solutions.

### Lesson 8.2 Solving Systems of Two Equations Using Substitution

In this lesson, students become aware that a graph does not always provide an exact solution. The focus for this lesson is on using an algebraic method to solve systems of two equations. The method discussed in this section is the substitution method. Students examine inconsistent systems (systems that have no solution), as well as consistent systems (systems that have one or more solutions).

### Lesson 8.3 Investigation: Solving Systems of Two Equations Using Elimination

In this Investigation, students use the elimination method as an alternative to the substitution method for solving a system of two equations. Students are guided through a solution requiring that only one of the equations be multiplied by a constant to produce identical coefficients in one of the variables before subtracting. Example 1 demonstrates the case in which both equations are multiplied by appropriate constants to produce identical coefficients in one of the variables. Example 2 demonstrates how to determine, algebraically, whether a system is a dependent system.

### Lesson 8.4 R.A.P.

In this lesson, students **R**eview **A**nd **P**ractice solving problems that require the use of skills and concepts taught in previous math levels. The skills reviewed in this lesson are skills that are needed as a basis for solving problems throughout this course.

### Lesson 8.5 Graphing Inequalities in Two Variables

In this lesson, students are transitioned from graphing a single variable inequality on a number line (Chapter 3) to graphing the same inequality on a coordinate plane that includes a second variable. Once students recognize that a region of the plane can be used to represent an inequality, they are introduced to graphs of two-variable inequalities. They recognize that the graph of a related equation in two variables becomes the boundary and every point inside the shaded region satisfies the inequality. They learn how to identify those inequalities for which the set of points on the boundary either do or do not satisfy the inequality, as well as how to interpret other boundaries described by the limits set forth in real-world situations.

### Lesson 8.6 Investigation: Systems of Linear Inequalities

In this Investigation, students use their knowledge of solving a system of equations and of graphing an inequality in two variables on a coordinate plane to find the region of a graph that contains the solution(s) to a system of inequalities on the coordinate plane.

### Chapter 8 Extension: Linear Programming

In this Extension, students use what they learned in Lesson 8.6 about graphing systems of inequalities to optimize profit or income from a business. They become familiar with and follow the guidelines for an optimization method called linear programming.

## Lesson Guide

| Lesson/Objectives | Materials | |
|---|---|---|
| **Chapter 8 Opener: How Are Business Decisions Made?**<br>• understand that equations can help people and businesses make decisions. | | |
| **8.1 Investigation: Using Tables and Graphs to Compare Linear Models**<br>• use a table to solve a system of two linear equations.<br>• use a graph to solve a system of two linear equations. | *Per student:*<br>• graphing calculator<br>• grid paper | |
| **8.2 Solving Systems of Two Equations Using Substitution**<br>• model a decision-making situation with a system of linear equations.<br>• use substitution to solve a system of two linear equations.<br>• recognize an inconsistent system of linear equations. | | *Optional:*<br>• graphing calculator |
| **8.3 Investigation: Solving Systems of Two Equations Using Elimination**<br>• use elimination to solve a system of two linear equations.<br>• recognize a dependent system of linear equations. | | *Optional:*<br>• grid paper |
| **8.4 R.A.P.**<br>• solve problems that require previously learned concepts and skills. | | |
| **8.5 Graphing Inequalities in Two Variables**<br>• draw a graph of a linear inequality involving one or two variables on a coordinate plane. | *Per student:*<br>• grid paper | *Optional:*<br>• your state's building code for stairs<br>• rulers for measuring the risers and treads of staircases in your school<br>• color pencils |
| **8.6 Investigation: Systems of Linear Inequalities**<br>• find the graphical solution to a system of linear inequalities in two variables. | *Per student:*<br>• grid paper | *Optional:*<br>• color pencils |
| **Chapter 8 Extension: Linear Programming**<br>• use a graphical method to solve a linear programming problem in two variables. | *Per student:*<br>• grid paper | *Optional:*<br>• graphing calculator<br>• straightedge<br>• color pencils<br>• TRM table shell for Question 4 |

## Pacing Guide

| | Day 1 | Day 2 | Day 3 | Day 4 | Day 5 | Day 6 | Day 7 | Day 8 | Day 9 | Day 10 |
|---|---|---|---|---|---|---|---|---|---|---|
| **Basic** | p. 261, 8.1 | 8.2 | 8.3 | 8.4 | 8.5 | 8.5, 8.6 | 8.6 | project | review | |
| **Standard** | p. 261, 8.1 | 8.2 | 8.3 | 8.4 | 8.5 | 8.5, 8.6 | 8.6 | project | review | extension |
| **Block** | p. 261, 8.1, 8.2 | 8.2, 8.3 | 8.4, 8.5 | 8.5, 8.6 | 8.6, project | review, extension | | | | |

### Supplement Support

See the Book Companion Website at www.highschool.bfwpub.com/ModelingwithMathematics and the Teacher's Resource Materials (TRM) for additional resources.

CHAPTER

**8**

# Systems of Equations and Inequalities

## CONTENTS

## Lesson Objective

- understand that equations can help people and businesses make decisions.

## Vocabulary

## Description

This Chapter Opener sets the stage for the use of systems of equations in decision-making by business managers as well as ordinary people.

> **TEACHING TIP**
>
> Ask students to think of other situations that may require consumers to choose between alternatives, such as those mentioned in the reading (cell phone plans and music services).

## How Are Business Decisions Made?

Most managers of businesses are faced with many decisions every day. Planning a new product or building, setting a price for a product, and choosing a supplier for materials are just a few of the things that people in business deal with frequently.

Business decision-making often requires weighing alternatives. Buying supplies in large quantities may save money. However, storing those large quantities until they are used can be a problem. It may be possible to determine the best quantity to order and store to minimize total cost.

You probably have already made or will make many business-related decisions in your life. Choosing a cell phone plan or a music service are two examples. Either of these decisions can be daunting, especially since there are so many options to consider. The best choice for a cell phone plan may depend on whether you expect to make many or just a few calls each month. The best choice for a music service may depend on whether you prefer buying songs one at a time or by subscription.

Decisions like these are frequently made with the aid of mathematical models. Equations and inequalities can often be used to clarify choices. You have seen in previous chapters how a single equation can help you make predictions. It is not unusual for complex business decisions to require solving hundreds of equations all at once. Fortunately, computers make finding such solutions easier.

In this chapter, you will learn how to model decision-making situations with a limited number of equations or inequalities. You will also explore a variety of methods for finding solutions.

**262** **Chapter 8** SYSTEMS OF EQUATIONS AND INEQUALITIES

You have used linear functions to model a variety of situations. There are times when more than one equation is needed to construct a model. In this lesson, you will use tables and graphs to solve such problems.

Text messaging using cell phones and similar mobile devices is the most widely used data application in the world. The first phone text message was sent in 1992. In less than 20 years, there were over 2 billion users of text messaging worldwide.

Most people with mobile communications devices buy a voice plan that includes text messaging. But there are many people that want only text messaging capability. These people may buy a *data only plan* from a service provider.

1. One company has a plan that costs $5 per month for up to 200 messages sent or received. Each additional message costs $0.10.
   a. Under this plan, how much would you pay if you send or receive 125 messages in one month?
   b. How much would you pay for 215 messages in one month?
   c. Write an equation that gives the total cost $C_1$ for a month with $n$ messages, if $n$ is greater than 200.

2. Another company also charges $5 per month but allows up to 250 messages. Each message above 250 costs $0.20. Write an equation that gives the total cost $C_2$ for a month with $n$ messages, if $n$ is greater than 250.

3. Compare the costs of the two plans for a month in which 150 messages are used.

4. Compare the costs of the two plans for a month in which 230 messages are used.

5. Compare the costs of the two plans for a month in which the number of messages used is (a) 280 messages and (b) 350 messages.

6. Your answers to Question 5, Parts (a) and (b) suggest that there may be some number of messages between 280 and 350 for which both plans cost the same. Explain why.

7. One way to find if there is a value of $n$ for which the costs of both plans are equal is to use a table. Enter both of your cost equations as functions on the function screen **Y=** of your calculator. Let **Y1** represent the cost of the first plan, $C_1$. Let **Y2** represent the cost of the second plan, $C_2$.

## Lesson 8.1
## Investigation Answers

**1a.** $5
**1b.** $5 + 15($0.10) = $6.50
**1c.** $C_1 = 5 + 0.10(n - 200)$
**2.** $C_2 = 5 + 0.20(n - 250)$
**3.** They are the same, $5.
**4.** Plan 2 costs $5. Plan 1 costs $8. Therefore, Plan 2 is cheaper.
**5a.** Plan 1 costs $13. Plan 2 costs $11. Therefore, Plan 2 is cheaper.
**5b.** Plan 1 costs $20. Plan 2 costs $25. Therefore, Plan 1 is cheaper.
**6.** Sample answer: Plan 2 is cheaper than Plan 1 for $n = 280$. Plan 1 is cheaper than Plan 2 for $n = 350$. The costs of both plans should be equal for some value of $n$ between 280 and 350, although it might not be for a whole number of messages.

**7.**

### CONNECTION

Point out to students that the Investigation compares costs for only the least expensive data plans offered by two companies. If a person consistently sends and/or receives more than the monthly allotment of messages, it would be cheaper to buy a plan that has a higher base charge but includes a larger number of messages.

**5e** Explore

## Lesson Objectives
- use a table to solve a system of two linear equations.
- use a graph to solve a system of two linear equations.

## Vocabulary
- solution to a system of equations
- system of equations

## Materials List
- grid paper

## Description

Students should work in pairs using graphing calculators. They are asked to create a table containing sequences of values of two linear functions in order to find an input value that makes the function values equal. Then they graph both functions and identify the coordinates of the intersection as the solution of the system of equations.

*Wrapping Up the Investigation:*

Conduct a whole-class discussion with students comparing their answers to **Question 13** regarding which data plan is preferable.

### TEACHING TIP

**Questions 1 and 2** If students struggle with writing the equations, remind them that they have modeled similar situations in Chapter 3.

### TEACHING TIP

**Questions 1 and 2** Students may not be familiar with the use of subscripts on variables. Point out that the use of subscripts allows two variables that describe the same type of quantity to be given the same descriptive symbol, but also to be distinguished from each other.

### TEACHING TIP

**Question 7** Remind students that many calculators only allow the use of **X** and **Y** as variables. For this situation, they should always interpret **X** as the variable $n$, **Y1** as $C_1$ and **Y2** as $C_2$.

# LESSON 8.1

**TEACHING TIP**

**Question 8** If students ask about the meaning of *increment*, tell them that it is the difference between successive values of the independent variable.

**COMMON ERROR**

If students do not see values for both of their equations in their tables, remind them that the = sign for both equations must be highlighted on the function screen.

**TEACHING TIP**

For **Question 11**, urge students to use the **TRACE** function of the calculator to find the approximate coordinates of the intersection point (although sometimes exact coordinates can be found in this way). Some students may be aware that it is possible to have the calculator automatically find the point by using the **[CALC] Intersect** function.

**8.**

**9.** $n = 300$ messages

**10.** $C_1 = 5 + 0.1(300 - 200) = 15$;
$C_2 = 5 + 0.2(300 - 250) = 15$

**11.** Sample answer: The graphs of the two cost equations intersect at a point where $n = 300$ and $c = 15$.

**[250, 350] × [5, 25]**

**8.** Use the Table Setup screen **[TBLSET]** to start a table at 280 messages with an increment **ΔTbl** of 1 message. Both the independent and dependent variables should be set to **Auto**.

**9.** Search the **[TABLE]** screen to find the number of messages **X** that results in the same cost for both plans, **Y1** and **Y2**. This number is the value of *n*. What is the value of *n*?

**10.** Substitute your answer to Question 9 into each of your cost equations and evaluate them to find $C_1$ and $C_2$.

**11.** Graph both equations using a window large enough to include your answer to Question 9. Describe the result.

**12.** Summarize your results by describing the intervals of messaging for which (a) both plans have equal costs, (b) Plan 2 is cheaper than Plan 1, and (c) Plan 1 is cheaper than Plan 2.

**13.** Suppose a friend wants to sign up for an inexpensive data-only plan and asks your advice on which of these two plans is better. How would you answer?

## SYSTEMS OF LINEAR EQUATIONS

In the Investigation, you found a coordinate pair $(n, C)$ that is a solution to two different equations. A collection of two or more equations that relate the same variables is called a **system of equations**.

A **solution to a system of equations** consists of a value or values of the variables that make all of the equations in the system true. If the graphs of two linear equations that contain the same two variables intersect at a single point, the coordinates of that point satisfy both equations and form the only solution of the system.

**Note**

Graphs of nonlinear systems of equations may intersect at multiple points.

### Practice for Lesson 8.1

**Connection**

*Revenue* is the total income of a business.

**For Exercises 1–6, use the following information.**

A talented teenage baker has agreed to supply a local cafe with pies for $15 each. She will need $525 in startup costs for her pie business. She also knows that it will cost her $8 to make each pie.

**1.** If *x* is the number of pies she sells to the cafe, write a function that models her total dollar revenue *R*.

**264**    **Chapter 8**    SYSTEMS OF EQUATIONS AND INEQUALITIES

**12a.** Both plans cost the same from 0 to 200 messages and for 300 messages.

**12b.** Plan 2 is cheaper than Plan 1 for between 200 and 300 messages.

**12c.** Plan 1 is cheaper than Plan 2 for more than 300 messages.

**13.** Sample answer: Plan 2 is probably better, since you get more messages for $5 and it is still cheaper if you exceed the 250 message allowance by a little bit. But if you think you might frequently use many more than the allowed number of messages, Plan 1 would be a better choice.

**CONNECTION**

You may wish to identify **Exercises 1–6** as an example of *Break-Even Analysis*, a widely used method for determining the level of output that must be reached before a profit can be made.

## Practice for Lesson 8.1 Answers

**1.** $R = 15x$

2. Write a function that models her total cost C.

3. Graph your revenue and total cost equations on the same set of axes. Find the coordinates of the intersection of the revenue and total cost functions.

4. Confirm your answer to Exercise 3 by using a table.

5. Explain the meaning of your answer to Exercises 3 and 4.

6. For what numbers of pies will the baker make a profit?

7. Consider this system of equations.

$$x = 2y - 4$$
$$5x + 15 = 3y$$

   a. Use grid paper to graph both equations on the same set of axes. Then estimate the solution to the system.

   b. Explain why this graphical method may not always be the best way to solve a system of two equations.

8. Use the [TABLE] feature of a graphing calculator to solve this system of equations.

$$y = 7x + 1$$
$$y = 2x + 9$$

   (Hint: Use an increment of 0.1.)

9. Graph this system of equations.

$$2y - 3x = 4$$
$$9x + 30 = 6y$$

   Explain how you know this system of equations has no solution.

10. Graph this system of equations.

$$y = -0.6x + 2$$
$$3x + 5y = 10$$

   Explain how you know this system of equations has an unlimited number of solutions.

**TEACHING TIP**

**Exercise 3** If students use a calculator to make their graphs, make sure that they can identify which graph represents the revenue function and which represents the cost function. In the sample answer, the revenue function is stored in **Y1** and the cost function in **Y2**.

**TEACHING TIP**

**Exercise 7** Students will only be able to approximate the solution using a graph. The exact solution is $\left(-\frac{18}{7}, \frac{5}{7}\right)$. The purpose of this exercise is to show students that graphing is usually not an optimal way to solve a system of equations.

**TEACHING TIP**

**Exercises 9 and 10** Make sure students understand that a system of two linear equations can have no, one, or infinitely many solutions.

2. $C = 8x + 525$

3. Sample answer: The intersection point is (75, 1,125).

[50, 100] × [1000, 2000]

4. Sample answer:

| X | Y1 | Y2 |
|---|---|---|
| 70 | 1050 | 1085 |
| 71 | 1065 | 1093 |
| 72 | 1080 | 1101 |
| 73 | 1095 | 1109 |
| 74 | 1110 | 1117 |
| 75 | 1125 | 1125 |
| 76 | 1140 | 1133 |

X=75

5. Sample answer: The total revenue of $1,125 from selling 75 pies is exactly equal to the total cost for baking 75 pies.

6. She must bake and sell more than 75 pies to make a profit.

7a. Sample answer: The solution is about (−2.6, 0.7).

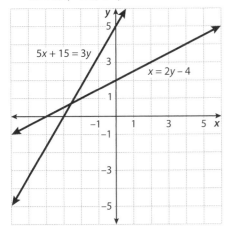

7b. Sample answer: The accuracy of the solution depends on the accuracy of the graph. The solution to this system does not involve integers, so it must be estimated.

8. Sample table:

| X | Y1 | Y2 |
|---|---|---|
| 1 | 8 | 11 |
| 1.1 | 8.7 | 11.2 |
| 1.2 | 9.4 | 11.4 |
| 1.3 | 10.1 | 11.6 |
| 1.4 | 10.8 | 11.8 |
| 1.5 | 11.5 | 12 |
| 1.6 | 12.2 | 12.2 |

X=1.6

Solution: (1.6, 12.2)

9–10. See answers beginning on page 622.

265

**5e** Explain

## Lesson Objectives

- model a decision-making situation with a system of linear equations.
- use substitution to solve a system of two linear equations.
- recognize an inconsistent system of linear equations.

## Vocabulary

- consistent
- inconsistent
- substitution method

## Description

This lesson introduces the first of two algebraic methods for solving a system of two linear equations. The substitution method is presented in the context of movie theater ticket sales. Writing equations to model situations similar to this is also emphasized.

### TEACHING TIP

Students often try to immediately write algebraic equations to model a problem. Point out that a more systematic process, beginning with equations written with words and gradually incorporating symbols, can be helpful in producing appropriate models.

Graphical methods can be used to solve some simple systems of equations. But graphs cannot always provide exact solutions. This lesson focuses on an algebraic method for solving a system of two linear equations.

### SOLVING A SYSTEM OF EQUATIONS ALGEBRAICALLY

A 600-seat movie theater sells regular price tickets for $10. It charges senior citizens only $7. The receipts for a particular sold-out movie are $5,730. How many of the tickets sold were regular price tickets? How many were senior tickets?

This situation can be modeled by a system of two equations.

- One equation can be written to model the total number of tickets sold.

Since the 600-seat theater was sold out, the total number of tickets sold must be 600. This fact can be stated in the form of an equation.

$$\text{Total number of tickets sold} = 600$$

Since two types of tickets were sold, the left side of the above equation can be written as a sum.

$$(\text{Number of regular tickets}) + (\text{Number of senior tickets}) = 600$$

Let $r$ represent the number of regular tickets sold. Let $s$ represent the number of senior tickets sold. The equation can now be written in algebraic form.

$$r + s = 600$$

- A second equation can be written to describe total receipts in dollars.

$$\text{Total receipts} = 5{,}730$$

The left side of this equation can also be written as a sum.

$$(\text{Total value of regular tickets}) + (\text{Total value of senior tickets}) = 5{,}730$$

The total value in each category equals the amount per ticket multiplied by the number of tickets.

$$10r + 7s = 5{,}730$$

The original situation is now modeled by a system of two linear equations.

$$r + s = 600$$
$$10r + 7s = 5{,}730$$

### Recall

A single equation that contains two variables does not have a unique solution.

A solution of this system of equations consists of an ordered pair $(r, s)$ that makes *both* equations true. In general, a solution is found by combining the information contained in both equations. This can be done in several ways. In Lesson 8.1, you saw that the coordinates of the intersection of the graphs of two equations satisfy both equations.

One algebraic method for solving a system of two equations involves substituting the information contained in one of the equations into the other equation. This process is called the **substitution method**.

The first step in the substitution method is to solve either equation for one of the variables. For example, the first equation can be solved for $r$.

| | |
|---|---|
| Original equation | $r + s = 600$ |
| Subtract $s$ from both sides. | $r = 600 - s$ |

Then substitute $600 - s$ for $r$ in the second equation, $10r + 7s = 5{,}730$.

$$10(600 - s) + 7s = 5{,}730$$

Now you have an equation with one unknown, $s$. Solve for $s$.

| | |
|---|---|
| New equation | $10(600 - s) + 7s = 5{,}730$ |
| Distributive Property | $6{,}000 - 10s + 7s = 5{,}730$ |
| Combine like terms. | $6{,}000 - 3s = 5{,}730$ |
| Subtract 6,000 from both sides. | $-3s = -270$ |
| Divide both sides by $-3$. | $s = 90$ |

To find $r$, substitute 90 for $s$ in either of the original equations.

$$r + 90 = 600$$
$$r = 600 - 90$$
$$r = 510$$

The solution to the system of equations is (510, 90). To check this solution, substitute the values in *both* original equations.

| | |
|---|---|
| $r + s = 600$ | $10r + 7s = 5{,}730$ |
| $510 + 90 \overset{?}{=} 600$ | $10(510) + 7(90) \overset{?}{=} 5{,}730$ |
| $600 \overset{?}{=} 600$ ✓ | $5{,}100 + 630 \overset{?}{=} 5{,}730$ |
| | $5{,}730 = 5{,}730$ ✓ |

So, 510 regular price tickets and 90 senior tickets were sold.

### THE SUBSTITUTION METHOD

If a system of two equations in two unknowns has a unique solution, the substitution method can always be used to find the solution.

To solve a system of two equations by substitution,
1. Solve either of the original equations for one of the variables.
2. Substitute the resulting expression in place of that variable in the *other* original equation.
3. Solve this new equation for the remaining variable to find its value.
4. Substitute the value from Step (3) in either of the original equations to find the value of the other variable.
5. Check your solution in both of the original equations.

**ADDITIONAL EXAMPLE**

A person has 20 coins. Some are nickels, and some are dimes. The total value of the coins is $1.30. How many are there of each coin?

6 dimes and 14 nickels

### E X A M P L E

A market has a total of 27 employees. Each full-time employee makes $375 per week and each part-time employee makes $160 per week. A total of $7,975 in wages is paid out each week. How many full-time employees work at the market? How many part-time employees work at the market?

**Solution:**

First, create a mathematical model of the situation. The first sentence, "A market has a total of 27 employees," can be written in equation form.

$$\text{Total number of employees} = 27$$

Let $f$ represent the number of full-time employees, and $p$ the number of part-time employees. Now the equation can be written in algebraic form.

$$f + p = 27$$

Next, the sentence "A total of $7,975 in wages is paid out each week" can be written in equation form.

$$\text{Total wages} = 7,975$$

The left side of the equation can be written as a sum.

$$(\text{Wages paid to full-time employees}) + (\text{Wages paid to part-time employees}) = 7,975$$

The total wages for each type of employee equals the number of employees multiplied by the amount paid to each employee.

$$375f + 160p = 7,975$$

The situation is modeled by this system of two linear equations.

$$f + p = 27$$
$$375f + 160p = 7,975$$

This system of equations can be solved by substitution using the steps shown on page 268.

Original system
$$f + p = 27$$
$$375f + 160p = 7{,}975$$

1.  Solve the first equation for $f$. $\qquad\qquad f = 27 - p$

2.  Substitute for $f$ in the second equation. $\qquad 375(27 - p) + 160p = 7{,}975$

3.  Solve for $p$.
    Simplify. $\qquad\qquad\qquad\qquad\qquad\qquad 10{,}125 - 215p = 7{,}975$
    Subtract 10,125 from both sides. $\qquad\qquad\quad -215p = -2{,}150$
    Divide by $-215$. $\qquad\qquad\qquad\qquad\qquad\qquad p = 10$

4.  Substitute 10 for $p$ in one of the $\qquad\qquad\quad f + 10 = 27$
    original equations.
    Simplify. $\qquad\qquad\qquad\qquad\qquad\qquad\qquad f = 17$

5.  Check to see whether these values satisfy both equations:

    $$f + p = 27 \qquad\qquad\qquad 375f + 160p = 7{,}975$$
    $$\overset{?}{17 + 10 = 27} \qquad\qquad\qquad 375(17) + 160(10) \overset{?}{=} 7{,}975$$
    $$27 = 27 \checkmark \qquad\qquad\qquad\qquad 6{,}375 + 1{,}600 \overset{?}{=} 7{,}975$$
    $$7{,}975 = 7{,}975 \checkmark$$

So, there are 17 full-time and 10 part-time employees.

## CONSISTENT AND INCONSISTENT SYSTEMS OF EQUATIONS

 **2**

Use substitution to solve this system of equations.

$$x - 3y = 4$$
$$6y + 5 = 2x$$

**Solution:**

| | |
|---|---|
| First original equation | $x - 3y = 4$ |
| Solve the first equation for $x$. | $x = 3y + 4$ |
| Substitute for $x$ in the second equation. | $6y + 5 = 2(3y + 4)$ |
| Simplify. | $6y + 5 = 6y + 8$ |
| Subtract $6y$ from both sides. | $5 = 8$ |

If you try to solve a system of equations and get a result that is a false statement, such as $5 = 8$, you can be sure that there are no values of the variables that make both equations in the system true. This means that there is no solution to the original system of equations.

**ADDITIONAL EXAMPLE**

Use substitution to solve this system of equations.

$$3y = x + 4$$
$$2x + 1 = 6y$$

no solution; The system is inconsistent.

A system of equations is **inconsistent** if it has no solutions. In Exercise 9 of Lesson 8.1, you found that the graphs of the given equations were parallel lines. This is what happens when a system of equations is inconsistent.

A system of equations is **consistent** if it has one or more solutions.

## Practice for Lesson 8.2

**For Exercises 1–4, use the substitution method to solve the system of equations. Identify any system that is inconsistent.**

**1.** $x - y = 2$
$2x + 3y = 9$

**2.** $2x = 3y + 19$
$4x - y = 13$

**3.** $5x - y = 20$
$2y = 10x - 8$

**4.** $5x = 4y - 26$
$3x + 2y = 2$

**5.** A coffee shop sells several different kinds of coffee. The shop also uses some of its coffees to make its own custom blends. Coffee A sells for $6.00 a pound. Coffee B sells for $10.00 a pound. The shop's manager wants to create a blend of types A and B that sells for $7.00 a pound. The manager wants to make 10 pounds of this blend.

   **a.** Write an equation that models the total number of pounds of coffees A and B in the blend. Use $a$ to represent the number of pounds of coffee A used in the blend. Use $b$ for the number of pounds of coffee B used in the blend.

   **b.** What is the total dollar value of the 10 pounds of blended coffees?

   **c.** Write an equation that represents this total dollar value in terms of $a$ and $b$.

   **d.** What is the number of pounds of each coffee in 10 pounds of the blend?

## Practice for Lesson 8.2 Answers

**1.** $(3, 1)$

**2.** $(2, -5)$

**3.** inconsistent

**4.** $(-2, 4)$

**5a.** $a + b = 10$

**5b.** $70

**5c.** $6a + 10b = 70$

**5d.** $7\frac{1}{2}$ pounds of coffee A and $2\frac{1}{2}$ pounds of coffee B

**6.** A young woman is saving money to buy a used car. The price of the car is $5,525, but it will be reduced by $150 for each month that the car remains unsold. She currently has $3,250 in her savings account and will be able to save an additional $175 each month.

   **a.** Write an equation that models the price in dollars $d$ of the car after $n$ months.

   **b.** Write an equation that models the number of dollars $d$ the woman will have saved after $n$ months.

   **c.** Determine the number of months until the woman can buy the car.

   **d.** Explain how you could use a graph to solve this problem.

   **e.** Explain how you could use a table to solve this problem.

**7.** The promotions manager for a baseball team is planning a special opening day giveaway. Each of the first 5,000 fans will receive either a souvenir cap or a blanket with the team logo. The manager knows that the caps cost $5 each and the blankets cost $12 each. The amount to be spent on purchasing the caps and blankets is $32,000.

   **a.** Write a system of equations that models this situation. Let $c$ represent the number of caps. Let $b$ represent the number of blankets.

   **b.** Solve the system algebraically.

   **c.** Use a graph to solve the system.

   **d.** Use a table to solve the system.

   **e.** How many caps and blankets should be purchased?

**8.** An order of smartphones and MP3 players totals $4,003 without any taxes or other charges. The cost of each smartphone is $194.50, and the cost of each MP3 player is $159.50. The shipment contains a total of 24 devices. How many of each device is in the order?

**9.** A corner stand sells peanuts for $1.00 per pound and walnuts for $2.00 per pound. The operator of the stand wants to make 50 pounds of peanut-walnut mix. He will maintain the cost per pound of each type of nut and sell the mix for $1.60 a pound. How many pounds of each type of nut should he put into the mix?

**10.** A car share company's "occasional driving" plan has a $50 annual fee and charges $8 per hour for a car. Another plan from the same company has a monthly fee of $50 but charges only $7.20 per hour.

   **a.** How many hours of driving in a year would result in equal total costs for both plans?

   **b.** If you use a car for 200 hours in a year, which plan is the better deal?

---

**Connection**

A car share company rents cars on a shared basis. Members usually pay an annual or monthly fee. They can then find a car on the street at a specified location. Rentals can be for intervals as short as one hour.

---

SOLVING SYSTEMS OF TWO EQUATIONS USING SUBSTITUTION    **Lesson 8.2**    **271**

---

**6a.** $d = 5,525 - 150n$

**6b.** $d = 3,250 + 175n$

**6c.** 7

**6d.** Sample answer: Graph both equations from Parts (a) and (b) on the same axes. Find the point of intersection of the lines. The coordinates of that point $(n, d)$ form the solution to the system.

**6e.** Make a table of $n$ and $d$ values for each equation from Parts (a) and (b). Examine the tables to find a value of $n$ for which the $d$ values are identical in both tables. The common $(n, d)$ pair is the solution to the system.

**7a.** $c + \phantom{0}b = 5,000$
$5c + 12b = 32,000$

---

**CONNECTION**

**Exercise 10** Car share companies are a recent innovation in car rentals. Available in many cities, they place cars in many locations. The cars can then be rented by the hour or by the day. Zipcar™ is one popular brand.

---

**COMMON ERROR**

**Exercise 10** Students may need to be reminded that the first plan includes an *annual* fee, while the second includes a *monthly* fee.

---

**7b.**
$$c + \phantom{0}b = 5,000$$
$$5c + 12b = 32,000$$
$$c = 5,000 - b$$
$$5(5,000 - b) + 12b = 32,000$$
$$25,000 + 7b = 32,000$$
$$7b = 7,000$$
$$b = 1,000$$
$$c = 4,000$$

**7c.** Sample answer: For $c = 5,000 - b$, let **Y1** $= 5,000 - $ **X**.
For $c = 6,400 - 2.4b$, let **Y2** $= 6,400 - 2.4$**X**.

$[0, 8000] \times [0, 5000]$

---

**7d.** Sample answer:

**7e.** The manager should purchase 4,000 caps and 1,000 blankets.

**8.** Sample answer:
$$s + m = 24$$
$$194.50s + 159.50m = 4,003$$
There are 5 smartphones and 19 MP3 players.

**9.** Sample answer:
$$p + w = 50$$
$$1.00p + 2.00w = 1.60(50)$$
He should use 20 pounds of peanuts and 30 pounds of walnuts.

**10a.** Sample answer:
$$C = 50 + 8h$$
$$C = 12(50) + 7.20h$$
For 687.5 hours, each plan costs $5,550.

**10b.** The first plan, with the annual fee, is the better bargain for any number of hours less than 687.5.

**5e** Explore

## Lesson Objectives
- use elimination to solve a system of two linear equations.
- recognize a dependent system of linear equations.

## Vocabulary
- dependent
- elimination method

## Materials List

## Description

The elimination method is presented as an alternative to the substitution method for solving a system of two linear equations. Students are guided through a relatively simple instance of using this method, requiring that only one of the equations be multiplied by a constant before subtracting the equations. Example 1 then illustrates the more general case of multiplying both equations by appropriate constants to produce identical coefficients for one of the variables. This method is sometimes called the "linear combination" method.

*Wrapping Up the Investigation:*
Remind students that the choice of which variable to eliminate is arbitrary, but that it may be easier to determine a common multiple for one of the variables rather than the other. It is not necessary to find the least common multiple (LCM), although using the LCM produces smaller numbers in the resulting equation.

### TEACHING TIP

**Question 3** Point out to students that adding (or subtracting) the two equations in a system is one way of combining the information contained in both equations into a single equation in one variable. In the substitution method, the "combining" is done in a different way, by inserting the information from one equation into the other.

### Lesson 8.3 INVESTIGATION: Solving Systems of Two Equations Using Elimination

The substitution method from the previous lesson works well for some systems of equations. This lesson introduces another algebraic method that is sometimes more efficient.

As you saw in Lesson 8.2, the substitution method is easy to use in principle. But for some systems, the solution process can become complicated. There is another algebraic method for solving a system of two linear equations.

Two friends have started a small business making unfinished furniture. Their first products are bookcases and small cabinets. Both items are made from wide boards and thin plywood.

One bookcase is built from 10 feet of board and 5 square feet of plywood. One cabinet requires 5 feet of board and 8 square feet of plywood.

There are 165 feet of wide board and 132 square feet of plywood on hand. How many bookcases and cabinets would use up all of the board and plywood material?

1. Let $B$ represent the number of bookcases made, and let $C$ represent the number of cabinets made. This situation can be modeled by the following system of equations:

$$10B + 5C = 165$$
$$5B + 8C = 132$$

Multiply both sides of the second equation by 2. Does this new equation have the same solutions as the original second equation? Explain.

2. Rewrite the system of equations, but replace the second equation with the new equation you found in Question 1.

3. Subtract the first equation from the new second equation. To do this, subtract the left side of the first equation from the left side of the second equation. Also, subtract the right side of the first equation from the right side of the second equation. Simplify both sides of the resulting equation.

4. Explain how you know that this new equation is true for the furniture situation.

5. Solve your equation from Question 3 and interpret the result.

6. You now have a value for $C$. Substitute this value back into either of the original equations to find $B$.

### TEACHING TIP

**Question 3** You may want to suggest that students continue to write the equations in vertical form, stacked one above the other, during the solution process (as done in the Examples).

### TEACHING TIP

**Question 4** Make sure students understand that the Properties of Equality justify adding or subtracting the equations.

## Lesson 8.3 Investigation Answers

1. $10B + 16C = 264$; Yes, multiplying both sides of an equation by any non-zero number produces an equivalent equation.

2. $10B + 5C = 165$
   $10B + 16C = 264$

3.
$$(10B + 16C) - (10B + 5C) = 264 - 165$$
$$10B + 16C - 10B - 5C = 99$$
$$11C = 99$$

4. Sample answer: Equal quantities have been subtracted from equal quantities, so according to the Properties of Equality, the results must be equal.

5. $C = 9$; Nine cabinets should be made.

6. Sample answer:
$$10B + 5C = 165$$
$$10B + 5(9) = 165$$
$$10B = 120$$
$$B = 12$$

**7.** Write the solution (B, C) to the system.

**8.** How many bookcases and cabinets would need to be built to use up all of the board and plywood material?

**9.** Check your answer to Question 8 to see that it satisfies all the requirements of the original problem statement.

## THE ELIMINATION METHOD

To solve for C in the Investigation, you combined the two equations in a way that eliminated B. This solution process is called the **elimination method** for solving a system of two linear equations in two variables. The key to this method is to make the coefficient of one of the variables the same in both equations.

> To solve a system of two equations by elimination,
>
> 1. Write the equations, one above the other, with like terms aligned.
> 2. Multiply one or both equations by numbers that will result in the same or opposite coefficients for one of the variables in both equations. *Be sure to multiply every term in an equation by the same number.*
> 3. Add or subtract the new equations in such a way that one variable is eliminated.
> 4. Solve for the remaining variable.
> 5. Substitute the result in one of the original equations to find the value of the other variable.
> 6. Check your solution in both of the original equations.

Sometimes the coefficients of neither variable can be made equal with a single multiplication by a whole number. In such cases, multiply each equation by a different number. Choose multipliers so that one of the variables has the same or opposite coefficients in both equations.

**7.** (12, 9)

**8.** Build 12 bookcases and 9 cabinets.

**9.** Twelve bookcases would use 12(10) = 120 feet of board, and 9 cabinets would use 9(5) = 45 feet of board, for a total of 165 feet. The bookcases would use 12(5) = 60 square feet of plywood and the cabinets would use 9(8) = 72 square feet of plywood, for a total of 132 square feet. All the available materials would be used.

> **TEACHING TIP**
>
> Students may find the elimination method easier to use if in Step (2), they produce opposite values for the coefficients of one of the variables. Then the equations can be added rather than subtracted.

> **TEACHING TIP**
>
> Point out to students that instead of using substitution to find the value of the second variable, it is sometimes easier to solve for the second variable by elimination.

> **TEACHING TIP**
>
> Point out to students that if one or both equations contain fractions or decimals, it is helpful if they use multiplication to "clear" them from the equation(s) before proceeding with the elimination method.

> **TEACHING TIP**
>
> If students ask about computer methods for solving large systems of equations, tell them that they involve representing all of the equations with matrices. Matrix methods are based in part on the elimination method.

## ADDITIONAL EXAMPLE

Solve this system of equations.

$$5x = 3y + 2$$
$$2x + 1 = 9y$$

$$\left(\frac{7}{13}, \frac{3}{13}\right)$$

Solve this system of equations.

$$3x + 8y = 1$$
$$5x = 6y + 21$$

**Solution:**

This system of equations can be solved by elimination using the steps shown on page 273.

1.  Begin by writing the equations so that like terms are aligned.

$$3x + 8y = 1$$
$$5x - 6y = 21$$

2.  Multiply every term of the first equation by 5 and every term of the second equation by 3.

$$5(3x + 8y) = 5(1)$$
$$3(5x - 6y) = 3(21)$$

Simplify.

$$15x + 40y = 5$$
$$15x - 18y = 63$$

3.  Subtract the second equation from the first. $\qquad 58y = -58$
4.  Solve for $y$. Divide both sides by 58. $\qquad y = -1$
5.  Substitute $-1$ for $y$ in the first equation. $\qquad 3x + 8(-1) = 1$

    Solve for $x$. Simplify. $\qquad 3x - 8 = 1$

    Add 8 to both sides. $\qquad 3x = 9$

    Divide both sides by 3. $\qquad x = 3$

6.  Check to see whether these values satisfy both equations:

$$3x + 8y = 1 \qquad\qquad 5x = 6y + 21$$
$$3(3) + 8(-1) \stackrel{?}{=} 1 \qquad\qquad 5(3) \stackrel{?}{=} 6(-1) + 21$$
$$9 - 8 \stackrel{?}{=} 1 \qquad\qquad 15 \stackrel{?}{=} -6 + 21$$
$$1 = 1 \checkmark \qquad\qquad 15 = 15 \checkmark$$

The solution is $(3, -1)$.

The elimination method requires a little more planning than the substitution method. You have to decide on the initial multipliers. But the tradeoff is that the algebra may be less complicated. Also, the elimination method can be generalized in a way that allows systems of large numbers of equations to be solved using computers.

### E X A M P L E ❷

Solve this system of equations.

$$6y = 2x + 10$$
$$x + 5 = 3y$$

**Solution:**

First, write the equations with like terms aligned.

$$-2x + 6y = 10$$
$$x - 3y = -5$$

Multiply the second equation by 2.

$$-2x + 6y = 10$$
$$2x - 6y = -10$$

Add the equations.                 0    0

Since this last equation is true, the system of equations is consistent. But it has more than one solution. The equations are equivalent, so any solution of one equation is also a solution of the other.

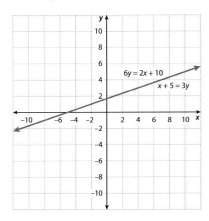

The graphs of both the equations are the same line. A system of equations such as this is called **dependent**.

## ADDITIONAL EXAMPLE ❷

Solve this system of equations.

$$2y = 5x - 3$$
$$15x = 6y + 9$$

This system is dependent and has infinitely many solutions.

**TEACHING TIP**

Students may wonder how any of the "infinitely many" solutions to a dependent system can be found. Tell them that they can choose any value for one of the variables and substitute it into one of the equations to find a value for the other variable. The resulting pair is a solution of both equations.

# LESSON 8.3

## Practice for Lesson 8.3 Answers

1. Sample answer: The coefficients of $x$ in the equations are 3 and 5, which are factors of 15. To produce a new system of equations in which the coefficients of $x$ are both equal to 15, multiply the first equation by 5 and the second equation by 3.

2. $(-7, -4)$

3. inconsistent

4. dependent

5. $(2, -1)$

6. $(2, -3)$

7. $\left(\dfrac{13}{31}, -\dfrac{1}{31}\right)$

8. Sample answer: When it is easy to solve one of the equations for one of the variables, such as when one of the coefficients is 1, substitution is the easier method to use. This is the case for Exercises 3 and 6.

9a. $2h + d = 7.50$

9b. $h + 2d = 6.00$

9c. A hamburger costs $3.00 and a soft drink costs $1.50.

10a. $20r + 34c = 50.40$
$15r + 17c = 32.70$

10b. Multiply $20r + 34c = 50.40$ by 3 and $15r + 17c = 32.70$ by 4.

10c. $0.60

---

## Practice for Lesson 8.3

1. In Example 1, explain how you know to multiply the first equation by 5 and the second equation by 3.

**For Exercises 2–7, use the elimination method to solve the system of equations. Identify any system that is either inconsistent or dependent.**

2. $5x = 9y + 1$
$3y = 2x + 2$

3. $a = 2b + 1$
$2a - 4b = 7$

4. $3s + 2t = 5$
$9s + 6t = 15$

5. $3x + 7y = -1$
$2x - 3y = 7$

6. $5C = D + 13$
$4C = 5 - D$

7. $5p + 3q = 2$
$7p - 2q = 3$

8. Identify any of Exercises 2–7 for which you might prefer to solve using the substitution method. Explain your choice.

**For Exercises 9–11, solve using the elimination method.**

9. At a ball game, one person bought 2 hamburgers and a soft drink for $7.50. Another person bought 1 hamburger and 2 soft drinks for $6.00.
   a. Write an equation that models the first person's total cost. Let $h$ represent the price of a hamburger and $d$ the price of a drink.
   b. Write an equation that models the second person's total cost.
   c. Find the cost of one hamburger and the cost of one soft drink.

10. A florist offers two package deals of roses and carnations. One package offers 20 roses and 34 carnations for $50.40. The other package contains 15 roses and 17 carnations for $32.70.
    a. Write a system of two equations that models the costs of both packages in terms of the cost $r$ of one rose and the cost $c$ of one carnation.
    b. What are the smallest numbers that you can multiply each equation by in order to eliminate $r$ from your system?
    c. Find the cost of one carnation.

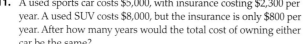

**11.** A used sports car costs \$5,000, with insurance costing \$2,300 per year. A used SUV costs \$8,000, but the insurance is only \$800 per year. After how many years would the total cost of owning either car be the same?

**For Exercises 12–14, solve using any method (table, graph, or algebra).**

**12.** A student has \$100 in the bank and is spending it at the rate of \$3 each day. His friend has \$20 in the bank and is adding to it by saving \$5 each day. How many days will it take for the two friends to have the same amount of money?

**13.** A carnival booth has small stuffed bears and large stuffed bears that it uses for prizes. Each small bear is worth \$2.50, and each large bear is worth \$5. If the booth has a total of 200 bears, with a total value of \$625, how many bears of each size are there?

**14.** One type of prepaid phone card offers two options for its use. You can make a call for 2.9 cents a minute with no extra charge. Or you can pay a "connection charge" of 40 cents and pay only 1 cent a minute.
   **a.** For how many minutes of calling is the total cost the same for both options?
   **b.** For what range of times is the connection charge option the less-expensive choice?
   **c.** For what range of times is the 2.9 cents per minute option the less-expensive choice?

**TEACHING TIP**

**Exercises 12–14** can be solved by any method of the student's choosing. You may want to ask why they chose the methods they used.

**11.** 2 years

**12.** Sample answer:
$A = 100 - 3d$
$A = 20 + 5d$
After 10 days, they will both have \$70

**13.** Sample answer:
$s + l = 200$
$2.50s + 5l = 625$
There are 150 small bears and 50 large bears.

**14a.** Sample answer:
$C = 2.9t$
$C = 40 + 1t$
For a call lasting 21 minutes, the total cost is approximately the same for both options.

**14b.** for calls over 21 minutes

**14c.** for calls under 21 minutes

# LESSON 8.4

## Lesson Objective

• solve problems that require previously learned concepts and skills.

## Exercise Reference

Exercise 1: Lesson 8.1

Exercise 2: Lesson 8.3

Exercises 3–4: Appendix C

Exercises 5–10: Appendix B

Exercises 11–16: Appendix E

Exercises 17–22: Appendix K

Exercise 23: Lesson 4.1

Exercise 24: Lesson 3.7

Exercise 25: Lesson 2.2

Exercise 26: Lesson 3.2

Exercises 27–30: Lesson 6.1

## Lesson 8.4
## R.A.P. Answers

1. system
2. dependent
3. C
4. B
5. 0.8
6. $0.\overline{27}$
7. 0.07
8. $\dfrac{9}{1,000}$
9. $\dfrac{82}{25}$ or $3\dfrac{7}{25}$
10. $\dfrac{4}{9}$
11. $\dfrac{3}{50}$, 0.06
12. $\dfrac{127}{100}$ or $1\dfrac{27}{100}$, 1.27
13. $\dfrac{1}{10}$, 0.1
14. 7%
15. 55%
16. 650%
17. $4.7 \times 10^3$
18. $8.1 \times 10^6$
19. $9.53 \times 10^1$
20. 600,000
21. 212.4
22. 3,800
23. 135°

---

## Lesson 8.4  |  R.A.P.

**Fill in the blank.**

1. Two or more equations that relate the same variables are called a(n) _____ of equations.

2. If the equations of a system of two equations are equivalent, then the system is called a(n) _____ system.

**Choose the correct answer.**

3. In a piggy bank, there are 25 nickels and 15 dimes. What is the ratio of the number of nickels to the total number of coins?

   A. $\dfrac{5}{3}$     B. $\dfrac{3}{5}$     C. $\dfrac{5}{8}$     D. $\dfrac{3}{8}$

4. There are 24 students in your class. Eleven of the students are males. Which expression shows the ratio of the number of males to females?

   A. $\dfrac{11}{24}$     B. $\dfrac{11}{13}$     C. $\dfrac{13}{24}$     D. $\dfrac{13}{11}$

**Write the fraction as a decimal.**

5. $\dfrac{4}{5}$           6. $\dfrac{3}{11}$           7. $\dfrac{7}{100}$

**Write the decimal as a fraction or mixed number.**

8. 0.009          9. 3.28          10. $0.\overline{4}$

**Write the percent as a fraction or mixed number and as a decimal.**

11. 6%          12. 127%          13. 10%

**Write the fraction or mixed number as a percent.**

14. $\dfrac{7}{100}$          15. $\dfrac{11}{20}$          16. $6\dfrac{1}{2}$

**Write the number in scientific notation.**

17. 4,700          18. 8,100,000          19. 95.3

**Write the number in standard form.**

20. $6 \times 10^5$          21. $2.124 \times 10^2$          22. $3.8 \times 10^3$

23. Find the measure of one angle in a regular octagon.

**24.** Write an inequality for the following statement. Then graph the inequality.

n is less than or equal to 5 and greater than −1.

**25 a.** The two variables in the table are proportional. Explain how you know.

| Weeks w | 6 | 7 | 8 | 9 | 10 |
|---------|---|---|---|---|----|
| Days d | 42 | 49 | 56 | 63 | 70 |

**b.** Find the constant of proportionality and write an equation for a direct variation function that models the data.

**26.** To reseed a yard, a landscaping company charges $50 for seed and fertilizer, plus $40 per hour for labor. Write an equation that models the total cost C for a job that takes t hours.

**For Exercises 27–30, use the circle graph below that shows the regions of birth for foreign-born people living in the United States.**

**Region of Birth**

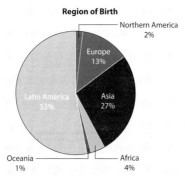

SOURCE: 2008 AMERICAN COMMUNITY SURVEY

**27.** What is the most common region of birth?

**28.** List the regions in order from most common to least common.

**29.** About how many times more people were born in Asia than in Europe?

**30.** Of all people living in the United States who are foreign-born, find the ratio of those born in the Western Hemisphere (Latin America and Northern America) to those born outside the Western Hemisphere.

LESSON 8.4

**24.** $-1 < n \le 5$

**25a.** Sample answer: The ratios of days d to weeks w are all equal to 7 days per week.

**25b.** constant of proportionality: 7 days per week; d = 7w

**26.** C = 50 + 40t

**27.** Latin America

**28.** Latin America, Asia, Europe, Africa, Northern America, Oceania

**29.** about twice as many

**30.** 55% to 45%, or 11 to 9

# LESSON 8.5

## Lesson Objective

- draw a graph of a linear inequality involving one or two variables on a coordinate plane.

## Vocabulary

## Description

This lesson begins with a transition from graphing a single-variable inequality on a number line to graphing the same inequality on a coordinate plane that includes a second variable. Once students see that a region of the plane can represent an inequality, they are introduced to graphs of two-variable inequalities.

### CONNECTION

You may want to suggest that students research their own state's building code to see if the requirements for staircases are similar to those discussed in this lesson. You could also have them measure the riser height and tread depth of staircases at your school to see how they compare to the code requirements.

In Chapter 3, you graphed inequalities in one variable on a number line. This lesson introduces the use of a coordinate plane to graph inequalities that involve two variables.

All states have building codes. Many of the codes can be expressed as mathematical inequalities because they establish limits on what can be done.

Have you ever thought the steps on a certain staircase were hard to climb? State building codes place limits on staircase design for safety reasons. A typical requirement for public buildings is stated in this way:

"Maximum riser height is 7 inches and minimum riser height is 4 inches."

The riser height code can be expressed as this compound inequality.

$$4 \le R \le 7$$

It can also be represented graphically on a number line.

But staircases have both risers and treads. So a two-dimensional grid can be used to show possible values for riser heights $R$ and tread depths $T$ at the same time. On such a grid, the graphs of $R = 4$ and $R = 7$ are vertical lines.

### Note

A *riser* is the vertical front of a stair. The horizontal surface that you step on is called a *tread*.

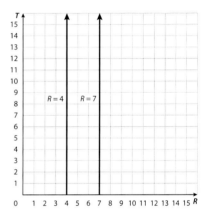

280    **Chapter 8**    SYSTEMS OF EQUATIONS AND INEQUALITIES

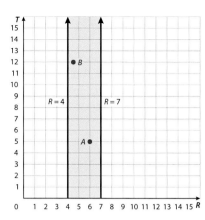

All points on or between the graphs of $R = 4$ and $R = 7$ satisfy the inequality $4 \leq R \leq 7$. Shading the region between the vertical lines shows this. The yellow-shaded region, including its boundaries, is the graph of the inequality $4 \leq R \leq 7$ in two dimensions.

Graphing this in the coordinate plane allows a relationship between $R$ and $T$ to be shown. Every point in the yellow-shaded region and on the boundary lines identifies a combination of riser height and tread depth that satisfies the riser code. For example, point $A$ corresponds to a riser height of 6 inches and a tread depth of 5 inches. Point $B$ corresponds to a riser height of $4\frac{1}{2}$ inches and a tread depth of 12 inches. Both combinations have riser heights between 4 and 7 inches. But there is usually also a code for tread depth, such as

"Minimum tread depth is 11 inches."

This requirement can be expressed as this inequality.

$$T \geq 11$$

It can be graphed as another shaded region on the grid.

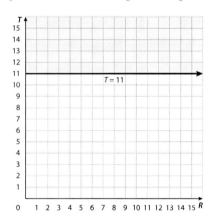

All points on or above the graph of $T = 11$ satisfy the inequality $T \geq 11$.

**Note**

The boundaries that represent limiting values are drawn as solid lines. Since there is no upper limit on the tread depth, there is no solid line at the top of the graph.

**TEACHING TIP**

Point out to students that in this situation, as well as in most of the contextual situations in this lesson and Lesson 8.6, either variable could be considered to be the independent variable. There is no natural dependence of one variable on the other. So, graphs can be constructed with either variable on the horizontal axis.

**TEACHING TIP**

Make sure students understand that the graph of an inequality is a two-dimensional region of the plane, not a point or a line.

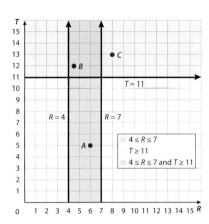

The two graphs can be combined to show both relationships, $4 \leq R \leq 7$ *and* $T \geq 11$.

Only points in the green region represent riser/tread combinations that satisfy both building codes. Point B still corresponds to a legal staircase with $4\frac{1}{2}$-inch risers and 12-inch treads. But the tread depth for point A is too short to satisfy the code. And point C satisfies the tread depth requirement but represents a riser height that is too great to satisfy the code.

## INEQUALITIES IN TWO VARIABLES

To graph an inequality in two variables, first determine the boundaries. Replace the inequality sign with an equal sign. Then graph the resulting equation.

The graph of the inequality is a shaded region on one side of the boundary. To determine which side of the boundary to shade, choose any point on one side of the line and substitute its coordinates in the inequality. If the point satisfies the inequality, shade the side containing that point. Otherwise, shade the opposite side. Every point in that shaded region satisfies the inequality.

## ADDITIONAL EXAMPLE ①

A medium men's baseball jersey requires $2\frac{1}{4}$ yards of fabric. A large jersey requires $3\frac{3}{4}$ yards of fabric. Draw a graph that shows the possible numbers of medium and large jerseys that can be made if 75 yards of fabric are available.

Sample graph:

## E X A M P L E ①

A fruit stand sells peaches for $0.40 each and apples for $0.30 each. Draw a graph that shows the possible numbers of peaches P and apples A that can be bought for any amount of money up to and including $5.00.

**Solution:**

The possible values of P and A must satisfy the inequality $0.40P + 0.30A \leq 5.00$. The upper limit of the inequality represents spending the entire $5.00, which can be expressed by the equation $0.40P + 0.30A = 5.00$. Its graph is a line that is a boundary of the graph of the inequality.

The line can be drawn most easily using intercepts. For $P = 0$, $A = 16\frac{2}{3}$. For $A = 0$, $P = 12\frac{1}{2}$.

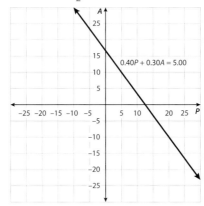

Substitute the coordinates of a few points in the inequality.

For the point $(0, 10)$,

$$0.40(0) + 0.30(10) \overset{?}{\le} 5.00$$
$$3 \le 5.00$$

For the point $(10, 0)$,

$$0.40(10) + 0.30(0) \overset{?}{\le} 5.00$$
$$4 \le 5.00$$

For the point $(10, 10)$,

$$0.40(10) + 0.30(10) \overset{?}{\le} 5.00$$
$$7 \nleq 5.00$$

For the point $(0, 0)$,

$$0.40(0) + 0.30(0) \overset{?}{\le} 5.00$$
$$0 \le 5.00$$

TEACHING TIP

Although the graphs of the boundaries in the Examples are drawn using intercepts, point out to students that they can solve an inequality for one of the variables in order to graph it in slope-intercept form, using methods from Lesson 3.6 and Chapter 5.

TEACHING TIP

Emphasize that *any* point not on a boundary of the graph of an inequality can be used to determine which side to shade. Ask students to explain why the origin $(0, 0)$ is often a convenient point to test.

**Note**

Any point not on a boundary of the graph of an inequality can be used to determine which region to shade. The origin (0, 0) is often the easiest point to check.

The points (0, 10), (10, 0), and (0, 0) all satisfy the inequality $0.40P + 0.30A \leq 5.00$, but (10, 10) does not. So shade the region to the side of the line that includes the first three points.

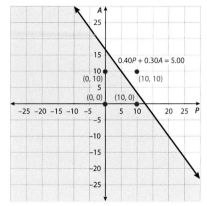

All points in the shaded region or on the boundary line satisfy the inequality $0.40P + 0.30A \leq 5.00$. But since $A$ and $P$ represent numbers of apples and peaches, negative values for these variables make no sense. So the graph of this problem situation should be limited to points in the first quadrant, as well as points on the boundaries of the shaded region that are on either the $P$-axis or the $A$-axis.

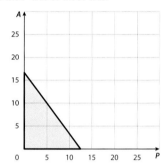

Since you cannot buy a fraction of a peach or apple, only points in the shaded region or its boundaries that have integer coordinates are possible solutions of the inequality.

**TEACHING TIP**

Point out to students that this graph is an enlarged portion of the first quadrant and axes of the previous graph on this page. The shaded area and darkened segments represent all of the ordered pairs whose first and second coordinates are non-negative and satisfy the inequality $0.40P + 0.30A \leq 5.00$. This is the region in which the possible solutions to the problem lie.

## GRAPHS FOR WHICH BOUNDARIES ARE NOT INCLUDED

Inequalities that describe limits in real-world situations often include the limiting value. But there are times when the boundaries are not included. The limiting boundary of the graph of a "greater than" or "less than" inequality is drawn as a dashed line.

 **2**

Graph the inequality $2x > 3y - 6$.

**Solution:**

Even though it is not included in the inequality, the boundary of the graph is the equation $2x = 3y - 6$. The intercepts for the graph of this equation are $(-3, 0)$ and $(0, 2)$.

Notice that in this case, negative values of the variables are allowed. So the graph includes all four quadrants. A dashed line is used to indicate that points on the boundary do not satisfy the inequality.

To decide which side of the boundary should be shaded, check to see if the point $(0, 0)$ makes a true statement.

$$2x > 3y - 6$$
$$2(0) \overset{?}{>} 3(0) - 6$$
$$0 > -6$$

Since $0 > -6$ is a true statement, shade the region that includes $(0, 0)$.

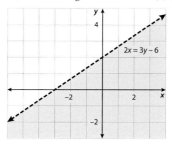

## ADDITIONAL EXAMPLE **2**

Graph the inequality $3x - 4y > 0$.

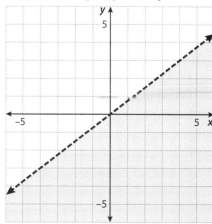

## Practice for Lesson 8.5
## Answers

**1a.** $A \leq 16.67 - 1.33P$

**1b.** No, it does not, because there is more than one value of $A$ for each value of $P$.

**1c.** They are discrete, since only whole numbers of peaches and apples can be bought.

**2.**

**3.**

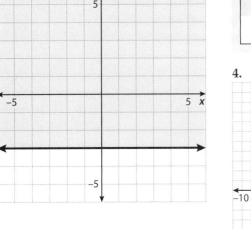

To graph an inequality containing two variables,

1. Replace the inequality symbol with an equal sign.

2. Graph the resulting equation. This is a boundary of the graph of the inequality. Use a solid line for inequalities with ≤ or ≥ and a dashed line for inequalities with < or >.

3. Shade the region on the side of the boundary line for which the inequality is true. To decide which side of the boundary line to shade, test one point that is on either side of the line. If the coordinates of the point satisfy the inequality, shade that side of the line. If they do not, shade the other side of the line.

## Practice for Lesson 8.5

1. Consider the inequality and the situation from Example 1.

$$0.40P + 0.30A \leq 5.00$$

   **a.** Solve the inequality for $A$.
   **b.** Does your answer to Part (a) represent a function? Explain.
   **c.** Are $P$ and $A$ discrete variables or continuous variables?

**For Exercises 2–5, graph the inequality on a coordinate plane.**

2. $x < 2$

3. $y \geq -3$

4. $x > 4$ and $y \leq 0$

5. $x \leq 0$ and $-2 \leq y \leq 2$

**For Exercises 6–7, complete Parts (a), (b), and (c).**
   **a.** Graph the boundary of the inequality on a coordinate plane.
   **b.** Test the following points to see if they satisfy the inequality, $(0, 5), (0, -5), (0, 0), (-5, 0), (5, 0)$.
   **c.** Shade the region containing points that satisfy the inequality.

6. $3x - 4y > 12$

7. $y \geq 1 - \dfrac{1}{2}x$

**4.**

**5.**

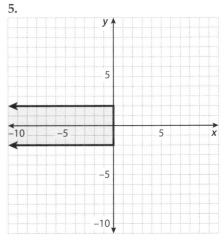

6–7. See answers beginning on page 622.

**For Exercises 8–9, shade a region of a graph that represents the given situation.**

**8.** In order to be eligible for the U.S. Army, a woman must be at least 58 inches tall but no more than 80 inches tall. Her weight can be no less than 109 pounds and no greater than 227 pounds.

**9.** Barker's classification system describes cider apples based on levels of acid (sour taste) and tannin ("pucker"). Apples having acid levels no greater than 0.45 percent and tannin less than 0.2 percent are classified as sweet.

**10.** Suppose that you want to buy chips and soda for a party. Each large bag of chips costs $2.40, and each large bottle of soda costs $2.00.

   **a.** Write an inequality that represents the limit on the number of bags of chips C and bottles of soda S that you can buy for $48.

   **b.** Draw a graph that represents the possible numbers of bags of chips and bottles of soda you can buy.

   **c.** Could you buy 15 bags of chips and 10 bottles of soda? Use the graph to justify your answer.

   **d.** Could you buy 5 bags of chips and 15 bottles of soda? Use the graph to justify your answer.

   **e.** If you buy 10 bags of chips, what is the largest number of bottles of soda you can buy?

**11.** A small vegetable garden is to be made in the shape of a rectangle. Exactly 30 feet of edging material is available to form the perimeter of the garden.

   **a.** Write an inequality that sets limits on the length $l$ and width $w$ that are possible for the garden.

   **b.** Draw a graph of the possible dimensions.

   **c.** Would a 10-foot by 3-foot garden be possible? Use the graph to justify your answer.

   **d.** Would a 12-foot by 5-foot garden be possible? Use the graph to justify your answer.

   **e.** Would a 9-foot by 6-foot garden be possible? Use the graph to justify your answer.

**CONNECTION**

**Exercise 8** The height and weight requirements for women entering the army are only the extremes. In fact, weight limits vary with height and are more restrictive. And the stated limits may occasionally be waived, with body fat percentage being a determining factor.

**TEACHING TIP**

**Exercises 9–11** Remind students that only the first quadrant and the axes that bound the shaded region are appropriate for most inequalities that model applied contexts, since variables that represent real-world quantities are often non-negative.

**8.**   Sample graph:

**9.**   Sample graph:

**10b.** Sample graph:

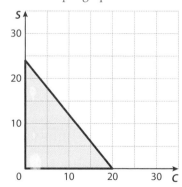

**10c.** No, the point (15, 10) is not on the graph.

**10d.** Yes, the point (5, 15) is on the graph.

**10e.** 12

**11a.** $2l + 2w \le 30$ or $l + w \le 15$

**11b.** Sample graph:

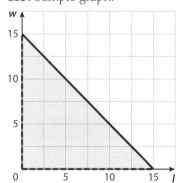

**11c.** Yes, the point (10, 3) is on the graph.

**11d.** No, the point (12, 5) is not on the graph.

**11e.** Yes, the point (9, 6) is on the included boundary of the graph.

**10a.** $2.40C + 2.00S \le 48$

287

# LESSON 8.6

## Lesson Objective

- find the graphical solution to a system of linear inequalities in two variables.

## Vocabulary

- solution to a system of inequalities
- system of inequalities

## Materials List

## Description

Building on the simpler graphs of Lesson 8.5, students are guided through the process of finding a region of a graph that represents the solution to a system of inequalities. That region is the intersection of the graphs of the individual inequalities.

*Wrapping Up the Investigation:*

It is important for students to recognize that the coordinates of all points in the solution region, including any solid boundaries, are part of the solution set (except when only whole numbers are allowed, as in this case). In **Question 11**, make sure students justify their answers to **Question 10** by substituting coordinates into the inequalities from **Questions 1 and 2**.

> ### TEACHING TIP
> When students graph a system of inequalities, suggest that they use a different color or type of shading for the graph of each inequality.

## Lesson 8.6 Investigation Answers

1. $15S + 30L \leq 300$
2. $5S + 20L \leq 160$
3. no
4. It is either in the first quadrant or on the axes.

---

## Lesson 8.6

### INVESTIGATION: Systems of Linear Inequalities

Earlier in this chapter, you learned how to solve systems of linear equations, and in Lesson 8.5, you graphed inequalities. In this lesson, you will learn how to find a graphical solution to a system of inequalities.

As you have seen, the graph of an inequality can be a region of the plane. This reflects the fact that there are usually many values of the variables that satisfy an inequality. There are many situations that are modeled by more than one inequality. You can solve such a **system of inequalities** by finding a region over which all the inequalities in the system are satisfied.

A musician has converted a garage into a recording studio. She plans to take on two types of projects. Large ensembles are expected to require 30 hours of studio time for recording and mixing. She will have to hire a recording engineer for 20 of those hours. Demo recordings of soloists will only require 15 hours. Since she can do the mixing of the demos herself, she only needs an engineer for 5 of these 15 hours.

1. She plans to work long hours. She estimates that she can put in a maximum of 300 hours in the studio each month. This can be done with many different combinations of soloists and large ensembles. Write an inequality that models the time spent to record and mix $S$ soloists and $L$ large groups if no more than 300 hours are available.

2. The recording engineer is only available for 160 hours per month. Write another inequality that models the time the recording engineer works in a month during which $S$ soloists and $L$ large groups are recorded.

3. Are negative values possible for the two variables?

4. Your answers to Questions 1 and 2 form a system of inequalities. The shaded region of a graph, including boundaries, represents the solution of the system. The coordinates of each point in that region must satisfy all of the inequalities in the system.

   What does your answer to Question 3 tell you about the graph of the solution?

---

**5.** Graph the inequality you wrote in Question 1. Does it matter which variable appears on the horizontal axis?

**6.** Graph your inequality from Question 2 on the same coordinate system that you used in Question 5.

**7.** What values of $S$ satisfy both inequalities for this situation?

**8.** What values of $L$ satisfy both inequalities for this situation?

**9.** Part of your shaded region is contained in the graphs of both of the inequalities from Questions 5 and 6. Shade this part a darker color.

**10.** Your answer to Question 9 represents the **solution to a system of inequalities** that began this Investigation. Only points in this region represent allowed combinations of the variables $S$ and $L$ for the music studio situation.

Use your graph to determine which of the following combinations of large ensembles and soloists are possible:
**a.** 7 large ensembles and no soloists
**b.** 8 large ensembles and 8 soloists
**c.** 4 large ensembles and 12 soloists
**d.** 3 large ensembles and 18 soloists

**11.** Verify your answers to Question 10 by substituting the values of the variables in both of the inequalities from Questions 1 and 2.

**11c.** 30(4) + 15(12) = 300; 20(4) + 5(12) = 140, which is less than 160.

**11d.** 30(3) + 15(18) = 360, which is greater than 300; 20(3) + 5(18) = 150, which is less than 160.

**5.** Sample answer: No, either variable can appear on the horizontal axis, since neither is dependent on the other.

**6.** Sample answer:

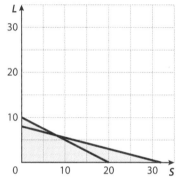

**7.** $0 \le S \le 20$

**8.** $0 \le L \le 8$

**9.**

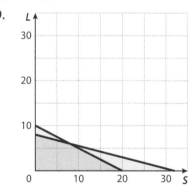

**10a.** yes

**10b.** No, the point is outside the graphs of both inequalities.

**10c.** yes

**10d.** No, the point is above the graph of the inequality for studio time.

**11a.** 30(7) + 15(0) = 210, which is less than 300; 20(7) + 5(0) = 140, which is less than 160.

**11b.** 30(8) + 15(8) = 360, which is greater than 300; 20(8) + 5(8) = 200, which is greater than 160.

To solve a system of inequalities graphically,

1. Graph a shaded region representing each inequality on the same coordinate grid.

2. Find the region where the individual graphs overlap and shade it a darker color.

3. Check at least one point in your solution region to verify that its coordinates satisfy all of the inequalities.

## ADDITIONAL EXAMPLE

**a.** Solve this system of inequalities.

$$y > -\frac{1}{3}x + 2$$
$$2y - x \leq 4$$

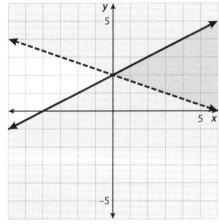

**b.** Describe the region of the graph that is the solution set for the system of inequalities. the region that is above the line $y = -\frac{1}{3}x + 2$ *and* beneath the line $2y - x = 4$, and including the portion of the line $2y - x = 4$ that is in the first quadrant

## E X A M P L E

**a.** Solve this system of inequalities.

$$y \geq 2x - 1$$
$$3y < 2x + 6$$

**b.** Describe the region of the graph that is the solution set for the system of inequalities.

**Solution:**

**a.** Graph the first inequality, $y \geq 2x - 1$.  Then graph the second inequality, $3y < 2x + 6$, on the same coordinate system.

 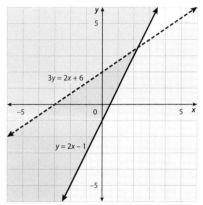

Use the point (0, 1) to check the answer.

$$y \overset{?}{\geq} 2x - 1 \qquad\qquad 3y \overset{?}{<} 2x + 6$$
$$1 \overset{?}{\geq} 2(0) - 1 \qquad\qquad 3(1) \overset{?}{<} 2(0) + 6$$
$$1 \geq -1 \checkmark \qquad\qquad 3 < 6 \checkmark$$

**b.** The solution set is the region on and above the graph of the line $y = 2x - 1$ and under the graph of the line $3y = 2x + 6$.

## Practice for Lesson 8.6

1  a. Graph the following system of inequalities:
$$y \leq 2x - 4$$
$$2x + 3y < 12$$

   b. Is $(4, -3)$ a part of the solution to the system of inequalities? Use your graph to justify your answer.

   c. Is $(7, 5)$ a part of the solution to the system of inequalities? Use your graph to justify your answer.

   d. Is $(3, 2)$ a part of the solution to the system of inequalities? Use your graph to justify your answer.

   e. Is the origin a part of the solution to the system of inequalities? Use your graph to justify your answer.

2  a. Graph the following system of inequalities:
$$x - 3y \geq 18$$
$$y \leq 3x + 10$$

   b. At what point do the boundary lines intersect? Is this point a part of the solution to the system of inequalities? Explain.

   c. Describe the region of the graph that is the solution set for the system of inequalities.

3. Write a system of inequalities that describes the graph below.

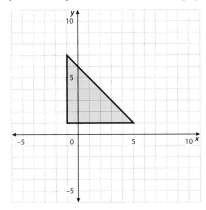

## Practice for Lesson 8.6 Answers

1a.

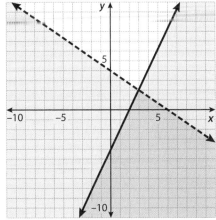

**1b.** Yes, it lies in the shaded region for both inequalities.

**1c.** No, it only lies in the shaded region for only one of the inequalities, $y \leq 2x - 4$.

**1d.** No, it lies at the intersection of the boundaries. The inequality $2x + 3y < 12$ is a "less than" relationship, so the boundary for this inequality is not included in the solution.

**1e.** No, it only lies in the shaded region for only one of the inequalities, $2x + 3y < 12$.

2a.

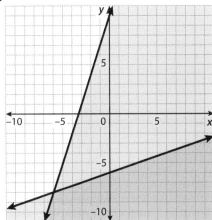

**2b.** The lines intersect at $(-6, -8)$. This point is part of the solution because the graphs of both inequalities include the boundary lines.

**2c.** The solution set is the region found beneath both lines, $y = 3x + 10$ and $x - 3y = 18$, as well as the section of each line that borders that region.

**3.** $x + y \leq 6$
   $x \geq -1$
   $y \geq 1$

**4.** D

**5a.** $40T + 20C \leq 2{,}000$
$6T + 8C \leq 600$

**5b.** Negative numbers of tables or chairs make no sense.

**5c.** Sample answer:

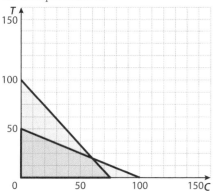

**5d.** Yes, the point (35, 30) is in the shaded region for both inequalities.

**5e.** No, the point (10, 50) lies in the shaded region of only one inequality.

**6a.** $45B + 120C \leq 1{,}200$
$B + C \geq 20$
$B \geq 0, C \geq 0$

**6b.** Sample graph:

**4.** Which region of the graph represents the solution set for the system of inequalities $y \geq x$ and $y \leq 2$?

**5.** A small company makes unfinished tables and chairs. Each table uses 40 board feet of wood, and each chair uses 20 board feet. It takes 6 hours of labor to make a table and 8 hours of labor to make a chair. There are 2,000 board feet of wood and 600 labor-hours available for the next week.

  **a.** Let *T* represent the number of tables made in the next week and *C* the number of chairs. Write inequalities that relate *T* and *C* to the total available amount of wood and to the total available labor.

  **b.** This situation can be further described by the inequalities $T \geq 0$ and $C \geq 0$. Why?

  **c.** Draw a graph of the solution set for this situation.

  **d.** Can the company produce 30 tables and 35 chairs in the next week? Explain.

  **e.** Can the company produce 50 tables and 10 chairs in the next week? Explain.

**6.** A principal has received a $1,200 grant to buy new printers for his school. He has a choice between buying black-and-white printers for $45 each and color printers for $120 each. He wants at least 20 new printers.

  **a.** Let *B* represent the number of black-and-white printers and *C* the number of color printers. Write a system of inequalities that models the situation.

  **b.** Draw a graph of the solution set.

  **c.** What is the largest number of color printers that will satisfy both requirements? Explain.

**6c.** The intersection of the boundaries of the solution set is (16, 4). So, 4 color printers and 16 black-and-white printers can be bought without exceeding the $1,200 limit.

**7.** A group of art students has formed an Arts Collective to organize an arts and crafts exhibition.

To publicize the event, they plan to use two methods. One method is to print one-page flyers and distribute them at schools and malls. The flyers will cost only 8 cents each to produce. Another method is to mail postcards about the event to selected people. This option is more expensive: 12 cents for each card, plus 18 cents per card for bulk postage. However, postcards are expected to be more effective than flyers. But to get the 12-cent rate, they must order at least 500 cards. The total budget for publicity is $300.

   **a.** Write a system of inequalities that models this situation.
   **b.** Draw a graph of the solution set.

**8.** A ballpark offers two packages for birthday party favors. Package A includes 5 tickets for a ball-toss game and 6 pennants for the home team. Package B includes 15 tickets for a ball-toss game and 3 pennants for the home team. The ballpark management wants to have at least 30 packages available. They also want to include at least 300 tickets but no more than 180 pennants.

   **a.** Write a system of inequalities that models this situation. Let $a$ represent the number of A packages and $b$ the number of B packages.
   **b.** Graph the system of inequalities to determine how many of each package can be assembled.
   **c.** Is it possible to assemble 10 of Package A and 40 of Package B? Explain.
   **d.** Is it possible to assemble 20 of Package A and 30 of Package B? Explain.

**7a.** Let $F$ represent the number of flyers. Let $C$ represent the number of postcards.
$$0.08F + 0.30C \leq 300$$
$$C \geq 500$$
$$F \geq 0$$

**7b.** Sample graph:

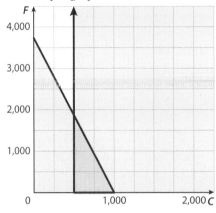

**8a.** $a + b \geq 30$
$5a + 15b \geq 300$
$6a + 3b \leq 180$
$a \geq 0, b \geq 0$

**8b.** Sample answer:

**8c.** Yes, the point (10, 40) is in the shaded region.

**8d.** No, the point (20, 30) is outside the shaded region.

# MODELING PROJECT

## Materials List

## Description

In this project, students use USPS information to form a system of four inequalities and then find the solutions of the system graphically. After they have completed the solution, they are asked to research other USPS size limits.

## Sample Answers

1. $w \geq 3\frac{1}{2}$ in.; $w \leq 6\frac{1}{8}$ in.;
   $l \geq 5$ in.; $l \leq 11\frac{1}{2}$ in.

2. The boundary of each inequality is either a horizontal or a vertical line.

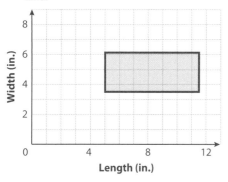

3. The solutions are in the shaded area.
4. Answers will vary depending on the envelopes chosen.
5. Yes, it does meet the size requirements. The USPS machines cannot find the stamp on a square envelope, so each square envelope must be handled by a person, who costs more than the machine that sorts the envelopes.
6. Answers will vary depending on the other size limits chosen.

---

**CHAPTER**

# 8

## Modeling Project

## Sizing Up the Mail

According to the United States Postal Service (USPS), letters that weigh one ounce or less can be mailed for the cost of a first-class stamp, if they meet these specific size limits.

- The letter must be rectangular. The length of the letter is the dimension parallel to the address.
- It must be at least $3\frac{1}{2}$ inches high by 5 inches long.
- It can be no more than $6\frac{1}{8}$ inches high by $11\frac{1}{2}$ inches long.

1. Use this information to write a system of four inequalities for the USPS size limits. Use $l$ for the length of the letter and $w$ for its width.
2. Graph each inequality on the same set of axes.
3. Where in the graph do you find the solutions to the system of inequalities?
4. Measure the lengths and widths of several envelopes. Use your model to determine whether the envelope meets the size requirements for a first-class envelope.
5. Consider a 5 in. × 5 in. envelope. The USPS charges more to send an envelope of this size. Does it meet the size requirements for a first-class envelope? If it does, why do you think they charge more?
6. Research other USPS first-class size limits, such as those for postcards and large envelopes. Write a report on what you found. Be sure to include a system of equations and a graph for each situation.

# Chapter 8 Review

## You Should Be Able to:

### Lesson 8.1
- use a table to solve a system of two linear equations.
- use a graph to solve a system of two linear equations.

### Lesson 8.2
- model a decision-making situation with a system of linear equations.
- use substitution to solve a system of two linear equations.
- recognize an inconsistent system of linear equations.

### Lesson 8.3
- use elimination to solve a system of two linear equations.

- recognize a dependent system of linear equations.

### Lesson 8.4
- solve problems that require previously learned concepts and skills.

### Lesson 8.5
- draw a graph of a linear inequality involving one or two variables on a coordinate plane.

### Lesson 8.6
- find the graphical solution to a system of linear inequalities in two variables.

## Key Vocabulary

system of equations (p. 264)

solution to a system of equations (p. 264)

substitution method (p. 267)

inconsistent (p. 270)

consistent (p. 270)

elimination method (p. 273)

dependent (p. 275)

system of inequalities (p. 288)

solution to a system of inequalities (p. 289)

## Chapter 8 Test Review

**For Exercises 1–4, fill in the blank.**

1. A system of equations that has no solutions is called a(n) _____ system.

2. A system of equations that has infinitely many solutions is called a(n) _____ system.

3. The boundary of the graph of a "greater than" or "less than" inequality is drawn as a(n) _____ line.

4. The boundary of the graph of an inequality that includes an equal sign is drawn as a(n) _____ line.

# CHAPTER REVIEW

 **5e**   Evaluate

## Chapter 8 Test Review Answers

1. inconsistent
2. dependent
3. dashed or broken
4. solid

5. Choose any point that is not on the boundary. If its coordinates satisfy the inequality, shade the region including that point. Otherwise, shade the other side.

6. The intersection shows the number of copies for which the total cost per month is the same for both companies.

7. $(-6, 8)$

8. dependent

9. $\left(\dfrac{27}{5}, -\dfrac{2}{5}\right)$

10. inconsistent

11a. For the retailer: $C = 0.0825p$; For the wholesaler: $C = 0.05p + 13$

11b. $(p, C) = (400, 33)$

11c. For a purchase price of $400, the additional costs will be the same from both suppliers.

11d. the retailer

11e. the wholesaler

12. For 8 prints, the total cost is the same at both stores.

5. On the graph of an inequality, explain how you can decide which side of a boundary to shade.

6. This graph was made to compare the costs of renting copy machines from Company A and Company B. What information does the point of intersection of the two lines give?

**Copy Machine Rental Cost**

**For Exercises 7–10, solve the system of equations. Identify any system that is either inconsistent or dependent.**

7. $2x + y = -4$
   $5x + 3y = -6$

8. $3x = 5y + 2$
   $15y = 9x - 6$

9. $2x - 3y = 12$
   $2x + 7y = 8$

10. $x - 2y = 8$
    $3x - 5 = 6y$

11. You are the owner of a shop that designs and sells T-shirts. You can buy plain shirts from a local retailer and pay 8.25% sales tax. Another option is to order shirts at the same price from an online wholesaler in another state, who is not required to collect sales tax. But the wholesaler charges a processing fee of $13 per order, plus 5% of the price of the shirts for shipping and handling.
    a. Write a system of equations that describes your options. Represent the value of the shirts purchased by $p$, and the additional costs for each order by $C$.
    b. Solve the system using a graph or table. Check your answer with an algebraic method.
    c. What does the solution mean in this context?
    d. If you plan to order $300 worth of materials, which option is cheaper?
    e. If you plan to order $500 worth of materials, which option is cheaper?

12. One store charges $1.60 for a photo print order, plus $0.10 per print. Another charges $1.20, plus $0.15 per print. For how many prints is the total cost the same?

**13.** A florist has 600 daisies and 450 irises with which to create some floral arrangements. She has decided on two basic combinations: the bargain assortment will contain 8 daisies and 3 irises, while the deluxe assortment will contain 4 daisies and 6 irises.

   **a.** She wants to use all of the available flowers. Write a system of equations that will allow her to determine how many bargain $b$ and deluxe $d$ assortments to make.

   **b.** How many of each type of arrangement will use all of the available flowers?

**14.** Which graph represents the inequality $3y \leq x + 6$?

**Graph A**

**Graph B**

**Graph C**

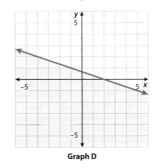

**Graph D**

**15.** Draw a graph of the solution set for the following system of inequalities:

$$y \leq x + 3$$
$$x + y \leq 4$$

**16.** A loaf of rye bread requires 3 cups of flour and $\frac{1}{2}$ cup of sugar. A loaf of pumpernickel bread requires $2\frac{1}{2}$ cups of flour and 1 cup of sugar. You have 40 cups of flour and 10 cups of sugar.

   **a.** Write a system of inequalities that models the numbers of loaves of rye $r$ and pumpernickel $p$ that could be baked.

   **b.** Graph the system of inequalities.

**13a.** $8b + 4d = 600$
     $3b + 6d = 450$

**13b.** $b = 50$, $d = 50$; 50 of each type should be created.

**14.** Graph A

**15.**

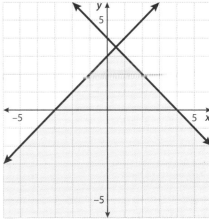

**16a.** Sample answer:
     $3r + 2.5p \leq 40$
     $0.5r + p \leq 10$
     $r \geq 0, p \geq 0$

**16b.** Sample graph:

# Chapter Extension
## Linear Programming

## Lesson Objective

- use a graphical method to solve a linear programming problem in two variables.

## Vocabulary

- constraints
- feasible region
- linear programming
- objective function
- optimization

## Materials List

## Description

In this lesson, students apply what they learned in Lesson 8.6 about graphing systems of inequalities to optimize profit or income from a business.

### CONNECTION

The variables in a linear programming problem are often called *decision variables*, because the purpose of the analysis is to decide which values of the variables will be optimal.

In Lesson 8.6, you solved a system of inequalities to find the region of a graph that contains the solutions to a system of inequalities. Points in this region can sometimes be examined to determine the best way to achieve a goal.

Some kinds of business decisions involve choosing between alternative options. Choosing the best option in a situation is called **optimization**.

One widely used optimization method is called **linear programming**. This method is based on finding the solutions to a system of linear inequalities that models a given situation. Then the various choices represented by combinations of variables in the region that indicates the solutions are examined to find the best course of action.

Consider again the music studio situation from the Investigation in Lesson 8.6. The following system of inequalities can be used to model that situation:

$$15S + 30L \leq 300$$
$$5S + 20L \leq 160$$
$$S \geq 0$$
$$L \geq 0$$

The graph below shows the solutions to the system of inequalities.

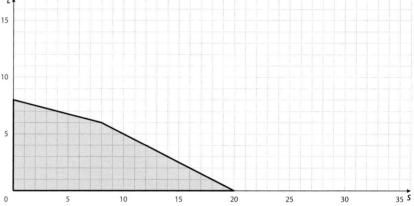

The green-shaded region of this graph is called the **feasible region** for the situation. The word *feasible* means "possible." The coordinates of each point in the region represent a combination of soloists and large ensembles that it would be possible to record in a month.

The inequalities that determine the feasible region are called **constraints**. Each inequality constrains, or limits, the possible values of $S$ and/or $L$. The last two listed inequalities, $S \geq 0$ and $L \geq 0$, require that the variables be non-negative. Similar constraints appear in many linear programming problems.

With more information, a decision can be made regarding the best combination of soloists and large ensembles to record.

1. The music studio will produce a profit of $750 for each large ensemble recording. Each solo recording will produce a profit of $250. Write an equation that models the total profit $P$ from recording $S$ soloists and $L$ ensembles.

2. The profit function that you have written is called the **objective function**. The objective of this analysis is to maximize profit. Use your equation to find the total profit in a month when 12 soloists and 3 large ensembles are recorded.

3. Identify all the vertices of the feasible region and determine their coordinates.

4. Use your profit function from Question 1 to find the profit for each combination in your answer to Question 3. Record your results in a table similar to the one below.

| Vertex (S, L) | Profit ($) |
|---|---|
|  |  |
|  |  |
|  |  |
|  |  |

5. Can you find a point in the feasible region for which the profit is greater than any of the profit values in your table? Remember that only integer-valued coordinates are valid for this situation.

6. What is the maximum possible monthly profit for the studio if none of the constraints are violated?

7. What combination of soloists and large ensembles should the studio owner try to schedule in a month to maximize profit?

8. How would your answers to Questions 4–7 change if the profit for recording a soloist were to increase from $250 to $400?

**TEACHING TIP**

If students have difficulty deciding how to find the vertex for which both variables are nonzero, suggest they write the equations of the boundary lines and find their intersection.

**TEACHING TIP**

Show students how the seven steps in the Guidelines for Linear Programming on page 300 are illustrated in the music studio example.

## Chapter 8 Extension Answers

1. $P = 250S + 750L$
2. $250(12) + 750(3) = \$5{,}250$
3. $(0, 0)$; $(20, 0)$; $(0, 8)$; $(8, 6)$
4.

| Vertex (S, L) | Profit ($) |
|---|---|
| (0, 0) | 0 |
| (20, 0) | 5,000 |
| (0, 8) | 6,000 |
| (8, 6) | 6,500 |

5. no
6. $6,500
7. 8 soloists and 6 large ensembles
8. The table shows the new profit amounts for the vertices of the feasible region.

| Vertex (S, L) | Profit ($) |
|---|---|
| (0, 0) | 0 |
| (20, 0) | 8,000 |
| (0, 8) | 6,000 |
| (8, 6) | 7,700 |

It would be more profitable to record only soloists.

**Guidelines for Linear Programming**

To solve a linear programming problem graphically,

1. Write an equation describing the quantity you wish to maximize or minimize. This equation is called the *objective function*.

2. Define a system of inequalities that models the *constraints*. The inequalities should be based on the same variables that appear in the objective function.

3. Graph the inequalities on the same coordinate plane.

4. Identify the *feasible region*. The feasible region is the solution set for the system of inequalities.

5. Find the coordinates of the vertices of the feasible region.

6. Substitute the coordinates of each vertex into the objective function and find its value.

7. Identify the coordinates that yield the maximum or minimum value of the objective function. This ordered pair is the optimum solution.

**For Questions 9–13, consider the following situation.**

Your sporting goods company plans to sell merchandise at a local stadium. At the souvenir stand, you will sell hats with the home team's logo for $12 and T-shirts for $20. Each hat costs $2 in materials and $5 in labor to produce, and each T-shirt costs $4 in material and $5 in labor to produce. After analyzing your business accounts, you decide that you can spend no more than $1,000 for materials and $1,500 for labor during one week.

In order to maximize your *total income,* how many hats and how many T-shirts should you make?

9. Begin by writing the objective function. In this context, the objective function is an equation that models income as a function of the numbers of hats $h$ and T-shirts $t$ that are produced and sold.

10. Write inequalities for each of the following constraints for this situation:
    **a.** Limit on spending for materials
    **b.** Limit on spending for labor
    **c.** Non-negativity (two inequalities)

11. Draw a graph of the feasible region.

12. Identify the vertices of the feasible region and find the resulting total income for each vertex.

13. How many hats and how many T-shirts should you make to maximize income?

**10c.** Non-negativity: $h \geq 0, t \geq 0$

**11.** Sample graph:

**9.** Income $= 12h + 20t$

**10a.** Limit on spending for materials:
$2h + 4t \leq 1,000$

**10b.** Limit on spending for labor:
$5h + 5t \leq 1,500$

**12.**

| Vertex | Income ($) |
|---|---|
| (0, 0) | 0 |
| (300, 0) | 3,600 |
| (0, 250) | 5,000 |
| (100, 200) | 5,200 |

**13.** 100 hats and 200 T-shirts

# Chapter 9
## Symmetry and Transformations

## Mathematical Overview

This chapter begins with students exploring two types of symmetry: rotational symmetry and line symmetry. As students continue through the chapter, they learn to identify four ways to move (or transform) an object in a plane so that the size and shape of the object does not change—this type of transformation is called an *isometry* or a *rigid motion*. The four types of rigid motions presented in this chapter are rotations, translations, reflections, and glide reflections. Students may have experienced the first three of these transformations under the names of *turns*, *slides*, and *flips*. Using rigid motions, students make connections to one- and two-dimensional patterns. The last lesson in this chapter focuses on using the coordinate plane and coordinate notation to describe, as well as sketch, the four types of rigid motion.

## Lesson Summaries

**Lesson 9.1    *Activity: Symmetry***

In this Activity, students explore the mathematical concepts of two types of symmetry: line symmetry and rotational symmetry. If a figure has line symmetry, students tell how many lines of symmetry the figure has. If a figure has rotational symmetry, students find the angle of rotation. This section concludes with students distinguishing between figures that have rotational symmetry with and without having point symmetry.

**Lesson 9.2    *Transformations and Rigid Motions***

In this lesson, students examine the four rigid motions (isometries): translations, reflections, rotations, and glide reflections. Two of these, reflection and rotation, help describe symmetry that students explored in Lesson 9.1. When defining a rotation, students identify three things: the center point, the angle (the number of degrees the figure is turned), and the direction of the rotation (clockwise or counterclockwise). Students become aware of the use of a translation vector when translating a figure and when examining a glide reflection of a figure.

**Lesson 9.3    *Investigation: Rigid Motions and Patterns***

In this Investigation, students read a discussion about repeated patterns and then develop their own strip pattern that has glide-reflection symmetry. After examining their own and other groups' patterns, they discover that all strip patterns and wallpaper designs have translation symmetry. During the Practice for this lesson, students investigate how changing a center of rotation or a line of symmetry affects a strip pattern.

**Lesson 9.4    *R.A.P.***

In this lesson, students **R**eview **A**nd **P**ractice solving problems that require the use of skills and concepts taught in previous math levels. The skills reviewed in this lesson are skills that are needed as a basis for solving problems throughout this course.

**Lesson 9.5    *Activity: Rigid Motions in the Coordinate Plane***

There are five parts to the Activity in this lesson. These parts cover translations in a coordinate plane, reflections in the $y$-axis, reflections in the $x$-axis, rotations in the coordinate plane, and glide reflections using the $x$-axis as the line of reflection. While working on each of the five parts of this Activity, students learn to use coordinate notation to describe rigid motions.

**Chapter 9    *Extension: Perspective in Art***

In this Extension, students analyze four works of art in which three-dimensional objects are depicted in two-dimensional scenes. They decide whether a given painting or sketch makes use of perspective. They also identify real-world inaccuracies in the painting titled *Perspective Absurdities* by William Hogarth. Once they have identified some of the factors that are important to the proper use of perspective in drawing and painting, students make four paper cubes, position them according to a diagram, and then draw a two-dimensional sketch of what they see from each of the four positions: North, South, East, and West.

## Lesson Guide

| Lesson/Objectives | Materials | |
|---|---|---|
| **Chapter 9 Opener: How Do Archaeologists Use Mathematics When Studying Past Civilizations?** <br> • recognize that mathematics is used to help make connections to past civilizations. | | *Optional:* <br> • strip patterns (such as those found on pottery and wallpaper borders) |
| **9.1 Activity: Symmetry** <br> • discover the characteristics of line and rotational symmetry. <br> • identify line symmetries of a figure. <br> • identify rotational symmetries of a figure. | *Per group:* <br> • flat-edged mirror <br> *Per student:* <br> • scissors <br> • ruler <br> • round coffee filters (at least 4) <br> • protractor | *Optional:* <br> • TRM geometric figure for Question 2 <br> • tracing (or patty) paper <br> • TRM geometric figures for Exercises 1–6, 9 |
| **9.2 Transformations and Rigid Motions** <br> • create images of figures using translations, reflections, rotations, and glide reflections. <br> • identify the rigid motion used to create the image of a given figure. | *Per student:* <br> • ruler <br> • protractor | *Optional:* <br> • tracing (or patty) paper <br> • scissors <br> • TRM geometric figures for Exercises 1–5 <br> • grid paper |
| **9.3 Investigation: Rigid Motions and Patterns** <br> • use rigid motions (isometries) to describe one- and two-dimensional repeated patterns. <br> • use rigid motions to create one-dimensional repeated patterns. | *Per group:* <br> • flat-edged mirror or MIRA™ geometry tools <br> *Per student:* <br> • ruler <br> • tracing (or patty) paper | *Optional:* <br> • photos of strip patterns found on buildings in your community |
| **9.4 R.A.P.** <br> • solve problems that require previously learned concepts and skills. | | *Optional:* <br> • grid paper <br> • color pencils |
| **9.5 Activity: Rigid Motions in the Coordinate Plane** <br> • use coordinate notation to describe rigid motions. <br> • sketch the image of a figure on the coordinate plane when given a rigid motion. | *Per group:* <br> • grid paper <br> • flat-edged mirrors <br> • rulers <br> • tracing (or patty) paper | *Optional:* <br> • TRM table shells for Questions 2, 4, 10, 16, 22, 25, and Exercise 1 |
| **Chapter 9 Extension: Perspective in Art** <br> • determine whether a painting or sketch makes use of perspective. <br> • use overlapping to represent three-dimensional objects in two-dimensional drawings. | *Per group:* <br> • centimeter grid paper printed on cardstock <br> • transparent tape <br> • masking tape or string <br> • meter stick <br> • scissors | *Optional:* <br> • TRM nets of cubes for Question 9 |

## Pacing Guide

| | Day 1 | Day 2 | Day 3 | Day 4 | Day 5 | Day 6 | Day 7 | Day 8 | Day 9 | Day 10 |
|---|---|---|---|---|---|---|---|---|---|---|
| **Basic** | p. 302, 9.1 | 9.1, 9.2 | 9.2 | 9.3 | 9.4 | 9.5 | 9.5 | project | review | |
| **Standard** | p. 302, 9.1 | 9.1, 9.2 | 9.2 | 9.3 | 9.4 | 9.5 | 9.5 | project | review | extension |
| **Block** | p. 302, 9.1 | 9.2, 9.3 | 9.3, 9.4 | 9.5 | project, review | review, extension | | | | |

### Supplement Support

See the Book Companion Website at www.highschool.bfwpub.com/ModelingwithMathematics and the Teacher's Resource Materials (TRM) for additional resources.

# Symmetry and Transformations

## CONTENTS

## Lesson Objective

- recognize that mathematics is used to help make connections to past civilizations.

## Vocabulary

## Description

This reading poses an out-of-the-ordinary situation in which mathematics is used to draw conclusions about the past. The purpose of the reading is to pique students' interest in the topics of symmetry and transformations.

### TEACHING TIP

After students have read the Chapter Opener, lead a whole-class discussion asking students if they have ever been to an archeological site. Explain, or have students explain, what an archeological excavation site might look like.

If possible, bring to class examples of strip patterns, such as those found around the edges of vases and pots. Sample wallpaper borders with geometric designs also provide good examples of strip patterns.

### TEACHING TIP

Describing a pattern (band or strip) as one-dimensional means that the pattern admits translations in one direction (and its opposite) along the band. Patterns in the plane that admit translations in many directions are called *two-dimensional*.

# How Do Archaeologists Use Mathematics When Studying Past Civilizations?

Archaeologists often find pieces of pottery called *shards* at excavation sites. These shards are examined and sorted in hopes of gaining information about the people who once lived at those locations.

Archaeologists often sort the pieces by their color and decorative patterns. They might even use a 19th-century discovery made by *crystallographers*, specialists in the science of crystal structure. These scientists discovered minerals in various shapes. They noticed that these shapes grew in certain patterns and fit together in certain ways.

Using the mathematical concepts of repeated patterns, scientists learned to classify the different crystal structure of the minerals. As they sorted the different shapes, they were able to define exactly 230 different categories.

These are the same classifications that archeologists use to help them categorize the patterns found on pottery shards. Crystal structures are just "space patterns." The same principles apply to patterns in the plane and even to patterns found in one-dimensional bands, which are called "strip patterns."

In this chapter, you will explore the mathematical concepts of rigid motion and symmetry. You will also examine how archaeologists use these concepts to better understand civilizations of the past.

### CONNECTION

This chapter provides an opportunity to explore other cultures, as many cultures use symmetry in their artistic designs. For example, symmetry is often seen in Navajo weavings, ancient Chinese bronze vessels, and in Islamic art. You may want to take this opportunity to team with a history teacher in your school to create a multidisciplinary unit on other cultures, using this chapter as the basis of the mathematics for the unit.

## LINE SYMMETRY

1. The figure below shows a geometric figure and a dashed, vertical line $\ell$.

Place a mirror on line $\ell$, perpendicular to the page. Look at the figure in the mirror. Line $\ell$, where you placed the mirror, is known as the **line of reflection**. And the reflection that you see in the mirror is called the **mirror image** or simply the *image*.

2. On a separate sheet of paper, copy the original figure and the line of reflection. Draw the image. (Use the mirror if you need to.) Describe the image.

3. Find the point on the image you drew that corresponds to point $A$ in the original figure. Label that point $A'$ (pronounced "A-prime"). Draw a line between $A$ and $A'$. What relationship do you notice between the segment $AA'$ and the line of reflection?

4. Look at point $B$ on the line of reflection. Where is its image? In general, what can be said about all points on the line of reflection?

A figure has **line symmetry** if you can fold the figure along a line (the line of reflection) so that the two parts coincide. This is the most common type of symmetry found in nature.

## Lesson 9.1 Activity Answers

2. It is congruent to the original figure.
3. The line $AA'$ is perpendicular to the line of reflection. The line of reflection bisects the line $AA'$.
4. Point $B$'s image is on the line of reflection. In general, all points on the line of reflection reflect onto themselves.

### TEACHING TIP

If a classroom set of mirrors is not available, have students share one or two, as it is important for students to actually "see" the reflection of the figure in the mirror. For many students, this Activity makes the new vocabulary that is introduced here more meaningful and relevant to their world.

## Lesson Objectives

- discover the characteristics of line and rotational symmetry.
- identify line symmetries of a figure.
- identify rotational symmetries of a figure.

## Vocabulary

- angle of rotation
- line of reflection
- line symmetry
- mirror image
- rotational symmetry

## Materials List

- flat-edged mirrors
- protractors
- round coffee filters
- rulers
- scissors

## Description

*Preparation:*

Have students work in groups of 2–4 students. Provide each group with a mirror, rulers, scissors, and coffee filters (at least four per person).

*During the Activity:*

In the first part of the Activity, have students take turns using a mirror and answering **Questions 2–4**.

In the second part of the Activity, have students work independently, folding and cutting their coffee filters and answering the questions. Then have students compare their answers with others in their group.

*Closing the Activity:*

Summarize the two types of symmetry explored in this lesson. Then ask students to name objects in the real world that have line symmetry or rotational symmetry.

**303**

As you look at certain geometric figures and pieces of art, you often feel a sense of balance and proportion. Informally in the world of art, this sense is often referred to as symmetry. In this lesson, you will explore the mathematical concepts of two types of symmetry: line symmetry and rotational symmetry.

# LESSON 9.1

## TEACHING TIP

Many students find it difficult to determine whether a figure has rotational symmetry. For these students, suggest that they trace the figure onto a small piece of paper, locate the center point, and then rotate the figure until it coincides with itself. Once they have done that, ask them how they can determine the angle of rotation without measuring.

**5a.** Yes, one line of symmetry.

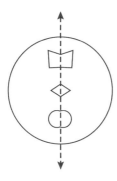

**5b.** Check students' work. The sample shown here does not have rotational symmetry.

**6a.** Sample answer: Yes, two lines of symmetry.

**6b.** Sample answer: Yes, the figure does have rotational symmetry. The angle of rotation is 180°.

**7a.** Sample answer: Yes, four lines of symmetry.

**Note**

Positive rotations go counterclockwise, and negative rotations go clockwise.

## ROTATIONAL SYMMETRY

A figure has **rotational symmetry** if there is a center point about which you can rotate the figure 180° or less so that the figure coincides with itself.

This figure has rotational symmetry because you can rotate it 45°, 135°, or 180° around the center of symmetry, and it will coincide with itself. For a figure with rotational symmetry, the **angle of rotation** is the least positive angle that causes the figure to coincide with itself.

5. Take a coffee filter and fold it in half. Make cuts along the folded edge to create a design. Then unfold the filter.

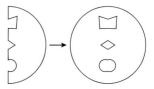

   a. Does your design have line symmetry? If so, how many lines of symmetry does it have?
   b. Does your design have rotational symmetry? If so, find the angle of rotation.

6. Take a new filter, fold it in half, and then fold it in half again. (You will have folded the filter into fourths.) Make cuts along the folded edges to create a design. Unfold the filter.
   a. Does your design have line symmetry? If so, how many lines of symmetry does it have?
   b. Does your design have rotational symmetry? If so, find the angle of rotation.

7. Take a new filter, fold it in half, fold it in half again, and then fold it in half a third time. (You will have folded the filter into eighths.) Make cuts along the folded edges to create a design. Unfold the filter.
   a. Does your design have line symmetry? If so, how many lines of symmetry does it have?

**304**    **Chapter 9**    SYMMETRY AND TRANSFORMATIONS

## TEACHING TIP

Vocabulary organizers, such as the one below, are particularly helpful for this chapter.

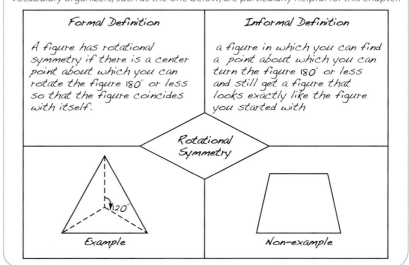

b. Does your design have rotational symmetry? If so, find the angle of rotation.

8. Take a new filter, fold it in half, and then fold that half into thirds. (You will have folded the filter into sixths.) Make cuts along the folded edges to create a design. Unfold the filter.
   a. Does your design have line symmetry? If so, how many lines of symmetry does it have?
   b. Does your design have rotational symmetry? If so, find the angle of rotation.

### Practice for Lesson 9.1

**For Exercises 1–6, answer the following questions:**
   a. Does the figure have line symmetry? If so, how many lines of symmetry does it have? If not, explain why not.
   b. Does the figure have rotational symmetry? If so, find the angle of rotation. If not, explain why not.

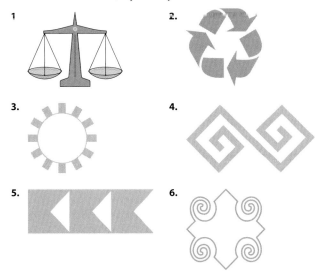

1.    2.

3.    4.

5.    6.

7. Describe the line symmetry and rotational symmetry of a square.

8. Draw a quadrilateral that has exactly two lines of symmetry and a rotational symmetry of 180°.

SYMMETRY    **Lesson 9.1**    305

7b. Sample answer: Yes, the figure does have rotational symmetry. The angle of rotation is 90°.
8a. Sample answer: Yes, the figure does have line symmetry; three lines of symmetry.
8b. Sample answer: Yes, the figure does have rotational symmetry. The angle of rotation is 120°.

**TEACHING TIP**

**Exercises 1–5** It may be helpful to some students to have them trace the figures and draw the line(s) of symmetry. If students are unsure, then have them fold the paper to check to see if their lines are actual lines of symmetry.

**COMMON ERROR**

**Exercises 1 and 5** Some students may think that these figures have rotational symmetry. Have them copy each figure onto tracing paper and rotate it to see if it coincides with the original figure.

**TEACHING TIP**

**Exercise 7** Students often have difficulty finding all of the lines of symmetry of a square, rhombus, rectangle, and parallelogram. In these cases, encourage them to draw a figure and, if necessary, use a mirror. They could also trace the figure on tracing paper and fold on what they think are lines of symmetry. Holding the folded paper up to the light helps them see whether or not the fold is a line of symmetry.

3a. Yes, there are 12 lines of symmetry.
3b. Yes, the least angle of rotation is 30°.
4a. No, there is no line symmetry. There is no line along which you can fold the figure so that the two parts coincide.
4b. Yes, the least angle of rotation is 180°.
5a. Yes, there is one line of symmetry.
5b. No, there is no rotational symmetry. There is no point about which you can rotate the figure 180° or less so that the figure coincides with itself.

6a. Yes, there are two lines of symmetry.
6b. Yes, the least angle of rotation is 180°.
7. A square has four lines of symmetry. It also has rotational symmetry. The angle of rotation is 90°.
8. Sample answer:

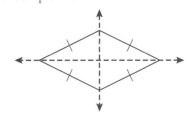

**Practice for Lesson 9.1 Answers**

1a. Yes, there is one line of symmetry.
1b. No, there is no rotational symmetry. There is no point about which you can rotate the figure 180° or less so that the figure coincides with itself.
2a. No, there is no line symmetry. There is no line along which you can fold the figure so that the two parts coincide.
2b. Yes, the least angle of rotation is 120°.

9. The three figures below show company logos. Describe the symmetry of each.

**Shell Oil logo**

**Gulf Oil logo with letters**

**Gulf Oil logo without letters**

10. A figure has *point symmetry* if it can be turned exactly 180° about a point and coincide with an image of itself. All figures that have point symmetry have rotational symmetry, but not all figures with rotational symmetry have point symmetry.

a. Look at the figures for Exercises 1–6 on page 305. Identify one figure that has point symmetry.

b. Identify one figure that has rotational symmetry but does not have point symmetry.

9. The first logo has line symmetry about a vertical line. The second logo has no symmetry. The third logo has two lines of symmetry, vertical and horizontal. It also has rotational symmetry with an angle of rotation of 180°.

10a. The figures in Exercises 3, 4, and 6 have point symmetry.

10b. The figure in Exercise 2 has rotational symmetry but does not have point symmetry.

## TRANSFORMATIONS

In Lesson 9.1 you explored line symmetry and rotational symmetry. In this lesson, you will learn to identify four ways to move an object in the plane so that the size and shape of the object does not change.

When you think about objects being transformed, you may think about them being changed in size or shape. For example, you may be familiar with a popular line of children's toys called Transformers®. The main feature of these toys is that an object such as a car, machine, or animal can be transformed into a robot. Objects can also be transformed mathematically.

A **transformation** is an operation that moves or changes a geometric figure into a new figure.

Not all transformations involve changing size and/or shape. For instance, an object sliding on a table can be moved to a different location. In this process, the object does not change size or shape, just location. This is an example of a rigid motion or isometry.

A transformation where size and shape do not change is called a **rigid motion** or **isometry**.

A rigid motion preserves distances. This means that the distance between any two points in the new figure (called the **image**) is equal to the distance between the corresponding two points in the original figure. It also means that lines that are straight in the original figure are straight in the image, and that angle measurement is also preserved. In other words, the image is always congruent to the original figure.

# LESSON 9.2

**5e**  Explain

## Lesson Objectives

- create images of figures using translations, reflections, rotations, and glide reflections.
- identify the rigid motion used to create the image of a given figure.

## Vocabulary

- glide reflection
- image
- isometry
- reflection
- rigid motion
- rotation
- transformation
- translation
- translation vector

## Materials List

- protractor
- ruler

## Description

In this lesson, students examine the four types of rigid motions (isometries): *translations, reflections, rotations,* and *glide reflections.* Two of these, *reflection* and *rotation,* help describe the symmetry that students saw in **Lesson 9.1**.

### TEACHING TIP

In this lesson, it may be helpful to provide students with tracing paper or patty paper, as they are often asked to copy or trace figures.

## RIGID MOTIONS

The simplest rigid motion is the **translation** or "slide." Imagine a photograph on a table. If you slide the photo to a new place on the table, each of the points of the original photo moves the same distance to the new location. The distance, together with the direction of the slide, defines the translation. This is called the **translation vector**.

translation vector

A second type of rigid motion is the **reflection** or "flip." A reflection uses a line of reflection to create a mirror image of the original shape or figure. In the Investigation in Lesson 9.1, you used a mirror to create a reflection of the original figure.

A **rotation** or "turn" is a third type of rigid motion. A rotation turns a figure a specific number of degrees about a specific point called the *center*. You can define a rotation by its center, the amount of rotation, and the direction of the rotation.

**Clockwise rotation**          **Counter-clockwise rotation**

The fourth type of rigid motion is called a **glide reflection.** A glide reflection combines a reflection in a line with a translation along that line. An example of a glide reflection can be seen in the pattern formed by the human footsteps straddling line $\ell$. In this figure, the dashed line indicates the line of reflection and the arrow indicates the translation vector. Notice that the translation vector and the line of reflection are parallel.

**LESSON 9.2**

## Practice for Lesson 9.2

1. Trace the figure onto your paper. Then use the given translation vector to draw the translated image.

2. Trace the figure onto your paper. Then draw the reflection about the given line.

3. Trace the figure onto your paper.
   a. Rotate the figure 90° clockwise about the given point. Sketch the image.

   b. Return to the original figure and this time, rotate it 180° about the same point of rotation.

The fourth type of rigid motion is called a **glide reflection.** A glide reflection combines a reflection in a line with a translation along that line. An example of a glide reflection can be seen in the pattern formed by the human footsteps straddling line $\ell$. In this figure, the dashed line indicates the line of reflection and the arrow indicates the translation vector. Notice that the translation vector and the line of reflection are parallel.

## Practice for Lesson 9.2

1. Trace the figure onto your paper. Then use the given translation vector to draw the translated image.

2. Trace the figure onto your paper. Then draw the reflection about the given line.

3. Trace the figure onto your paper.
   a. Rotate the figure 90° clockwise about the given point. Sketch the image.

   b. Return to the original figure and this time, rotate it 180° about the same point of rotation.

**TEACHING TIP**

When discussing glide reflections be sure to point out that the translation vector, which shows the distance and direction the figure is translated, must be parallel to the line of symmetry.

**TEACHING TIP**

**Exercises 1–5** For students who are experiencing difficulty with rotations or glide reflections, have them cut out copies of the figures, then rotate or reflect and slide them. Many students need to see the figures actually move.

## Practice for Lesson 9.2 Answers

1. Sample answer:

2. Sample answer:

3a. Sample answer:

3b. Sample answer:

**4.** Trace the figures and draw the line(s) of reflection for each.

**a.**                  **b.**

**5.** Trace the figure, the line of reflection, and the translation vector. Sketch three glide-reflected images.

**6.** The figure below shows the original figure used to make the images in Parts (a–d).

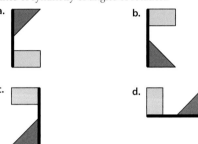

Name the rigid motion used to achieve the image. Describe any lines of symmetry or angles of rotation.

**a.**                      **b.**

**c.**                      **d.**

**7.** Follow these directions to create a figure and two images.
- Draw a triangle and label the vertices *A*, *B*, and *C*.
- Draw a vertical line $\ell_1$ to the right of your triangle and reflect the triangle about $\ell_1$.
- Now draw a second line $\ell_2$ parallel to $\ell_1$ and to the right of the image of your triangle.
- Reflect the image about $\ell_2$.

How is the final image related to your original triangle?

---

**4a.**

**4b.**

**5.**

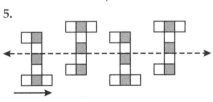

**6a.** reflection; The line of symmetry could be any vertical line.

**6b.** rotation of 180°

**6c.** reflection; The line of symmetry could be any horizontal line.

**6d.** rotation of 90° clockwise or 270° counterclockwise

**7.** Sample figure:

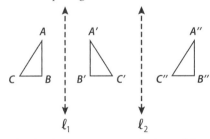

The final image is a translation of the original triangle. The length of the translation vector appears to be double the distance between $\ell_1$ and $\ell_2$.

As you saw in Lesson 9.2, rigid motions can be used to describe movements of figures in the plane. In this lesson, you will investigate how a repeated pattern can be affected by a rigid motion.

### REPEATED PATTERNS

Figure 1 shows a one-dimensional pattern called a *strip pattern*, and Figure 2 shows a two-dimensional pattern called a *wallpaper pattern*.

**Figure 1**

When each of these patterns is extended indefinitely, the pattern in each can be moved by translation to coincide with itself. Some of the translation vectors are shown in red on the figures. In one-dimensional patterns, the translation vectors that move the pattern onto itself are all along the line of the pattern. In two-dimensional patterns, there are translation vectors in more than one direction.

The term *symmetry* is often used to describe infinite patterns, both strip and wallpaper types. In this lesson, symmetry is defined in terms of rigid motions. For example, in the previous two figures, when the patterns underwent a certain translation, the resulting images coincided with the original figures. For this reason, we say the patterns have **translation symmetry**.

Notice that the pattern in Figure 3 can be reflected in vertical lines. The pattern in Figure 4 on the next page can be reflected in a horizontal line. The pattern in Figure 5 on the next page can be reflected in a horizontal line and in vertical lines. All three patterns have line symmetry.

**Vertical line of reflection**
**Figure 3**

## Lesson Objectives

- use rigid motions (isometries) to describe one- and two-dimensional repeated patterns.
- use rigid motions to create one-dimensional repeated patterns.

## Vocabulary

- glide-reflection symmetry
- rotational symmetry
- translation symmetry

## Materials List

- ruler
- mirrors or MIRA™ geometry tools
- tracing paper or patty paper

## Description

This Investigation works best with students working in pairs. Have students read the section "Repeated Patterns." Then discuss the patterns shown in this section.

In groups, have students work through **Questions 1–5**.

*Wrapping Up the Investigation:*

Once all groups have completed the Investigation, ask each group to share its pattern with the class and discuss its symmetry. Does it have translation, rotational, or line symmetry in addition to the glide-reflection symmetry? Some of the patterns will have line symmetry and some may have rotational symmetry. But *all* will have translation symmetry if it is an infinite pattern. Make sure that this point is brought out in the Investigation.

Again, mirrors, tracing paper and/or patty paper should be available to all students who need them.

Below Figure 1, in the left margin:

**Figure 2**

**Horizontal line of reflection**
**Figure 4**

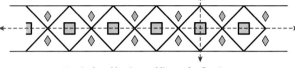

**Vertical and horizontal lines of reflection**
**Figure 5**

## TEACHING TIP

When looking for line symmetry as in the two-dimensional design in **Figure 6**, students often stop examining the pattern when one line of symmetry is found. Encourage them to search for others.

## Lesson 9.3 Investigation Answers

1. Sample patterns; one showing a simple pattern and another showing a more complex pattern:

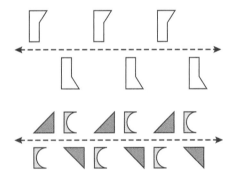

2. Answers will vary.
3. Some of the patterns will have line symmetry, and some may have rotational symmetry. But all will have translation symmetry if they are infinite patterns.
4. Figures 3, 4, 5, and 6 have line symmetry, and Figures 5, 6, and the green and blue figure have rotational symmetry. Each will have translation symmetry if they are infinite patterns.
5. Yes, they all have translation symmetry.

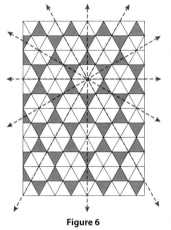

**Figure 6**

Figure 6 shows a two-dimensional design that has vertical and horizontal lines of reflection as well as lines of reflection at 30°, 60°, 120°, and 150°.

Some infinite patterns have **rotational symmetry** (but not line symmetry). One such pattern is shown below.

1. Work with a partner or small group. Develop a strip pattern that has **glide-reflection symmetry**.
2. Once your group has completed your pattern, exchange it with another group. Does the pattern from the other group have glide-reflection symmetry?
3. Look at both your group's pattern and another group's pattern. Do they have any of the other symmetries (translation symmetry, line symmetry, rotation symmetry)?
4. Look back at the figures in this lesson and find one with line symmetry and one with rotational symmetry. What other symmetry or symmetries do these figures have?
5. Do you think that all strip patterns and wallpaper designs have a particular symmetry in common? If so, name the type of symmetry.

## Practice for Lesson 9.3

1. For Parts (a–d), each of the infinite patterns illustrates at least one type of symmetry. Describe the symmetries of each pattern.

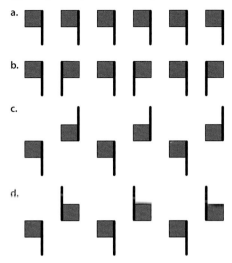

a.

b.

c.

d.

2. Describe the symmetry of each infinite pattern.

a.

b.

3. Use a block letter "F" to create the strip patterns as described.
   a. a pattern with line symmetry (vertical line of reflection only)
   b. a pattern with line symmetry (horizontal line of reflection only)
   c. a pattern with line symmetry (both vertical and horizontal lines of reflection)

RIGID MOTIONS AND PATTERNS    Lesson 9.3    313

**CONNECTION**

Teachers sometimes ask if strip patterns are only related to the geometry of works of art. The pattern below was generated in a college differential equations class, and is purely mathematical in origin. It shows the family of curves $y = \arcsin(c - \cos x)$ for various values of $c$ between $-2$ and $2$.

**LESSON 9.3**

**COMMON ERROR**

**Exercise 1** Students often have trouble distinguishing between glide-reflection and rotational symmetry (half turns) as in Parts (c) and (d). If they are having difficulty, have them check for symmetry using tracing paper.

**CONNECTION**

Encourage students to look for strip patterns on buildings around their community. Suggest that they take photos and write a short report describing the symmetry of the pattern. Use these photos and papers to create a display in the classroom or hallway.

## Practice for Lesson 9.3 Answers
1a. translation symmetry
1b. line symmetry (vertical), translation
1c. glide-reflection symmetry, translation
1d. rotational symmetry, translation
2a. glide-reflection symmetry, translation
2b. rotational symmetry, translation
3a. Sample pattern:

3b. Sample pattern:

3c. Sample pattern:

313

**4a.** Sample pattern:

**4b.** Sample pattern:

Yes, it looks different.

**4c.** The dots are in the center of the strip.

**5a.** translation symmetry and horizontal line symmetry

**5b.** Sample pattern:

**5c.** Answers will vary. One possible pattern is that it will look like the answer to Part (b).

**5d.** The two patterns may be the same. If the pattern from Part (b) has both vertical and horizontal line symmetry, it will also have rotational symmetry.

**4  a.** Use a block letter "E" to create a strip pattern with rotational symmetry. Place a dot at your center of rotation.
**b.** Move your center of rotation. For example, if your center of rotation in Part (a) was near the bottom of the "E," move it up toward the middle of the letter. Redraw your pattern. Does it look different?
**c.** For Parts (a) and (b), where are each of your dots in relation to your pattern?

**5  a.** Identify the symmetry for the flower pattern in the figure below.

**88**<◁<▷◁◁<**88**<◁<▷◁◁<**88**<◁<▷◁◁<**88**<◁<▷◁◁<**88**

**b.** Redraw this pattern so that it has a vertical line symmetry in the center of the part of the pattern that looks like **88**.
**c.** Redraw the pattern in Part (a), giving it rotational symmetry with the point of rotation being the center of the flower.
**d.** What do you observe about your patterns from Parts (b) and (c)? Why do you think this happened?

**Fill in the blank.**

1. A(n) _____ is an operation that moves or changes a geometric figure into a new figure.

2. A transformation that does *not* change the size or shape of a figure is called a(n) _____.

**Choose the correct answer.**

3. Which number is *not* a rational number?

   A. $-1$    B. $0$    C. $\dfrac{2}{3}$    D. $\pi$

4. Which number is equivalent to $|5 - 8|$?

   A. $-3$    B. $13$    C. $3$    D. $-13$

**Add, subtract, multiply, or divide.**

5. $4.6 + 11.32 + 0.154$    6. $5 - 0.67$

7. $4 - 3.2 + 8.01$    8. $7.1 \times 0.002$

9. $2(0.03 + 1.3)$    10. $16 \div 0.02$

**Evaluate the expression.**

11. $3 + 8 \div 2 \times 5$    12. $(2 + 4) \times 7$

13. $2 + 4 \times 7$    14. $\dfrac{50 - 8}{2 \times 7}$

15. $21 \div (10 + 2 - 9)$    16. $20 - 5 + \dfrac{20 - 8}{6}$

**Combine like terms.**

17. $4(m + 2n) - 3n$    18. $2(3x + 5) + 4x - 5x$

19. $8 - 3z + 4(1 - z)$    20. $0.8(3 + y) + 2(1.2 - z)$

21. Solve the system of inequalities by graphing.

$$y \geq 2x + 1$$
$$y < -x + 1$$

22. Write an equation of the line that is perpendicular to the graph of $y = 2x + 5$ and passes through the point $(1, -2)$.

**The square root is between which two consecutive integers?**

23. $\sqrt{52}$    24. $\sqrt{134}$

21.

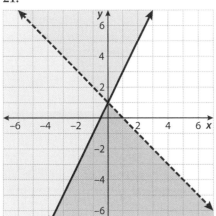

22. $y = -\dfrac{1}{2}x - \dfrac{3}{2}$

23. 7 and 8

24. 11 and 12

**5e**  Evaluate

## Lesson Objective

- solve problems that require previously learned concepts and skills.

## Exercise Reference

Exercises 1–2: Lesson 9.2

Exercise 3: Appendix J

Exercise 4: Appendix G

Exercises 5–10: Appendix B

Exercises 11–16: Appendix H

Exercises 17–20: Lesson 3.5

Exercise 21: Lesson 8.6

Exercise 22: Lesson 5.7

Exercises 23–24: Appendix P

Exercises 25–28: Appendix M

Exercises 29–32: Lesson 2.5

Exercise 33: Lesson 4.7

## Lesson 9.4 R.A.P. Answers

1. transformation
2. rigid motion or isometry
3. D
4. C
5. 16.074
6. 4.33
7. 8.81
8. 0.0142
9. 2.66
10. 800
11. 23
12. 42
13. 30
14. 3
15. 7
16. 17
17. $4m + 5n$
18. $5x + 10$
19. $12 - 7z$
20. $0.8y - 2z + 4.8$

**25.** $3\sqrt{5}$

**26.** $\dfrac{\sqrt{3}}{5}$

**27.** $\dfrac{\sqrt{5}}{5}$

**28.** $\dfrac{\sqrt{6}}{4}$

**29.** 1

**30.** 0

**31.** $-\dfrac{2}{3}$

**32.** undefined

**33a.** 2 : 5 or 1 : 2.5

**33b.** $\left(\dfrac{2}{5}\right)^2 = \dfrac{4}{25}$

**33c.** $\left(\dfrac{2}{5}\right)^3 = \dfrac{8}{125}$

**Simplify the expression.**

**25.** $\sqrt{45}$

**26.** $\sqrt{\dfrac{3}{25}}$

**27.** $\sqrt{\dfrac{1}{5}}$

**28.** $\sqrt{\dfrac{3}{8}}$

**Find the slope of the line that passes through the given pair of points.**

**29.** (3, 7), (0, 4)

**30.** (−4, 4), (2, 4)

**31.** (1, −2), (4, −4)

**32.** (−4, 5), (−4, −1)

**33.** These two square pyramids are similar.

10 cm        4 cm

a. What is the scale factor of the smaller pyramid to the larger one?

b. What is the ratio of the surface area of the smaller pyramid to the surface area of the larger one?

c. What is the ratio of the volume of the smaller pyramid to the volume of the larger one?

In previous lessons in this chapter, you found that all rigid motions change a figure's location but not its size or shape. In this lesson, you will explore how you can use graphs and coordinate notation to describe rigid motions.

People who use rigid motions in their work often need to describe locations precisely. When a precise location is important, coordinates are used. For example, every pixel on a computer screen has coordinates that identify its location. These coordinates can be used to transform objects that are composed of one or more pixels.

### PART A: TRANSLATIONS IN A COORDINATE PLANE

Recall that a translation slides an object a given distance in a given direction. Thus, every translation has a distance and direction associated with it.

1. On a sheet of grid paper, plot △*ABC* as shown. Trace an image of △*ABC* onto a sheet of patty paper. Label the vertices of the image *A'*, *B'* and *C'*.

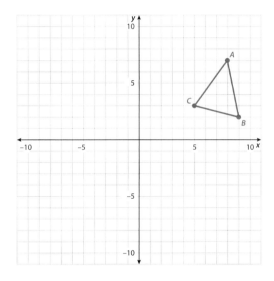

## Lesson 9.5 Activity Answers

1. Check students' graphs.

---

## Lesson Objectives

- use coordinate notation to describe rigid motions.
- sketch the image of a figure on the coordinate plane when given a rigid motion.

## Vocabulary

## Materials List

*Per group:*

- grid paper
- tracing paper or patty paper
- ruler
- flat-edged mirrors

## Description

*Preparation:*

Have students work in groups of 2–4 students. Provide each group with rulers and tracing paper.

*During the Activity:*

Take a moment to review the four rigid motions that students have studied. Then have a volunteer read the lesson's introductory paragraph to the class.

Have groups work on **Parts A–E** of the Activity. Since students are asked to give the coordinates of their images, suggest that they make their drawings of the original triangle and the axes on grid paper.

*Closing the Activity:*

Once all students have completed the Activity, have them confirm their coordinate notations for translations, reflections in the *y*-axis, reflections in the *x*-axis, rotations of 90°, 180°, and 270°, and glide reflections using the *x*-axis as the line of symmetry.

If groups are unable to complete the Activity in one class period, you may either assign the remaining work as homework or choose to complete the Activity the next day in class.

**2.**

**Slide 5 units to the left and 2 units up.**

| Original Vertex | Original Position | Image Vertex | Position of Image |
|:---:|:---:|:---:|:---:|
| $A$ | $(8, 7)$ | $A'$ | $(3, 9)$ |
| $B$ | $(9, 2)$ | $B'$ | $(4, 4)$ |
| $C$ | $(5, 3)$ | $C'$ | $(0, 5)$ |

**3.** No.

**4.** Answers will vary.

**5.** the $y$-coordinate; $-8$

**6.** the $x$-coordinate; $-2$

**7.** $A'(4, 7)$, $B'(6, 11)$, $C'(9, 9)$, $D'(7, 5)$

**8.** $(x, y) \rightarrow (x + h, y + k)$

**9.** Check students' graphs.

**2.** Place the image ($\triangle A'B'C'$), on top of the original ($\triangle ABC$). Slide the image 5 units to the left and 2 units up. Then copy and complete a table similar to the one below.

**Slide 5 units to the left and 2 units up**

| Original Vertex | Original Position | Image Vertex | Position of Image |
|:---:|:---:|:---:|:---:|
| $A$ | $(8, 7)$ | $A'$ | |
| $B$ | | $B'$ | |
| $C$ | | $C'$ | |

**3.** Did the triangle change size or shape?

**4.** Return the image to its original position and repeat Question 2 two more times using different values for the horizontal and the vertical shifts.

**5.** Which coordinate is affected when a point or figure is translated down 5 units? If that coordinate was $-3$, what will the new coordinate be?

**6.** Which coordinate is affected when a point or figure is translated to the right 4 units? If that coordinate was $-6$, what will the new coordinate be?

**7.** Figure $ABCD$ has vertices at $A(3, 2)$, $B(5, 6)$, $C(8, 4)$, and $D(6, 0)$. If the figure is translated 1 unit to the right and 5 units up, find the coordinates of the vertices of the image $A'B'C'D'$.

**8.** A translation of 3 units to the right and 1 unit up can be written in coordinate notation: $(x, y) \rightarrow (x + 3, y + 1)$. Use coordinate notation to describe a translation of $(x, y)$ horizontally $h$ units and vertically $k$ units.

$$(x, y) \rightarrow (\blacksquare, \blacksquare)$$

## PART B: REFLECTIONS IN THE Y-AXIS

**9.** Return to the original triangle ($\triangle ABC$). Place your image ($\triangle A'B'C'$) from Question 1 on top of the original and trace the axes on the patty paper.

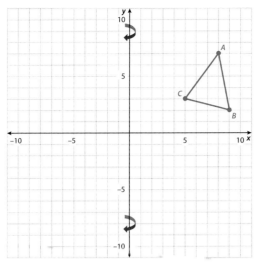

**10.** Reflect the triangle ($\triangle ABC$) in the $y$-axis (the line of reflection) by flipping the paper across the $y$-axis and realigning the axes. Then copy and complete a table similar to the one below.

| Reflect across the $y$-axis | | | |
|---|---|---|---|
| Original Vertex | Original Position | Image Vertex | Position of Image |
| $A$ | $(8, 7)$ | $A'$ | |
| $B$ | | $B'$ | |
| $C$ | | $C'$ | |

**11.** Did the triangle change its size or shape?

**12.** What happens to the $x$- and $y$-coordinates when a point or figure is reflected across the $y$-axis?

**13.** Figure $ABCD$ has vertices at $A(3, 2)$, $B(5, 6)$, $C(8, 4)$, and $D(6, 0)$. If the figure is reflected in the $y$-axis, find the coordinates of the image $A'B'C'D'$.

**14.** Use coordinate notation to describe a reflection in the $y$-axis.

$$(x, y) \rightarrow (\blacksquare, \blacksquare)$$

**10.**

| Reflect across the $y$-axis. | | | |
|---|---|---|---|
| Original Vertex | Original Position | Image Vertex | Position of Image |
| $A$ | $(8, 7)$ | $A'$ | $(-8, 7)$ |
| $B$ | $(9, 2)$ | $B'$ | $(-9, 2)$ |
| $C$ | $(5, 3)$ | $C'$ | $(-5, 3)$ |

**11.** No.

**12.** Sample answer: The new $x$-coordinate is the opposite of the original $x$-coordinate. The $y$-coordinate stays the same.

**13.** $A'(-3, 2)$, $B'(-5, 6)$, $C'(-8, 4)$, $D'(-6, 0)$

**14.** $(x, y) \rightarrow (-x, y)$

# LESSON 9.5

**15.** Check students' graphs.

**16.**

| Reflect across the *x*-axis. | | | |
|---|---|---|---|
| Original Vertex | Original Position | Image Vertex | Position of Image |
| *A* | (8, 7) | *A′* | (8, −7) |
| *B* | (9, 2) | *B′* | (9, −2) |
| *C* | (5, 3) | *C′* | (5, −3) |

**17.** No.

**18.** Sample answer: The *x*-coordinate stays the same. The new *y*-coordinate is the opposite of the original *y*-coordinate.

**19.** *A′*(3, −2), *B′*(5, −6), *C′*(8, −4), *D′*(6, 0)

---

**15.** Return to the original triangle (△*ABC*). Place your image (△*A′B′C′*) from Question 1 and axes from Question 9 on top of the original.

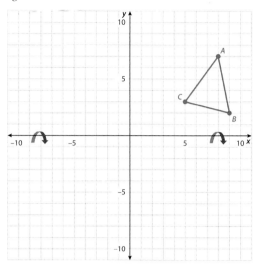

**16.** Reflect the triangle (△*ABC*) in the *x*-axis (the line of reflection) by flipping the paper across the *x*-axis and realigning the axes. Then copy and complete a table similar to the one below.

| Reflect across the *x*-axis | | | |
|---|---|---|---|
| Original Vertex | Original Position | Image Vertex | Position of Image |
| *A* | (8, 7) | *A′* | |
| *B* | | *B′* | |
| *C* | | *C′* | |

**17.** Did the triangle change its size or shape?

**18.** What happens to the *x*- and *y*-coordinates when a point or figure is reflected across the *x*-axis?

**19.** Figure *ABCD* has vertices *A*(3, 2), *B*(5, 6), *C*(8, 4), and *D*(6, 0). If the figure is reflected in the *x*-axis, find the coordinates of the image *A′B′C′D′*.

**20.** Use coordinate notation to describe a reflection in the $x$-axis.

$$(x, y) \rightarrow (\blacksquare, \blacksquare)$$

## PART D: ROTATIONS IN THE COORDINATE PLANE

**21.** Trace an image of $\triangle ABC$ and the coordinate axes from Question 1 on a new sheet of patty paper. Label the vertices of the image $A'$, $B'$ and $C'$.

**22.** Place the image ($\triangle A'B'C'$) and the axes on top of the original. Rotate the image and axes $90°$ about the origin by turning the copy counterclockwise. Then copy and complete a table similar to the one below.

| Rotate about the origin | | | | |
|---|---|---|---|---|
| Angle of Rotation | Original Vertex | Original Position | Image Vertex | Position of Image |
| | $A$ | $(8, 7)$ | $A'$ | |
| $90°$ | $B$ | | $B'$ | |
| | $C$ | | $C'$ | |

**23.** Did the triangle change its size or shape?

**24.** Use coordinate notation to describe a $90°$ rotation about the origin.

$$(x, y) \rightarrow (\blacksquare, \blacksquare)$$

**25.** Repeat Question 22 for the rotations of $180°$ and $270°$.

**26 a.** Use coordinate notation to describe a rotation of $180°$ about the origin.

$$(x, y) \rightarrow (\blacksquare, \blacksquare)$$

**b.** Repeat Part (a) for a rotation of $270°$ about the origin.

## PART E: GLIDE REFLECTIONS USING THE X-AXIS

Since a glide reflection is a combination of a translation and a reflection, it requires a distance, a direction, and a line of reflection. In this Investigation, only horizontal translations will be explored since the translation vector must be parallel to the line of reflection.

**27.** Conduct an investigation into glide reflections using the $x$-axis as the line of reflection.

**a.** Use grid paper and draw a triangle in one of the quadrants.

**20.** $(x, y) \rightarrow (x, -y)$

### CONNECTION

Coordinate descriptions of rotations that are not multiples of $90°$ use trigonometry and are not discussed in this text.

**21.** Check students' graphs.

**22.**

| Rotate about the origin. | | | | |
|---|---|---|---|---|
| Angle of Rotation | Original Vertex | Original Position | Image Vertex | Position of Image |
| | $A$ | $(8, 7)$ | $A'$ | $(-7, 8)$ |
| $90°$ | $B$ | $(9, 2)$ | $B'$ | $(-2, 9)$ |
| | $C$ | $(5, 3)$ | $C'$ | $(-3, 5)$ |

**23.** No.

**24.** $(x, y) \rightarrow (-y, x)$

**25.**

| Rotate about the origin. | | | | |
|---|---|---|---|---|
| Angle of Rotation | Original Vertex | Original Position | Image Vertex | Position of Image |
| | $A$ | $(8, 7)$ | $A'$ | $(-8, -7)$ |
| $180°$ | $B$ | $(9, 2)$ | $B'$ | $(-9, -2)$ |
| | $C$ | $(5, 3)$ | $C'$ | $(-5, -3)$ |
| | $A$ | $(8, 7)$ | $A'$ | $(7, -8)$ |
| $270°$ | $B$ | $(9, 2)$ | $B'$ | $(2, -9)$ |
| | $C$ | $(5, 3)$ | $C'$ | $(3, -5)$ |

**26a.** $(x, y) \rightarrow (-x, -y)$
**26b.** $(x, y) \rightarrow (y, -x)$
**27.** Answers will vary.

**28.** $(x, y) \rightarrow (x + h, -y)$

## Practice for Lesson 9.5
## Answers

**1a.** Transformation I

Transformation II

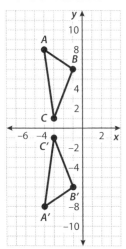

**b.** Select a horizontal distance to use in the translation. (Remember that the translation must be parallel to the *x*-axis if you want to reflect the figure in the *x*–axis.)

**c.** Translate the figure. Then reflect the image across the *x*-axis.

**d.** Record the results.

**e.** Repeat with different triangles until you see a pattern.

**28.** Use coordinate notation to describe a glide reflection of the point $(x, y)$ if the point is translated *h* units horizontally and then reflected in the *x*-axis.

**Practice** for Lesson 9.5

1. Triangle *ABC* has the vertices $A(-4, 8)$, $B(-1, 6)$, and $C(-3, 1)$.
   **a.** Sketch △*ABC* and its images after the following transformations:

   | | |
   |---|---|
   | Transformation I: | $(x, y) \rightarrow (x + 8, y + 2)$ |
   | Transformation II: | $(x, y) \rightarrow (x, -y)$ |
   | Transformation III: | $(x, y) \rightarrow (-y, x)$ |
   | Transformation IV: | $(x, y) \rightarrow (-x, y)$ |

   **b.** Describe each transformation.

2. **a.** Follow these steps to conduct an investigation into glide reflections using the *y*-axis as the line of reflection.

   Step 1: On grid paper, draw a scalene triangle in one of the four quadrants of a coordinate grid.

   Step 2: Select a vertical distance to use in the translation. (Remember that the translation must be parallel to the *y*-axis if you want to reflect the figure in the *y*-axis.)

   Step 3: Translate the figure. Then reflect the image across the *y*-axis.

   Step 4: Record the results.

   Step 5: Repeat with different triangles until you see a pattern.

   **b.** Use coordinate notation to describe a glide reflection of the point $(x, y)$ if the point is translated *k* units vertically and then reflected in the *y*-axis.

Transformation III

Transformation IV

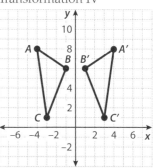

**1b.** Transformation I is a translation of 8 units to the right and up 2 units. Transformation II is a reflection in the *x*-axis. Transformation III is a rotation of 90° counterclockwise. Transformation IV is a reflection in the *y*-axis.

**2a.** Answers will vary.

**2b.** $(x, y) \rightarrow (-x, y + k)$

CHAPTER

# 9

# Modeling Project

## It's a Masterpiece!

In this chapter you have seen a number of ways people use mathematics to create art. Now it is your turn to be creative. Use the tools you have developed in this chapter to create five different one-dimensional "strip" patterns, one with translation symmetry only, one with vertical line symmetry, one with horizontal symmetry, one with rotational symmetry, and one with glide reflection symmetry. While the patterns and colors can be anything you would like, include notes with each that describe how you used mathematics to transform your objects in order to create the patterns. These notes should include the types of transformations that you used to create your work.

Be creative and have fun. Be ready to share your drawings with the class and answer questions about your work.

## Materials List

- ruler
- colored pencils
- protractor

## Description

Students are asked to use what they know about symmetry and transformations to create five one-dimensional patterns. This project works best when individual students create their own patterns.

## Sample Answers

Patterns will vary depending on each student's level of creativity and knowledge of the chapter.

# Chapter 9  Review

## You Should Be Able to:

### Lesson 9.1

- discover the characteristics of line and rotational symmetry.
- identify line symmetries of a figure.
- identify rotational symmetries of a figure.

### Lesson 9.2

- create images of figures using translations, reflections, rotations, and glide reflections.
- identify the rigid motion used to create the image of a given figure.

### Lesson 9.3

- use rigid motions (isometries) to describe one- and two-dimensional repeated patterns.
- use rigid motions to create one-dimensional repeated patterns.

### Lesson 9.4

- solve problems that require previously learned concepts and skills.

### Lesson 9.5

- use coordinate notation to describe rigid motions.
- sketch the image of a figure on the coordinate plane when given a rigid motion.

## Key Vocabulary

line of reflection (p. 303)

mirror image (p. 303)

line symmetry (p. 303)

rotational symmetry (p. 304)

angle of rotation (p. 304)

transformation (p. 307)

rigid motion (p. 307)

isometry (p. 307)

image (p. 307)

translation (p. 308)

translation vector (p. 308)

reflection (p. 308)

rotation (p. 308)

glide reflection (p. 309)

translation symmetry (p. 311)

rotational symmetry (p. 312)

glide-reflection symmetry (p. 312)

## Chapter 9  Test Review

1. Describe the symmetry in the figure below.

2. Which statement *best* identifies the line symmetry and rotational symmetry of the capital letter H?

   A. It has one line of symmetry and rotational symmetry with an angle of rotation of 180°.

   B. It has two lines of symmetry and no rotational symmetry.

   C. It has two lines of symmetry and rotational symmetry with an angle of rotation of 180°.

   D. It had two lines of symmetry and rotational symmetry with an angle of rotation of 90°.

3. Describe the line symmetry and rotational symmetry of a regular pentagon.

4. Describe the lines of symmetry of a regular polygon with *n* sides,

   a. if *n* is even.

   b. if *n* is odd.

5 a. Reflect the letter in the figure about the reflection line ℓ. Draw the image.

   b. Now reflect the image from Part (a) about the reflection line ℓ. What do you observe?

6. Describe the symmetry of the capital letter N.

## Chapter 9 Test Review Answers

1. The figure has 2 lines of symmetry: vertical and horizontal. It also has rotational symmetry about the point where the two non-horizontal lines intersect with an angle of rotation of 180°.

2. C

3. A regular pentagon has 5 lines of symmetry. It also has rotational symmetry. The angle of rotation is 72°.

4a. If *n* is even, it will have *n* lines of symmetry, half of them pass through a pair of vertices and half are perpendicular bisectors of a pair of sides.

4b. If *n* is odd, it will have *n* lines of symmetry. These lines are the perpendicular bisectors of the sides.

5a.

5b.

If the figure is reflected twice about the same reflection line, the image is congruent to the original figure and has the same orientation.

6. It has rotational symmetry with an angle of rotation of 180°.

# CHAPTER REVIEW

**7a.** glide reflection

**7b.** rotation (90° clockwise or 270° counterclockwise)

**7c.** reflection (vertical line of reflection)

**7d.** reflection (horizontal line of reflection)

**8.** glide-reflection symmetry and translation symmetry

**9.** horizontal and vertical line symmetry, rotational symmetry (180° rotation), translation symmetry

**7.** The figure below shows the original figure used to make the images in Parts (a–d).

Name the rigid motion used to achieve each of the images.

**a.**

**b.**

**c.**    **d.**

**8.** Describe the symmetry in the infinite pattern.

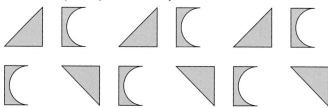

**9.** Identify the symmetries for the pattern below.

**10.** In the figure shown, which of these do *not* produce an image of the rectangle with two of its vertices lying on the y-axis?

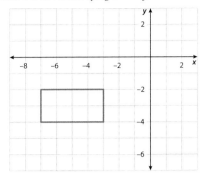

**A.** a reflection across the x-axis   **B.** a translation 3 units to the right
**C.** a translation up 2 units       **D.** a reflection across the y-axis

**11.** Triangle ABC is shown in the figure below.

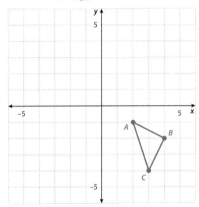

Sketch △ABC and its images after the following transformations:

**a.** a reflection across the x-axis. Label this image A'B'C'.

**b.** a rotation of 180°. Label this image A''B''C''.

**c.** a translation of 7 units to the left and 2 units down. Label this image A'''B'''C'''.

**12.** The line segment AB has endpoints at (1, 5) and (−4, −2). If the segment is rotated 90° counterclockwise, what are the endpoints of the image of segment AB?

**10.** A, C, and D
**11(a−c).**

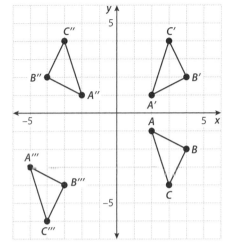

**12.** (−5, 1) and (2, −4)

**5e** Elaborate

## Lesson Objectives

- determine whether a painting or sketch makes use of perspective.
- use overlapping to represent three-dimensional objects in two-dimensional drawings.

## Vocabulary

- perspective

## Materials List

- centimeter grid paper printed on cardstock
- transparent tape
- masking tape or string
- meter stick
- scissors

## Description

Students work in groups of 3–4 students, and each group should be assigned one of the four works of art (A, B, C, or D). As they compare their art pieces, they are asked to make note of which ones *best* represent real-life situations. They are also asked to make observations about the relative sizes of objects in the works of art. In doing so they learn that objects closer to the viewer appear larger than similar items that are farther away.

**Questions 1–8** prepare students for further exploration of techniques, such as overlapping, that are used to create perspective. In **Questions 9–14**, students create models of cubes and arrange them based on a top view. Then they shift their perspective on the cubes by viewing the arrangements from the north, south, east, and west. After each different view, they create a sketch of what they see. They should notice in their sketches that cubes closest to them overlap the ones in the background.

---

# Chapter Extension
## Perspective in Art

Throughout Chapter 9, you examined one-dimensional strip patterns, a type of art that is often used to decorate objects and buildings. Because of the sense of balance and proportion found in these symmetrical patterns, many people find them to be esthetically pleasing. In this Extension, you will explore some other techniques used by artists as they try to paint and draw three-dimensional objects and scenes on two-dimensional canvas and paper.

Examine the piece of art assigned to your group.

**Cave drawings similar to those found at Hamangala**
**Figure A**

**Architectural rendering of a building**
**Figure B**

---

7. Below are a few of the many possible answers:
   - The woman learning out the window is lighting the pipe of the person walking on a distant hill.
   - The trees on the distant hill overlap the sign on the garage.
   - The fishing pole closest to the viewer hangs over the fishing pole that is farthest from the viewer.
   - The swan on the lake is larger than the cattle and sheep that are closer.
   - The man walking on the distant hill is larger than the coach crossing the bridge.
   - The lines on the building make the side of the building appear to be in two different planes.

*Perspective Absurdities* by William Hogarth.
**Figure C**

**Ancient Egyptian art**
**Figure D**

1. What do you notice about your assigned piece of art?

2. What do you notice about the sizes of the different people and animals in the picture?

3. What do you notice about the relationships between the sizes of the different objects and their placement in the picture?

4. Which pictures most accurately depict a real-life scene? Explain.

5. Which pictures least accurately depict a real-life scene? Explain.

**Perspective** is the technique of representing objects from three-dimensional space in a two-dimensional plane. Through the use of perspective, an artist's two-dimensional drawing or painting imitates the appearance of a three-dimensional object or scene.

6. Which pictures seem to make use of perspective?

7. The engraving shown in Figure C is titled *Perspective Absurdities* by William Hogarth. Work with your group to identify the real-world inaccuracies in the painting. Describe each error in detail.

CHAPTER EXTENSION    **Chapter 9**    329

## Chapter 9 Extension Answers

1. Figure A: Sample answer: Students should see that while the picture is primitive, it seems to represents people and animals.
   Figure B: Sample answer: Students should recognize that the architectural drawing looks realistic.
   Figure C: Sample answer: Students should notice that some of the things in the picture do not look possible.
   Figure D: Sample answer: Students should notice that the picture does not seem to try to render the four people accurately.

2. Figure A: Sample answer: The animals are larger than the humans. The humans are all approximately the same size.
   Figure B: Sample answer: The people in the foreground are larger than the people near the car.
   Figure C: Sample answer: The person walking on the hill seems too large when compared to the horses that are pulling the wagon on the bridge.
   Figure D: Sample answer: The sitting people are one size and the other person is a much smaller size.

3. Figure A: Sample answer: The placement of the animals makes them appear to be floating above the humans. The hunters appear to be riding on the backs of the animals.
   Figure B: Sample answer: The trees get smaller as they get farther away, as do the people.
   Figure C: Sample answer: Some objects that are closer to the viewer appear to be larger than those object that are farther from the viewer, but some objects in the distance appear larger than objects in the foreground of the painting.
   Figure D: Sample answer: All subjects (objects and people) appear to be in the same plane.

4. Answers may vary. Students will probably answer Figures B and C. Students looking closely at Figure C may decide that it is not accurate.

5. Answers may vary. Students most likely will choose Figures A and D.

6. Sample answer: Figure B seems to make use of perspective. Some students may recognize that the Hogarth painting (Figure C) uses perspective in a funny and impossible way. Students may even suggest that the artist is doing this on purpose.

7. See answer on page 328.

329

**8a.** Sample diagram:

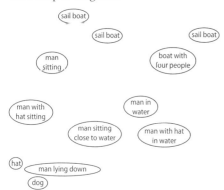

**8b.** Sample answer: Possible clues include relative sizes of objects, positions of objects in the picture, overlapping of objects, and shading.

**8c.** Sample answer: Seurat put some objects in front of other objects. The objects that are in front appear closer to the view because they are larger in size and cover (overlap) objects behind them. Objects that are farther away are drawn smaller, and objects in the far distance show less detail.

---

**TEACHING TIP**

If students have forgotten how to make a net of a solid cube, have them refer back to **Lesson 4.6**.

---

**8.** The painting *Bathers at Asnieres* by George Seurat is shown below. In this painting, the artist tried to represent a three-dimensional subject on the surface of canvas or paper.

***The Bathers at Asnieres* by George Seurat**

a. Imagine that you are in a hot-air balloon floating over the subjects in this picture. Draw a bird's-eye view of what you would see. You do not have to sketch every detail. For example, you might use ovals labeled as dog, man lying down, man wearing hat, or sailboat to indicate the positions of people and objects.

b. Describe the clues in the original picture that helped you decide where to place the people and objects in your drawing.

c. Explain how the artist tried to convey depth.

In Questions 1–8, you identified factors that are important to the proper use of perspective in drawing and painting. One of these is the location of objects with respect to each other. That is, objects close to the viewer often overlap those that are behind them. Another factor is the relative size of objects. Objects far away from the viewer are drawn smaller than those close to the viewer.

Within your group, use centimeter grid paper to create 4 cubes as described in the table.

Use masking tape or string to mark a 35-cm by 35-cm square region on a flat surface such as a table. Label the sides of the square "North," "South," "East," and "West."

| Cube | Side Length (cm) |
|------|------------------|
| A | 2 |
| B | 4 |
| C | 6 |
| D | 8 |

Position the cubes according to the diagram shown below.

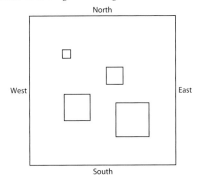

**Cube placement**

**9.** Lower yourself so that you are at eye level with the cubes. Draw a two-dimensional sketch of what you see from the north, south, east, and west.

**10.** How are the sketches alike?

**11.** How are the sketches different?

**12.** How does overlapping reveal which cube is in front of another cube?

**13.** The figure below shows the top view of a table on which three cubes are sitting. Draw four eye-level views of what you would see if you were sitting at positions *A*, *B*, *C*, and *D*.

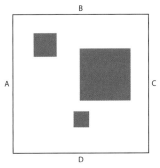

**Top view of three cubes on a table**

**14.** Explain how to draw images of objects so that the person looking at the image knows which objects are closer than other objects.

**9.** Sample sketches:

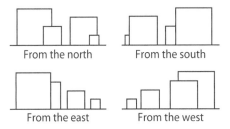

**10.** Sample answer: All four sketches contain the same four cubes.

**11.** Sample answer: The cube that appears to be closest to the eye of the viewer varies as the location of the viewer varies.

**12.** Sample answer: If a cube is in the foreground, then the drawing of that cube overlaps any of the cubes that appear to be behind it.

**13.** Sample answers:

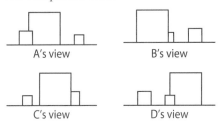

**14.** Sample answer: Objects that are closest to the viewer may overlap objects that are farthest from the viewer.

# Chapter 10
# Exponential Functions

## Mathematical Overview

Describing and predicting change is an important use of mathematics. In Chapter 5, students used mathematics to describe and predict linear change. In this chapter, students focus on examining the Properties of Exponents and their use in modeling and predicting exponential growth and decay—types of nonlinear change. Lessons 10.2 and 10.3 review the Properties of Exponents and explain how the properties are applied when working with very large numbers, as well as very small numbers, expressed in scientific notation. Throughout the chapter, students examine tables of data, equations, and graphs of exponential growth or decay functions.

## Lesson Summaries

### Lesson 10.1  *Activity: Nonlinear Change*

In this Activity, students working in pairs use a paper-cutting activity to discover an exponential function that models the relationship between the number of layers of paper and the number of cuts made. After collecting data, students show how powers of 2 can be used to compute the number of layers of paper after each cut. They write a function that models their data, and then use graphing calculators to make scatter plots that show the function is nonlinear. This Activity provides the foundation for the Investigation in Lesson 10.5.

### Lesson 10.2  *Properties of Exponents*

In this lesson, students review the Properties of Exponents in order to simplify expressions involving positive integer exponents. Students then write very large numbers using exponents when they express these numbers in scientific notation. Students use scientific notation to rewrite computations with very large numbers, and then they apply the Properties of Exponents to perform the computations. The skills reviewed and polished in this lesson are the foundations for the Investigation in Lesson 10.3.

### Lesson 10.3  *Investigation: Negative Exponents*

In this Investigation, a brief introduction to negative exponents is provided. Then, using the Sierpinski Triangle, students work in pairs to investigate the area of the smallest triangle formed in each term of the pattern. Students use graphing calculators to make scatter plots of the data collected and discover that the function modeling their data is an example of exponential decay. This lesson concludes with a review of the following topics: the Quotient of Powers Property to show the meaning of an exponent of 0, negative exponents used in scientific notation, monomials expressed with either positive or negative exponents, and an expanded list of the Properties of Exponents.

### Lesson 10.4  *R.A.P.*

In this lesson, students **R**eview **A**nd **P**ractice solving problems that require the use of skills and concepts taught in previous math levels. The skills reviewed in this lesson are skills that are needed as a basis for solving problems throughout this course.

### Lesson 10.5  *Investigation: Modeling Exponential Growth*

In this Investigation, students work in pairs to build on their work with exponential growth in Lesson 10.1. They construct two growth models. The first model represents the relationship between the thickness of paper and the number of cuts, using the process they used in Lesson 10.1. The second model represents the data provided about the number of mosquitoes testing positive for the West Nile virus. Students practice identifying relationships as linear growth, exponential growth, or neither, and then write equations that model the patterns. Then they use a graphing calculator to determine if their models fit the given data.

### Lesson 10.6  *Investigation: Modeling Exponential Decay*

In this Investigation, students work in pairs to investigate building a model for exponential decay via a water pollution cleanup scenario. During the Investigation students explore the concept of asymptotes. They practice classifying the graphs of functions as exponential growth or exponential decay and identifying characteristics of the graphs without ever graphing the given functions.

### Chapter 10  *Extension: Newton's Law of Cooling*

In this Extension, students collect data regarding the temperature of cooling water, create models exemplifying Newton's Law of Cooling (which states that the rate of change of the temperature of an object is proportional to the difference between its own temperature and the temperature of its surroundings), and then make scatter plots to model the data.

## Lesson Guide

| Lesson/Objectives | Materials | |
|---|---|---|
| **Chapter 10 Opener: Will the World Have Enough Water?**<br>• understand that exponential change is modeled with a nonlinear function. | | |
| **10.1 Activity: Nonlinear Change**<br>• recognize exponential functions. | *Per pair:*<br>• one $8\frac{1}{2}'' \times 11''$ sheet of paper<br>• scissors | *Optional:*<br>• TRM table shells for Questions 1, 5, 8, and 9<br>• TRM scatter plot shell for Question 2<br>• graphing calculator<br>• TRM table shells for Exercise 6, Part (b) |
| **10.2 Properties of Exponents**<br>• use properties of exponents to simplify expressions.<br>• use scientific notation to compute with large numbers. | | |
| **10.3 Investigation: Negative Exponents**<br>• define and use negative exponents.<br>• define and use 0 as an exponent.<br>• simplify monomials. | *Per pair:*<br>• graphing calculator | *Optional:*<br>• TRM table shell for Question 1<br>• TRM table shell for Exercise 18, Part (a) |
| **10.4 R.A.P.**<br>• solve problems that require previously learned concepts and skills. | | |
| **10.5 Investigation: Modeling Exponential Growth**<br>• identify situations involving exponential growth.<br>• model situations involving exponential growth. | *Per pair:*<br>• graphing calculator | *Optional:*<br>• TRM table shells for Questions 2, 4, and 14<br>• TRM table shells for Exercises 4, 5, 6<br>• TRM table shell for the Additional Example |
| **10.6 Investigation: Modeling Exponential Decay**<br>• identify situations involving exponential decay.<br>• model situations involving exponential decay. | *Per pair:*<br>• graphing calculator | *Optional:*<br>• TRM table shell for Question 5<br>• TRM table shell for the Additional Example |
| **Chapter 10 Extension: Newton's Law of Cooling**<br>• use technology to collect and analyze data for exponential decay involving a nonzero limiting value. | *Per group:*<br>• calculator-based data collection device (such as a CBL2)<br>• graphing calculator with data collection program<br>• temperature probe<br>• 2 paper or Styrofoam cups<br>• hot and cold water | *Optional:*<br>• TRM table shell for Questions 3 and 5<br>• thermometer accurate to 0.5°C |

## Pacing Guide

| | Day 1 | Day 2 | Day 3 | Day 4 | Day 5 | Day 6 | Day 7 | Day 8 | Day 9 | Day 10 | Day 11 |
|---|---|---|---|---|---|---|---|---|---|---|---|
| **Basic** | p. 334, 10.1 | 10.1, 10.2 | 10.2, 10.3 | 10.3 | 10.4 | 10.5 | 10.5 | 10.6 | project | review | |
| **Standard** | p. 334, 10.1 | 10.1, 10.2 | 10.2, 10.3 | 10.3 | 10.4 | 10.5 | 10.5 | 10.6 | project | review | extension |
| **Block** | p. 334, 10.1 | 10.2, 10.3 | 10.3, 10.4 | 10.5 | 10.6, project | review, extension | | | | | |

**Supplement Support**

See the Book Companion Website at www.highschool.bfwpub.com/ModelingwithMathematics and the Teacher's Resource Materials (TRM) for additional resources.

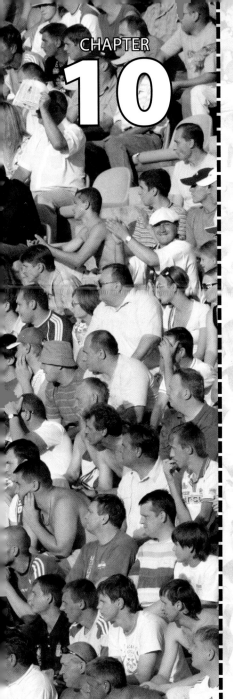

# Exponential Functions

## CONTENTS

## Lesson Objective

- understand that exponential change is modeled with a nonlinear function.

## Vocabulary

## Description

The Chapter Opener gives an example of a situation that involves exponential growth.

### CONNECTION

You may wish to point out to students that "one thousand trillion" is called a *quadrillion*. Note that in many countries, the usage of the words *billion*, *trillion*, and *quadrillion* differs from their meanings in the U.S. and scientific communities.

### TEACHING TIP

Ask students whether they have heard of changes in other quantities (such as populations) described as exponential growth. Also, ask them how they might recognize that a change in a variable is not linear.

### CONNECTION

Matt Damon's 2006 film *Running the Sahara* depicted the water crisis in North Africa. His group, H2O Africa, is affiliated with Water.org, a U.S.-based nonprofit organization committed to providing safe drinking water and sanitation to people in developing countries. The www.water .org website contains timely information about water issues.

## Will the World Have Enough Water?

This may seem like a silly question, but in reality it is a very serious question.

Consider the following facts:

- Three-fourths of the world is covered with water. But most of that is salt water, which is not good for most people's water needs.
- Fresh water is needed for drinking, bathing, and other household activities.
- Cropland irrigation accounts for 70% of all fresh water use.
- In all, the use of fresh water by all the nations of the world amounts to about one thousand trillion gallons per year.
- The United Nations predicts that demand for water will be greater than the available supply within a few decades.
- Some American companies are already shipping clean lake water from Alaska to India and other places that are experiencing water shortages.
- It has been estimated that global water consumption is doubling every 20 years.

You have probably heard something described as "growing exponentially." World water usage is one of many things that grow exponentially. But just what does exponential growth mean? You have already studied linear growth, as well as things that decrease linearly. Exponential growth and decay are examples of nonlinear change.

It is no surprise that a process with the name "exponential" is described mathematically using exponents. This chapter includes an examination of properties of exponents and their use in modeling growth and decay.

Growth can occur in a variety of ways that require different mathematical models. In this lesson, you will examine a kind of growth that can be modeled with increasing powers of a given number.

Some things never change. There are always 7 days in a week. The meter is a unit of length that is the same everywhere. The ratio of a circle's circumference to its diameter always equals the number $\pi$. Such quantities are described mathematically as *constants*.

But many things in our world change over time. Sometimes the change happens quickly, such as a teenager's growth spurt over a summer or an increase of thousands of bacteria in a container of water. Other changes occur slowly, for example the erosion of a mountain peak or a change in the Earth's surface temperature. Changing quantities are described mathematically with *variables*. One of the most important uses of mathematics is describing and predicting change.

In previous chapters, you have studied changes that involve constant rates. Linear functions can model processes that increase or decrease at a constant rate. But if the rate of change of a quantity is not constant, a nonlinear function is needed.

1.  Cut a piece of paper in half. Lay the half-sheets on top of each other. Count and record the number of sheets in the pile. Cut each of the two half-sheets in half again. Count and record. Continue stacking and cutting the paper. Each time, count the number of layers of paper in the stack and record the result in a table like the one shown below.

| Number of Cuts | Number of Layers of Paper | | | |
|---|---|---|---|---|
| 0 | 1 | | | |
| 1 | 2 | | | |
| 2 | | | | |
| 3 | | | | |
| 4 | | | | |
| 5 | | | | |
| 6 | | | | |

NONLINEAR CHANGE    **Lesson 10.1**    **335**

## Lesson Objective

-  recognize exponential functions.

## Vocabulary

-  base
-  exponent
-  exponential function
-  exponential growth

## Materials List

-  one $8\frac{1}{2}'' \times 11''$ sheet of paper
-  scissors

## Description

*Preparation:*

Have students work in pairs. Each pair should be provided with paper and scissors. Have them read the introductory paragraphs before beginning the Activity.

*During the Activity:*

In this Activity, students cut a sheet of paper in half, then cut those sheets in half, and continue the process, stacking the sheets after each cut. They will see how quickly the number of sheets increases and gain an appreciation of the meaning of exponential change. They should see that the number of layers of paper doubles with each cut, and that this pattern can be described by a simple base 2 exponential function.

*Closing the Activity:*

Debrief the Activity by going over the answers to the questions with the students. Make sure that their summaries in **Question 16** include a recognition that the ratios of numbers of layers are constant.

## Lesson 10.1 Activity Answers

1.  See the completed table in Question 9 on page 337.

**2.**

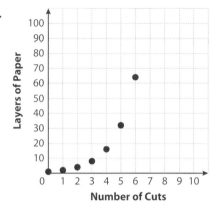

3. It is discrete, since the number of cuts is a whole number.
4. Sample answer: Domain is whole numbers. Range is natural numbers.
5. See the completed table in Question 9 on page 337.
6. Sample answer: Beginning with the second cut, the changes double with each cut.
7. No, the rate of change of a linear function is constant.
8. The ratios are constant. See the completed table in Question 9 on page 337.

**2.** Make a scatter plot of your data on a grid similar to the one below.

3. Is the function you have graphed continuous or discrete? Explain.
4. What are the domain and range of the function?
5. Label the third column of your table "Change in Number of Layers." For each cut, write the difference between the number of layers after the cut and before the cut.

| Number of Cuts | Number of Layers of Paper | Change in Number of Layers | | |
|---|---|---|---|---|
| 0 | 1 | — | | |
| 1 | 2 | $2 - 1 = 1$ | | |
| 2 | | | | |
| 3 | | | | |
| 4 | | | | |
| 5 | | | | |
| 6 | | | | |

6. Describe the pattern of the changes in the number of layers.
7. Is the change in the number of layers a linear function of the number of cuts? Explain.
8. Label the fourth column of your table "Ratio of Successive Numbers of Layers." For each cut, write the ratio of the number of layers after the cut to the number of layers before the cut. For example, after the first cut,

$$\frac{\text{number of layers after 1 cut}}{\text{number of layers after 0 cuts}} = \frac{2}{1} = 2$$

**Note**

The numbers in the third column are called *successive differences*. Each entry in this column is found by subtracting the number of layers in the preceding row from the number in the current, or *succeeding*, row. Successive differences can be helpful in analyzing data in a table when the changes in the independent variable are constant.

Describe any pattern you see in the fourth column.

| Number of Cuts | Number of Layers of Paper | Change in Number of Layers | Ratio of Successive Numbers of Layers |
|---|---|---|---|
| 0 | 1 | — | — |
| 1 | 2 | $2 - 1 = 1$ | $\frac{2}{1} = 2$ |
| 2 | | | |
| 3 | | | |
| 4 | | | |
| 5 | | | |
| 6 | | | |

**9.** Label the fifth column of your table "Computing Process for Column 2." In this column, show how powers of 2 can be used to compute the number of layers of paper after each cut. For example, after the second cut, the number of layers is $2 \cdot 2 = 2^2$.

**Recall**

Recall that repeated multiplication can be written with a **base** and an **exponent**. For example, $5 \cdot 5 \cdot 5$ can be rewritten as $5^3$. The factor 5 is the base. The number 3, which tells how many factors are multiplied, is the exponent.

| Number of Cuts | Number of Layers of Paper | Change in Number of Layers | Ratio of Successive Numbers of Layers | Computing Process for Column 2 |
|---|---|---|---|---|
| 0 | 1 | — | — | — |
| 1 | 2 | $2 - 1 = 1$ | $\frac{2}{1} = 2$ | $2 = 2^1$ |
| 2 | 4 | $4 - 2 = 2$ | $\frac{4}{2} = 2$ | $2 \cdot 2 = 2^2$ |
| 3 | | | | |
| 4 | | | | |
| 5 | | | | |
| 6 | | | | |

**10.** Look at the first and fifth columns of your table. Describe any connection you see between the number of cuts and the expressions in the "Computing Process for Column 2" column.

**11.** Write a function for the number of layers of paper $L$ if you cut the paper $n$ times.

**12.** Use a graphing calculator to make a scatter plot of the data from your first table in Question 1. Then graph your function from Question 11 on the scatter plot and record your window. Does your function describe the points in the scatter plot?

NONLINEAR CHANGE    **Lesson 10.1**    **337**

**9.**

| Number of Cuts | Number of Layers of Paper | Change in Number of Layers | Ratio of Successive Numbers of Layers | Computing Process for Column 2 |
|---|---|---|---|---|
| 0 | 1 | — | — | — |
| 1 | 2 | $2 - 1 = 1$ | $\frac{2}{1} = 2$ | $2 = 2^1$ |
| 2 | 4 | $4 - 2 = 2$ | $\frac{4}{2} = 2$ | $2 \cdot 2 = 2^2$ |
| 3 | 8 | $8 - 4 = 4$ | $\frac{8}{4} = 2$ | $2 \cdot 2 \cdot 2 = 2^3$ |
| 4 | 16 | $16 - 8 = 8$ | $\frac{16}{8} = 2$ | $2 \cdot 2 \cdot 2 \cdot 2 = 2^4$ |
| 5 | 32 | $32 - 16 = 16$ | $\frac{32}{16} = 2$ | $2 \cdot 2 \cdot 2 \cdot 2 \cdot 2 = 2^5$ |
| 6 | 64 | $64 - 32 = 32$ | $\frac{64}{32} = 2$ | $2 \cdot 2 \cdot 2 \cdot 2 \cdot 2 \cdot 2 = 2^6$ |

**10.** The exponent equals the number of cuts.

**11.** $L = 2^n$

**12.** Sample answer: The graph of the function passes through all the points.

$[-0.2, 6.2] \times [-1, 70]$

# LESSON 10.1

**TEACHING TIP**

For **Question 13**, you may wish to show students how a TI-83/84 graphing calculator can be used to create and extend a repeated pattern. For example, to generate the second column of the table in the Activity,

- Press **1** **ENTER**;
- Press **2nd** **ANS**;
- Enter the operation to be repeated, in this case **x** **2**;
- Press the **ENTER** key repeatedly as many times as needed.

**TEACHING TIP**

Ask students to explain why, for an exponential function $y = a \cdot b^x$, $a$ cannot be 0 and $b$ cannot be 1. (The function would be constant in both cases, either $y = 0$ or $y = a$.)

**TEACHING TIP**

Point out to students that in an exponential function, $a$ and $b$ do not change but $x$ does.

**TEACHING TIP**

The domain of an exponential function is defined as including all real numbers. At this point, students may not understand the meaning of negative, zero, or fractional exponents. Negative exponents and the 0 exponent are discussed in **Lesson 10.3**, and fractional exponents will be defined in a later course.

**TEACHING TIP**

It is stated that the range of an exponential function includes either positive real numbers or negative real numbers, but not both. This assumes that the $x$-axis is an asymptote. If the function is shifted vertically, the range may include both positive and negative numbers.

**13.** Use your function to predict how many layers of paper there would be after 10 cuts.

**14.** What happens as the number of cuts increases?

**15.** What is the vertical intercept of the graph of your function?

**16.** Write a summary of what you have found out about the properties of the function that relates the number of layers of paper to the number of cuts.

## EXPONENTIAL FUNCTIONS

The function you investigated in the Activity is an example of an **exponential function**. The equation of an exponential function consists of

- an *initial value a,* where $a \neq 0$,
- a *constant base b,*
- a *variable exponent x.*

Using these symbols, the general form is

$y = a \cdot b^x$, where $a$ is the initial value of the dependent variable $y$.

An exponential function has the following properties:

- The base $b$ can be any positive real number except 1.
- The domain includes all real numbers.
- The range includes either positive real numbers or negative real numbers, but not both.
- The $y$-intercept of the graph of the function is $(0, a)$.
- As $x$ increases by constant amounts, the *ratios* of successive values of the function are constant.

When the ratios of successive values of the function are positive, as in the Activity, the base $b$ is greater than 1. In such cases, the function $y = a \cdot b^x$ describes **exponential growth**.

## Practice for Lesson 10.1

**1.** In Question 11 of the Activity, you found an exponential function that models the increase in the number of layers of paper.

  **a.** What is the initial value of your function?

  **b.** What is the base of your function?

  **c.** What is the exponent?

  **d.** Does the problem domain for your function include all real numbers? Explain.

**COMMON ERROR**

Students may assume that the common ratio of successive terms is always equal to $b$, the base of the exponential function. This is only true if the successive values of $x$ increase by 1.

**13.** $2^{10} = 1{,}024$ layers

**14.** The number of layers continues to double without limit.

**15.** 1

**16.** Sample answer: The function is nonlinear, and the ratios of successive pairs of values are constant. The domain is whole numbers and the range is natural numbers.

## Practice for Lesson 10.1 Answers

**1a.** The initial value is 1.

**1b.** The base is 2.

**1c.** The exponent is $n$.

**1d.** No, the number of cuts must be a whole number.

**2.** Examine the "Computing Process" column of your table in Question 9. Continue the pattern of exponents in this column to find a value for the expression $2^0$.

**3.** Explain why 1 is not a useful value for the base of an exponential function.

**4.** A student in a biology lab places a sample of bacteria in a culture dish. She counts and records the number of bacteria present every hour beginning at noon.

| Hour | Time $t$ (hours) | Number of Bacteria Present |
|---|---|---|
| 12:00 p.m. | 0 | 15 |
| 1:00 p.m. | 1 | 60 |
| 2:00 p.m. | 2 | 240 |
| 3:00 p.m. | 3 | 960 |

  **a.** Can the relationship between time and number of bacteria be described by an exponential function? Explain.

  **b.** Write an equation that models the number of bacteria $N$ as a function of the time $t$ in hours.

  **c.** Use your function to predict the number of bacteria that will be present at 6:00 p.m. if this pattern continues.

**5.** *Chain letters* appear frequently on the Internet. One person starts a chain letter by sending an e-mail message to several friends. Each recipient is asked to forward the letter to an equal number of friends. The pattern can be repeated for a number of rounds to establish more links in the chain.

  **a.** Write an expression for the total number of people who have received a chain letter after $n$ rounds if each person sends the letter to 5 friends. Each person receives the chain letter only once.

  **b.** Suppose that two friends decide to begin a chain letter by each sending a message to six of their friends and asking them to forward it to six more friends, etc. No one receives the letter more than once, and the two friends do not send it to each other. Write an expression for the total number of people who have received the chain letter after $n$ rounds.

**6.** The sequence of numbers 4, 12, 36, 108, . . . is an example of a *geometric sequence*.

  **a.** What does this sequence have in common with the exponential function $y = a(3)^x$?

  **b.** Number each term in the sequence. Let 4, the first number in the sequence, be term number 0. Write an expression for the $n$th term in the sequence that is valid for each term starting with term number 1.

**TEACHING TIP**

In **Exercise 2**, students are asked to discover the meaning of $2^0$ by continuing a pattern. If they wonder how it can be that $2^0 = 1$, tell them that the concept of a 0 exponent will be revisited in **Lesson 10.3**.

**2.** Sample answer: If the pattern is continued, $2^0$ should equal 1.

**3.** Sample answer: If $b = 1$ in $y = a \cdot b^x$, the value of the function would be constant, since 1 to any power equals 1.

**4a.** Yes, the ratios of successive numbers of bacteria are all equal to 4.

**4b.** $N = 15 \cdot 4^t$

**4c.** $15 \cdot 4^6 = 61{,}440$

**5a.** $5^n$

**5b.** $2 \cdot 6^n$

**6a.** The ratios of successive terms are constant and equal to 3.

**6b.** $4 \cdot 3^n$

**TEACHING TIP**

**Exercise 6** Suggest that students make a table to help them see the pattern in the terms, with headings "Term Number," "Term Value," "Computing Process." Note that **Part (b)** asks for an expression that is valid for each term starting with term number 1. This is because students may not recognize the meaning of a zero exponent for term 0 at this point.

# LESSON 10.2

**5e** Explain

## Lesson Objectives

- use properties of exponents to simplify expressions.
- use scientific notation to compute with large numbers.

## Vocabulary

- scientific notation

## Description

This lesson provides a review of the Properties of Exponents, which are used to simplify expressions involving positive integer exponents. Computations involving scientific notation are also introduced.

---

## TEACHING TIP

Point out to students that if they ever have trouble remembering a particular property, a demonstration like the one shown in Example 1 may help them use it correctly.

---

You have seen that variable exponents are used to model some kinds of growth. In this lesson, you will review the properties of exponents.

### REPEATED MULTIPLICATION

Exponential functions involve exponents that vary. Exponents that are variable share properties with exponents that are constant. Those properties are based on the fact that a natural number used as an exponent stands for the number of times a base is used as a factor. For example, $3^4$ is equivalent to $3 \cdot 3 \cdot 3 \cdot 3$. This relationship can account for all of the following properties of exponents.

#### Properties of Exponents

Product of Powers: $a^m \cdot a^n = a^{m+n}$

Quotient of Powers: $\dfrac{a^m}{a^n} = a^{m-n}$ for $a \neq 0$

Power of a Product: $(a \cdot b)^n = a^n \cdot b^n$

Power of a Quotient: $\left(\dfrac{a}{b}\right)^n = \dfrac{a^n}{b^n}$ for $b \neq 0$

Power of a Power: $(a^m)^n = a^{mn}$

### E X A M P L E ❶

**a.** Use the definition of exponents to verify that $(2^4)(2^3) = 2^7$.

**b.** Use the Product of Powers Property to verify that $(2^4)(2^3) = 2^7$.

**Solution:**

**a.** Using the definition of exponents:

| | |
|---|---|
| Definition of exponents | $(2^4)(2^3) = (2 \cdot 2 \cdot 2 \cdot 2)(2 \cdot 2 \cdot 2)$ |
| Commutative Property | $= 2 \cdot 2 \cdot 2 \cdot 2 \cdot 2 \cdot 2 \cdot 2$ |
| Definition of exponents | $= 2^7$ |

**b.** Using the Product of Powers Property:

| | |
|---|---|
| Product of Powers Property | $(2^4)(2^3) = 2^{4+3}$ |
| Simplify. | $= 2^7$ |

---

## ADDITIONAL EXAMPLE ❶

**a.** Use the definition of exponents to verify that $\left(4^3\right)^2 = 4^6$.

**b.** Use the Power of a Power Property to verify that $\left(4^3\right)^2 = 4^6$.

**a.** Definition of exponents $\left(4^3\right)^2 = (4 \cdot 4 \cdot 4)^2$

    Definition of exponents $\quad = (4 \cdot 4 \cdot 4)(4 \cdot 4 \cdot 4)$

    Simplify. $\quad = 4^6$

**b.** Product of Powers Property $\left(4^3\right)^2 = 4^{(3)(2)}$

    Simplify. $\quad\quad\quad\quad = 4^6$

## SIMPLIFYING EXPRESSIONS CONTAINING EXPONENTS

The Properties of Exponents can often be used to rewrite an algebraic expression in a simpler way.

**Note**

It may not always be obvious what it means to simplify an expression. Simplifying usually involves writing an expression in a more compact form.

### E X A M P L E ❷

Simplify $\dfrac{28t^6}{7t^2}$.

**Solution:**

| | |
|---|---|
| Original expression | $\dfrac{28t^6}{7t^2}$ |
| Divide the coefficients; then use the Quotient of Powers Property. | $\dfrac{28}{7}(t^{6-2})$ |
| Simplify. | $4t^4$ |

### E X A M P L E ❸

Simplify $\left(\dfrac{2a^2}{bc^3}\right)^4$.

**Solution:**

| | |
|---|---|
| Original expression | $\left(\dfrac{2a^2}{bc^3}\right)^4$ |
| Use the Power of a Quotient Property. | $\dfrac{(2a^2)^4}{(bc^3)^4}$ |
| Use the Power of a Product Property. | $\dfrac{2^4(a^2)^4}{b^4(c^3)^4}$ |
| Use the Power of a Power Property. | $\dfrac{16a^8}{b^4c^{12}}$ |

Sometimes more than one sequence of steps can be used to simplify an expression. Use any method that involves correct mathematical properties.

**ADDITIONAL EXAMPLE ❷**

Simplify $(3v^5)(8v^6)$. $24v^{11}$

**ADDITIONAL EXAMPLE ❸**

Simplify $\left(\dfrac{3j^5k^4}{l^2}\right)^3$. $\dfrac{27j^{15}k^{12}}{l^6}$

# LESSON 10.2

## ADDITIONAL EXAMPLE 4

Use two different methods to simplify $\left(\dfrac{y^7}{4y^6}\right)^3$.

Sample answer:

Method 1:

$$\left(\frac{y^7}{4y^6}\right)^3 = \left(\frac{y^1}{4}\right)^3 = \frac{y^3}{4^3} = \frac{y^3}{64}$$

Method 2:

$$\left(\frac{y^7}{4y^6}\right)^3 = \frac{(y^7)^3}{4^3(y^6)^3} = \frac{y^{21}}{64y^{18}} = \frac{y^3}{64}$$

---

### TEACHING TIP

Use a few simple examples to illustrate operations with scientific notation, such as

$$\frac{8 \times 10^3}{2 \times 10^2} = \frac{8}{2} \times 10^{3-2}$$

$$= 4 \times 10^1$$

---

Use two different methods to simplify $(3x^3 \cdot x^5)^2$.

**Solution:**

**Method 1:**

| Original expression | $(3x^3 \cdot x^5)^2$ |
| Use the Power of a Product Property. | $3^2(x^3)^2(x^5)^2$ |
| Use the Power of a Power Property. | $9x^6x^{10}$ |
| Use the Product of Powers Property. | $9x^{16}$ |

**Method 2:**

| Original expression | $(3x^3 \cdot x^5)^2$ |
| Use the Product of Powers Property. | $(3x^8)^2$ |
| Use the Power of a Product Property. | $3^2(x^8)^2$ |
| Use the Power of a Power Property. | $9x^{16}$ |

## SCIENTIFIC NOTATION

Recall that very large numbers can be written using exponents. For example, a hard disk on a computer may hold 20 billion bytes (20 gigabytes) of information. But 20 billion can also be expressed as $20 \times 10^9$. And since 20 is $2 \times 10$, the same number can be written as $2 \times 10^{10}$. Other possibilities include $200 \times 10^8$ and $2{,}000 \times 10^7$. But the most common form to use is $2 \times 10^{10}$.

> A number is in **scientific notation** if it is written in the form $a \times 10^n$, where $1 \le a < 10$ and $n$ is an integer.

The Properties of Exponents can be used to carry out operations with numbers written in scientific notation.

EXAMPLE 5

The diameter of the Earth is about 12,700,000 meters, and the diameter of Jupiter is about 143,000,000 meters. Use scientific notation to find about how many Earth diameters would stretch across the diameter of Jupiter.

**Solution:**

Divide the diameter of Jupiter by the diameter of Earth.

$$\dfrac{143,000,000 \text{ m}}{12,700,000 \text{ m}}$$

Express each number in scientific notation.

$$\dfrac{1.43 \times 10^8 \text{ m}}{1.27 \times 10^7 \text{ m}}$$

Divide and use the Quotient of Powers Property.

$$\dfrac{1.43}{1.27} \times 10^{8-7}$$

Simplify.

$$1.13 \times 10^1 \text{ or } 11.3$$

About 11 Earth diameters would stretch across the diameter of Jupiter.

---

**Practice for Lesson 10.2**

1  **a.** Use the definition of exponents to verify that $\dfrac{3^7}{3^5} = 3^2$.

   **b.** Use the Quotient of Powers Property to verify that $\dfrac{3^7}{3^5} = 3^2$.

2. Use two different methods to simplify $\left(\dfrac{4r^8}{2r^2}\right)^3$.

---

**ADDITIONAL EXAMPLE 5**

There are one billion nanometers (nm) in a meter, and the radius of the Earth is about 6,370,000 meters. Use scientific notation to compute the radius of the Earth in nanometers.
$(6.37 \times 10^6)(10^9) = 6.37 \times 10^{15}$ nm

**2.** Sample answer:
Method 1:

$$\left(\dfrac{4r^8}{2r^2}\right)^3 = (2r^6)^3$$

$$= (2)^3(r^6)^3$$

$$= 8r^{18}$$

Method 2:

$$\left(\dfrac{4r^8}{2r^2}\right)^3 = \dfrac{(4r^8)^3}{(2r^2)^3}$$

$$= \dfrac{4^3(r^8)^3}{2^3(r^2)^3}$$

$$= \dfrac{64r^{24}}{8r^6}$$

$$= 8r^{18}$$

---

**Practice for Lesson 10.2 Answers**

**1a.** By definition:

Definition of exponents

$$\dfrac{3^7}{3^5} = \dfrac{3 \cdot 3 \cdot 3 \cdot 3 \cdot 3 \cdot 3 \cdot 3}{3 \cdot 3 \cdot 3 \cdot 3 \cdot 3}$$

Simplify.

$$= 3 \cdot 3$$

Definition of exponents

$$= 3^2$$

**1b.** Using the Quotient of Powers Property:

Quotient of Powers Property

$$\dfrac{3^7}{3^5} = 3^{7-5}$$

Simplify.

$$= 3^2$$

**3a.** $2^{a+3} = (2^a)(2^3)$
$\phantom{2^{a+3}} = 8(2^a)$

**3b.** $3^{4n} = (3^n)^4$

**3c.** $3^{4n} = (3^4)^n$
$\phantom{3^{4n}} = 81^n$

**4a.** $W = 1{,}000{,}000{,}000{,}000{,}000(2^t)$

**4b.** $W = (1 \times 10^{15})(2^t)$

**5.** $x^{11}$

**6.** $12c^8 d^6$

**7.** $64h^6$

**8.** $5M^3$

**9.** $y^{15}$

**10.** $25A^6 B^8$

**11.** $\dfrac{27s^{18}}{t^6}$

**12.** $\dfrac{p^{24}q^6}{r^{12}}$

**13.** $\dfrac{x^{12}y^4}{16}$

**14a.**
$(3.4 \times 10^8)(1.2 \times 10^6) = (3.4 \times 1.2)$
$(10^8 \times 10^6)$
$\phantom{(3.4 \times 10^8)(1.2 \times 10^6)} = 4.08 \times 10^{14}$

**14b.** $\dfrac{18{,}000{,}000{,}000}{600{,}000} = \dfrac{1.8 \times 10^{10}}{6 \times 10^5}$
$\phantom{\dfrac{18{,}000{,}000{,}000}{600{,}000}} = \dfrac{1.8}{6} \times \dfrac{10^{10}}{10^5}$
$\phantom{\dfrac{18{,}000{,}000{,}000}{600{,}000}} = 0.3 \times 10^5$
$\phantom{\dfrac{18{,}000{,}000{,}000}{600{,}000}} = 3 \times 10^4$

**14c.** $(20{,}000{,}000)^4 = (2 \times 10^7)^4$
$\phantom{(20{,}000{,}000)^4} = 2^4 (10^7)^4$
$\phantom{(20{,}000{,}000)^4} = 16 \times 10^{28}$
$\phantom{(20{,}000{,}000)^4} = 1.6 \times 10^{29}$

**15.** $2 \times 10^2 = 200$ seconds

---

**3** **a.** Use the Product of Powers Property to rewrite $2^{a+3}$ as the product of a number greater than 1 and a power of 2.

   **b.** Use a Property of Exponents to rewrite $3^{4n}$ as a power of $3^n$.

   **c.** Use a Property of Exponents to rewrite $3^{4n}$ as a power of 81.

**4.** In the Chapter Opener of this chapter, it was stated that global water consumption is doubling every 20 years. It was also stated that current yearly water use by all the nations of the world is about one thousand trillion gallons.

   **a.** Write an exponential function that models expected future global water use. Let $W$ represent total water used in a year. Let $t$ represent time measured in units of 20-year intervals.

   **b.** Rewrite your answer to Part (a) using scientific notation.

**For Exercises 5–13, simplify the given expression.**

**5.** $(x^4)(x^7)$

**6.** $(2c^5 d^2)(6c^3 d^4)$

**7.** $(4h^2)^3$

**8.** $\dfrac{10M^{12}}{2M^9}$

**9.** $(y^3)^5$

**10.** $(5A^3 B^4)^2$

**11.** $\left(\dfrac{6s^6}{2t^2}\right)^3$

**12.** $\left(\dfrac{p^4 q}{r^2}\right)^6$

**13.** $\left(\dfrac{3x^9 y^5}{12x^3 y^3}\right)^2$

**14.** Use scientific notation to rewrite each computation. Then use Properties of Exponents to calculate the result. Express the answer in scientific notation.

   **a.** $(340{,}000{,}000)(1{,}200{,}000)$

   **b.** $\dfrac{18{,}000{,}000{,}000}{600{,}000}$

   **c.** $(20{,}000{,}000)^4$

**15.** The speed of light is approximately $3 \times 10^{10}$ centimeters per second. How long will it take light to travel $6 \times 10^{12}$ centimeters?

You have seen how exponents can be used to create functions that model growth. You have also reviewed several Properties of Exponents. In this lesson, you will see how exponential functions can be used to model one type of decreasing behavior.

In the study of mathematics, something that at first seems to have no meaning may later turn out to be very useful. At first glance, the expression $2^{-3}$ does not appear to make sense. After all, an exponent is supposed to count factors of a product. How can there be a negative number of factors?

An answer is provided by one of the Properties of Exponents. Look at the quotient $\frac{2^4}{2^7}$. Since it literally means $\frac{2 \cdot 2 \cdot 2 \cdot 2}{2 \cdot 2 \cdot 2 \cdot 2 \cdot 2 \cdot 2 \cdot 2}$ it must equal $\frac{1}{2 \cdot 2 \cdot 2}$ or $\frac{1}{2^3}$. But, according to the Quotient of Powers Property, $\frac{2^4}{2^7} = 2^{4-7} = 2^{-3}$. If the Properties of Exponents are always to be true for all real numbers, then they must allow for **negative exponents.**

> **Negative Exponents**
>
> If a number or variable is raised to a negative exponent, the result is equal to the *reciprocal* of the corresponding positive power of the same number or variable.
>
> $$a^{-n} = \frac{1}{a^n} \quad \text{and} \quad \frac{1}{a^{-n}} = a^n$$

**1.** A geometric design can be created by repeating a process over and over. The three triangles below show such a process.

Notice that the second figure is created by connecting the midpoints of the sides of the first unshaded triangle, forming four smaller congruent triangles. Then the central triangle of those four smaller triangles is shaded red.

The third figure is formed by repeating the process of dividing each of the three unshaded triangles in the second figure into four smaller congruent triangles and then shading the central triangles red.

## Lesson Objectives

- define and use negative exponents.
- define and use 0 as an exponent.
- simplify monomials.

## Vocabulary

- degree of a monomial
- exponential decay
- monomial
- negative exponent
- zero exponent

## Materials List

## Description

Students should work in pairs in this Investigation to explore how an equilateral triangle can be subdivided into smaller and smaller equilateral triangles through an iterative process. They do not need to create the drawings themselves.

Students observe an exponential decrease in the area of one of the smallest triangles as the process is repeated. They see that an exponential function with a fractional base (or, alternatively, a negative exponent) models this exponential decay.

*Wrapping Up the Investigation:*

Lead a whole-class discussion to ensure that students see both the similarities and the differences between exponential growth and exponential decay.

> **CONNECTION**
>
> The figure described in this Investigation is similar to the *Sierpinski Triangle*, first described in 1915 by the Polish mathematician Waclaw Sierpinski. It is an example of *fractal geometry*, a figure that appears the same at any level of magnification and which is produced by an infinite iterative process.

## Lesson 10.3 Investigation Answers

**1.**

| Term Number | Picture | Area of the Smallest Triangle (in.²) |
|---|---|---|
| 0 | | 1 |
| 1 | | $\frac{1}{4}$ |
| 2 | | $\frac{1}{16}$ |

| Term Number | Picture | Area of the Smallest Triangle (in.²) |
|---|---|---|
| 3 | | $\frac{1}{64}$ |
| 4 | | $\frac{1}{256}$ |

**2.** Sample answer: The heights of the points decrease, but by smaller amounts as $n$ increases.

**[−0.2, 4.2] × [−0.2, 1.2]**

**3.** $A = \dfrac{1}{4^n}$ or $A = \left(\dfrac{1}{4}\right)^n$

**4.** The function fits the points in the scatter plot.

**[−0.2, 4.2] × [−0.2, 1.2]**

**5.** $A = \left(\dfrac{1}{4}\right)^n$ or $A = \dfrac{1}{4^n}$, $A = 4^{-n}$

---

**TEACHING TIP**

For **Questions 5 and 6**, make sure that students see the equivalence of all three forms of the decay function:

$$A = \left(\dfrac{1}{4}\right)^n, A = \dfrac{1}{4^n}, \text{ and } A = 4^{-n}.$$

---

Assume that this pattern could be continued indefinitely. If the area of the first triangle is exactly 1 square inch, complete the third column of a table like the one below.

| Term Number | Picture | Area of the Smallest Triangle (in²) |
|:---:|:---:|:---:|
| 0 | | 1 |
| 1 | | $\dfrac{1}{4}$ |
| 2 | | ? |
| 3 | | ? |
| 4 | | ? |

**2.** Use a graphing calculator to make a scatter plot of the area of the smallest triangle vs the term number as the term number increases from 0 to 4. Describe the scatter plot.

**3.** Write an equation that expresses the area of the smallest triangle $A$ as a function of the term number $n$.

**4.** Graph your function on your scatter plot. Does your function fit the scatterplot? If not, revise your function.

**5.** Use exponent properties to write your function in two different forms. One form should have a positive exponent $n$. The other should have a negative exponent $-n$.

6. Graph both of your functions from Question 5. Do they produce the same graph as in Question 4?

7. What will be the exact area of the smallest triangle if the pattern is continued to the sixth term?

8. As $n$ gets larger and larger, what happens to $A$?

9. According to your function, can the area of the smallest triangle ever be 0?

10. The function you found in this Investigation is an example of **exponential decay**. Summarize the properties of this function.

Functions that describe exponential decay have all of the properties of exponential functions $y = a \cdot b^x$ that were discussed in Lesson 10.1. Decay functions can be written in two ways,

- with a base $b$ between 0 and 1, or
- with a base $b$ that is greater than 1 and has a negative exponent.

For most practical applications, a negative exponent is used. See Lesson 10.6 for more examples.

## ZERO EXPONENT

The Quotient of Powers Property can also be used to show the meaning of an exponent of 0. Consider the expression $\frac{x^5}{x^5}$. This ratio must equal 1 for any value of $x$ except 0. But according to the Quotient of Powers Property, it must also equal $x^{5-5} = x^0$. Again, you would not expect an exponent of 0 to make sense. Its meaning comes from the requirement that the Properties of Exponents should be true for all numbers.

> ### Zero Exponent
>
> If a non-zero number or variable is raised to the 0 power, the result is always 1.
>
> $$a^0 = 1 \text{ for } a \neq 0$$

You first learned that an exponent counts the number of identical factors in a product. But in general, it is best to think of an exponent as a number that can symbolize one of several types of operations.

- A positive integer exponent represents the number of factors in a product.
- A negative exponent represents a reciprocal.
- An exponent of 0 means that an expression is equal to 1 unless the base is 0.

You may explore other types of exponents in future courses.

> **TEACHING TIP**
>
> In **Question 8**, make sure students recognize the characteristics of the asymptotic behavior of the decay function for larger values of $n$. A formal definition of an asymptote will be given in **Lesson 10.6**.

6. Yes.

7. $\dfrac{1}{4^6} = \dfrac{1}{4{,}096}$

8. Sample answer: $A$ gets closer and closer to 0.

9. No, but it can be very small, and can get very close to 0.

10. Sample answer: The function decreases as the values of the independent variable increase, but it is not linear. It has a vertical intercept of 1, but no horizontal intercept. The domain includes all whole numbers for this situation. The range includes only positive numbers that are less than or equal to 1.

In Lesson 10.2, you used scientific notation with positive exponents to write large numbers. You can use negative exponents to express very small numbers in scientific notation. For example, the time it takes for a typical personal computer to carry out a single instruction is 0.00000000036 second. To express this number in scientific notation, write it in the form $a \times 10^n$, where $1 \le a < 10$, and $n$ is an integer.

$$0.00000000036 = 3.6 \times 0.0000000001$$
$$= 3.6 \times \frac{1}{10,000,000,000}$$
$$= 3.6 \times \frac{1}{10^{10}}$$
$$= 3.6 \times 10^{-10} \text{ second}$$

### Note

A simple way of converting a number to scientific notation is as follows:

Count the number of places the decimal point must be moved to produce a 1 or a number between 1 and 10. If the decimal point is moved to the left, use a positive power of 10. If the decimal point is moved to the right, use a negative power of 10.

Check to see whether evaluating the scientific notation product produces the correct size number.

**E X A M P L E**

Write 0.00000724 in scientific notation.

**Solution:**

$$0.00000724 = 7.24 \times 0.000001$$
$$= 7.24 \times \frac{1}{1,000,000}$$
$$= 7.24 \times \frac{1}{10^6}$$
$$= 7.24 \times 10^{-6}$$

## ADDITIONAL EXAMPLE ❶

Write 0.000059 in scientific notation.
$5.9 \times 10^{-5}$

## MONOMIALS

Some expressions can be written with either positive or negative exponents. Simplifying such expressions often means rewriting them with only positive exponents.

E X A M P L E **2**

Simplify each expression.

**a.** $w^7 \cdot w^{-2}$    **b.** $\dfrac{3x^4}{y^{-5}}$    **c.** $\dfrac{s^3 t^{-6}}{r^0 s^{-1}}$

**Solution:**

**a.** Original expression                    $w^7 \cdot w^{-2}$

  Product of Powers Property         $w^{7+(-2)}$

  Simplify.                                       $w^5$

**b.** Original expression                    $\dfrac{3x^4}{y^{-5}}$

  Definition of negative exponent   $\dfrac{3x^4}{\frac{1}{y^5}}$

  Multiply by the reciprocal.         $3x^4 \cdot \dfrac{y^5}{1}$

  Simplify.                                       $3x^4 y^5$

**c.** Original expression                    $\dfrac{s^3 t^{-6}}{r^0 s^{-1}}$

  Definition of 0 exponent             $\dfrac{s^3 t^{-6}}{1 \cdot s^{-1}}$

  Quotient of Powers Property        $s^{3-(-1)} t^{-6}$

  Simplify.                                       $s^4 t^{-6}$

  Definition of negative exponent   $s^4 \left( \dfrac{1}{t^6} \right)$

  Simplify.                                       $\dfrac{s^4}{t^6}$

The answers to Parts (a) and (b) of Example 2 are members of a special class of expressions called monomials.

## ADDITIONAL EXAMPLE **2**

Simplify each expression.

**a.** $z^9 \cdot z^{-5}$    $z^4$

**b.** $\dfrac{5a^3}{b^{-7}}$    $5a^3 b^7$

**c.** $\dfrac{p^{-2} q^0 r^5}{p^{-3} r^{-6}}$    $pr^{11}$

A **monomial** is the product of a coefficient and one or more variables raised to non-negative integer powers. A monomial in one variable has the form $ax^k$, where $k$ is called the **degree of the monomial**.

The following expanded list of exponent properties can be used to simplify algebraic expressions.

## Properties of Exponents

Product of Powers:   $a^m \cdot a^n = a^{m+n}$

Quotient of Powers:   $\dfrac{a^m}{a^n} = a^{m-n}$ for $a \neq 0$

Power of a Product:   $(a \cdot b)^n = a^n \cdot b^n$

Power of a Quotient:   $\left(\dfrac{a}{b}\right)^n = \dfrac{a^n}{b^n}$ for $b \neq 0$

Power of a Power:   $(a^m)^n = a^{mn}$

Negative Exponent:   $a^{-n} = \dfrac{1}{a^n}$ for $a \neq 0$

Reciprocal:   $a^{-1} = \dfrac{1}{a}$ for $a \neq 0$

Zero Exponent:   $a^0 = 1$ for $a \neq 0$

## Practice for Lesson 10.3

1. As stated in Lesson 10.1, the ratios of consecutive values of an exponential function are constant. Explain how this requirement is satisfied by your function for the geometric pattern from the Investigation in this lesson.

2. Technetium-99 (Tc-99) is a radioactive element used in bone marrow scans. It has a *half-life* of 6 hours. This means that the number of radioactive emissions per second drops by one-half of its value every 6 hours. Suppose that a dose with an activity of 200 million emissions per second is given to a patient.
    a. What will the activity of the dose be after 6 hours? What will the activity of the dose be after 12 hours?
    b. Write an equation that models the rate of radioactivity $R$ in emissions per second as a function of time $t$ measured in units of 6-hour intervals. Use scientific notation in your answer.
    c. Express your answer to Part (b) in two additional ways.

## Practice for Lesson 10.3 Answers

1. Sample answer: The area of the smallest triangle goes from 1 in.$^2$ to $\frac{1}{4}$ in.$^2$ to $\frac{1}{16}$ in.$^2$, etc. The ratios of consecutive terms are all equal to $\frac{1}{4}$.

2a. 100 million emissions per second; 50 million emissions per second

2b. Sample answer:
$R = (2 \times 10^8) \cdot 2^{-t}$

2c. Sample answer: $R = (2 \times 10^8)\left(\frac{1}{2}\right)^t$
or $R = \dfrac{2 \times 10^8}{2^t}$

3. In Exercise 4, Part (b) of Lesson 10.1, you found that the function $N = 15 \cdot 4^t$ modeled the number of bacteria in a culture as a function of time $t$ in hours. The *initial value* for the bacteria population at 12:00 p.m. was given as 15 bacteria. Show that the function includes the initial value.

4. Explain why $a = 0$ is excluded from the definition $a^0 = 1$ in the Zero Exponent Property.

5. Write an expression for the $n$th term of the sequence $5, \frac{5}{3}, \frac{5}{9}, \frac{5}{27}, \ldots$. Let 5 be term 0.

6. Write the number in scientific notation.
   a. 0.00000005
   b. 0.0028
   c. 0.81

7. Write the number in standard notation.
   a. $4 \times 10^{-5}$
   b. $9.35 \times 10^{-2}$
   c. $6.72 \times 10^0$

8. Use scientific notation to rewrite the computation. Then use properties of exponents to calculate the result. Express the answer in scientific notation.
   a. $(23,000,000)(0.000000002)$
   b. $\dfrac{0.0003}{0.0000015}$

**For Exercises 9–13, simplify the expression and write the answer with only positive exponents.**

9. $5t^{-2}$          10. $(2d)^{-3}$

11. $B^{-4} + (2AB)^0$      12. $(-3x^2y^{-2})^3$

13. $\dfrac{9a^{-1}b^2c}{12a^3b^{-2}c^4}$

14. Match the expression in Column 1 with an equivalent expression in Column 2.

|   | Column 1 | Column 2 |
|---|----------|----------|
| a. | $3^{-2}$ | $9$ |
| b. | $-3^2$ | $\frac{1}{9}$ |
| c. | $(-3)^{-2}$ | $-9$ |
| d. | $-(-3)^{-2}$ | $-\frac{1}{9}$ |

**For Exercises 15–17, state the degree of the monomial.**

15. $5x^3$          16. $p^7$

17. $10$

NEGATIVE EXPONENTS   Lesson 10.3   351

9. $\dfrac{5}{t^2}$

10. $\dfrac{1}{8d^3}$

11. $\dfrac{1}{B^4} + 1$

12. $-\dfrac{27x^6}{y^6}$

13. $\dfrac{3b^4}{4a^4c^3}$

14a. $\dfrac{1}{9}$

14b. $-9$

14c. $\dfrac{1}{9}$

14d. $-\dfrac{1}{9}$

15. 3

16. 7

17. 0

**LESSON 10.3**

**COMMON ERROR**

Students may incorrectly write the answer to **Exercise 9** as $\dfrac{1}{25t^2}$. Remind them that, since there are no parentheses around $5t$, the exponent operates only on the variable $t$.

**TEACHING TIP**

**Exercise 13** Students often have difficulty using the Quotient of Powers Property in problems with negative exponents. You may want to show them that problems such as this one can be simplified by first converting to positive exponents and then using the Quotient of Powers Property.

**COMMON ERROR**

**Exercise 13** Some students may need to be reminded that an exponent of 1 is implied when no exponent is shown.

**COMMON ERROR**

If students have difficulty recognizing the degree of the monomial in **Exercise 17**, remind them that the constant 10 can be thought of as $10x^0$.

3. Sample answer: When $t = 0$, $N = 15 \cdot 4^0 = 15 \cdot 1 = 15$.

4. Sample answer: As discussed in the lesson, the definition of the zero exponent is based on the expression $\dfrac{a^n}{a^n}$. If $a = 0$, this expression becomes $\dfrac{0}{0}$, which is undefined.

5. $5\left(\dfrac{1}{3}\right)^n$ or $5 \cdot 3^{-n}$

6a. $5 \times 10^{-8}$
6b. $2.8 \times 10^{-3}$
6c. $8.1 \times 10^{-1}$
7a. 0.00004
7b. 0.0935
7c. 6.72
8a. $(2.3 \times 10^7)(2 \times 10^{-9})$
$= (2.3 \times 2)(10^7 \times 10^{-9})$
$= 4.6 \times 10^{-2}$

8b. $\dfrac{3 \times 10^{-4}}{1.5 \times 10^{-6}} = \left(\dfrac{3}{1.5}\right)\left(\dfrac{10^{-4}}{10^{-6}}\right)$
$= 2 \times 10^2$

351

**18a.**

| $n$ | $-a^n$ | $(-a)^n$ |
|-----|--------|----------|
| 2 | $-9$ | 9 |
| 3 | $-27$ | $-27$ |
| 4 | $-81$ | 81 |
| 5 | $-243$ | $-243$ |
| 6 | $-729$ | 729 |

**18b.** Sample answer: When $n$ is even, the expressions are opposites of each other. When $n$ is odd, they are equal to each other.

**18.** In some cases $-a^n$ and $(-a)^n$ are equal and in some cases they are not.

    **a.** Complete the table for $a = 3$.

| $n$ | $-a^n$ | $(-a)^n$ |
|-----|--------|----------|
| 2 | | |
| 3 | | |
| 4 | | |
| 5 | | |
| 6 | | |

    **b.** In general, when are $-a^n$ and $(-a)^n$ equal and when are they opposites?

**Fill in the blank.**

1. For an exponential function of the form $y = ab^x$, if the $x$-values change by constant amounts, the _____ of successive $y$-values are constant.

2. For any nonzero number $a$, the value of $a^0$ is _____.

**Choose the correct answer.**

3. Which example illustrates the Commutative Property of Addition?

   **A.** $(3 + 2) + 5 = 3 + (2 + 5)$     **B.** $(3 + 2) + 5 = 5 + (2 + 3)$

   **C.** $3 + 0 = 3$                      **D.** $3 + (-3) = 0$

4. Which graph represents a direct variation function?

**A.** 

**B.** 

**C.** 

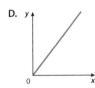

**D.** 

**Add or subtract.**

5. $\dfrac{3}{4} - \dfrac{5}{8}$     6. $\dfrac{2}{3} + \dfrac{7}{12}$     7. $\dfrac{7}{10} + \dfrac{3}{20} - \dfrac{2}{5}$

8. $1\dfrac{2}{3} + \dfrac{5}{6}$     9. $1\dfrac{3}{8} - \dfrac{7}{8}$     10. $2\dfrac{1}{4} - 1\dfrac{3}{16}$

**Solve.**

11. What is 70% of 20?            12. What is 150% of 12?

13. What percent of 80 is 32?     14. What percent of 200 is 250?

15. 21 is 35% of what number?     16. 5 is 0.5% of what number?

**Identify the property illustrated.**

17. $6\left(\dfrac{1}{6}\right) = 1$            18. $6 - 15 = 3(2 - 5)$

## Lesson Objective

- solve problems that require previously learned concepts and skills.

## Exercise Reference

Exercise 1: Lesson 10.1

Exercise 2: Lesson 10.3

Exercise 3: Appendix J

Exercise 4: Lesson 2.3

Exercises 5–10: Appendix A

Exercises 11–16: Appendix F

Exercises 17–18: Appendix J

Exercises 19–22: Appendix M

Exercise 23: Appendix N

Exercise 24: Lesson 6.3

Exercise 25: Lesson 1.2

Exercise 26: Lesson 3.1

Exercise 27: Lesson 4.2

Exercise 28: Lesson 7.2

Exercise 29: Lesson 8.3

Exercise 30: Lesson 9.3

Exercise 31: Lesson 10.2

## Lesson 10.4 R.A.P. Answers

1. ratios
2. 1
3. B
4. D
5. $\dfrac{1}{8}$
6. $1\dfrac{1}{4}$
7. $\dfrac{9}{20}$
8. $2\dfrac{1}{2}$
9. $\dfrac{1}{2}$
10. $1\dfrac{1}{16}$
11. 14
12. 18
13. 40%
14. 125%
15. 60
16. 1,000
17. Inverse Property of Multiplication
18. Distributive Property

**19.** $7\sqrt{2}$

**20.** $4\sqrt{5}$

**21.** $\dfrac{\sqrt{3}}{3}$

**22.** $\dfrac{\sqrt{35}}{14}$

**23a.** 48.83 s

**23b.** 48.4 s

**23c.** 49.8 s

**23d.** 6.5 s

**24.**

**Race Times**

```
45 | 8
46 |
47 | 2 4 8
48 | 0 1 7
49 | 5 8 8
50 |
51 | 6
52 | 3
```

Key: 45 | 8 represents 45.8 seconds.

**25.** $8\dfrac{3}{4}$ feet, or 8 feet 9 inches

**26.**

Subtract 2        Multiply by 4

$n \qquad n-2 \qquad 4(n-2)$

**27.** $m = \dfrac{Fr^2}{GM}$

**28a.** See answer to Part (b).

**28b.** Sample answer:

**28c.** Sample answer: $c = \dfrac{5}{8}h + \dfrac{3}{16}$

**29.** $\left(2, \dfrac{1}{2}\right)$

**30.** translation symmetry, vertical line symmetry, rotational symmetry, glide-reflection symmetry

**31.** $\dfrac{25s^4}{9r^2}$

**Simplify.**

**19.** $\sqrt{98}$

**20.** $\sqrt{80}$

**21.** $\sqrt{\dfrac{1}{3}}$

**22.** $\sqrt{\dfrac{5}{28}}$

**23.** The 12 members of a swimming team had the following times (in seconds) for the 100-yard freestyle race: 47.2, 49.8, 47.4, 45.8, 51.6, 49.5, 48.1, 49.8, 48.7, 52.3, 47.8, 48.0. Find (a) the mean, (b) the median, (c) the mode, and (d) the range of the data.

**24.** Make a stem-and-leaf diagram for the data in Exercise 23.

**25.** The scale of a drawing is $\dfrac{1}{4}$-inch = 1 foot. What actual length is represented by a line that is $2\dfrac{3}{16}$ inches long on the drawing?

**26.** Draw an arrow diagram that represents the expression $4(n-2)$.

**27.** Newton's Law of Universal Gravitation is described by the formula $F = \dfrac{GMm}{r^2}$. Solve for $m$.

**28.** The table to the left shows data on some of the shortest trees in a forest. The *crown* is the leafy top part of a tree.
  **a.** Make a scatter plot of crown width $c$ vs height $h$.
  **b.** Draw a line on the scatter plot that models the trend in the data.
  **c.** Find an equation for your line in slope-intercept form.

| Height (m) | Crown Width (m) |
|---|---|
| 0.9 | 0.7 |
| 1.5 | 1.0 |
| 2.4 | 1.2 |
| 2.5 | 1.3 |
| 3.0 | 2.9 |
| 3.3 | 1.4 |
| 4.5 | 2.8 |
| 5.0 | 4.2 |
| 5.5 | 3.5 |

**29.** Solve the system.
$$3x - 4y = 4$$
$$2x - 6y = 1$$

**30.** Describe the symmetries for the pattern shown below.

**31.** Simplify $\left(\dfrac{5r^2s^5}{3r^3s^3}\right)^2$.

**INVESTIGATION: Modeling Exponential Growth**

**5e** Explore

## Lesson Objectives

- identify situations involving exponential growth.
- model situations involving exponential growth.

## Vocabulary

## Materials List

## Description

Students should work in pairs on this Investigation. Building on their work with exponential growth from Lesson 10.1, they construct growth models for two different situations. In both, they determine the base $b$ from examining the constant growth ratios.

*Wrapping Up the Investigation:*

Be sure to discuss the Example in the text with students because it helps them make the connection between percents of increase and the successive ratios. Point out that either can be used to determine whether a function is exponential.

You have seen that a type of increase called *exponential growth* and a type of decrease called *exponential decay* involve variable exponents. You have also studied the Properties of Exponents. In this lesson, you will examine the properties of exponential growth functions in more detail.

As you saw in the Activity in Lesson 10.1, the number of *layers* of paper doubles with each cut. The total number of sheets after each cut can be modeled by an exponential function of the form $y = a \cdot b^x$, which in this case is $L = 2^n$, where $L$ is the number of layers and $n$ is the number of cuts. In this Investigation, you will focus on the *thickness* of the paper.

1. A *ream* of paper contains 500 sheets. It is almost 2 inches thick. About how thick is one sheet of paper?

2. Complete the table below for the process you used in the Activity in Lesson 10.1, which involved cutting and stacking paper.

| Number of Cuts | Number of Layers | Total Thickness of Paper (in.) | Change in Thicknesses (in.) |
|---|---|---|---|
| 0 | 1 | 0.004 | — |
| 1 | 2 | 0.008 | $0.008 - 0.004 = 0.004$ |
| 2 | | | |
| 3 | | | |
| 4 | | | |
| 5 | | | |
| 6 | | | |

MODELING EXPONENTIAL GROWTH    **Lesson 10.5**    **355**

## Lesson 10.5 Investigation Answers

1. About 0.004 inches
2.

| Number of Cuts | Number of Layers | Total Thickness of Paper (in.) | Change in Thicknesses (in.) |
|---|---|---|---|
| 0 | 1 | 0.004 | — |
| 1 | 2 | 0.008 | $0.008 - 0.004 = 0.004$ |
| 2 | 4 | 0.016 | $0.016 - 0.008 = 0.008$ |
| 3 | 8 | 0.032 | $0.032 - 0.016 = 0.016$ |
| 4 | 16 | 0.064 | $0.064 - 0.032 = 0.032$ |
| 5 | 32 | 0.128 | $0.128 - 0.064 = 0.064$ |
| 6 | 64 | 0.256 | $0.256 - 0.128 = 0.128$ |

**3.** No, it is not a linear relationship because the rate of change is not constant.

**4.**

| Number of Cuts | Number of Layers | Total Thickness of Paper (in.) | Ratios of Successive Thicknesses |
|---|---|---|---|
| 0 | 1 | 0.004 | — |
| 1 | 2 | 0.008 | $\frac{0.008}{0.004} = 2$ |
| 2 | 4 | 0.016 | $\frac{0.016}{0.008} = 2$ |
| 3 | 8 | 0.032 | $\frac{0.032}{0.016} = 2$ |
| 4 | 16 | 0.064 | $\frac{0.064}{0.032} = 2$ |
| 5 | 32 | 0.128 | $\frac{0.128}{0.064} = 2$ |
| 6 | 64 | 0.256 | $\frac{0.256}{0.128} = 2$ |

**TEACHING TIP**

Point out to students that their graph for **Question 10** exhibits an end behavior similar to what they saw in Lesson 10.3. However, instead of approaching the horizontal axis for positive values of the independent variable, here the graph approaches the axis for negative values. It is important that students recognize that the value of an exponential function of the form $y = ab^x$ can never be 0 (**Question 11**).

**TEACHING TIP**

**Question 13** Point out to students that the total thickness after 10 cuts is about 4 inches, and after 11 cuts, it is about 8 inches. So, it takes 11 cuts to achieve a thickness of *at least* 6 inches.

**5.** Yes, it is an exponential relationship because the ratios of successive thicknesses are constant.

**6.** $T = (0.004) \cdot 2^n$

**7.** The initial value is 0.004, when $n = 0$. The base is 2.

**8.** Both functions involve the same base 2. The initial values are different.

**9.** about 4,194 inches, or almost 350 feet

**3.** Consider the relationship between the total thickness and the number of cuts. Is this a linear relationship? Explain.

**4.** Using the same data as in Question 3, calculate the *ratios* of successive thicknesses and complete the table below.

| Number of Cuts | Number of Layers | Total Thickness of Paper (in.) | Ratios of Successive Thicknesses |
|---|---|---|---|
| 0 | 1 | 0.004 | — |
| 1 | 2 | 0.008 | $\frac{0.008}{0.004} = 2$ |
| 2 | | | |
| 3 | | | |
| 4 | | | |
| 5 | | | |
| 6 | | | |

**5.** Consider the relationship between the total thickness and the number of cuts. Is this an exponential relationship? Explain.

**6.** Write an equation that describes total thickness $T$ as a function of the number of cuts $n$.

**7.** What is the initial value of your function? What is the base?

**8.** How is this function similar to the function $L = 2^n$ that described the number of layers of paper in the Activity in Lesson 10.1? How is it different?

**9.** If you could cut the paper 20 times, how thick would the stack be?

**10.** Use a graphing calculator to graph your function. Use a window of $[-3, 3] \times [0, 0.032]$.

**11.** Can the value of your function ever be 0?

**12.** What are the problem domain and range? Explain.

**13.** Change the window on your graph, as needed, to answer this question. How many cuts would be needed to produce a paper stack at least 6 inches thick?

**10.** Sample answer:

$[-3, 3] \times [0, 0.032]$

**11.** No.

**12.** problem domain: whole numbers; problem range: $T \geq 0.004$; A negative number of cuts makes no sense, and the thickness cannot be less than the thickness of one sheet of paper.

**13.** 11 cuts

**14.** A mosquito control scientist collected a large sample of mosquitoes each month for five months. The number of mosquitoes in each sample that were infected with West Nile virus were counted.

| Month | Month Number | Number of Mosquitoes Testing Positive for West Nile Virus | Successive Ratios |
|---|---|---|---|
| May | 0 | 400 | — |
| June | 1 | 600 | |
| July | 2 | 900 | |
| August | 3 | 1,350 | |
| September | 4 | 2,025 | |

Complete the last column of the table and describe what you find.

**15.** Write an equation that models the number of infected mosquitoes $M$ as a function of the month number $n$.

**16.** Use a graphing calculator to graph your function for the months of May through September.

**17.** Describe how you can use a table of values such as the one in Question 14 to determine the equation of an exponential growth function $y = a \cdot b^x$.

Recall that the base $b$ of an exponential function can be any positive number except 1. Only numbers greater than 1 produce exponential growth. But as you saw in the Investigation, the base does not have to be an integer.

The constant ratio of successive values for an exponential function is equal to the base $b$ only if the values of the independent variable increase by 1 in successive rows of the table.

---

**LESSON 10.5**

**14.** The ratios all equal 1.5.

| Month | Month Number | Number of Mosquitoes Testing Positive for West Nile Virus | Successive Ratios |
|---|---|---|---|
| May | 0 | 400 | — |
| June | 1 | 600 | 1.5 |
| July | 2 | 900 | 1.5 |
| August | 3 | 1,350 | 1.5 |
| September | 4 | 2,025 | 1.5 |

**15.** $M = 400(1.5)^n$

**16.** Sample graph:

**[0, 4] × [0, 2100]**

**17.** Sample answer: The initial value of the function (when $x = 0$) is equal to $a$. The constant ratio of successive values is equal to $b$.

**TEACHING TIP**

If necessary, remind students how to determine percents of change (increase or decrease).

$$\frac{\text{change}}{\text{original number}} = \frac{\text{percent}}{100}$$

## ADDITIONAL EXAMPLE

The table shows the population of a city over several years.

| Year | Population |
|------|-----------|
| 2006 | 46,050 |
| 2007 | 47,432 |
| 2008 | 48,854 |
| 2009 | 50,320 |
| 2010 | 51,830 |

**a.** Add a third column to the table and calculate the successive ratios. The ratios of successive values are approximately constant and equal 1.03.

**b.** Add a fourth column to the table and calculate the percents of increase. The percents of increase are approximately constant and equal 0.03.

**c.** Find a function that fits the data well. Let $t = 0$ in 2006.
$P = 46,050(1.03)^t$

**a.** Consider your table of values for the mosquito control situation from the Investigation. Add a fifth column to your table and calculate the percent of increase in the number of mosquitoes testing positive for West Nile virus for each month beginning with June.

| Month | Month Number | Number of Mosquitoes Testing Positive for West Nile Virus | Successive Ratios | Percent of Increase |
|-------|-------------|----------------------------------------------------------|-------------------|---------------------|
| May | 0 | 400 | — | — |
| June | 1 | 600 | 1.5 | |
| July | 2 | 900 | 1.5 | |
| August | 3 | 1,350 | 1.5 | |
| September | 4 | 2,025 | 1.5 | |

**b.** What relationship exists between the successive ratios and the percents of increase?

**Solution:**

**a.** The percents of increase all equal 50%.

| Month | Month Number | Number of Mosquitoes Testing Positive for West Nile Virus | Successive Ratios | Percent of Increase |
|-------|-------------|----------------------------------------------------------|-------------------|---------------------|
| May | 0 | 400 | — | — |
| June | 1 | 600 | 1.5 | $\frac{600-400}{400} = \frac{p}{100}; p = 50\%$ |
| July | 2 | 900 | 1.5 | $\frac{900-600}{600} = \frac{p}{100}; p = 50\%$ |
| August | 3 | 1,350 | 1.5 | $\frac{1,350-900}{900} = \frac{p}{100}; p = 50\%$ |
| September | 4 | 2,025 | 1.5 | $\frac{2,025-1,350}{1,350} = \frac{p}{100}; p = 50\%$ |

**b.** The successive ratios are equal to 1 plus the percent of increase when the percent of increase is written in decimal form.

If you observe constant successive ratios or constant percents of change in a table, then you know that a function is exponential. If the values of the independent variable increase by 1 in successive rows of the table, and if the percent of increase $p$ is expressed in decimal form as $0.01p$, then the base of the exponential function is $(1 + 0.01p)$.

## Practice for Lesson 10.5

**For Exercises 1–3, complete Parts (a), (b), and (c).**

   **a.** Identify each relationship as linear growth, exponential growth, or neither. Explain your answer.

   **b.** If the growth is linear or exponential, write an equation that models the pattern.

   **c.** Check your function with a graphing calculator to see if your model fits the given data.

**1.**

| x | y |
|---|---|
| 0 | 2 |
| 1 | 77 |
| 2 | 302 |
| 3 | 677 |
| 4 | 1,202 |

**2.**

| x | y |
|---|---|
| 0 | 2 |
| 1 | 10 |
| 2 | 50 |
| 3 | 250 |
| 4 | 1,250 |

**3.**

| x | y |
|---|---|
| 0 | 2 |
| 1 | 302 |
| 2 | 602 |
| 3 | 902 |
| 4 | 1,202 |

## Practice for Lesson 10.5 Answers

**1a.** Neither; the rate of change is not constant, and neither are the successive ratios.

**2a.** exponential growth; The successive ratios are all 5.

**2b.** $y = 2 \cdot 5^x$

**2c.**

$[-0.5, 5] \times [0, 1300]$

**3a.** linear growth; The rate of change is constant at 300.

**3b.** $y = 2 + 300x$

**3c.**

$[-0.5, 5] \times [0, 1300]$

# LESSON 10.5

**4a.** Sample answer: The successive ratios are almost constant at 1.20, so an exponential function should model the data.

| Census Year | Decade Number | Population | Successive Ratios |
|---|---|---|---|
| 1950 | 0 | 2,378,963 | — |
| 1960 | 1 | 2,853,214 | 1.20 |
| 1970 | 2 | 3,409,169 | 1.19 |
| 1980 | 3 | 4,132,156 | 1.21 |
| 1990 | 4 | 4,866,692 | 1.18 |
| 2000 | 5 | 5,894,121 | 1.21 |

**4b.** Sample answer: $P = 2,378,963(1.20)^t$, where $t$ measures time in decades.

**4c.** $2,378,963(1.20)^7 \approx 8,520,000$

**4d.** Sample answer: $t \approx 8$ decades or 80 years, so the year should be about 2030.

[−0.5, 10] × [0, 11,000,000]

**5a.** The successive ratios of the numbers of centenarians are constant. An exponential function of the form $y = a \cdot b^x$ should fit the data.

| Year | Year Number | Number of Centenarians | Successive Ratios |
|---|---|---|---|
| 2000 | 0 | 50,454 | — |
| 2001 | 1 | 53,986 | 1.07 |
| 2002 | 2 | 57,765 | 1.07 |
| 2003 | 3 | 61,808 | 1.07 |
| 2004 | 4 | 66,135 | 1.07 |
| 2005 | 5 | 70,764 | 1.07 |
| 2006 | 6 | 75,718 | 1.07 |
| 2007 | 7 | 81,018 | 1.07 |
| 2008 | 8 | 86,689 | 1.07 |
| 2009 | 9 | 92,758 | 1.07 |

**5b.** The constant ratio is 1.07, so $b = 1.07$. The initial value in year number 0 is 50,454, so $a = 50,454$. The function $C = 50,454 \cdot (1.07)^n$ should closely model the data.

**4.** The table shows how the population of the state of Washington changed from the year 1950 to 2000.

| Census Year | Decade Number | Population |
|---|---|---|
| 1950 | 0 | 2,378,963 |
| 1960 | 1 | 2,853,214 |
| 1970 | 2 | 3,409,169 |
| 1980 | 3 | 4,132,156 |
| 1990 | 4 | 4,866,692 |
| 2000 | 5 | 5,894,121 |

  **a.** Explain what type of function fits the data.
  **b.** Write a function that closely models the data.
  **c.** If your model continues to hold into the future, what will the population of Washington be in 2020?
  **d.** Graph your function and use it to predict when Washington's population will be 10,000,000.

**5.** According to the U.S. Census Bureau, in 2000 there were 50,454 *centenarians* in the United States. A centenarian is a person at least 100 years old. Suppose that a researcher continued to collect data through 2009.

| Year | Year Number | Number of Centenarians |
|---|---|---|
| 2000 | 0 | 50,454 |
| 2001 | 1 | 53,986 |
| 2002 | 2 | 57,765 |
| 2003 | 3 | 61,808 |
| 2004 | 4 | 66,135 |
| 2005 | 5 | 70,764 |
| 2006 | 6 | 75,718 |
| 2007 | 7 | 81,018 |
| 2008 | 8 | 86,689 |
| 2009 | 9 | 92,758 |

  **a.** Explain what type of function fits the data.
  **b.** Write a function that closely models the data.
  **c.** If the model continues to hold into the future, how many centenarians will there be in 2017?
  **d.** Graph your function and use it to predict when the number of centenarians will reach 1,000,000.

**5c.** 2017 is 17 years after 2000, and $50,454 \cdot (1.07)^{17} \approx 159,375$ centenarians.

**5d.** The number will pass 1,000,000 sometime during 2044 (year number 44).

[0, 50] × [0, 1,200,000]

6. Wildlife scientists use mathematical models to predict animal populations. The data in the table show the growth of the buffalo population in a national park.

| Year | Population |
|------|-----------|
| 2005 | 125 |
| 2006 | 160 |
| 2007 | 205 |
| 2008 | 260 |
| 2009 | 335 |

a. Find the growth rate each year, as a percent of increase from the previous year's population. Round to the nearest percent.

| Year | Population | Percent of Increase |
|------|-----------|---------------------|
| 2005 | 125 | — |
| 2006 | 160 | |
| 2007 | 205 | |
| 2008 | 260 | |
| 2009 | 335 | |

b. Write an equation that models the buffalo population as a function of time. (Use $t = 0$ to represent the year 2005.)
c. Use a calculator to verify your model using the data from 2005 to 2009. How well does your model fit the data?
d. Use your function to predict how many buffalo will be in the park in 2015.

7. The 2010 Census found that the population of the United States on April 1, 2010 was about 309 million. This figure represented an increase of about 28 million from the 2000 census figure. This is an annual percent of increase of about 0.95%.
a. Find a model that could be used to predict the population of the United States after the year 2010. Assume a constant growth rate.
b. At the same rate of increase, what would be the population of the United States on April 1, 2013?
c. Write your answer to Part (b) in scientific notation.
d. From 1990 to 2000, the U.S. population grew at a rate of 1.25% per year. If this rate is used to answer Part (b), what effect would it have on the population estimate for 2013?

MODELING EXPONENTIAL GROWTH    Lesson 10.5    361

COMMON ERROR

**Exercises 6 and 7** Some students may forget how to determine the base of their exponential function when the percent of increase is known. If that is the case, they will find that their graphs will not fit the data. If necessary, remind them of the **Example** in the lesson and point out that the base of their exponential equation will be equal to 1 + the percent of increase (written as a decimal).

6d.

| Year | Population | Percent of Increase |
|------|-----------|---------------------|
| 2005 | 125 | — |
| 2006 | 160 | 28% |
| 2007 | 205 | 28% |
| 2008 | 260 | 27% |
| 2009 | 335 | 29% |

6b. Sample answer: $P = 125(1 + 0.28)^t$ or $P = 125(1.28)^t$
6c. The function models the data very well.

$[-0.5, 5] \times [0, 400]$

6d. $125(1.28)^{10} \approx 1,476$ buffalo
7a. $P = 309(1 + 0.0095)^t$ or $P = 309(1.0095)^t$
7b. $309(1.0095)^3 \approx 318$, or about 318 million people
7c. $3.18 \times 10^8$
7d. $309(1.0125)^3 \approx 321$, or 321 million in 2013, a difference of about 3 million people

361

# LESSON 10.6

## Lesson Objectives

- identify situations involving exponential decay.
- model situations involving exponential decay.

## Vocabulary

- asymptote
- horizontal asymptote

## Materials List

## Description

Students should work in pairs on this Investigation. Through a context of water pollution cleanup, they build a model for exponential decay.

*Wrapping Up the Investigation:*

Lead a class discussion that focuses on the problem domain and range for exponential decay. Students should see that, while the complete range of a decay function of the form $y = ab^x$ may include all positive numbers (see the graph in the answer to **Question 9**), the range for a context like the one in the Investigation is more limited.

## Lesson 10.6 Investigation Answers

1. 10%
2. also 10%
3. $0.1(50) = 5$ pounds
4. 45 pounds
5.

| Weeks of Cleaning | Amount of Contaminant Remaining (pounds) |
| --- | --- |
| 0 | 50 |
| 1 | 45 |
| 2 | 40.5 |
| 3 | 36.45 |
| 4 | 32.805 |
| 5 | 29.525 |

In Lesson 10.5, you used exponential functions to model growth. In this lesson, you will explore models for exponential decay.

Polluted water is a problem in many areas of the United States and around the world. Chemicals from industrial and household uses can get into ground water and contaminate it. One way to clean polluted water is to pump some of it out of the ground and remove the pollutants. The cleaned water is then returned to the ground. Through this process, the ground water gradually becomes cleaner.

1. Suppose that 10,000 gallons of water are contaminated with 50 pounds of a chemical. One thousand gallons are removed, cleaned and returned to the ground. What percent of the total volume of water was removed?
2. What percent of the 50 pounds of chemical contaminant has been removed?
3. How many pounds of contaminant were removed?
4. How many pounds of contaminant remain in the ground?
5. If this process is repeated once a week for 5 weeks, complete the table to show how the amount of chemical contaminant changes.

| Weeks of Cleaning | Amount of Contaminant Remaining (pounds) |
| --- | --- |
| 0 | 50 |
| 1 | |
| 2 | |
| 3 | |
| 4 | |
| 5 | |

6. What type of function can be used to model the amount of chemical in the ground water during this process? Explain.
7. Write an equation that models the amount of contaminant $C$ in pounds as a function of the number of weeks of cleaning $n$.

6. Sample answer: The successive ratios of contaminant amounts are all equal to 0.9, so an exponential model will work.
7. $C = 50(0.9)^n$

8. Use your function to find the amount of contaminant remaining in the ground water after 10 weeks of cleaning.

9. Use a graphing calculator to graph your function. Use a window of $[-10, 10] \times [0, 150]$.

10. Change your window and use your graph, or use a table, to find how many weeks it would take to reduce the amount of contaminant to 1 pound.

11. What do you expect would happen to the value of $C$ if the cleaning process were continued indefinitely into the future?

12. What are the problem domain and range?

The cleanup of polluted water is another example of exponential decay. For both exponential growth and exponential decay, the base of the function $y = ab^x$ is equal to the constant ratio of successive values of the function.

- If the base $b$ in $y = ab^x$ is greater than 1, the function models exponential growth.
- If the base $b$ in $y = ab^x$ is between 0 and 1, the function models exponential decay.

And as you saw in Lesson 10.3, exponential decay can also be modeled by $y = ab^{-x}$, where $b$ is greater than 1.

## ASYMPTOTES

In the Investigation, you observed a graph that approached the $x$-axis but never actually reached it. Throughout this chapter, you have observed similar behavior in other exponential graphs. In these graphs, the $x$-axis is an **asymptote**.

> An **asymptote** is a line that is not part of a graph but is one that the graph approaches at its extremes. In particular, a line $y = k$ is a **horizontal asymptote** if the value of a function approaches the number $k$ as $x$ gets very large or very small.

MODELING EXPONENTIAL DECAY    **Lesson 10.6**    **363**

## LESSON 10.6

8. 17.434 pounds

9.

$[-10, 10] \times [0, 150]$

10. slightly more than 37 weeks
11. Sample answer: $C$ would continue to decrease but could never reach 0.
12. Problem domain: whole numbers; problem range: $0 < C \le 50$; A negative number of weeks makes no sense, and the amount decreases from 50 but can never reach 0.

### TEACHING TIP

Take time to talk about the information immediately following **Question 12** of the Investigation because this will help students examine equations and determine whether they represent exponential growth or exponential decay.

### TEACHING TIP

Avoid defining an asymptote as a line that "the graph approaches but never reaches." A graph may intersect a horizontal asymptote $y = k$ even as the value of $y$ approaches $k$. For example, the graph of $y = e^{-5x} - e^{-x}$ crosses the $x$-axis, even though the $x$-axis is a horizontal asymptote.

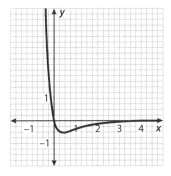

363

# LESSON 10.6

## ADDITIONAL EXAMPLE

A can of soda contains 20 mg of dissolved carbon dioxide ($CO_2$). The amount of dissolved $CO_2$ decreases by 70% every hour after the can is opened.

**a.** Find the amount of dissolved $CO_2$ in the can each hour for 4 hours.

| Number of Hours | Dissolved $CO_2$ (mg) |
|---|---|
| 0 | 20 |
| 1 | |
| 2 | |
| 3 | |
| 4 | |

| Number of Hours | Dissolved $CO_2$ (mg) |
|---|---|
| 0 | 20 |
| 1 | 6 |
| 2 | 1.8 |
| 3 | 0.54 |
| 4 | 0.162 |

**b.** Find a function that models the amount of dissolved $CO_2$ as a function of time. $A = 20(0.30)^t$

**c.** Use a table or graph to find when the amount will be reduced to 0.01 mg. a little after 6 hours

**d.** Does the graph have an asymptote? Yes, there is a horizontal asymptote, the line $A = 0$.

## EXAMPLE

A used car is purchased for $8,400. It depreciates (loses value) by 12% of its value each year.

**a.** Determine the value of the car each year for 4 years after purchase.

**b.** Find a function that models the car's depreciation.

**c.** The car's owner plans to keep the car until its value reaches $3,000. Use a table or graph to find how many years it will take until the car's value falls below $3,000. (Assume that it continues to depreciate 12% every year.)

**d.** Does the graph of the car's value have an asymptote? Explain.

### Solution:

**a.** For a 12% decrease, the car's value will be 0.88 times its value in the previous year. Amounts are rounded to the nearest dollar.

| Years from Purchase | Value |
|---|---|
| 0 | $8,400 |
| 1 | $7,392 |
| 2 | $6,505 |
| 3 | $5,724 |
| 4 | $5,037 |

**b.** The initial value (in dollars) is 8,400, and the base is 0.88. The value after $n$ years is $V = 8,400(0.88)^n$.

**c.** The car's value will fall below $3,000 shortly after 8 years.

$$[0, 10] \times [0, 9000]$$

**d.** The $n$-axis ($V = 0$) is a horizontal asymptote. As $n$ gets very large, the car's value approaches 0, but the expression $8,400(0.88)^n$ can never equal 0.

1. Without graphing, classify the graph of each function as exponential growth or decay, then identify at least three additional characteristics of the graph.
   a. $y = 3^x$
   b. $y = 6(0.5)^x$
   c. $y = 4(1.25)^x$

2. Exponential decay can always be modeled using a negative exponent.
   a. Use your knowledge of negative exponents to explain why $(0.25)^x = 4^{-x}$.
   b. Rewrite your function from Question 7 of the Investigation using a negative exponent.

**For Exercises 3–8, use the following information.**

Caffeine is an ingredient in coffee, tea, and some soft drinks. A typical cup of coffee may contain 150 milligrams of caffeine. Caffeine is removed from the bloodstream by the kidneys.

The table shows how the amount of caffeine in a person's bloodstream might change after drinking a cup of coffee.

| Time (hours) | Amount of Caffeine in Bloodstream (mg) |
|---|---|
| 0 | 150 |
| 1 | 120 |
| 2 | 96 |
| 3 | 76.8 |

3. What type of function can be used to model the amount of caffeine in the bloodstream during this process? Explain.

4. Find an equation that models the amount of caffeine $C$ (in mg) as a function of the time $t$ (in hours) after drinking the coffee.

5. Does this equation model exponential growth or exponential decay? Explain.

6. State the problem domain and range of your function.

7. Use your function to find the amount of caffeine remaining in the bloodstream after 6 hours.

8. Use a graphing calculator to determine how long it will take for the amount of caffeine to be reduced to 20 mg.

8. a little over 9 hours

[0, 10] × [0, 150]

**TEACHING TIP**

**Exercise 2, Part (b)** Point out to students that, even though a fractional base may be more convenient for this exercise, exponential decay is almost always modeled using a negative exponent.

## Practice for Lesson 10.6 Answers

**1a.** exponential growth; Its domain is all real numbers, its range is all positive real numbers, the $x$-axis is a horizontal asymptote, it has no $x$-intercepts, its $y$-intercept is 1, and it is an increasing function.

**1b.** exponential decay; Its domain is all real numbers, its range is all positive real numbers, the $x$-axis is a horizontal asymptote, it has no $x$-intercepts, its $y$-intercept is 6, and it is a decreasing function.

**1c.** exponential growth; Its domain is all real numbers, its range is all positive real numbers, the $x$-axis is a horizontal asymptote, it has no $x$-intercepts, its $y$-intercept is 4, and it is an increasing function.

**2a.** $(0.25)^x = \left(\dfrac{1}{4}\right)^x = (4^{-1})^x = 4^{-x}$

**2b.** $C = 50(0.9)^n = 50\left(\dfrac{1}{0.9}\right)^{-n} = 50\left(\dfrac{10}{9}\right)^{-n}$, so $C \approx 50(1.11)^{-n}$.

3. Sample answer: The successive ratios of amounts of caffeine are all equal to 0.8, so an exponential decay model will work.

4. $C = 150(0.8)^t$ or $C = 150(1.25)^{-t}$

5. It models exponential decay because the base is 0.8, a number between 0 and 1.

6. problem domain: non-negative real numbers; range: $0 < C \le 150$

7. 39.3 mg

9. Sample answer: $V = 16,000(0.85)^t$
10. about $7,099
11. between 7 and 8 years
12. No, the rate of change is not constant.
13. Yes, the ratios of successive population values are all approximately 0.95.
14. Sample answer: $P = 600(0.95)^t$, with $t = 0$ in 2002.
15. Sample graph:

$$[-1, 20] \times [0, 700]$$

16. When $t = 10$, $P = 359$.
17. after about 13.5 years; so probably sometime in 2015
18. Sample answer: Yes, $P = 0$ is a horizontal asymptote. If the model continues to hold, the value of $P$ can never actually be 0, since $(0.95)^t$ is positive for any value of $t$. But since only whole numbers of bears make sense for this situation, when $P$ becomes less than 0.5, it would *round* to 0.
19. Sample answer: The half-life of the carbon-14 is 5,730 years, because that is how long it takes for the amount to be reduced by one-half. The function $C = 1,000 \left(\dfrac{1}{2}\right)^n$ can be used to model the amount remaining

**For Exercises 9–11, use the following information.**

A car is purchased for $16,000. Its value depreciates by 15% each year.

9. Write an equation that gives the car's value as a function of time.
10. What is the car's value after 5 years?
11. When will the car's value fall below $5,000?

**For Exercises 12–18, use the following information.**

The bear population in a wildlife preserve changed as shown in the table to the left.

| Year | Bear Population |
|------|-----------------|
| 2002 | 600 |
| 2003 | 570 |
| 2004 | 542 |
| 2005 | 514 |
| 2006 | 489 |
| 2007 | 464 |
| 2008 | 441 |
| 2009 | 419 |

12. Do the data show a linear relationship? Explain.
13. Do the data show an exponential relationship? Explain.
14. Write an equation that models the bear population as a function of time.
15. Use a graphing calculator to graph your function and the data. Include a time interval of 20 years beginning in 2002.
16. Predict the bear population in 2012.
17. When will the bear population be 300?
18. Does the graph contain an asymptote? Explain.
19. The amount of radioactive carbon-14 ($C_{14}$) in a fossil can be used to determine the age of the fossil. The table below shows the amount of carbon-14 remaining from a sample of 1,000 grams after a given number of years.

| Time (years) | $C_{14}$ Remaining (grams) |
|--------------|----------------------------|
| 0 | 1,000 |
| 5,730 | 500 |
| 11,460 | 250 |
| 17,190 | 125 |

Explain how to determine the number of years that have passed when the sample of carbon-14 has a mass of 31.25 grams.

20. A trout farm is estimated to have around 5,000 fish when it opens. Each day, approximately 2% of the fish in the lake are caught. At the end of the week, the lake is restocked with 1,200 fish.
    a. How many fish are caught by the end of the first week?
    b. Will the lake run out of fish? Explain.

after $n$ half-lives. $C$ will equal 31.25 when $n = 5$, and $5(5,730) = 28,650$ years.
20a. $5,000 - 5,000(0.98)^7 \approx 659$ fish
20b. No, because the amount added to the population exceeds what was taken out.

## My, How You've Grown!

As you have seen in this chapter, one type of nonlinear growth is called *exponential growth*. One characteristic of an exponential function $y = ab^x$ is that when $x$ changes by constant amounts, the *ratios* of successive $y$-values are constant. This behavior is equivalent to a constant percent of change in successive $y$-values.

Populations of people, animals, and even plants sometimes grow exponentially. You saw some examples of this in Lesson 10.5. In this project you will investigate the growth of human populations.

Pick one of the nations of the world and explore historical data for its population. Find population figures that span several decades if possible.

1. Construct a table that lists years in the first column and population in the second column. If the years are not consecutive, list them so that the differences between successive years are constant (for example, every 5 years or every 10 years).

2. Identify time periods for which growth appears to be approximately exponential.

3. For a period of exponential growth, find an equation of the form $p = ab^t$ that models the data reasonably well. Let $t$ be the time measured from the beginning of the exponential growth period. Then $a$ represents the initial value of population at the start of the exponential growth period.

4. Use your model to predict the population at the end of the exponential growth period. Comment on the accuracy of the prediction.

5. Include a graph of the nation's population that includes the time period you investigated.

6. Cite the source of your data.

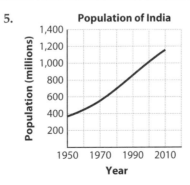

MODELING PROJECT      **Chapter 10**      **367**

# MODELING PROJECT

**5e** Elaborate

## Materials List

## Description

In this project, students conduct research on the population growth of a nation of their choice. Historical data are available on the Internet for many of the nations of the world, although the geography and history sections of your school library may also have good sources of data.

Students should examine historical records to look for exponential growth patterns. They can examine ratios for successive time intervals, or percent growth, looking for periods over which the ratios or percents are approximately constant. Underdeveloped countries are more likely to exhibit exponential growth, as growth often slows for developed nations.

### TEACHING TIP

A computer spreadsheet program is ideal for exploring population trends and calculating year-to-year ratios or percent changes. Calculator lists are another good option.

### CONNECTION

This project provides an opportunity to make a connection with a teacher of world history or geography. Students may want to research population growth for a country they are studying in another course.

## Sample Answers

1.

| Population of India | |
|---|---|
| Year | Population (millions) |
| 1950 | 370 |
| 1960 | 446 |
| 1970 | 555 |
| 1980 | 692 |
| 1990 | 856 |
| 2000 | 1,013 |
| 2010 | 1,156 |

2. From 1950 to 1990, the population increased at approximately 23% each decade.

3. A model is $P = 370(1.23)^t$, where $t$ measures time in decades after 1950.

4. For 1990 (4 decades after 1950), the model predicts a population of $P = 370(1.23)^4 = 847$ million. This figure is only about 1% less than the actual 1990 population.

5.

**Population of India**

Population (millions): 1,400 / 1,200 / 1,000 / 800 / 600 / 400 / 200

Year: 1950  1970  1990  2010

6. Internet source: http://www.cs.colostate.edu/ ~malaiya/india.html#Populations in the Subcontinent

## Chapter 10 Review

### You Should Be Able to:

**Lesson 10.1**

- recognize exponential functions.

**Lesson 10.2**

- use properties of exponents to simplify expressions.
- use scientific notation to compute with large numbers.

**Lesson 10.3**

- define and use negative exponents.
- define and use 0 as an exponent.
- simplify monomials.

**Lesson 10.4**

- solve problems that require previously learned concepts and skills.

**Lesson 10.5**

- identify situations involving exponential growth.
- model situations involving exponential growth.

**Lesson 10.6**

- identify situations involving exponential decay.
- model situations involving exponential decay.

### Key Vocabulary

base (p. 337)

exponent (p. 337)

exponential function (p. 338)

exponential growth (p. 338)

scientific notation (p. 342)

negative exponent (p. 345)

exponential decay (p. 347)

zero exponent (p. 347)

monomial (p. 350)

degree of a monomial (p. 350)

asymptote (p. 363)

horizontal asymptote (p. 363)

## Chapter 10 Test Review Answers

**1a.** initial value
**1b.** base
**2.** monomial
**3.** asymptote

### Chapter 10 Test Review

**For Exercises 1–6, fill in the blank.**

1. For the exponential function $y = 3 \cdot 2^x$,
   a. 3 is called the _____.
   b. 2 is called the _____.

2. The product of a coefficient and one or more variables raised to non-negative powers is called a(n) _____.

3. If the value of a function approaches the number $k$ as $x$ gets very large or very small, the line $y = k$ is a horizontal _____.

**4.** A function of the form $y = ab^x$ with $b > 1$ models exponential _____.

**5.** A function of the form $y = ab^x$ with $0 < b < 1$ models exponential _____.

**6.** A function of the form $y = ab^{-x}$ with $b > 1$ models exponential _____.

**7.** You are given a table of data relating two variables. The independent variable increases at a constant rate. Explain how you can tell if
   **a.** a linear function is a good model for the data.
   **b.** an exponential function is a good model for the data.

**For Exercises 8–12, simplify the expression. Write your answer with positive exponents only.**

**8.** $(y^3)(y^9)$

**9.** $\dfrac{t^8}{t^2}$

**10.** $3d^{-4}$

**11.** $\left(\dfrac{2p^4}{q^{-2}r^5}\right)^3$

**12.** $\dfrac{4a^3bc^{-5}}{12a^5b^{-4}c^2}$

**13.** Write 0.0000000025 in scientific notation.

**14.** The diameter of the period at the end of this sentence is about $3 \times 10^{-2}$ centimeter. Write this length using standard notation.

**15.** The population of a town has been increasing as shown in the table.

| Year | Population |
|------|------------|
| 1970 | 6,451 |
| 1980 | 7,423 |
| 1990 | 8,548 |
| 2000 | 9,814 |
| 2010 | 11,280 |

   **a.** If the pattern continues, find a function that models the population $P$ of the town in terms of the number $n$ of decades after 1970.

   **b.** If the pattern continues, predict the town's population in 2030.

CHAPTER REVIEW

**4.** growth
**5.** decay
**6.** decay
**7a.** If the rate of change of the dependent variable is constant, a linear function is a good model for the data.
**7b.** If the ratios of successive values of the dependent variable are constant, an exponential function is a good model for the data.
**8.** $y^{12}$
**9.** $t^6$
**10.** $\dfrac{3}{d^4}$
**11.** $\dfrac{8p^{12}q^6}{r^{15}}$
**12.** $\dfrac{b^5}{3a^2c^7}$
**13.** $2.5 \times 10^{-9}$
**14.** 0.03 centimeter
**15a.** Sample answer: $P = 6,451(1.15)^n$
**15b.** When $n = 6$, $P = 14,922$.

**16a.** Sample answer: $A = 93.5 \left(\frac{1}{2}\right)^n$ or $A = 93.5(2)^{-n}$

**16b.** 1.46 square inches

**17a.** $h = 200(0.75)^n$ or $h = 200(1.33)^{-n}$

**17b.** about 27 cm

**18a.** $M = 27 + 3t$

**18b.** 72 moose

**18c.** $M = 27(1 + 0.0924)^t$; $M = 27(1.0924)^t$

**18d.** about 102 moose

---

**16.** Suppose you take a sheet of $8\frac{1}{2}$-inch by 11-inch paper and fold it in half, then fold in half again, and continue to repeat the process.

   **a.** Find an equation that describes the area of the top surface of the folded paper as a function of the number of folds

   **b.** What will the area be after the 6th fold?

**17.** A ball is dropped from a height of 200 centimeters. The table shows the height of the ball after each of the first 4 bounces.

| Number of Bounces | Height (cm) |
|---|---|
| 0 | 200 |
| 1 | 150 |
| 2 | 112.5 |
| 3 | 84.4 |
| 4 | 63.3 |

   **a.** If the pattern continues, write an equation that gives the height of the ball $h$ after $n$ bounces.

   **b.** Use your equation to predict the height of the ball after the 7th bounce.

**18.** The moose population in a state park in 2005 was 27. In 2010 the moose population had grown to 42.

   **a.** If the growth is caused only by migration, the yearly change in the number of moose can be assumed to be constant. In that case, write an equation that models the number of moose $M$ in the park as a function of time $t$ (in years) beginning in 2005.

   **b.** Use your equation from Part (a) to predict the number of moose in the park in 2020 if the same pattern continues.

   **c.** On the other hand, if the growth is solely due to reproduction, the population would have grown by 9.24% each year from 2005 to 2010. Find a model for the moose population in that case.

   **d.** Use your equation from Part (c) to predict the number of moose in the park in 2020.

# CHAPTER 10

# Chapter Extension
## Newton's Law of Cooling

A lake or pool that is fed by a spring usually has a constant temperature. For example, Barton Springs in Austin, Texas, feeds a man-made pool in Zilker Park near downtown Austin. The water from the springs is always 68°F, making the pool cool and popular on hot summer afternoons.

Since the temperature of the water is constant at 68°F, objects that are put in the pool cool to that temperature. Park managers can calculate how long it takes an object in the pool to reach 68°F using Newton's Law of Cooling.

1. Fill a cup with hot water and a second cup with cold water. Place a temperature probe in the hot water for 30 seconds. Then move the probe to the cold water and immediately begin collecting data. Measure the temperature every second for 40 seconds. Make a scatter plot of temperature vs time.

2. Record the final temperature of the probe in the cold water.

3. Copy the data for the first 7 seconds into a table like the one shown here. Calculate the successive ratios and record them in the third column.

| Time (seconds) | Temperature (°C) | Successive Ratios | | |
|---|---|---|---|---|
| 0 | | — | | |
| 1 | | | | |
| 2 | | | | |
| 3 | | | | |
| 4 | | | | |
| 5 | | | | |
| 6 | | | | |
| 7 | | | | |

4. Would an exponential function describe the data well? Explain.

## Lesson Objective

- use technology to collect and analyze data for exponential decay involving a nonzero limiting value.

## Vocabulary

## Materials List

- CBL2 or other calculator-based data collection device, or a thermometer accurate to 0.5°C
- calculator with data collection program
- temperature probe
- 2 paper or Styrofoam cups
- hot and cold water

## Description

Students should work in small groups to collect data on the cooling of a temperature probe. They will observe that successive temperature ratios are not constant. But if the data are transformed by subtracting the final temperature (the lowest temperature recorded by the probe) from each data value, the exponential nature of the data becomes apparent.

If CBL2s are not available, students can use thermometers. In which case, have them record temperatures every 5 seconds instead of every second, until the temperature levels off.

If it is not possible to have students collect their own data, either do the experiment as a class demonstration or have them use the sample data given in the answer to **Question 3**.

*Using the CBL2*

The steps for using the CBL2 to collect temperature data are as follows:

1. Connect the TI-83+/TI-84 to the CBL2.

2. Place the temperature probe in Channel 1.

3. Press the **APPS** button.

4. Choose CBL/CBR.*

---

5. Choose DATA LOGGER from the menu.

6. Choose the following settings for the next screen:
   PROBE: TEMP
   #SAMPLES: 40
   INTRVL(SEC): 1
   UNITS: °C
   PLOT: RealTme
   DIRECTNS: On

7. Arrow down to GO and follow the directions.

*Note: Some calculators may have different versions of this program.

### TEACHING TIP

**Questions 2 and 3** If necessary, point out to students that the temperatures can be found by using the left and right arrow keys to trace the graph on the calculator. The "final temperature" is the lowest temperature recorded by the probe at the end of the data collection period.

## Chapter 10 Extension Answers

1.–3.   See answers on page 372.

# CHAPTER 10 EXTENSION

The ratios in **Question 5** will not be exactly equal. Suggest that students use the average ratio over the first 7 seconds as the base for their exponential function.

## Chapter 10 Extension Answers

1. Sample scatter plot:

[–3, 43] × [0, 42]

2. Sample answer: 20.5581°C
3. See the completed table in Question 5 below.

TEACHING TIP

Make sure that students can use the results of their experiment to analyze the new situation presented in **Question 12**. They should recognize that 25 is the constant in the function, and also that 25 should be subtracted from the initial temperature value of 100 to find the coefficient for the exponential term $b^t$.

4. No, the successive ratios are continually increasing.

5.

| Time (seconds) | Temperature (°C) | Successive Ratios | (Temperature – Final Temperature) | Successive Ratios |
|---|---|---|---|---|
| 0 | 40.3 | — | 19.7419 | — |
| 1 | 36.439 | 0.904194 | 15.8809 | 0.804426 |
| 2 | 33.3571 | 0.915423 | 12.799 | 0.805937 |
| 3 | 30.9070 | 0.926549 | 10.3489 | 0.808571 |
| 4 | 28.9302 | 0.936040 | 8.3721 | 0.808985 |
| 5 | 27.3488 | 0.945337 | 6.7907 | 0.811111 |
| 6 | 26.0465 | 0.952382 | 5.4884 | 0.808223 |
| 7 | 24.9535 | 0.958037 | 4.3954 | 0.800853 |

Note: This assumes a "Final Temperature" of 20.5581°C.

6. Yes, the successive ratios for these values are approximately constant at 0.81.
7. $(T - 20.5581) = 19.7419(0.81)^t$
8. $T = 19.7419(0.81)^t + 20.5581$

---

5. Complete the last two columns of your table. Subtract your final temperature (see Question 2) from the temperatures in the second column and record the results in the fourth column. Then calculate successive ratios of these values.

| Time (seconds) | Temperature (°C) | Successive Ratios | (Temperature – Final Temperature) | Successive Ratios |
|---|---|---|---|---|
| 0 | | — | | |
| 1 | | | | |
| 2 | | | | |
| 3 | | | | |
| 4 | | | | |
| 5 | | | | |
| 6 | | | | |
| 7 | | | | |

6. Would an exponential function describe the relationship between the quantity (Temperature – Final Temperature) and time? Explain.
7. Write an equation that models the quantity (Temperature – Final Temperature) as a function of time $t$. Let $T$ represent the temperature measured by the temperature probe. Use your answer to Question 2 for the final temperature.
8. Solve for $T$ and write temperature $T$ as a function of time $t$.
9. Graph your function from Question 8 on a scatter plot of the original time and temperature data for the first 7 seconds.
10. Does your model describe the data well?
11. Write your function from Question 8 using a negative exponent.
12. Suppose you were to take an object from a pot of boiling water at 100°C and place it where room temperature is 25°C. Write a function that might model the object's temperature $T$ as a function of time $t$ in minutes.

9. Sample graph:

[–2, 10] × [0, 43]

10. Sample answer: Yes, all the data points are on or near the graph of the function.
11. Sample answer: $T = 19.7419(1.23)^{-t} + 20.5581$
12. Sample answer:
    $T - 25 = ($ Initial Temperature $-$ Final Temperature $)b^t$, where $b$ equals the successive ratios of values of the quantity.
    (Temperature $-$ Final Temperature). One possibility is $T - 25 = (100 - 25)b^t$ or $T = 75(0.8)^t + 25$. This is equivalent to $T = 75(1.25)^{-t} + 25$.

# Chapter 11
## Quadratic Functions

## Mathematical Overview

The relationship among parabolas, quadratic functions, and quadratic equations is investigated through activities that explore both the geometric and algebraic properties of parabolas. Students look at the characteristics of three special cases of the quadratic function in standard form ($y = ax^2 + bx + c$, where $a \neq 0$), and at using graphs, factoring, and the quadratic formula as methods for solving quadratic equations. This chapter examines how parabolic shapes focus energy, how quadratic functions can be used to model real-world situations, and how the solutions to quadratic equations can help answer questions about real-world quadratic models.

## Lesson Summaries

### Lesson 11.1   *Investigation: Parabolas–A Geometric Look*

In this Investigation, students use focus-directrix paper to investigate the geometric properties of parabolas that make it possible for parabolic-shaped objects to focus sound, light, radio waves, etc. to a single point. Students examine the location of the focus, directrix, axis of symmetry, vertex, points on the graph, and whether the graph is increasing or decreasing. With the information they gather, students write an equation of the form $x^2 = 4py$ for the parabola. Students extend their knowledge of transformations to include writing equations of the form $(x - h)^2 = 4p(y - k)$ for parabolas.

### Lesson 11.2   *Activity: Parabolas–An Algebraic Look*

In this Activity, students construct physical models of a suspension bridge cable on a coordinate grid. They answer questions about the geometric characteristics of parabolas introduced in Lesson 11.1. Students then write an equation that models the curve formed when weights are added to the chains in their model. They make connections between the equation and its graph. They also use their algebraic skills to determine that the equation is a quadratic function that represents a smooth U-shaped curve called a parabola.

### Lesson 11.3   *Investigation: Graphing Quadratic Functions*

This Investigation is designed to help students make the connection between a quadratic function and its graph. Students are given a function in standard form $y = ax^2 + bx + c$, where $a \neq 0$. They locate the vertex, create a table of values, and then sketch the graph. The effects that the constants $a$, $b$, and $c$ have on a graph are explored by looking at three special cases: $y = ax^2$, $y = ax^2 + c$, and $y = ax^2 + bx$. The Investigation concludes with a summary of important concepts and skills that can be used to help sketch the graph of any quadratic function.

### Lesson 11.4   *R.A.P.*

In this lesson, students **R**eview **A**nd **P**ractice solving problems that require the use of skills and concepts taught in previous math levels. The skills reviewed in this lesson are skills that are needed as a basis for solving problems throughout this course.

### Lesson 11.5   *Polynomial Arithmetic*

In this lesson, students extend their study of monomials from Chapter 10 to adding, subtracting, and multiplying algebraic expressions that are monomials or sums of monomials (polynomials). Students use the acronym F.O.I.L. and visual models known as area models to assist them when multiplying binomials.

### Lessons 11.6   *Investigation: Solving Quadratic Equations* and 11.7   *Investigation: The Quadratic Formula*

In Lesson 11.6, students solve quadratic equations both graphically and algebraically. They examine how the intercepts of the graph of a quadratic function relate to the factors in the factored form of the function set equal to 0. In Lesson 11.7, students use the quadratic formula to solve quadratic equations. They investigate the discriminant to find the connections among the value of the discriminant, the number of roots of the equation, and the graph of the related function.

### Lesson 11.8   *Modeling with Quadratic Functions*

In this lesson, students use quadratic models to describe real-world situations involving free-fall motion and the relationship between time and the height of an object.

### Chapter 11   *Extension: Exploring Quadratic Data*

In the first section of this Extension, students examine distance-versus-time graphs of data collected by a motion detector. In the second section, students use first and second differences to distinguish between linear and quadratic data given in tables.

## Lesson Guide

| Lesson/Objectives | Materials | |
|---|---|---|
| **Chapter 11 Opener: Is It a Parabola?**<br>• recognize the usefulness of parabolas in the daily lives of people. | | |
| **11.1 Investigation: Parabolas–A Geometric Look**<br>• graph a parabola given the focus and directrix.<br>• write an equation of a parabola when the distance from the vertex to the focus is known.<br>• identify the vertex and axis of symmetry of a parabola.<br>• use an equation of a parabola to model a real-world situation. | *Per pair:*<br>• focus-directrix paper or Handout 11A (several copies)<br>• ruler<br>• grid paper | *Optional.*<br>• color pencils |
| **11.2 Activity: Parabolas–An Algebraic Look**<br>• identify the mathematical properties of a model of a suspension bridge cable.<br>• find an equation of a parabola that passes through the origin given a point on the graph and the other *x*-intercept. | *Per group:*<br>• $\frac{1}{4}$-inch grid paper<br>• bulletin board or cardboard<br>• straight pins or tacks<br>• paper clips<br>• lightweight chain<br>• weights (e.g., large metal washers) | *Optional:*<br>• Handout 11B |
| **11.3 Investigation: Graphing Quadratic Functions**<br>• find the coordinates of the vertex of a graph of a quadratic function.<br>• sketch the graph of a quadratic function.<br>• identify whether a parabola opens upward or downward by examining the function.<br>• identify the range and domain of a given quadratic function. | *Per pair:*<br>• grid paper<br>• graphing calculator or computer | *Optional:*<br>• TRM table shell for Question 1, Part (b) |
| **11.4 R.A.P.**<br>• solve problems that require previously learned concepts and skills. | | • TRM for Exercises 28, 29 |
| **11.5 Polynomial Arithmetic**<br>• add and subtract polynomials.<br>• multiply a polynomial by a monomial.<br>• multiply two binomials. | | |
| **11.6 Investigation: Solving Quadratic Equations**<br>• use graphs to solve quadratic equations.<br>• solve quadratic equations by factoring.<br>• make connections between the roots of a quadratic equation and the zeros of the graph of the related quadratic function. | *Per student:*<br>• graphing calculator | *Optional:*<br>• grid paper<br>• color pencils<br>• algebra tiles |
| **11.7 Investigation: The Quadratic Formula**<br>• use the quadratic formula to solve quadratic equations.<br>• select and defend a method of solving a quadratic equation. | *Per group:*<br>• graphing calculator | *Optional:*<br>• grid paper<br>• TRM for Exercise 18 |
| **11.8 Modeling with Quadratic Functions**<br>• use a quadratic function to model a real-world situation. | | *Optional:*<br>• grid paper |
| **Chapter 11 Extension: Exploring Quadratic Data**<br>• investigate distance-versus-time graphs.<br>• use first and second differences to identify quadratic functions. | *Per student:*<br>• graphing calculator | *Optional:*<br>• TRM table shells for Questions 13, 15, 17, 19<br>• motion detector |

## Pacing Guide

| | Day 1 | Day 2 | Day 3 | Day 4 | Day 5 | Day 6 | Day 7 | Day 8 | Day 9 | Day 10 | Day 11 | Day 12 | Day 13 |
|---|---|---|---|---|---|---|---|---|---|---|---|---|---|
| **Basic** | p. 374, 11.1 | 11.1 | 11.2 | 11.3 | 11.4 | 11.5 | 11.5 | 11.6 | 11.6 | 11.7 | 11.8 | project | review |
| **Standard** | p. 374, 11.1 | 11.1 | 11.2 | 11.3 | 11.4 | 11.5 | 11.6 | 11.6 | 11.7 | 11.8 | project | review | extension |
| **Block** | p. 374, 11.1 | 11.2, 11.3 | 11.3, 11.4 | 11.5 | 11.6 | 11.7, 11.8 | project, review | extension | | | | | |

**Supplement Support**

See the Book Companion Website at www.highschool.bfwpub.com/ModelingwithMathematics and the Teacher's Resource Materials (TRM) for additional resources.

# Quadratic Functions

## CONTENTS

# CHAPTER 11 OPENER

**5e**  Engage

## Lesson Objective

- recognize the usefulness of parabolas in the daily lives of people.

## Vocabulary

## Description

This reading helps students understand the applications of the reflective properties of parabolas.

## Is It a Parabola?

You may already know that a mathematical curve called a *parabola* is used in the design of structures such as suspension bridges and in the modeling of projectile motion. But did you know that the same curve has a reflection or focusing property?

When a parabola is rotated around its line of symmetry, it forms a three-dimensional surface. This surface is used in the design of car headlights and satellite dishes because of its reflection property.

The reflection property of the parabola can be shown using a parabolic surface that is a mirror as shown in the figure to the left. If a light is placed at a particular point, all of the light rays will reflect off the mirror in lines parallel to the line of symmetry. Car headlights, flashlights, and searchlights demonstrate this property.

This reflection property also works in reverse, as shown in the figure below. If energy such as light or sound comes to a parabolic receiver, such as a satellite dish, it is reflected by the surface of the receiver to a single point. Applications of this property are used in communication systems, radar systems, reflector microphones found on the sidelines of football games, telescopes, and solar furnaces.

Another application that is familiar to most people is the cupping of your hands around your ears in order to hear distant sounds. Believe it or not, the ideal shape for your hands is a parabola!

In this chapter, you will explore both the geometric and algebraic properties of this special curve.

In addition to focusing sound and light, parabola-shaped objects can focus radio waves and other forms of energy. In this lesson, you will examine the geometric properties of parabolas that make this possible.

As you saw in the Chapter Opener, the shape of a parabola makes it ideal for applications that involve reflecting and focusing. Telescopes, satellite dishes, car headlights, cameras, and even flashlights are just a few of the things that depend on the reflection (or focusing) property of parabolas. The ability of a parabola to focus energy is a direct result of its special geometric properties.

A **parabola** can be defined as the set of points in a plane that are equidistant from a given line and a given point not on the line. The given line is called the **directrix** of the parabola, and the given point is called the **focus**.

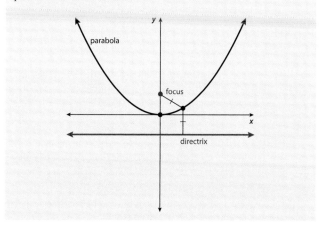

In this Investigation, you will create a graph of a set of points in a plane that are equidistant from a given line and a given point not on the line, and examine some of the special characteristics of your parabola.

1. Examine a piece of focus-directrix paper. What do you notice about the paper?

## Lesson Objectives

- graph a parabola given the focus and directrix.
- write an equation of a parabola when the distance from the vertex to the focus is known.
- identify the vertex and axis of symmetry of a parabola.
- use an equation of a parabola to model a real-world situation.

## Vocabulary

- axis of symmetry
- directrix
- focus
- parabola
- vertex (of a parabola)

## Materials List

- focus-directrix paper or Handout 11A
- rulers
- grid paper

## Description

This lesson works best as a two-day lesson with students working in pairs. On Day 1 have students work through the Investigation, **Questions 1–18**.

In this lesson, students are given the geometric definition of a parabola. Then during the Investigation, they use focus-directrix paper (**Handout 11A**) to create several parabolas and investigate their properties. Once all groups are finished, debrief the results of the Investigation and go over the Example given.

*Wrapping Up the Investigation:*

On Day 2, have students work with a partner on the exercises. Make sure that plenty of focus-directrix paper is available for students who wish to explore.

## Lesson 11.1 Investigation Answers

1. Sample answer: It has several parallel, horizontal lines and there are several concentric circles with their centers at the point shown on the paper. The distance between the circles is equal to the distance between the parallel lines.

2. See students' work.
3. The distance from the focus to the point is one unit and the distance from the directrix to the point is one unit, so the distances are equal.

4. Sample graph:

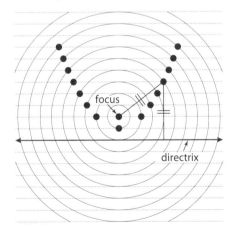

2. On your piece of focus-directrix paper, draw a horizontal line that is two units below the point at the center of the circles. Label the center point "focus" and the line "directrix." You will use this focus and directrix to create a parabola.

3. In the figure shown below, a second point is shown in red. What can you say about the distance between this point and the focus and the distance between this point and the directrix?

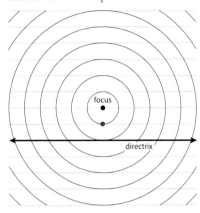

4. Use the circles and lines on the paper to help you locate at least ten more points that are equally distant from the focus and the directrix. Find points that are to the left and to the right of the focus. (Recall that the distance between a point and a line is the length of the perpendicular from the given point to the line.)

5. Connect the points with a smooth curve. Since all points on your curve are equidistant from a given point (the focus) and a given line (the directrix) all of the points you plotted lie on the graph of a parabola.

6. Describe your graph.

7 a. Does the graph show line symmetry? If so, describe the line of symmetry.
   b. For a parabola, the line of symmetry of the graph is called the **axis of symmetry**. Draw the line of symmetry for your graph and label it "axis of symmetry."

8. Now draw a horizontal axis and vertical axis on your paper. Place the origin where your axis of symmetry intersects the parabola. This lowest point on this graph is the *minimum value* and is called the **vertex** of the parabola. Label the horizontal axis "$x$" and the vertical axis "$y$."

9. Does your graph represent a function? Explain.

5. Sample graph:

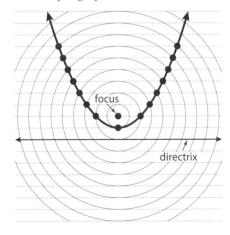

6. Sample answer: It is "U" shaped and opens upward.
7a. Yes; the line of symmetry passes through the focus and is perpendicular to the directrix.
7b–9. See answers on page 377.

**10 a.** Examine only the portion of the graph where $x > 0$. Look at the curve from left to right. Is the graph increasing or decreasing?

**b.** Now examine only the portion of the graph where $x < 0$. Look from left to right at the curve. Is the graph increasing or decreasing?

**11 a.** What happens to the height of the graph as $x$ increases without bound? (Hint: to answer this question, look at the graph to see what happens to it as you move farther and farther to the right along the horizontal axis.)

**b.** What happens to the height of the graph as $x$ decreases without bound? (Hint: to answer this question, look at the graph to see what happens to it as you move farther and farther to the left along the horizontal axis.)

If a parabola has a vertex at the origin, a focus at $(0, p)$, and a directrix $y = -p$, the standard-form equation of the parabola is $x^2 = 4py$. Notice that the value of $p$ can be positive or negative as $p$ represents the directed distance from the vertex to the focus.

**12.** Find an equation for your parabola in Question 8.

**13 a.** Use another piece of focus-directrix paper. In this construction, draw the directrix two units *above* the focus at the center of the circles. Then construct the parabola with the given focus and directrix.

**b.** Again draw a horizontal axis and vertical axis on your paper with the origin at the vertex of your parabola.

**14.** Does the parabola open up or down?

**15.** What are the coordinates of the vertex of this parabola?

**16.** Describe when the graph is increasing and when it is decreasing. (Hint: be sure to look at the curve from left to right as you describe the curve.)

**17.** What is the directed distance from the vertex to the focus?

**18.** What is the value of $p$?

**19.** Write an equation for the parabola.

**10a.** increasing
**10b.** decreasing
**11a.** It increases.
**11b.** It increases.
**12.** $p = 1$, so the equation is $x^2 = 4(1)y$ or $x^2 = 4y$.
**13a.** Sample graph:

**13b.** Sample graph:

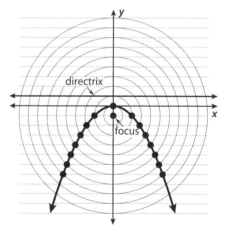

**14.** down
**15.** $(0, 0)$
**16.** When $x < 0$, the graph is increasing. When $x > 0$, the graph is decreasing.
**17.** $-1$
**18.** $-1$
**19.** $x^2 = -4y$

**7b.** Sample graph:

**8.** Sample graph:

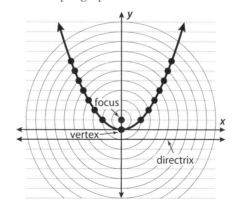

**9.** Yes, for each input value, there is exactly one output value.

## ADDITIONAL EXAMPLE

The vertex of a parabola is at the origin and its focus is located at the point (0, 7). Find equations for the directrix and the parabola. Then graph the parabola.

Directrix: $y = -7$;
Parabola: $x^2 = 28y$
Sample graph:

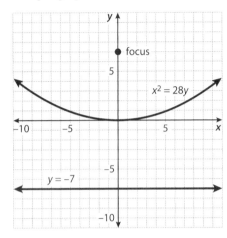

### TEACHING TIP

In **Exercise 1**, students explore what happens to the shape of a parabola as the focus and directrix are moved. If students struggle with answering these questions, have them use focus-directrix paper to create parabolas as described.

## Practice for Lesson 11.1 Answers

**1a.** Sample answer: It appears to be more narrow.

**1b.** As you move the focus away from the directrix, the parabola appears to open wider.

**1c.** Construct a vertical directrix and place the focus to the right of it.

Find equations of the directrix and the parabola if the focus of the parabola is the point (0, −3) and the vertex is the origin. Graph the parabola.

**Solution:**

First sketch the given information. From that information and the definition of a parabola, you know that the directrix is a horizontal line 3 units above the vertex, since the focus is 3 units below the vertex. So, an equation of the directrix is $y = 3$.

You also know that the directed distance from the vertex to the focus is −3. So, $p = -3$, and an equation of the parabola is

$$x^2 = 4py$$
$$x^2 = 4(-3)y$$
$$x^2 = -12y$$

To graph the parabola, it is helpful to locate a few points on the parabola.

| $x$ | $y$ |
|-----|-----|
| 0   | 0   |
| 6   | −3  |
| −6  | −3  |

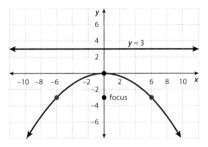

### Practice for Lesson 11.1

**1** **a.** The directrix of the parabola in the first part of the Investigation was below the focus. What happens as you move the focus closer to the directrix? (If you are not sure, use focus-directrix paper and try placing the directrix 1 unit away from the focus, rather than 2 units. What happens to the parabola?)

   **b.** What happens if you move the directrix farther away from the focus? (For example, place the directrix 4 units away from the focus, rather than 1 or 2 units.)

   **c.** How can you create a parabola so that it opens to the right? (Hint: try drawing a graph.)

**d.** How can you create a parabola so that it opens to the left?

**e.** Do the graphs in Parts (c) and (d) represent functions? Explain.

2. Think about a parabola with its vertex at the origin and the $y$-axis as its axis of symmetry. If the parabola is shifted $h$ units horizontally and $k$ units vertically, then the result is a parabola with its vertex at $(h, k)$ and an axis of symmetry parallel to the $y$-axis. The standard form of an equation for this parabola is $(x - h)^2 = 4p(y - k)$.

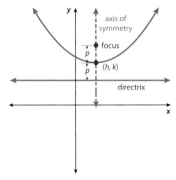

**a.** What are the coordinates of the focus?

**b.** What is the equation of the axis of symmetry?

**c.** What is the equation of the directrix?

3. Find equations of the directrix and the parabola.

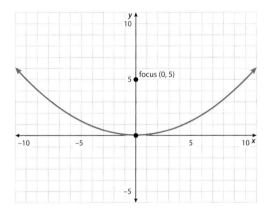

**TEACHING TIP**

If students struggle with **Exercise 2**, remind them of their work in **Lesson 9.5** on "Translations in a Coordinate Plane." If necessary, take time to review that section of **Lesson 9.5** with the students. This Exercise provides a foundation for **Exercises 5, 8, and 9**.

**1d.** Construct a vertical directrix and place the focus to the left of it.

**1e.** No, both graphs show more than one output value for some input values. Neither passes the vertical line test.

**2a.** $(h, k + p)$ or $(h, p + k)$

**2b.** $x = h$

**2c.** $y = -p + k$ or $y = k + (-p)$

**3.** $p = 5$; directrix: $y = -5$; equation: $x^2 = 4(5)y$; $x^2 = 20y$

**4.** $p = -4$; focus: $(0, -4)$; equation:
$x^2 = 4(-4)y$; $x^2 = -16y$

**5.** $h = -3, k = -4, p = 6$; directrix:
$y = -10$; equation:
$(x - (-3))^2 = 4(6)(y - (-4))$;
$(x + 3)^2 = 24(y + 4)$

**4.** Find the focus and an equation of the parabola.

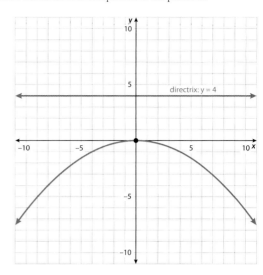

**5.** Find an equation of the directrix and an equation of the parabola.

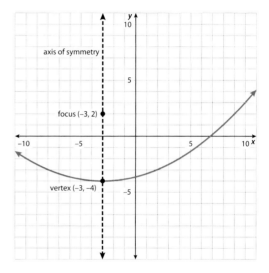

**For Exercises 6–9, find the vertex, the focus, and the equation of the directrix for each parabola. Then draw the graph.**

6. $x^2 = 8y$

7. $x^2 = -16y$

8. $(x - 1)^2 = -4(y + 3)$

9. $(x + 2)^2 = 2(y - 5)$

10. State whether the following statements are true or false. Then explain your reasoning.

    Statement A: All parabolas are graphs of functions.

    Statement B: All equations of the form $x^2 = 4py$ are functions and can be represented by parabolas.

11. A satellite dish has a diameter of 20 inches and a depth of 2 inches. Where should the receiver be located? Explain.

6. vertex: $(0, 0)$; focus: $(0, 2)$; directrix: $y = -2$

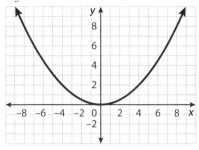

**TEACHING TIP**

**Exercise 11** If students struggle getting started with this exercise, have them draw a cross-section of the satellite dish on a coordinate plane. If the vertex is placed at the origin, the point $(10, 2)$ will be on the parabola. Using that information and the equation $x^2 = 4py$, they can find the value of $p$, the distance from the vertex to the focus.

7. vertex: $(0, 0)$; focus: $(0, -4)$; directrix: $y = 4$

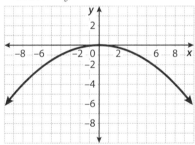

8. vertex: $(1, -3)$; focus: $(1, -4)$; directrix: $y = -2$

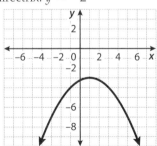

9. vertex: $(-2, 5)$; focus: $(-2, 5.5)$; directrix: $y = 4.5$

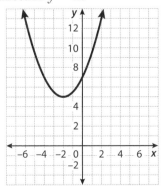

10. Statement A is false. Sample answer: As we saw in this Investigation, some parabolas can open to the right or left. These are not functions.
Statement B is true. Sample answer: The graphs of $x^2 = 4py$ are parabolas that open up or down and are functions.

11. Sample solution:

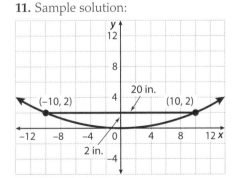

Since the point $(10, 2)$ is on the graph, $10^2 = 4(p)(2)$ and $p = \frac{100}{8} = 12.5$ inches. The receiver should be located at the focus which is outside the satellite dish, 12.5 inches from the vertex of the parabola.

**381**

**5e** Engage

## Lesson Objectives

- identify the mathematical properties of a model of a suspension bridge cable.
- find an equation of a parabola that passes through the origin given a point on the graph and the other $x$-intercept.

## Vocabulary

- quadratic function

## Materials List

*Per group:*

- $\frac{1}{4}$-inch grid paper
- bulletin board or cardboard
- tacks or pushpins
- lightweight chain
- paper clips
- weights such as large metal washers

or

- a copy of Handout 11B

## Description

*Preparation:*

Have students work in groups of two or three. Provide each group with the materials needed for the Activity. If it is not possible to provide students with the needed materials, give each group a copy of **Handout 11B.**

*During the Activity:*

In this Activity, students use simple materials to create models of suspension bridge cables. Once the models are created, they answer questions about the parabolas formed by their weighted chains.

Some of the questions posed in the Activity focus on the physical characteristics of parabolas that were introduced in **Lesson 11.1**. New to this lesson is the concept of finding an equation that can be used to model the curve. It is not intended for students to learn the form $y = ax(x - d)$ of a quadratic function, nor is the derivation of this equation discussed in this lesson. The purpose of giving the students the equation

is to allow them to easily write an equation for a parabola and then make connections between the equation and its graph.

Focus attention on **Questions 5 and 6.** These questions reinforce the concept that if a point lies on a graph, then it satisfies the equation of that graph and vice versa. After **Question 7**, a definition of quadratic functions is introduced.

Continue to reinforce the concept that all quadratic functions can be modeled by a parabola, but not all parabolas can be modeled by a quadratic function.

*Closing the Activity:*

Have students compare their simulated suspension cables and the equations that model them with those of other groups.

---

**TEACHING TIP**

If it is not possible to have students create a model of a suspension bridge cable as described in **Question 1**, provide them with a copy of **Handout 11B,** and then have them read through **Question 1** and begin the Activity with **Question 2**.

---

## Lesson 11.2 Activity Answers

1. See students' models.

---

**Lesson 11.2** ACTIVITY: **Parabolas— An Algebraic Look**

One of the most common types of bridges, especially for spanning large distances over rivers and harbors, is the suspension bridge. There are many such bridges throughout the world, but one of the most famous is the Golden Gate Bridge in San Francisco. In this lesson, you will create models of curved suspension bridge cables and explore their algebraic form.

In this Activity, you will construct a small model of a suspension bridge cable and then explore its mathematical properties. The properties are essentially the same for all suspension bridges.

1. Use the following directions to create a model of a suspension bridge.

- Attach a sheet of grid paper to a piece of cardboard or a bulletin board.
- Choose a point near the upper-left corner of the paper as the origin. Then draw $x$- and $y$-axes through that point. Note that only Quadrant IV of the coordinate plane appears on your paper.
- Label the axes with any convenient scale. Use the same scale on each axis.
- Use a pin or tack to attach one end of a chain at the origin. Then attach another link of the chain somewhere on the $x$-axis so that the chain hangs in the shape of a suspension bridge cable.

- To complete your model, use small hooks, such as opened paper clips, to place identical weights at *equally spaced horizontal intervals* along the curved chain. Caution: These weights will not be equally spaced along the chain.

2. When a chain or cable supports a load that is evenly spaced in the horizontal direction, it assumes the approximate shape of a parabola.
   **a.** Identify the two points where your parabola intersects the $x$-axis.
   **b.** What is the vertex of your parabola?
   **c.** Find an equation of the axis of symmetry.

3. Does the graph that is modeled by your chain represent a function? Explain.

4. The equation $y = ax(x - d)$ represents a parabola that crosses the $x$-axis at the origin and at the point $(d, 0)$. Since your curve goes through the origin and another point on the $x$-axis, you can use this form to find an equation for your chain's parabolic shape. Find the equation of your parabola. (Hint: To find the value of $a$, substitute the coordinates of the vertex and the value of $d$ in the equation $y = ax(x - d)$.)

5. You can check to see if your function actually describes the curved shape of your chain. Evaluate the function when $x = 10$, $15$, and $20$. Check to see if these $(x, y)$ pairs are on your chain.

6. Does the point $(4, -10)$ lie on your chain? Use your equation from Question 4 to justify your answer.

7. Use the Distributive Property to rewrite your equation from Question 4.

---

A **quadratic function** is a function that can be represented by the equation $y = ax^2 + bx + c$, where $a$, $b$, and $c$ are real numbers and $a \neq 0$. The graphs of quadratic functions are parabolas.

---

8. Does your model represent a quadratic function? Explain.

**CONNECTIONS**

A true parabola will result only from a uniform horizontal loading of a cable, that is, one where the load is continuously applied to the cable at a constant horizontal rate. For a real suspension bridge, as well as for the model in this lesson, the load is not continuous but is applied at fixed horizontal intervals. Therefore, the shape is only approximately parabolic.

A cable or chain supporting no load at all has a slightly different shape, called a *catenary*, which has a mathematical form different from that of a parabola. The catenary curve is not discussed in this course as it involves the hyperbolic cosine function.

**TEACHING TIP**

When students hang the weights on the chain, point out that this is intended to simulate the hanging of a road using vertical cables. The change in the shape of the chain after the weights are hung is probably insignificant because a parabola and catenary are almost identical on this scale.

**2a.** A sample answer using $\frac{1}{4}$-inch grid paper: $(0, 0)$ and $(42, 0)$

**2b.** Sample answer: $(21, -13)$

**2c.** Sample answer: $x = 21$

**3.** Yes, for each input value, there is exactly one output value. It also passes the vertical line test.

**4.** Sample answer: For the points $(0, 0)$, $(42, 0)$ and $(21, -13)$, $d = 42$, $x = 21$, $y = -13$. So, $a = 0.0295$ and the equation of the parabolic shape is $y = 0.0295x(x - 42)$.

**5.** The $(x, y)$ pairs should be close to points on the chain.

**6.** Sample answer: No, the point does not lie on the chain, because the ordered pair $(4, -10)$ is not a solution to the equation $y = 0.0295x(x - 42)$.

**7.** Sample answer: $y = 0.0295x^2 - 1.24x$

**8.** Yes, it represents a function and its equation can be written in the form $y = ax^2 + bx + c$.

## ADDITIONAL EXAMPLE

Find an equation of the graph of a quadratic function that crosses the $x$-axis at $(0, 0)$ and $(12, 0)$ and passes through the point $(4, -16)$.
$y = 0.5x(x - 12)$

**E X A M P L E**

Find an equation of the graph of a quadratic function that crosses the $x$-axis at $(0, 0)$ and $(-8, 0)$ and passes through the point $(-4, 12)$.

**Solution:**

First sketch a graph of the parabola using the given information.

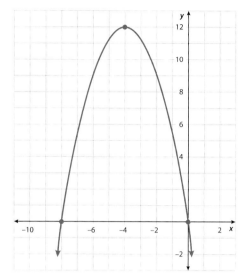

You know that the graph passes through the origin and that $d = -8$. Use the point $(-4, 12)$ to find $a$.

$$y = ax(x - d)$$
$$12 = a(-4)(-4 - (-8))$$
$$12 = a(-4)(4)$$
$$12 = -16a$$
$$-\frac{3}{4} = a$$

So, an equation of the graph is $y = -\frac{3}{4}x(x - (-8))$ or

$y = -\frac{3}{4}x(x + 8)$.

**9a.** Sample graphs:

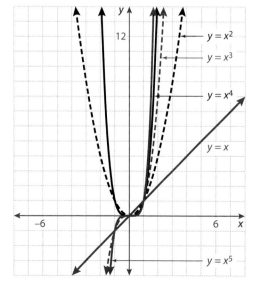

**9b.** Sample answer: All but $y = x$ are curves. Every graph passes through the origin and $(1, 1)$. The functions with even powers are U-shaped, pass through the point $(-1, 1)$, and have the $y$-axis as an axis of symmetry. The functions with odd powers are not U-shaped, and they all pass through $(-1, -1)$.

**9c.** Sample answer: The graph should be a U-shaped curve that passes through $(0, 0)$, $(1, 1)$, and $(-1, 1)$. Its axis of symmetry will be the $y$-axis, and it will be narrower than the other graphs.

**Practice** for Lesson 11.2

For Exercises 1–6, use the information shown in the figure below.

1. What is the equation of the parabola in the form $y = ax(x - d)$?
2. Use the Distributive Property to rewrite your equation from Exercise 1 in the form $y = ax^2 + bx$.
3. Does your equation represent a quadratic function? Explain.
4. Use one of your equations to find the coordinates of the vertex of the parabola.
5. Describe where the axis of symmetry in the parabola is located. Find its equation.
6. Which of these points lie on the parabola?

   $(4, -4)$     $(8, -6)$     $(14, -7)$     $(18, -5.4)$     $(20, 4)$

7  **a.** Find an equation of a quadratic function that passes through the following points: the origin, $(5, 0)$, and $(2, 6)$.
   **b.** Does the graph open upward or downward?
   **c.** What do you notice about the coefficient of the $x^2$ term of your equation?
8. The equation of a quadratic function that passes through the origin is $y = 5x(x - 25)$.
   **a.** Suppose the graph of the original function is translated 2 units to the right. Find an equation of the new function.
   **b.** Suppose the graph of the original function is translated 3 units to the left. Find an equation of the new function.
   **c.** Suppose the graph of the original function is translated $h$ units horizontally. Find an equation of the new function.
9. It is very difficult to just look at a graph and tell whether it is or is not a parabola because not all U-shaped graphs are parabolas.
   **a.** On the same set of axes, graph the functions $y = x$, $y = x^2$, $y = x^3$, $y = x^4$, and $y = x^5$.
   **b.** What do you notice about these graphs?
   **c.** Using your observations, how would you expect the graph of $y = x^6$ to look?

PARABOLAS—AN ALGEBRAIC LOOK     **Lesson 11.2**     **385**

## LESSON 11.2

**TEACHING TIP**

**Exercises 1–6** are designed to reinforce the concepts, skills, and vocabulary introduced in the Activity.

## Practice for Lesson 11.2 Answers

1. From the figure, $d = 24$ (the distance between the origin and the second point on the $x$-axis). Then substituting the coordinates of the point $(10, -7)$ in the equation $y = ax(x - 24)$, the value of $a$ can be calculated. Since $a = 0.05$, the equation is $y = 0.05x(x - 24)$.

**TEACHING TIP**

**Exercise 8** If students have difficulty with the translations, suggest that they refer back to **Lesson 9.5**. If students ask if the translation is to the left or right in **Part (c)**, point out that they do not need to assign a sign to $h$ as values for $h$ will be negative if the translation is to the left and positive if the translation is to the right.

**TEACHING TIP**

**Exercise 9** How students create the graphs in this exercise does not matter. They may use calculators, computers, or create them by hand. It is their observations that are important.

6. $(4, -4)$, $(14, -7)$, and $(18, -5.4)$ lie on the parabola.
**7a.** $y = -x(x - 5)$
**7b.** downward
**7c.** It is negative.
**8a.** $y = 5(x - 2)((x - 2) - 25) = 5(x - 2)(x - 27)$
**8b.** $y = 5(x - (-3))((x - (-3)) - 25) = 5(x + 3)(x - 22)$
**8c.** $y = 5(x - h)((x - h) - 25) = 5(x - h)(x - h - 25)$ or $y = 5(x - h)(x - (25 + h))$
**9a–c.** See answers on page 384.

2. $y = 0.05x^2 - 1.2x$
3. Yes, it is of the form $y = ax^2 + bx + c$ with $a = 0.05$, $b = -1.2$, and $c = 0$.
4. The axis of symmetry is the line $x = 12$. So, the $x$-coordinate of the vertex is 12. Use that value in the equation $y = 0.05x^2 - 1.2x$ to find the $y$-coordinate. The vertex is located at $(12, -7.2)$.
5. It is a vertical line passing through the vertex $(12, -7.2)$. An equation of the axis is $x = 12$.

**5e** Explore

## Lesson Objectives

- find the coordinates of the vertex of a graph of a quadratic function.
- sketch the graph of a quadratic function.
- identify whether a parabola opens upward or downward by examining the function.
- identify the range and domain of a given quadratic function.

## Vocabulary

- standard form (of a quadratic function)

## Materials

- grid paper

## Description

This Investigation works best if students work in pairs. **Question 1** asks students to use a table of values to sketch the graph of a quadratic function. In all questions beyond that one, students will need graphing calculators or computers as they investigate the questions.

This Investigation is designed to help students make the connections between a function and its graph. In order to help students accomplish this goal, they are given the expression $-\frac{b}{2a}$ for the $x$-coordinate of the vertex. Verification of this appears in **Exercise 17** of **Lesson 11.7**.

A summary of important concepts and skills is provided for the student at the end of the Investigation.

*Wrapping Up the Investigation:*

After going through the answers to the questions in the Investigation, focus on the summary provided at the end. Ask students how this summary can be used to help them sketch the graph of any given quadratic function.

## Lesson 11.3 Investigation Answers

**1a.** $-\frac{b}{2a} = -\frac{2}{2(1)} = -1$; The $y$-coordinate of the vertex is

$(-1)^2 + 2(-1) - 4 = -5$. So, the coordinates of the vertex are $(-1, -5)$.

---

**Lesson 11.3** | **INVESTIGATION:** **Graphing Quadratic Functions**

In Lesson 11.2, you explored several quadratic functions and found that their graphs are smooth, U-shaped curves called parabolas. In this lesson, you will continue to explore the graphs of quadratic functions.

Recall that a quadratic function is a function that can be written in the **standard form** $y = ax^2 + bx + c$, where $a \neq 0$. When sketching the graph of a quadratic function, it is helpful to first locate the vertex.

**Note**

You will be asked to show why this is true in Lesson 11.7, Exercise 17.

For a function written in standard form $y = ax^2 + bx + c$, the $x$-coordinate of the vertex is $-\frac{b}{2a}$.

Once you have found the coordinates of the vertex, create a table of values with several $x$-values less than the $x$-value of the vertex and several greater than the $x$-value of the vertex.

1. Consider the function $y = x^2 + 2x - 4$.
   **a.** Find the coordinates of the vertex.
   **b.** Use the function to complete this table.

| x | y | |
|---|---|---|
| −4 | | |
| −3 | | |
| −2 | | |
| −1 | | ← vertex |
| 0 | | |
| 1 | | |
| 2 | | |

   **c.** Sketch the graph by plotting the points in your table and connecting them with a smooth curve.

In the following questions, you will investigate the effects that the constants $a$, $b$, and $c$, have on the graphs of quadratic functions. You will consider three special cases of the graphs of $y = ax^2 + bx + c$. In order to explore the characteristics of these graphs, it is helpful to use either a graphing calculator or a computer.

---

**1b.**

| x | y |
|---|---|
| −4 | 4 |
| −3 | −1 |
| −2 | −4 |
| −1 | −5 |
| 0 | −4 |
| 1 | −1 |
| 2 | 4 |

**1c.** Sample graph:

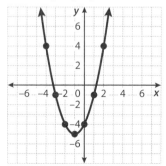

**CASE 1:** $y = ax^2$ (when $b = 0$ and $c = 0$)

**2.** Consider the graphs of quadratic functions whose general form is $y = ax^2$. For any value of $a$, what are the coordinates of the vertex? Explain.

**3** **a.** Using a calculator or computer, graph $y = ax^2$ on the same set of axes using 5, 3, 1, and 0.5 for the values of $a$. What do you observe as the values of $a$ become smaller?

**b.** Name three things that these four parabolas have in common.

**4.** Now graph $y = ax^2$ on the same set of axes using 5, $-5$, 3, and $-3$ for the values of $a$. What do you observe when $a > 0$? What do you observe when $a < 0$?

**5.** Without graphing, how can you tell whether the vertex is a maximum or a minimum?

**6.** What is the domain of the function $y = ax^2$?

**7** **a.** What is the range of the function $y = ax^2$ when $a > 0$?

**b.** What is the range of the function $y = ax^2$ when $a < 0$?

**CASE 2:** $y = ax^2 + c$ (when $b = 0$)

**8.** Investigate the effect that the value of $a$ has on the graph of $y = ax^2 + 3$ by graphing $y = ax^2 + 3$ for various values of $a$ on the same set of axes.

**a.** What do all of the graphs have in common?

**b.** What happens to the graph when $a > 0$?

**c.** What happens to the graph when $a < 0$?

**9.** Investigate the effect that the value of $c$ has on the graph by graphing $y = 2x^2 + c$ for various values of $c$ on the same set of axes. (Hint: Be sure to use values of $c$ that are greater than 0, equal to 0, and less than 0.)

**a.** What do you observe about the general shape of each of the graphs?

**b.** What do you observe about the axis of symmetry for each graph?

**c.** What do you observe about the vertices?

**10** **a.** What is the $x$-coordinate of the vertex of the graph of $y = ax^2 + c$ for any value of $a$ or $c$?

**b.** What is the $y$-coordinate of the vertex?

**11.** When $a$ is positive, how many $x$-intercepts does the graph of $y = ax^2 + c$ have? (Hint: Be sure to consider values of $c$ that are greater than 0, equal to 0, and less than 0.)

**10a.** The $x$-coordinate of the vertex is 0.

**10b.** The $y$-coordinate of the vertex is $c$.

**11.** When $a$ is positive and $c < 0$, there are two $x$-intercepts, and when $c = 0$, there is one $x$-intercept, and when $c > 0$, there are no $x$-intercepts.

**TEACHING TIP**

In **Questions 2–14**, students need graphing calculators or computers so they can explore many different graphs quickly and make conjectures from what they see.

**TEACHING TIP**

**Question 5** If students do not understand the term *maximum* or *minimum*, point out that a vertex is a *maximum* if it is the highest point, the point with the greatest $y$-value, of the graph. The vertex is a *minimum* if it is the lowest point, the point with the least $y$-value, of the graph.

**2.** $(0, 0)$; When $b = 0$, the $x$-coordinate of the vertex is $-\dfrac{b}{2a} = 0$, and when $x = 0$, $y = 0$.

**3a.** As $a$ gets smaller, the parabola appears wider.

**3b.** The vertex and the axis of symmetry are the same for each parabola and each parabola opens up.

**4.** When $a > 0$, the parabola opens upward. When $a < 0$, it opens downward.

**5.** If $a > 0$, the parabola opens upward and the vertex is a minimum. If $a < 0$, it opens downward and the vertex is a maximum.

**6.** all real numbers

**7a.** When $a > 0$, the range is all real numbers greater than or equal to 0.

**7b.** When $a < 0$, the range is all real numbers less than or equal to 0.

**8a.** The vertex of each graph is the same $(0, 3)$. The axis of symmetry for each graph is the $y$-axis.

**8b.** The parabola opens upward.

**8c.** The parabola opens downward.

**9a.** The general shapes of the graphs are the same.

**9b.** The axis of symmetry is the $y$-axis for each graph.

**9c.** The vertex of each graph lies on the $y$-axis.

# LESSON 11.3

**12.** When $a$ is negative and $c > 0$, there are two $x$-intercepts, and when $c = 0$, there is one $x$-intercept, and when $c < 0$, there are no $x$-intercepts.

**13.** There is only one $y$-intercept and its coordinates are $(0, c)$.

**14a.** The graph opens upward when $a > 0$. It opens downward when $a < 0$.

**14b.** Sample answer: The axis of symmetry varies, but it is not the $y$-axis in any of the graphs.

**14c.** In each graph, one of the $x$-intercepts is the origin.

## Practice for Lesson 11.3 Answers

**1.** Sample graph:

**2.** Sample graph:

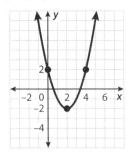

> **TEACHING TIP**
>
> In **Exercises 1–3**, the sketching should be done without the help of technology.

**3.** Sample graph:

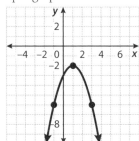

**4.** $(1, 2)$; maximum
**5.** $(0, -5)$; minimum
**6.** $(2, 8)$; maximum

388

---

**12.** When $a$ is negative, how many $x$-intercepts does the graph of $y = ax^2 + c$ have? (Hint: Be sure to consider values of $c$ that are greater than 0, equal to 0, and less than 0.)

**13.** How many $y$-intercepts does the graph of $y = ax^2 + c$ have? What are the coordinates?

### CASE 3: $y = ax^2 + bx$ (when $c = 0$)

**14.** Consider the graphs of quadratic functions whose general form is $y = ax^2 + bx$. Graph the function for various non-zero values of $a$ and $b$.
  **a.** When does the graph open upward? When does it open downward?
  **b.** For each graph, what do you notice about its axis of symmetry?
  **c.** For each graph, what do you notice about the $x$-intercepts?

In this Investigation, you found that the graphs of quadratic functions in the form $y = ax^2 + bx + c$ have the following properties:
  - There is a single maximum or minimum point called the vertex that lies on the axis of symmetry. The $x$-coordinate of that point is $-\frac{b}{2a}$.
  - The graph of a quadratic function is a U-shaped curve called a parabola. When $a$ is positive, the parabola opens upward. When $a$ is negative, it opens downward.
  - The domain of a quadratic function includes all real numbers.
  - For parabolas that open upward, the range includes all numbers greater than or equal to the $y$ coordinate of the vertex. For those that open downward, the range includes all numbers less than or equal to the $y$-coordinate of the vertex.
  - All quadratic functions have exactly one $y$-intercept, but there may be zero, one, or two $x$-intercepts.

## Practice for Lesson 11.3

**For Exercises 1–3, sketch the graph of the function.**

  **1.** $y = x^2 + 2x + 2$
  **2.** $y = x^2 - 4x + 2$
  **3.** $y = -x^2 + 2x - 3$

388    **Chapter 11**    QUADRATIC FUNCTIONS

---

**7a.** It opens upward because $a > 0$.
**7b.** $(2, -3)$; It is a minimum since the graph opens upward.
**7c.** the vertical line $x = 2$
**7d.** The domain is all real numbers. The range is all real numbers greater than or equal to $-3$.
**7e.** Sample graph:

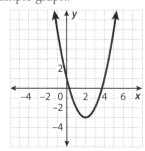

**8a.** Answers will vary. Some things that should be predicted are that the graphs have different axes of symmetry and that neither of these axes is the $y$-axis. They have different vertices. The vertex of $y = 2x^2 + 3x + 6$ is a minimum, and its graph opens upward. The vertex of $y = -3x^2 + 12x + 6$ is a maximum, and its graph opens downward.

**For Exercises 4–6, find the vertex of the function and determine whether it is a maximum or minimum.**

4. $y = -3x^2 + 6x - 1$

5. $y = x^2 - 5$

6. $y = 8x - 2x^2$

7. Consider the graph of $y = x^2 - 4x + 1$. *Before* graphing this function, use the observations you made about graphs of quadratic functions in the Investigation to answer the questions in Parts (a)–(d).
   a. Does the graph open upward or downward? Explain how you know.
   b. What are the coordinates of the vertex of the graph? Is it a maximum or minimum? Explain how you know.
   c. What is the equation of the axis of symmetry of the graph?
   d. What is the domain of the function? What is the range?
   e. Graph the function.

8. a. Without graphing the functions $y = 2x^2 + 3x + 6$ and $y = -3x^2 + 12x + 6$, predict how they differ.
   b. Graph each function to see if your prediction in Part (a) is correct.

9. A model rocket rises vertically so that its height $h$ above the ground (in feet) is given by $h = -16t^2 + 300t$, with time $t$ measured in seconds.
   a. In how many seconds after the rocket is launched will it reach its maximum height?
   b. What is the maximum height that the rocket will reach before it begins its descent?

10. Many functions have graphs that are transformations of graphs of simpler functions. For example, the graph of $y = x^2 + 3$ is a vertical shift of $y = x^2$ upward by three units. For Parts (a)–(d), compare the graph of the given function to the graph of $y = x^2$.
    a. $y = x^2 - 2$    b. $y = -x^2$
    c. $y = (x - 3)^2$    d. $y = (x + 5)^2 + 4$

11. Compare the graph of the given function to the graph of $y = x^2$. Let $c$ be a positive real number.
    a. $y = (x - c)^2$    b. $y = (x + c)^2$
    c. $y = x^2 + c$    d. $y = x^2 - c$

9b. $h \approx -16(9.4)^2 + 300(9.4) \approx$ 1,406 feet

10a. It is the graph of $y = x^2$ shifted downward two units.

10b. It is the graph of $y = x^2$ reflected in the $x$-axis.

10c. It is the graph of $y = x^2$ shifted three units to the right.

10d. It is the graph of $y = x^2$ shifted five units to the left and four units up.

11a. It is the graph of $y = x^2$ shifted $c$ units to the right.

11b. It is the graph of $y = x^2$ shifted $c$ units to the left.

11c. It is the graph of $y = x^2$ shifted upward $c$ units.

11d. It is the graph of $y = x^2$ shifted downward $c$ units.

**COMMON ERROR**

**Exercise 6** Some students will use 8 for $a$ and $-2$ for $b$ when finding the vertex of the parabola. Remind them that $a$ is the coefficient of the $x^2$ term and $b$ is the coefficient of the $x$ term in the standard form of a quadratic function regardless of the order of the terms.

**TEACHING TIP**

**Exercises 7 and 8** Encourage students to answer the questions before graphing the function, as one of the goals of this lesson is to be able to predict what the graph of a quadratic function might look like without actually drawing the graph.

**TEACHING TIP**

**Exercise 10** If students have difficulty recognizing the translations of the parent function $y = x^2$, encourage them to graph both $y = x^2$ and the given function on the same set of axes.

**TEACHING TIP**

**Exercise 11** This exercise is designed to help students generalize what they discovered in **Exercise 10**.

8b. Sample graphs:

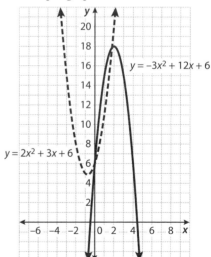

9a. The $t$-coordinate of the vertex of the graph is $-\frac{b}{2a} = -\frac{300}{2(-16)} \approx$ 9.375. So, the maximum height is reached at about 9.4 seconds.

**389**

# LESSON 11.4

**5e** Evaluate

## Lesson Objective

- solve problems that require previously learned concepts and skills.

## Exercise Reference

## Lesson 11.4 R.A.P. Answers

1. vertex
2. axis of symmetry
3. A
4. B
5. $\frac{3}{8}$
6. $\frac{16}{27}$
7. $\frac{9}{32}$
8. $11\frac{2}{3}$
9. $24\frac{1}{2}$
10. $\frac{3}{20}$
11. $\frac{3}{2}$
12. $\frac{2}{11}$
13. $\frac{6}{5}$
14. $\frac{\sqrt{3}}{4}$
15. $2\sqrt{2}$
16. $\frac{\sqrt{5}}{5}$

---

## Lesson 11.4 — R.A.P.

**Fill in the blank.**

1. The minimum point of a parabola that opens upward is called the _____ of the parabola.

2. The line of symmetry of the graph of a parabola is called the _____.

**Choose the correct answer.**

3. Triangle $XYZ$ has vertices $X(4, 3)$, $Y(2, 1)$, and $Z(-1, -3)$. What are the coordinates of the image $X'Y'Z'$ if triangle $XYZ$ is reflected in the $x$-axis?

   A. $X(4, -3)$, $Y(2, -1)$, and $Z(-1, 3)$
   B. $X(-4, -3)$, $Y(-2, -1)$, and $Z(1, 3)$
   C. $X(-4, 3)$, $Y(-2, 1)$, and $Z(1, -3)$
   D. $X(3, 4)$, $Y(1, 2)$, and $Z(-3, -1)$

4. How many lines of symmetry does the rectangle have?

   A. one
   B. two
   C. four
   D. none

**Multiply or divide. Write your answer in simplest form.**

5. $\frac{2}{3} \times \frac{9}{14} \times \frac{7}{8}$
6. $\frac{2}{9} \div \frac{3}{8}$
7. $\frac{3}{8} \times \frac{5}{12} \div \frac{5}{9}$
8. $\left(2\frac{1}{2}\right)\left(4\frac{2}{3}\right)$
9. $4 \times 6\frac{1}{8}$
10. $\frac{3}{5} \div 4$

**For Exercises 11–13, use the diagram to the left.**

11. What is the ratio of the number of blue marbles to the number of red marbles?

12. What is the ratio of the number of red marbles to the total number of marbles?

13. What is the ratio of the number of yellow marbles to the number of marbles that are not yellow?

**Simplify the radical.**

14. $\sqrt{\frac{3}{16}}$
15. $\sqrt{8}$
16. $\sqrt{\frac{1}{5}}$

**Evaluate the expression for the given value of the variable.**

**17.** $3y - 5, y = 5$

**18.** $5(6 - b), b = 7$

**19.** $9c + c^2 - 25, c = 4$

**20.** $8x - 4(x + 1)^2, x = -2$

**21.** $\dfrac{51 - t}{t + 3}, t = 6$

**22.** $\dfrac{44 + 2v}{2^2 + 2v}, v = 3$

**Solve.**

**23.** $\dfrac{t + 2}{2} = \dfrac{9}{6}$

**24.** $\dfrac{7}{5} = \dfrac{3n - 4}{n}$

**25.** $\dfrac{1.6}{7.2} = \dfrac{0.6}{d}$

**For Exercises 26–27, consider the following system of equations.**

$$6x - 2y = -2$$
$$y - 3x = 1$$

**26.** Is (1, 4) a solution of the system? Explain.

**27.** Is it the only solution? Explain.

**For Exercises 28–29, use the figure below**

**28.** Does the figure have line symmetry? If so, how many lines of symmetry does it have? If not, explain why not.

**29.** Does the figure have rotational symmetry? If so, find the angle of rotation. If not, explain why not.

**Simplify.**

**30.** $(3m^4)^3$

**31.** $(2x^3)(6x^5)$

**32.** $\left|\dfrac{12g^8}{3h^2}\right|^2$

**33.** The data below show the amount of time in minutes, in the last 10 days, that a musician spent practicing his trombone.

55, 45, 30, 20, 60, 55, 80, 60, 50, 15

**a.** What is the median of the data?

**b.** Identify the lower and upper extremes.

**c.** Identify the lower and upper quartiles.

**17.** 10

**18.** $-5$

**19.** 27

**20.** $-20$

**21.** 5

**22.** 5

**23.** 1

**24.** 2.5

**25.** 2.7

**26.** Yes, it satisfies both equations.

**27.** No, the system of equations is dependent

**28.** Yes, there are six lines of symmetry.

**29.** Yes, the least angle of rotation is 60°.

**30.** $27m^{12}$

**31.** $12x^8$

**32.** $\dfrac{16g^{16}}{h^4}$

**33a.** 52.5 minutes

**33b.** lower extreme: 15 minutes; upper extreme: 80 minutes

**33c.** lower quartile: 30 minutes; upper quartile: 60 minutes

# LESSON 11.5

## Lesson Objectives

- add and subtract polynomials.
- multiply a polynomial by a monomial.
- multiply two binomials.

## Vocabulary

- binomial
- polynomial
- trinomial

## Description

This lesson focuses on the skills needed to add, subtract, and multiply polynomials. The number of days spent on this lesson depends on the skill level of the students in the class. If students recall these skills from previous courses, use this as a one-day review and move on. If students struggle, you may want to consider spending two days teaching these skills. If that is the case, spend one day on adding, subtracting, and multiplying a polynomial by a monomial. Spend the second day on multiplying polynomials.

## ADDITIONAL EXAMPLE ❶

Add.

$(3t^2 - t + 5) + (6t^2 - 1)$
$9t^2 - t + 4$

## ADDITIONAL EXAMPLE ❷

Subtract.

$(x^2 + 6x + 7) - (x^2 - 2x + 7)$
$8x$

---

| Lesson 11.5 | **Polynomial Arithmetic** |

In Chapter 10, you worked with monomials, expressions that are the product of a coefficient and one or more variables raised to non-negative integer powers. In this lesson you will add, subtract, and multiply algebraic expressions that are monomials or sums of monomials.

A **polynomial** can be defined as a monomial or a sum of monomials. If a polynomial has two terms, such as $7a + 6$, it is called a **binomial**. If it has three terms, such as $5x^2 - 3y + 8$, it is called a **trinomial**.

**Recall**

If the variable parts of two terms are exactly the same, the terms are called *like terms*.

### ADDING AND SUBTRACTING POLYNOMIALS

To add and subtract two polynomial expressions, add or subtract the coefficients of the like terms.

Add.

$(2x^2 + 7x - 5) + (6x^2 - 4x + 1)$

**Solution:**

Group like terms.　　$(2x^2 + 7x - 5) + (6x^2 - 4x + 1) = (2x^2 + 6x^2) + [7x + (-4x)] + (-5 + 1)$

Combine like terms.　　　　　　　　　　　　　$= 8x^2 + 3x - 4$

Subtract.

$(3x^2 - 8x - 7) - (x^2 - 3x + 2)$

**Solution:**

Add the opposite. $(3x^2 - 8x - 7) - (x^2 - 3x + 2) = (3x^2 - 8x - 7) + (-x^2 + 3x - 2)$

Group like terms.　　　　　　　　　　$= [3x^2 + (-x^2)] + (-8x + 3x) + [(-7) + (-2)]$

Combine like terms.　　　　　　　　$= 2x^2 - 5x - 9$

## MULTIPLYING A POLYNOMIAL BY A MONOMIAL

To multiply a polynomial by a monomial, you can use the Distributive Property and either a horizontal or vertical format.

 **3**

Multiply.                    $2y(3y^3 + 4y - 5)$

**Solution:**

**Horizontal format:**

Distributive Property  $2y(3y^3 + 4y - 5) = 2y(3y^3) + 2y(4y) + 2y(-5)$

Multiply.                                $= 6y^4 + 8y^2 - 10y$

**Vertical format:**

$$3y^3 + 4y - 5$$

Distributive Property  $\times \qquad\qquad 2y$

Multiply.                    $6y^4 + 8y^2 - 10y$

## MULTIPLYING TWO BINOMIALS

To multiply a binomial by a binomial, use the Distributive Property twice and make sure that each term of one binomial is multiplied by each term of the other binomial. Either a horizontal or a vertical format can be used.

 **4**

Multiply.                    $(x + 2)(x - 5)$

**Solution:**

**Horizontal format:**

Distributive Property     $(x + 2)(x - 5) = x(x - 5) + 2(x - 5)$

Distributive Property                    $= x^2 - 5x + 2x - 10$

Combine like terms.                      $= x^2 - 3x - 10$

**Vertical format:**

$$x - 5$$
$$\times \quad x + 2$$

Multiply by 2.            $2x - 10$

Multiply by $x$.          $x^2 - 5x$

Combine like terms.       $x^2 - 3x - 10$

**ADDITIONAL EXAMPLE** **3**

Multiply.

$5n(2n^4 - 3n^2 + 1)$
$10n^5 - 15n^3 + 5n$

**ADDITIONAL EXAMPLE** **4**

Multiply.

$(y - 7)(y - 3)$
$y^2 - 10y + 21$

**ADDITIONAL EXAMPLE** 5

A parallelogram has a base of $(n + 1)$ cm and a height of $(2n - 3)$ cm. Write an expression to represent the area of the parallelogram.

$2n^2 - n - 3$

---

**TEACHING TIP**

Many students will have learned to use the F.O.I.L. pattern to multiply binomials in previous courses. The acronym F.O.I.L. provides students with a way of making sure that each term in one binomial is multiplied by each term of the other binomial.

Continue to remind students that this pattern is a way of making sure that the Distributive Property is used twice correctly.

---

**ADDITIONAL EXAMPLE** 6

Multiply.

$(3x + 5)(4x - 5)$

$12x^2 + 5x - 25$

---

**E X A M P L E** 5

Write an expression in the form of a trinomial that represents the volume of this rectangular solid.

**Solution:**

| Formula for the volume of a rectangular solid | $V = lwh$ |
|---|---|
| Substitution | $= x(x + 2)(x + 5)$ |
| Distributive Property | $= x[x(x + 5) + 2(x + 5)]$ |
| Distributive Property | $= x[(x \cdot x) + x(5) + 2(x) + 2(5)]$ |
| Multiply. | $= x(x^2 + 5x + 2x + 10)$ |
| Combine like terms. | $= x(x^2 + 7x + 10)$ |
| Distributive Property | $= x^3 + 7x^2 + 10x$ |

To multiply binomials mentally, make sure that each term of one binomial is multiplied by each term of the other binomial. It may be helpful to notice the F.O.I.L. pattern where the **f**irst terms of the two binomials are multiplied, then the **o**uter terms, then the **i**nner terms, and finally the **l**ast terms.

**E X A M P L E** 6

Multiply.

$(2x - 5)(3x + 7)$

**Solution:**

| Distributive Property | $(2x - 5)(3x + 7) = 2x(3x + 7) - 5(3x + 7)$ |
|---|---|
| Distributive Property | $= 2x(3x) + 2x(7) - 5(3x) - 5(7)$ |
| Combine like terms. | $= 6x^2 + 14x - 15x - 35$ |

$\qquad\qquad\qquad\uparrow\qquad\quad\uparrow\qquad\quad\uparrow\qquad\quad\uparrow$
$\qquad$ product of $\quad$ product of $\quad$ product of $\quad$ product of
$\qquad$ the first terms $\quad$ the outer terms $\quad$ the inner terms $\quad$ the last terms

| Combine like terms. | $= 6x^2 - x - 35$ |
|---|---|

## USING AREA MODELS TO MULTIPLY BINOMIALS

You can use area models to multiply two binomials. For example, the area model below can be used to find $(x + 4)(x + 8)$.

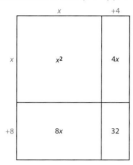

To find the area of the model, find the sum of the smaller areas.

$$(x + 4)(x + 8) = x^2 + 8x + 4x + 32$$
$$= x^2 + 12x + 32$$

So, $(x + 4)(x + 8) = x^2 + 12x + 32$.

## Practice for Lesson 11.5

**Find the sum or difference.**

1. $(x^3 + 2x - 10) + (x^3 - x^2 + 4)$
2. $(2x - 3y - 1) + (4x - y + 9)$
3. $(2a + 4b - 4c) - (5a + 2b - c)$
4. $(2xy - 3y^2 - 3x) - (5y^2 + 2x - 4xy)$
5. $(x^2 - 10) + (x^2 - 3x + 7) - (3x^2 + x - 8)$
6. $(2a^2 - 5ab - b^2) - (4a^2 + ab + 5b^2) - (ab + a^2)$

**Find the product.**

7. $5(p^2 - 4p - 2)$
8. $3y(2y^2 - y + 1)$
9. $(2t + 6)(3t + 5)$
10. $(6 - 2w)(w + 7)$
11. $(2x + 3y)(2x - y)$
12. $(2m^2 - 5n)(m^2 - 3n)$
13. $2(3h - 2)(4h + 7)$
14. $4(a + 4b)(a - 3b)$

POLYNOMIAL ARITHMETIC    **Lesson 11.5**    **395**

### LESSON 11.5

## Practice for Lesson 11.5 Answers

1. $2x^3 - x^2 + 2x - 6$
2. $6x - 4y + 8$
3. $-3a + 2b - 3c$
4. $6xy - 8y^2 - 5x$
5. $-x^2 - 4x + 5$
6. $-3a^2 - 7ab - 6b^2$
7. $5p^2 - 20p - 10$
8. $6y^3 - 3y^2 + 3y$
9. $6t^2 + 28t + 30$
10. $2w^2 - 8w + 42$
11. $4x^2 + 4xy - 3y^2$
12. $2m^4 - 11m^2n + 15n^2$
13. $24h^2 + 26h - 28$
14. $4a^2 + 4ab - 48b^2$

**15.** Sample answer: $x^3 + x^2 - 7x + 3$ and $2x^3 + x^2 + 2x$

**16.** Sample answer: $y^2 + 2y - 4$ and $6y^2 + 9y - 2$

**17a.** $2(6x + 1) + 2(3x - 1) = 18x$

**17b.** $(6x + 1)(3x - 1) = 18x^2 - 3x - 1$

**18a.** Sample answer:

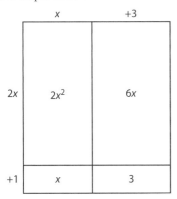

**18b.** $2x^2 + 6x + x + 3 = 2x^2 + 7x + 3$

**18c.** $(2x + 1)(x + 3) = 2x^2 + 7x + 3$

**19a.** $x^2 + 10x + 25$

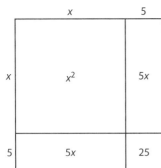

**19b.** $y^2 + 16y + 64$

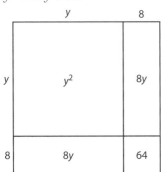

---

**15.** Write two polynomials whose sum is $3x^3 + 2x^2 - 5x + 3$.

**16.** Write two polynomials whose difference is $-5y^2 - 7y - 2$.

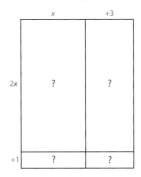

**17 a.** Write an expression to represent the perimeter of the rectangle to the left.

**b.** Write an expression to represent the area of the rectangle.

**18.** The area model shown in the figure below can be used to show the product of $(2x + 1)$ and $(x + 3)$.

**a.** Complete the model by replacing each question mark with the area of the indicated rectangle.

**b.** Use your model from Part (a) to find a polynomial expression for $(2x + 1)(x + 3)$.

**c.** Verify your results algebraically.

**19.** You can also use an area model to help you find the square of a binomial. Draw an area model for each expression. Find the total sum of the areas of the rectangles and write your sum as a trinomial.

**a.** $(x + 5)^2$

**b.** $(y + 8)^2$

**c.** Look carefully at your answers to Parts (a) and (b). Use your observations to fill in the blanks in the following:

$(a + b)^2 = $ _____

The square of $a + b$ is the square of _____ plus twice the product of _____ plus the square of _____.

**d.** Find $(x - 7)^2$. Use an area model if needed.

**e.** What number would you add to the expression below to make it a perfect square trinomial? Use an area model if needed.

$$x^2 + 12x + \blacksquare$$

**19c.** $a^2 + 2ab + b^2$; $a$; $a$ and $b$; $b$

**19d.** $x^2 - 14x + 49$

**19e.** 36

**20.** If you cut the corners out of a rectangular piece of cardboard and then fold up the flaps, you can make a box.

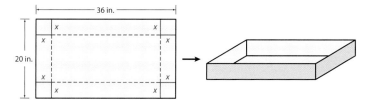

    **a.** Once the cardboard is folded, what are the length, width, and height of the box in terms of $x$?

    **b.** What is the volume of the box?

    **c.** Assuming that the box has no lid, what is the outside surface area of the box?

**21.** The owner of a lot that is 40 feet wide by 60 feet long must give up a strip of land from one of the shorter sides of her lot for street improvements. The strip that is to be removed must be of uniform width, but it is not yet known how wide the strip will be. The owner will be paid $15 per square foot for the land.

    **a.** Draw a picture to model this situation. Label the width of the strip $w$.

    **b.** Write an expression for the land area to be taken by the street improvements.

    **c.** Write an expression for the amount of money that the owner will be paid.

    **d.** Write an expression for the land area that the owner will have left.

**22.** Multiply $(x + 1)(2x^2 + x + 4)$.

### TEACHING TIP

**Exercise 20c** Point out that there is more than one way to find the surface area of the box. One way is to find the sum of the areas of the five sides of the box. Another way is to consider the area of the original rectangular piece of cardboard and subtract the areas of the four corners that were removed before folding.

**20a.** $l = (36 - 2x)$ in.; $w = (20 - 2x)$ in.; $h = x$ in.

**20b.** $V = x(20 - 2x)(36 - 2x) = 4x^3 - 112x^2 + 720x$ in.$^3$

**20c.** $SA = (20 - 2x)(36 - 2x) + 2x(20 - 2x) + 2x(36 - 2x) = 720 - 4x^2$ in.$^2$

### COMMON ERROR

**Exercise 22** Some students may try to use the F.O.I.L. pattern to multiply these two expressions. Point out that the F.O.I.L. pattern only works for multiplying binomials. To multiply other polynomials, the Distributive Property must be used.

**21a.** Sample answer:

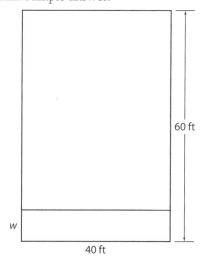

**21b.** $40w$ square feet

**21c.** $15(40w) = 600w$ dollars

**21d.** $40(60 - w) = 2,400 - 40w$

**22.** $2x^3 + 3x^2 + 5x + 4$

**5e** Explore

## Lesson Objectives

- use graphs to solve quadratic equations.
- solve quadratic equations by factoring.
- make connections between the roots of a quadratic equation and the zeros of the graph of the related quadratic function.

## Vocabulary

- quadratic equation
- roots
- Zero Product Property
- zeros

## Materials List

## Description

This lesson may require more than one day, depending on the students' backgrounds in factoring. If you choose to make this a two-day lesson, have students work through the first two sections of the Investigation on Day 1. Then on Day 2 have them work through the third section. If students need more help with factoring, you may want to spend time reviewing the different methods of factoring.

In this lesson, students use their calculators to formalize the connection between the zeros of a function and the factors contained in the factored form of the related quadratic equation. They also use factoring to solve quadratic equations and formalize the Zero Product Property.

*Wrapping Up the Investigation:*

Once students have completed answering all of the questions in the Investigation, debrief by having them share their answers. Then go over the final section of the lesson, the examples, and the steps that are used to solve a quadratic equation by factoring. It might be helpful to go over the steps as you work through an additional example.

In Lesson 11.2, quadratic functions were used to model the shapes of curved suspension bridge cables. You can also use quadratic functions to model paths of rockets and objects thrown into the air. In this lesson, you will use graphs and algebraic methods to solve quadratic equations. In turn, these solutions will help you answer questions about your quadratic models.

A **quadratic equation** is an equation that can be written in the standard form $ax^2 + bx + c = 0$, where $a \neq 0$.

### SOLVING QUADRATIC EQUATIONS BY GRAPHING

One way to solve a quadratic equation is to graph its related function and then find the point or points where the function crosses the $x$-axis.

1. Suppose that an object is dropped from the top of a 400-foot building. The height of the object, in feet, $t$ seconds after it has been dropped can be modeled by the function $h = -16t^2 + 400$. What are the coordinates of the vertex of the graph of this function?

2. Use a graphing calculator and a viewing window of $[-6, 6] \times [0, 500]$ to graph this function. Sketch the graph.

3. Use your graph to approximate the coordinates of the points where $h = 0$.

4. The $t$-coordinates of the points where the function crosses the horizontal axis are the solutions of the quadratic equation $-16t^2 + 400 = 0$. These solutions are also called **roots** of the equation $-16t^2 + 400 = 0$ or **zeros** of the function $y = -16t^2 + 400$. What are the roots of the equation?

5. Interpret a real-world meaning for each of these roots, if possible.

**Recall**

Factoring a quadratic expression means finding two or more expressions whose product is the given quadratic expression. For example, the expression $x^2 - x - 20$ can be written in factored form as $(x - 5)(x + 4)$.

### SOLVING QUADRATIC EQUATIONS BY FACTORING

A quadratic equation can also be solved algebraically. One way to do this is to rewrite the equation so that one side of the equation is equal to 0. Then factor the quadratic expression on the other side, if possible.

6. Suppose the height $h$ in feet of a rocket after $t$ seconds is given by the function $h = -16t^2 + 80t$. Write a related equation in standard form that can be solved to find the times when the height $h$ of the rocket is 64 feet above the ground.

## Lesson 11.6 Investigation Answers

1. The $t$-coordinate of the vertex is $-\frac{b}{2a} = -\frac{0}{-32} = 0$. The $h$-coordinate is 400. So the coordinates of the vertex are $(0, 400)$.

2. Sample graph:

$[-6, 6] \times [0, 500]$

3. Sample answer: $(-5, 0)$ and $(5, 0)$

4. $-5$ and $5$

5. When $t = 5$, the height of the object $= 0$. This means that the ball hits the ground after 5 seconds. There is no real-world meaning for $t = -5$ because the time must be positive.

6. $-16t^2 + 80t = 64$; $-16t^2 + 80t - 64 = 0$

7. Use a graphing calculator to graph $h = -16t^2 + 80t - 64$. Sketch the graph and record your viewing window.

8. At which $t$-values does the graph cross the horizontal axis?

9. Use a graphing calculator to make a table of values for $h = -16t^2 + 80t - 64$. At which $t$-values does $h$ equal 0? How do these values relate to the horizontal intercepts of your graph from Question 8?

10. The factored form of $-16t^2 + 80t - 64 = 0$ is $-16(t - 4)(t - 1) = 0$. Explain how you know that this is a true statement.

11. How do the intercepts in Questions 8 and 9 relate to the factors $(t - 4)$ and $(t - 1)$ in the factored form of the equation in Question 10?

12. What happens when you substitute the $t$-value for each intercept into the factored form of the equation?

13. When is the rocket 64 feet above the ground?

14. Consider the function $y = -0.5(x - 1)(x - 5)$, which is written in factored form.
    a. Use a graphing calculator to graph the function.
    b. Where does the graph cross the $x$-axis?
    c. Substitute the $x$-intercepts into the function. What $y$-values do they yield?
    d. Why do you think that an $x$-intercept is called a zero?

The factored form of a quadratic function, $y = a(x - r_1)(x - r_2)$, is a useful way to write a function because the values $r_1$ and $r_2$ are the $x$-intercepts or zeros of the graph of the function. These values are also the roots of the related quadratic equation $a(x - r_1)(x - r_2) = 0$.

In the factored form of a quadratic function, the only things that change are the numbers. In general, it can be written as:

$$y = \underline{\ ?\ }\,(x - \underline{\ ?\ })(x - \underline{\ ?\ })$$

The challenge is to replace the question marks with the correct values.

15. Write a quadratic function in factored form that has $x$-intercepts at $-4$ and 2. Use your graphing calculator to graph the function, sketch the graph, and record your window.

16. Revise your answer to Question 15 so that the vertex of the parabola is located at the point $(-1, -3.6)$. Explain how you determined your answer.

17. Write your answer from Question 16 in standard form $(y = ax^2 + bx + c)$. Then use your calculator to display the graph of the function in standard form and the graph of the function in factored form at the same time. Compare the graphs.

SOLVING QUADRATIC EQUATIONS    **Lesson 11.6**    **399**

LESSON 11.6

TEACHING TIP

In **Questions 7 and 8,** students may struggle relating the function $h = -16t^2 + 80t - 64$, which is written in terms of the variables $h$ and $t$, to the graph and table of the related function, $y = -16x^2 + 80x - 64$, given in $x$ and $y$ on the calculator. If this is the case, help students make the connections among the variables by asking which variable is the independent variable and which is the dependent variable in each equation.

7.

8. The graph crosses the horizontal axis when $t = 1$ or $t = 4$.

9. When $t = 1$ and $t = 4$, $h = 0$ in the table. These are the same values where the graph crosses the horizontal axis.

10. Sample answer: If you find the product of $-16(t - 4)(t - 1)$, you get $-16t^2 + 80t - 64$.

11. Sample answer: They are the values that are found when the factors are set equal to 0 and the resulting equations are solved.

12. When $t = 4$ is substituted into $-16(t - 4)(t - 1) = 0$, it makes the equation true. When $t = 1$ is substituted into the equation, it also makes the equation true.

13. one second after the rocket was launched and 4 seconds after launch

14a.

14b. The graph crosses the $x$-axis when $x = 1$ and when $x = 5$.

14c. When $x = 1$, $y = 0$. When $x = 5$, $y = 0$.

14d. Sample answer: When the $x$-value of the horizontal intercept is substituted into the function, $y = 0$.

15. Sample answer: This graph shows $2(x + 4)(x - 2)$.

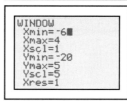

16–17. See answers beginning on page 623.

399

## ADDITIONAL EXAMPLE

Solve $x^2 - 12 = 4x$ for $x$.

$x = 6$ or $x = -2$

## FACTORING QUADRATIC EQUATIONS

When you used factoring to solve quadratic equations, you may have noticed that when an expression is in factored form and one of the factors is equal to 0, then the expression is equal to 0. For example,

$$4(0) = 0 \qquad 5(-3 + 3) = 0 \qquad -4(8 - 8) = 0 \qquad 5(x + 2)(0) = 0$$

This property is called the **Zero Product Property**.

> **Zero Product Property**
>
> If $a$ and $b$ are real numbers and $ab = 0$, then $a$ or $b$ (or both) is equal to 0.

## EXAMPLE ❶

Solve $x^2 - 6x = -5$ for $x$.

**Solution:**

| | |
|---|---|
| Original equation | $x^2 - 6x = -5$ |
| Add 5 to each side. | $x^2 - 6x + 5 = 0$ |
| Factor the trinomial. Use an area model if needed. | $(x - 5)(x - 1) = 0$ |
| Zero Product Property | $x - 5 = 0 \quad \text{or} \quad x - 1 = 0$ |
| Solve each equation for $x$. | $x = 5 \qquad\qquad x = 1$ |

*Check:*

Substitute 5 and 1 for $x$ in the original equation.

$$
\begin{aligned}
x^2 - 6x &= -5 & x^2 - 6x &= -5 \\
5^2 - 6(5) &\overset{?}{=} -5 & 1^2 - 6(1) &\overset{?}{=} -5 \\
25 - 30 &\overset{?}{=} -5 & 1 - 6 &\overset{?}{=} -5 \\
-5 &= -5 \checkmark & -5 &= -5 \checkmark
\end{aligned}
$$

The roots of the equation are 5 and 1.

**E X A M P L E** ❷

Solve $2x^2 - 7x + 3 = 0$ for $x$.

**Solution:**

| | |
|---|---|
| Original equation | $2x^2 - 7x + 3 = 0$ |
| Factor the trinomial.<br>Use an area model if needed. | $\left.\begin{array}{l}\\ \\ \end{array}\right\}$ $(2x - 1)(x - 3) = 0$ |
| Zero Product Property | $2x - 1 = 0 \quad \text{or} \quad x - 3 = 0$ |
| Solve each equation for $x$. | $2x = 1 \qquad\qquad x = 3$ |
| | $x = \dfrac{1}{2}$ |

*Check:*

Substitute $\dfrac{1}{2}$ and 3 for $x$ in the original equation.

$$2x^2 - 7x + 3 = 0 \qquad\qquad 2x^2 - 7x + 3 = 0$$

$$2\left(\tfrac{1}{2}\right)^2 - 7\left(\tfrac{1}{2}\right) + 3 \overset{?}{=} 0 \qquad 2(3)^2 - 7(3) + 3 \overset{?}{=} 0$$

$$\tfrac{1}{2} - \tfrac{7}{2} + 3 \overset{?}{=} 0 \qquad\qquad 18 - 21 + 3 \overset{?}{=} 0$$

$$0 = 0 \checkmark \qquad\qquad\qquad 0 = 0 \checkmark$$

The roots of the equation are $\dfrac{1}{2}$ and 3.

---

To solve a quadratic equation by factoring:

• Write the equation in standard form, $ax^2 + bx + c = 0$.

• Write the equation in factored form if possible.

• Set each factor equal to zero.

• Solve each of these equations.

• Since each of these roots makes at least one factor equal to 0, according to the Zero Product Property, each of these roots is a solution to the equation.

**ADDITIONAL EXAMPLE** ❷

Solve $3x^2 + 7x + 2 = 0$ for $x$.

$x = -\dfrac{1}{3}$ or $x = -2$

**TEACHING TIP**

Students may or may not be familiar with the following method of factoring a trinomial of the form $ax^2 + bx + c$. Point out that when they are factoring a trinomial of the form $ax^2 + bx + c$, they should look for two numbers, $r$ and $s$, such that $r + s = b$ and $rs = ac$.

Then they should factor as shown:

$$ax^2 + bx + c = \frac{(ax + r)(ax + s)}{a}$$

One (or both) of the factors in the numerator will have common factors which will divide out the $a$ in the denominator. This will yield the standard factored form.

# LESSON 11.6

## Practice for Lesson 11.6
## Answers

**1a.** Sample sketch:

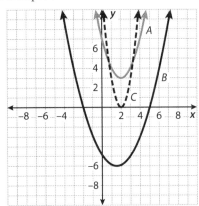

**1b.** No, it is not possible to sketch a parabola with more than two zeros.

**2.** The factors are $x + 2$ and $x + 6$.

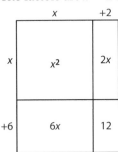

**3.** $t(2t + 5)$
**4.** $(m + 2)(m + 10)$
**5.** $(y - 18)(y + 1)$
**6.** $2(x - 5)(x - 2)$
**7.** $-7, 3$

---

**Practice** for Lesson 11.6

1. **a.** On the same set of axes, sketch three parabolas. Sketch one that has no zeros and label it $A$. Sketch a second one that has two zeros and label it $B$. Sketch a third one that has exactly one zero and label it $C$.
   **b.** Is it possible to sketch a parabola with more than two zeros? If so, make a sketch of it.

2. Complete the area model to the right to show the factors of the trinomial $x^2 + 8x + 12$. What are the factors?

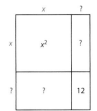

**Factor the polynomial. Use an area model if needed.**

3. $2t^2 + 5t$      4. $m^2 + 12m + 20$
5. $y^2 - 17y - 18$      6. $2x^2 - 14x + 20$

**Solve the equation by graphing. Estimate the solution if necessary.**

7. $x^2 + 4x - 21 = 0$     8. $9k^2 = 144$     9. $4d^2 - 9d = 25$

**Solve the equation by factoring.**

10. $3x^2 - 5x = 0$     11. $2n^2 + 7n + 3 = 0$     12. $y^2 + 16 = 8y$

13. Knowing the roots of a quadratic equation can help you factor the equation. For example, if the roots to the equation $x^2 - 7x + 10 = 0$ are 2 and 5, then $x = 2$ or $x = 5$. So the factors must be $(x - 2)$ and $(x - 5)$. You can check your factors by multiplying $(x - 2)$ by $(x - 5)$. The product $x^2 - 7x + 10$ confirms your factors.
    **a.** The roots to the equation $x^2 - 3x - 4 = 0$ are 4 and $-1$. Use this information to factor $x^2 - 3x - 4$.
    **b.** The roots to the equation $x^2 + 8x + 12 = 0$ are $-6$ and $-2$. Use this information to factor $x^2 + 8x + 12$.

14. A flare is launched from a life raft. The function $h = 192t - 16t^2$, where $h$ represents the height of the flare in feet after $t$ seconds, can be used to model the path of the flare.
    **a.** When is the flare 512 feet above the raft?
    **b.** How long is the flare in the air?

---

8. $\pm 4$
9. $-1.62, 3.87$
10. $0, \dfrac{5}{3}$
11. $-\dfrac{1}{2}, -3$
12. $4$
13a. $(x - 4)(x + 1)$
13b. $(x + 6)(x + 2)$
14a. $192t - 16t^2 = 512$; The flare is 512 feet when $t = 4$ seconds and again when $t = 8$ seconds.
14b. $192t - 16t^2 = 0$; The flare is on the ground when $t = 0$ and again when $t = 12$. It is in the air for 12 seconds.

**15.** A heavy brick is tossed into the air from a height of 48 feet. The function $h = -16t^2 + 32t + 48$ can be used to model the height $h$ of the brick after $t$ seconds. How long will it take for the brick to hit the ground?

**16.** Solve $(x + 2)(x + 8) = 40$ by factoring.

**17.** Some quadratic equations can be solved by taking the square root of each side of the equation. For example,

| | |
|---|---|
| Original equation | $3t^2 = 36$ |
| Divide both sides by 3. | $t^2 = 12$ |
| Take the square root of each side. | $t = \pm\sqrt{12}$ |
| Simplify. | $t = \pm 2\sqrt{3}$ |
| Approximate the roots. | $t \approx 3.5$ and $t \approx -3.5$ |

**a.** Solve $8x^2 - 32 = 0$ for $x$.

**b.** Solve $(x + 4)^2 = 7$ for $x$. Leave your answer in radical form.

**18.** You can also solve quadratic equations that do not factor into perfect squares by using an algebraic method called *completing the square*. In this method, a quadratic expression is made into a perfect square. For example,

| | |
|---|---|
| Original equation | $x^2 + 6x + 4 = 0$ |
| Subtract 4 from both sides. | $x^2 + 6x = -4$ |
| Add 9 to both sides of the equation to make one side of the equation into a perfect square trinomial. | $x^2 + 6x + 9 = -4 + 9$ |
| Simplify. | $x^2 + 6x + 9 = 5$ |
| Factor the trinomial. | $(x + 3)^2 = 5$ |
| Take the square root of both sides. | $x + 3 = \pm\sqrt{5}$ |
| Subtract 3 from both sides. | $x = -3 \pm\sqrt{5}$ |

The solutions in radical form are $-3 + \sqrt{5}$ and $-3 - \sqrt{5}$.

**a.** Solve $x^2 + 10x - 56 = 0$ by completing the square. Leave your answer in radical form, if necessary.

**b.** Solve $y^2 - 4y - 5 = 0$ by completing the square. Leave your answer in radical form, if necessary.

**c.** Solve $x^2 + 4x + 1 = 0$ by completing the square. Leave your answer in radical form, if necessary.

SOLVING QUADRATIC EQUATIONS    **Lesson 11.6**    403

**TEACHING TIP**

**Exercise 15** Point out that there are two solutions (3 and $-1$) to the *equation* $-16t^2 + 32t + 48 = 0$. Ask students why there is only one solution to the *problem*.

**COMMON ERROR**

**Exercise 16** If students try to solve this quadratic equation and get 32 and 38 for roots, remind them that the Zero Product Property cannot be used on this equation as it is written. One side of the equation must first be 0. Also point out the importance of checking solutions in the original equation.

**TEACHING TIP**

**Exercise 18** This exercise is optional. If your curriculum includes solving quadratics by completing the square, be sure to assign this exercise and go over it in class. Point out that the method of completing the square can be used to solve any quadratic equation.

**COMMON ERROR**

**Exercise 18** If students fail to find the number that is needed to complete the square, have them look at the diagram that is used to complete the square. Then have them generalize the method. To find the value that completes the square for the expression $x^2 + bx$, take half the $b$ and square the result.

**15.** 3 seconds

**16.** $x^2 + 10x - 24 = 0$; The roots are 2 and $-12$.

**17a.** $2, -2$

**17b.** $-4 \pm \sqrt{7}$

**18a.** $4, -14$

**18b.** $5, -1$

**18c.** $-2 \pm\sqrt{3}$

## Lesson Objectives

- use the quadratic formula to solve quadratic equations.
- select and defend a method of solving a quadratic equation.

## Vocabulary

- discriminant
- quadratic formula

## Materials List

## Description

As a class, have students read through the first part of the lesson where the quadratic formula is given to students. (Note: the derivation of this formula is given in **Exercise 18**.) Then have them work through **Example 1**. Take a few minutes to discuss the example before having students work in small groups or pairs to complete the Investigation portion of this lesson.

In the Investigation, students explore the usefulness of knowing the value of the discriminant of a quadratic equation in determining the number and types of roots for any quadratic equation.

*Wrapping Up the Investigation:*

Once students have completed answering all of the questions in the Investigation, debrief by having them share their answers. Then go over the final section of the lesson. Work through **Example 2** as a class, taking time to talk about the different methods they have used in solving quadratic equations.

---

## Lesson 11.7    INVESTIGATION: The Quadratic Formula

In Lesson 11.6, you learned how to solve quadratic equations both algebraically and graphically. In this lesson, you will learn to use the quadratic formula to solve quadratic equations.

### USING THE QUADRATIC FORMULA TO SOLVE QUADRATIC EQUATIONS

Not all quadratic equations are easily factored. In fact, only a small percent of all quadratic functions that are used to model real-world situations can be factored easily. The good news is that there is an algebraic method that can be used to find the exact roots of any quadratic equation. This method uses a formula known as the **quadratic formula**.

> **The Quadratic Formula**
>
> If $a$, $b$, and $c$ are real numbers and $a \neq 0$, then the solutions to a quadratic equation written in standard form ($ax^2 + bx + c = 0$) are given by the formula $x = \dfrac{-b \pm \sqrt{b^2 - 4ac}}{2a}$.

Notice that this formula represents two solutions:

$$x = \frac{-b + \sqrt{b^2 - 4ac}}{2a} \quad \text{and} \quad x = \frac{-b - \sqrt{b^2 - 4ac}}{2a}$$

### E X A M P L E ❶

Use the quadratic formula to solve the equation $5x^2 + 11x = -4$. If necessary, round answers to the nearest hundredth.

**Solution:**

Begin by writing the equation in standard form and identifying $a$, $b$, and $c$.

| | |
|---|---|
| Original equation | $5x^2 + 11x = -4$ |
| Add 4 to both sides. | $5x^2 + 11x + 4 = 0$ |
| | $\downarrow \quad\quad \downarrow \quad\quad \downarrow$ |
| | $a = 5 \quad b = 11 \quad c = 4$ |

---

### TEACHING TIP

Take time to look at the two solutions that arise from the quadratic formula. Rewrite each solution as the sum (or difference) of two fractions:

$x = -\dfrac{b}{2a} + \dfrac{\sqrt{b^2 - 4ac}}{2a}$ and

$x = -\dfrac{b}{2a} - \dfrac{\sqrt{b^2 - 4ac}}{2a}$. Then ask students what they notice. They should notice that the first fraction in each solution $\left(-\dfrac{b}{2a}\right)$ is the *x*-coordinate of the vertex. The second fraction in each solution must then be the distance from the *x*-coordinate of the vertex to the *x*-coordinate of each zero.

### COMMON ERROR

**Example 1** Students often forget to write their equations in standard form before applying the quadratic formula. Take time to point out that in this example, the equation $5x^2 + 11x = -4$ was written in standard form before the values of $a$, $b$, and $c$ were determined.

### ADDITIONAL EXAMPLE ❶

Use the quadratic formula to solve the equation $2x^2 + x = 14$. If necessary, round answers to the nearest hundredth. $x \approx -2.91$ or $x \approx 2.41$

Quadratic formula

$$x = \frac{-b \pm \sqrt{b^2 - 4ac}}{2a}$$

Substitute values for $a$, $b$, and $c$.

$$= \frac{-11 \pm \sqrt{11^2 - 4(5)(4)}}{2(5)}$$

Simplify.

$$= \frac{-11 \pm \sqrt{41}}{10}$$

Separate the solutions and evaluate.

$$x = \frac{-11 + \sqrt{41}}{10} \qquad \text{or} \qquad x = \frac{-11 - \sqrt{41}}{10}$$
$$\approx -0.46 \qquad\qquad\qquad \approx -1.74$$

The approximate roots of the equation are $-0.46$ and $-1.74$.

## THE DISCRIMINANT

In the quadratic formula, the expression under the radical sign, $b^2 - 4ac$, is called the **discriminant**. In the following Investigation, you will explore the connections among the value of the discriminant of an equation, the number of roots of the equation, and the graph of the related function.

**1 a.** Use the quadratic formula to solve $2x^2 + 5x - 3 = 0$.
  **b.** How many real roots does the equation have?
  **c.** Use a calculator to graph the related function. How many $x$-intercepts does the graph have?
  **d.** Is the value of the discriminant greater than 0, less than 0, or equal to 0?

**2 a.** Use the quadratic formula to solve $4x^2 + 4x + 1 = 0$.
  **b.** How many real roots does the equation have?
  **c.** Use a calculator to graph the related function. How many $x$-intercepts does the graph have?
  **d.** Is the value of the discriminant greater than 0, less than 0, or equal to 0?

**3 a.** Use the quadratic equation to solve $x^2 + 2x + 5 = 0$.
  **b.** How many real roots does the equation have?
  **c.** Use a calculator to graph the related function. How many $x$-intercepts does the graph have?
  **d.** Is the value of the discriminant greater than 0, less than 0, or equal to 0?

**4.** Summarize what you learned about the value of the discriminant of a quadratic equation, the number of roots of the equation, and the graph of the related function.

**Note**

Recall that the square root of a negative number is not a real number.

## Lesson 11.7 Investigation Answers

**1a.** $\frac{1}{2}$, $-3$

**1b.** two

**1c.** The graph has two $x$-intercepts.

**1d.** greater than 0

**2a.** $-\frac{1}{2}$

**2b.** one

**2c.** The graph has one $x$-intercept.

**2d.** equal to 0

**3a.** no real solutions

**3b.** none

**3c.** none

**3d.** less than 0

**4.** Sample answer: If the discriminant is positive, then the equation has two real roots, and the graph crosses the $x$-axis twice. If the discriminant is 0, then the equation has one real root, and the graph touches the $x$-axis at one point. If the discriminant is negative, the equation has no real roots and the graph does not intersect the $x$-axis.

THE QUADRATIC FORMULA   **Lesson 11.7**   **405**

## ADDITIONAL EXAMPLE ❷

Solve $2x^2 - x - 21 = 0$ by using the quadratic formula and by factoring.
$x = -3$ or $x = 3.5$

**TEACHING TIP**

If students are familiar with the *Completing the Square* method (**Lesson 11.6, Exercise 18**) of solving quadratic equations, talk about adding a fourth row to this table. When discussing the pros and cons of this method, be sure that students understand that this method works for all quadratic equations. Point out that it works best for equations in which the coefficient of the first-degree term is an even number.

Solve the equation $2t^2 - 3t - 5 = 0$ by first using the quadratic formula, and then solve it by factoring.

**Solution:**

• Using the quadratic formula ($a = 2$, $b = -3$, and $c = -5$):

Quadratic formula
$$t = \frac{-b \pm \sqrt{b^2 - 4ac}}{2a}$$

Substitute values for $a$, $b$, and $c$.
$$= \frac{-(-3) \pm \sqrt{(-3)^2 - 4(2)(-5)}}{2(2)}$$

Simplify.
$$= \frac{3 \pm \sqrt{49}}{4}$$

Separate the solutions and simplify.

$$t = \frac{3 + \sqrt{49}}{4} \quad \text{or} \quad t = \frac{3 - \sqrt{49}}{4}$$

$$= \frac{3 + 7}{4} \qquad\qquad = \frac{3 - 7}{4}$$

$$= 2.5 \qquad\qquad\quad = -1$$

The roots of the equation are $-1$ and $2.5$.

• Using factoring:

Original equation $\qquad\qquad\qquad 2t^2 - 3t - 5 = 0$

Factor the trinomial.
Use an area model if needed. $\Big\}$ $\qquad (2t - 5)(t + 1) = 0$

Zero Product Property $\qquad 2t - 5 = 0 \quad$ or $\quad t + 1 = 0$

Solve each equation for $t$. $\qquad\qquad t = 2.5 \qquad\qquad t = -1$

|  | $t$ | $+1$ |
|---|---|---|
| $2t$ | $2t^2$ | $2t$ |
| $-5$ | $-5t$ | $-5$ |

The roots of the equation are $-1$ and $2.5$.

Even though the quadratic formula can be used to solve any quadratic equation, it may not always be the most efficient method. Below are some pros and cons for the different methods you have used to solve a quadratic equation.

| Method | Pros and Cons |
|---|---|
| graphing | This method can be used sometimes, but the solutions may not be exact. Use this method when an approximate solution is good enough. |
| factoring | This method can be used when the factors are easy to find. This method is generally quicker than the others. |
| quadratic formula | This method always works, and it always gives accurate solutions. The drawback is that other methods may be easier in some cases. |

**406** **Chapter 11** QUADRATIC FUNCTIONS

## Practice for Lesson 11.7

Use the quadratic formula to solve the equation. If necessary, round answers to the nearest hundredth.

**1.** $n^2 + 8n + 15 = 0$      **2.** $6x^2 - 5x = 4$

**3.** $4t^2 - 8t + 1 = 0$      **4.** $-3(x^2 + 2x) + 4 = 0$

For the equation, state the value of the discriminant. Then state the number of real roots for the equation.

**5.** $4x^2 - 28x + 49 = 0$      **6.** $x^2 - 3x + 6 = 0$

**7.** $9x^2 - 12x - 1 = 0$      **8.** $4x^2 = 4x + 4$

Use either factoring or the quadratic formula to solve the equation. Round to the nearest tenth if necessary.

**9.** $2t^2 - 12t + 16 = 0$      **10.** $3x^2 + 8x - 3 = 0$

**11.** $3r^2 + 10r + 7 = 0$      **12.** $2x^2 + 5x = 9$

**13.** Without graphing, determine the $x$-intercepts of $y = x^2 - 6x - 16$.

**14.** A stone is thrown from a catapult. The function $h = -16t^2 + 80t$ describes the height $h$ of the stone as a function of time $t$.

  **a.** How high is the stone at 3.5 seconds?

  **b.** Write a related equation in standard form that can be solved to find the times when the stone will be 84 feet above the ground.

  **c.** Using any method you prefer, solve your equation to find the times that the stone is 84 feet above the ground. Round your answer to the nearest tenth, if necessary.

  **d.** When will the stone be 36 feet high?

**15.** The main cable of a suspension bridge can be modeled by the function $h = 0.00234x^2 - 0.75x + 80$, where $h$ represents the height of the cable above the roadway and $x$ measures the horizontal distance across the bridge starting from the left tower.

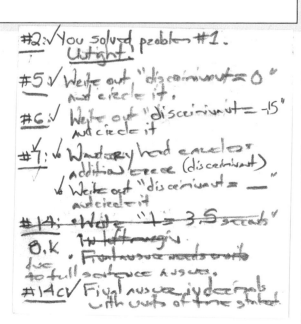

At what positions will the vertical support cables be 50 feet long?

---

## Practice for Lesson 11.7 Answers

1. $-5, -3$
2. $-\dfrac{1}{2}, \dfrac{4}{3}$
3. $0.13, 1.87$
4. $-2.53, 0.53$
5. $0$; 1 real root
6. $-15$, 0 real roots
7. $180$; 2 real roots
8. $80$; 2 real roots
9. $2, 4$
10. $-3, \dfrac{1}{3}$
11. $-1, -\dfrac{7}{3}$
12. $-3.7, 1.2$
13. The $x$-intercepts are $-2$ and $8$.
14a. 84 feet high
14b. $-16t^2 + 80t - 84 = 0$ or $16t^2 - 80t + 84 = 0$
14c. 1.5 seconds and 3.5 seconds
14d. 0.5 seconds and again at 4.5 seconds
15. $0.00234x^2 - 0.75x + 80 = 50$; $0.00234x^2 - 0.75x + 30 = 0$; $x$ is about 47 or 274

---

*(handwritten notes at bottom of page)*

#2: ✓ You solved problem #1. Watch it!

#5 ✓ Write out "discriminant = 0" and circle it.

#6 ✓ Write out "discriminant = -15" and circle it

#7: ✓ Watch... had enclose additional brace (discriminant)
✓ Write out "discriminant = ___" and circle it

#14: Write "t = 3.5 secs" ✓
o.k. • Find answers work to full sentence answers.

#14c ✓ Final answer(s) in decimals with units of time stated.

#14d: Final answer(s) decimals with units of time stated. ✓

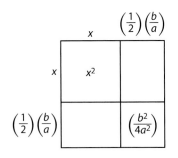

16. The function $d = 0.08s^2 - 2s + 28$ can be used to model the braking distance (in feet) of a certain car traveling at a given speed $s$ (in miles per hour).
    a. What braking distance does this function predict for a speed of 27 miles per hour?
    b. If the vehicle takes 64 feet to brake to a complete stop, what speed does the function predict?

17. The quadratic formula $x = \dfrac{-b \pm \sqrt{b^2 - 4ac}}{2a}$ gives the $x$-intercepts of the points where the graph of the quadratic equation in standard form crosses the $x$-axis. Use this information and the fact that the $x$-coordinate of the vertex is midway between the two zeros to determine the $x$-coordinate of the vertex of the graph. (Hint: Consider the two $x$-intercepts, $x = \dfrac{-b + \sqrt{b^2 - 4ac}}{2a}$ and $x = \dfrac{-b - \sqrt{b^2 - 4ac}}{2a}$.)

18. The quadratic formula can be derived by solving the general form of a quadratic equation. Copy the derivation below and supply the missing reasons.

| | |
|---|---|
| Original equation | $ax^2 + bx + c = 0$ |
| a. _____ | $ax^2 + bx = -c$ |
| b. _____ | $\dfrac{ax^2}{a} + \dfrac{bx}{a} = -\dfrac{c}{a}$ |
| Simplify. | $x^2 + \dfrac{b}{a}x = -\dfrac{c}{a}$ |
| Complete the square. | $x^2 + \dfrac{b}{a}x + \dfrac{b^2}{4a^2} = \dfrac{b^2}{4a^2} - \dfrac{c}{a}$ |
| Factor the left side, and simplify the right side. | $\left(x + \dfrac{b}{2a}\right)^2 = \dfrac{b^2 - 4ac}{4a^2}$ |
| c. _____ | $x + \dfrac{b}{2a} = \pm\sqrt{\dfrac{b^2 - 4ac}{4a^2}}$ |
| d. _____ | $x = -\dfrac{b}{2a} \pm \sqrt{\dfrac{b^2 - 4ac}{4a^2}}$ |
| Simplify. | $x = -\dfrac{b}{2a} \pm \dfrac{\sqrt{b^2 - 4ac}}{2a}$ |
| Combine the fractions. | $x = \dfrac{-b \pm \sqrt{b^2 - 4ac}}{2a}$ |

(The coefficient of $x^2$ is 1. So you can complete the square on the left side of the equation by adding the square of $\frac{1}{2} \cdot \frac{b}{a}$.)

**16a.** about 32.3 feet
**16b.** about 37.1 miles per hour
**17.** The $x$-intercept of the vertex is midway between the two $x$-intercepts. So, it is the average of the two $x$-intercepts.

$$x = \dfrac{\dfrac{-b + \sqrt{b^2 - 4ac}}{2a} + \dfrac{-b - \sqrt{b^2 - 4ac}}{2a}}{2}$$

$$= \dfrac{\dfrac{-b + \sqrt{b^2 - 4ac} + -b - \sqrt{b^2 - 4ac}}{2a}}{2}$$

$$= \dfrac{-2b}{4a}$$

$$= -\dfrac{b}{2a}$$

18. Sample answers:
    a. Subtract $c$ from each side.
    b. Divide each side by $a$.
    c. Take the square root of each side.
    d. Subtract $\dfrac{b}{2a}$ from each side.

In previous lessons, you have used quadratic functions to model such things as suspension bridge cables and the motion of an object thrown into the air. In this lesson, you will examine these and other applications of quadratic functions.

If an object is dropped downward and has little air resistance, it will continue to speed up due to the force of gravity. Consider the velocity of an object to be positive when it is moving upward, negative when it is moving downward, and zero when it is not moving. Problems of this type are generally referred to as *free-fall* problems, in which the relationship between the height of an object and time is modeled with a quadratic function. In general, the height of an object $h$ is given by

acceleration due to gravity

$$h = -\frac{1}{2}gt^2 + v_0t + h_0 \quad \text{initial height}$$

initial velocity

### Note

The acceleration $g$ due to the force of gravity is a constant value that is equal to about 32 ft/s$^2$ in U.S. Customary units or about 9.8 m/s$^2$ in SI units.

Consider these three functions.

$$h = -\frac{1}{2}(32)t^2 + 45t + 12$$

$$h = -\frac{1}{2}(9.8)t^2 - 2t + 112$$

$$h = -\frac{1}{2}(32)t^2 + 450$$

- In the first function, an object whose height is given in feet is thrown or shot upward with an initial velocity of 45 ft/s from a height of 12 feet above the ground.
- In the second, the object, whose height is given in meters, is thrown downward with a velocity of $-2$ m/s from a height of 112 meters.
- In the third function, the object is simply dropped from a height of 450 feet.

## Lesson Objective

- use a quadratic function to model a real-world situation.

## Vocabulary

## Description

This lesson focuses on using quadratic models to describe real-world situations. Free-fall motion is described and a function that can be used to express the height of an object in terms of time is explained.

### TEACHING TIP

Have students carefully read the **Note** on this page. Be sure to point out that the value of the constant $g$ tells you the units to use in free-fall problems. It is important for students to understand that the functions that are used to model free-fall motion describe the height of the object vs time, and that the graph of the function does not show the path of the object. In free-fall situations, the actual motion of the object is one-dimensional because the object only moves up and down.

# LESSON 11.8

## TEACHING TIP

Have students work through **Example 1** on their own, using the quadratic formula to confirm that the solutions are correct. Also take time to interpret the two zeros in **Part (b)**.

## ADDITIONAL EXAMPLE

A juggler throws a ball into the air. Its height $h$ in feet above the ground at time $t$ is given by $h = -16t^2 + 20t + 4$. At what time will the ball hit the ground?

It hits the ground about 1.4 seconds after it was thrown upward.

A model rocket rises vertically so that its height in feet above the ground is given by $h = 300t - 16t^2$.

 **a.** At what time will the rocket return to the ground?

 **b.** At what time will the rocket be at a height of 1,000 feet?

 **c.** At what time will the rocket be at a height of 2,000 feet?

**Solution:**

 **a.** At ground level, $h = 0$. So, $300t - 16t^2 = 0$.

This equation can be solved by factoring.

| | |
|---|---|
| Original equation | $300t - 16t^2 = 0$ |
| Factor. | $4t(75 - 4t) = 0$ |
| Zero Product Property | $4t = 0$   or   $75 - 4t = 0$ |
| Solve each equation for $t$. | $t = 0$    $-4t = -75$ |
| | $t = 18.75$ |

So, the rocket is on the ground at 0 seconds when it is launched. It returns to the ground after 18.75 seconds.

 **b.** To find when the rocket is at a height of 1,000 feet, solve the equation $300t - 16t^2 = 1{,}000$ or $16t^2 - 300t + 1{,}000 = 0$. Using the quadratic formula, the solutions are $t \approx 4.34$ seconds and $t \approx 14.41$ seconds.

 **c.** To find when the rocket is at a height of 2,000 feet, solve the equation $300t - 16t^2 = 2{,}000$ or $16t^2 - 300t + 2{,}000 = 0$. But the discriminant of this equation is negative.

$$b^2 - 4ac = (-300)^2 - 4(16)(2{,}000)$$
$$= -38{,}000$$

This indicates that there are no real solutions to the equation. The rocket will never reach a height of 2,000 feet.

**410**  **Chapter 11**  QUADRATIC FUNCTIONS

A model rocket blasts off from the ground and peaks in 3 seconds at 144 feet.

    **a.** When will the rocket hit the ground?

    **b.** Write a function for the height $h$ feet of the rocket at time $t$ seconds.

    **c.** How high will the rocket be 2 seconds after launch?

    **d.** When will the rocket again be at the same height as in Part (c)? Explain.

**Solution:**

    **a.** Since it takes 3 seconds for the rocket to reach its peak, it will be on the ground again 3 seconds after it peaks. So, the rocket will hit the ground 6 seconds after it blasts off.

    **b.** The roots of the function are 0 and 6, so, $h = a(t - 0)(t - 6)$. It is possible to find the value of $a$ since the ordered pair (3, 144), makes the equation true.

$$h = a(t - 0)(t - 6)$$
$$144 = a(3 - 0)(3 - 6)$$
$$144 = -9a$$
$$-16 = a$$

Therefore, the function is $h = -16(t - 0)(t - 6)$ or $h = -16t^2 + 96t$.

    **c.** $h = -16t^2 + 96t$
$$= -16(2)^2 + 96(2)$$
$$= 128$$

So, 2 seconds after the rocket is launched, it will be 128 feet above the ground.

    **d.** Substitute 128 for $h$ in $h = -16t^2 + 96t$, and solve for $t$.

$$h = -16t^2 + 96t$$
$$128 = -16t^2 + 96t$$
$$0 = -16t^2 + 96t - 128$$
$$0 = -16(t^2 - 6t + 8)$$
$$0 = -16(t - 2)(t - 4)$$
$$t - 2 = 0 \quad \text{or} \quad t - 4 = 0$$
$$t = 2 \qquad\qquad t = 4$$

The rocket will be 128 feet above the ground again at 4 seconds after launch.

**TEACHING TIP**

After students have worked through **Example 2**, take time to reinforce how to find the equation of a parabola when the two zeros and a point are known. If students questioned the equation $y = ax(x - d)$ that was introduced in **Lesson 11.2**, this is a good time to discuss where it comes from.

## ADDITIONAL EXAMPLE

A parabola crosses the $x$-axis at the origin and has a minimum at $(4, -12)$.

    **a.** What is the other $x$-intercept?

    **b.** Write an equation of the parabola.

    **a.** $(8, 0)$

    **b.** $y = \dfrac{3}{4}x(x - 8)$ or $y = \dfrac{3}{4}x^2 - 6x$

# LESSON 11.8

**Practice** for Lesson 11.8

For Exercises 1–3, describe the vertical motion of the object that is modeled by the given function.

1. $h = -16t^2 + 650$
2. $h = -4.9t^2 + 55t + 1$
3. $h = -16t^2 - 2t + 800$
4. Write an equation for the parabola that passes through the point (2, 7) and has a vertex at the origin.
5. Write an equation for the parabola that crosses the $x$-axis at the points (0, 0) and (20, 0) and passes through the point (−2, 22).
6. A golf ball hit by a professional player from an elevated tee follows a path given by the equation $h = -0.003x^2 + 0.9x + 2.5$ until it hits the fairway. For this function, $x$ represents the horizontal distance of the ball from the tee (in yards) and $h$ is the height of the ball (in yards) measured from the level of the flat fairway.
   a. What is the height of the tee?
   b. What is the height of the ball above the fairway after it has traveled 100 yards horizontally from the tee?
   c. How far does the ball travel horizontally before it hits the fairway?
7. The Golden Gate Bridge in San Francisco is a suspension bridge in which the two towers are about 1,280 meters apart. The two main suspension cables are attached to the tops of the towers 213 meters above the mean high-water level in the bay. The lowest point of each cable is 67 meters above the water.

As you saw in the Activity in Lesson 11.2, the main cables of a suspension bridge hang in the shape of a parabola. Find an equation for the shape of one of the cables of the Golden Gate Bridge. (Assume that the origin is placed at the lowest point of the cable, as shown in the figure.)

**TEACHING TIP**

**Exercises 1–3** If students question the units they should use in their descriptions, have them look at the coefficient of the $t^2$ term. If the coefficient is $-\frac{1}{2}(32)$ or −16, they know that they are working in the Customary system because the acceleration of gravity in that system is 32 ft/s². If the coefficient is $-\frac{1}{2}(9.8)$ or −4.9, they know that they are working in the metric system because the acceleration of gravity in that system is 9.8 m/s².

**TEACHING TIP**

If students have difficulty getting started with **Exercises 4 and 5**, suggest that they revisit **Example 2** to see how to find the equation of a parabola when both zeros and a third point on the parabola is known.

**TEACHING TIP**

**Exercise 6** Point out to students that the equation in this problem describes the actual path (height vs distance) of an object. Previous problems that involved free fall have described one-dimensional up-and-down motion (height vs time).

## Practice for Lesson 11.8 Answers

1. Sample answer: An object is dropped from the height of 650 feet.
2. Sample answer: An object is projected upward into the air from a location that is 1 meter above the ground. The initial velocity is 55 m/s.
3. Sample answer: An object is thrown downward from a location that is 800 feet above the ground. The initial velocity is −2 feet per second.
4. Since the vertex is at the origin, the function is of the form $y = ax^2$. Using the point (2, 7), $a = 1.75$. So, an equation for the parabola is $y = 1.75x^2$.

5. The zeros of the function are 0 and 20. So, $y = a(x − 0)(x − 20)$. It is possible to find the value of $a$ since the ordered pair (−2, 22), makes the equation true. Because $a = 0.5$, the function is $y = 0.5(x − 0)(x − 20)$ or $y = 0.5x^2 − 10x$.

6a. 2.5 yards
6b. When $x = 100$, $h = 62.5$ yards.

6c. The ball hits the fairway when $h = 0$. Solving $-0.003x^2 + 0.9x + 2.5 = 0$ for $x$ yields two solutions: $x \approx -2.75$ and $x \approx 302.8$. The positive result is the only root that makes sense in this context. So, the ball travels about 303 yards horizontally.

7. If the origin is placed at the vertex of the parabola, the equation is of the form $y = ax^2$. One end of the cable is at the point (640, 146). So, $a(640)^2 = 146$, and $a = 0.0003564$. Hence, a function that models one of the cables is $y = 0.0003564x^2$.

8. The freshman class is deciding whether or not to raise the price of tickets to the spring dance. The function $p = 75 + 100d - 20d^2$ can be used to estimate the total profit $p$ if the ticket price is raised $d$ dollars.
   a. What profit is expected if the ticket price is not raised?
   b. What is the least amount the ticket price can be raised if they want to make a profit of $155?

9. A ball is shot straight up from a cannon. After 6 seconds, its maximum height is 576 feet.
   a. Write a function that can be used to model the height of the ball.
   b. Use your function to find the height of the ball 4 seconds after launch.
   c. At what time will the ball be 320 feet above the ground?

10. The figure below shows a computer circuit board that is 10 cm by 8 cm. The circuit components are to be printed onto a rectangular area in the interior of the board, leaving a border of uniform width. If the interior must have an area of 72 cm², determine the width of the border.

11. A football is kicked into the air. It hits the ground 60 yards away from where it was kicked. At its highest point, the ball is 7 yards above the ground. Assume the relationship between height and distance is quadratic.
    a. Sketch a graph of the relationship between height and distance.
    b. Label the vertex with its coordinates. What does this point mean in this situation?
    c. Write a function that can be used to model the relationship between the height of the ball and the distance downfield.
    d. Assume that the ball is being kicked for a 51-yard field goal where the height of the crossbar is 10 feet. Will the ball make it through the goal posts? Explain.

# LESSON 11.8

8a. Letting $d = 0$, the profit is $75.

8b. $155 = 75 + 100d - 20d^2$; $d = 1$ or $d = 4$. The least amount is $d = 1$. Profit will be above $155 for $d$ between 1 and 4, and below $155 again for $d > 4$.

9a. $h = -16(t)(t - 12)$ or $h = -16t^2 + 192t$

9b. 512 feet

9c. at 2 and 10 seconds

10. Using $(10 - 2w)(8 - 2w) = 72$ and solving for $w$, the border width is about 0.23 cm.

11a.

11b. Vertex: (30, 7); At 30 yards downfield from where the ball is kicked, the ball is 7 yards above the playing field.

11c. $h = a(d - 0)(d - 60)$; Using the point (30, 7), $a = -\frac{7}{900}$. So the function is $h = -\frac{7}{900}d^2 + \frac{7}{15}d$ or $h = -\frac{7}{900}(d^2 - 60d)$.

11d. Yes. At a distance of 51 yards downfield, it will be 3.57 yards, or 10.71 feet, off the ground.

**12.** The roots of the equation are 0 and 630.
So, $y = a(x - 0)(x - 630)$. It is possible to find the value of $a$ since the ordered pair (315, 630) makes the equation true. Because $a = -0.00635$, the equation is $y = -0.00635(x - 0)(x - 630)$ or $y = -0.00635x^2 + 4.0005x$.

**13a.**

**[0, 100] × [0, 500]**

**12.** The Gateway Arch in St. Louis, Missouri, is 630 feet high and 630 feet wide at its outermost extremes. Even though its shape is actually a curve called a *catenary*, it can be approximated by a parabola.

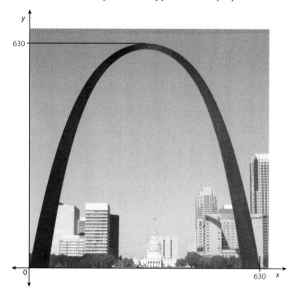

Find an equation for a parabola that approximates the outside edge of the arch if the origin of its graph is located on the ground at the leftmost edge of the arch.

**13.** The table below shows the distances required for a car to stop when braking at different speeds.

| Speed (mph) | Stopping Distance (ft) |
|---|---|
| 20 | 42 |
| 30 | 73.5 |
| 40 | 116 |
| 50 | 173 |
| 60 | 248 |
| 70 | 343 |
| 80 | 464 |

**a.** Use a graphing calculator to make a scatter plot of the data.

**b.** Use quadratic regression on the data to find a quadratic function that best fits the data. Write the regression equation expressing stopping distance $d$ as a function of speed $s$.

**c.** Use the model found in Part (b) to predict the stopping distance for a speed of 75 miles per hour.

**14.** Consider the following system of equations:

$$x + 4y = 14$$
$$x^2 - y = 1$$

**a.** What kind of equation is $x + 4y = 14$?

**b.** What kind of equation is $x^2 - y = 1$?

**c.** Solve the system of equations.

**d.** Suppose that one equation of a system is linear and the other is quadratic. Sketch three graphical situations, one that shows no real solutions, one that shows one real solution, and one that shows two real solutions to the system.

# LESSON 11.8

**13b.** $d = 0.0888s^2 - 1.96s + 49.1$

**13c.** $d = 0.0888(75)^2 - 1.96(75) + 49.1 \approx 402$ mph

**14a.** linear

**14b.** quadratic

**14c.** $(2, 3), \left(-\dfrac{9}{4}, 4\dfrac{1}{16}\right)$

**14d.** Sample answers:

No real solutions:

One real solution:

Two real solutions:

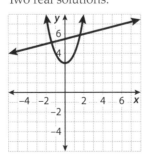

415

**Materials List**

**Description**

In this project students use what they know about quadratic functions to model a free-fall situation. This project can be done in small groups or by individual students.

**Sample Answers**

This sample answer is based on the following assumptions:

- The height of the building is 30 feet.
- The stagecoach is 10 feet long and 9 feet high.
- The stagecoach will maintain a constant speed of 20 mph at least 50 feet before and during the fall.

1. The hero's initial height is 30 feet and the acceleration due to gravity is 32 ft/s². Substitute these values into the function that represents free-fall motion.

$$h = -\frac{1}{2}gt^2 + h_0$$

$$h = -\frac{1}{2}(32)t^2 + 30$$

$$h = -16t^2 + 30$$

2. The height of the stagecoach roof is 9 feet. So, solve the equation $9 = -16t^2 + 30$. The hero will reach the height of the stagecoach in 1.146 seconds.

3. about 29.3 feet per second

4. Since the hero will be 9 feet above the ground in 1.146 seconds, the mark should be set so that it will take the stagecoach 1.146 seconds to get to the drop point.

$$d = (1.146 \text{ s})(29.3 \text{ ft/sec})$$
$$= 33.58 \text{ feet}$$

So, the mark should be set at 33.58 feet before the drop point.

---

## Designing a Hero's Fall

In this project you will design a stunt for a Western movie in which the hero falls off a rooftop onto the roof of a stagecoach being drawn by a team of horses. In order to make your plans, you will need to choose the height of the building and the dimensions (length and height) of the stagecoach. Assume that the stagecoach travels at a speed of 20 miles per hour.

In order to make your stunt work so that the hero does not get hurt, it is important for the person to know when to jump.

1. What function will you use to model the motion of the hero during the fall? Explain your reasoning.

2. How long will it take the hero to fall from the top of the building to the top of the stagecoach?

3. In this situation, height is calculated in feet, and time is calculated in seconds. However, the speed of the stagecoach is 20 miles per hour. Convert the speed of the stagecoach to feet per second.

4. The hero should begin the fall the instant the center of the stagecoach (not including the horses) reaches a mark in the road. Where should you place this mark so that the hero will land safely on top of the stagecoach?

   Recall that when an object falls freely from rest, its height can be modeled by the function

   $$h = -\frac{1}{2}gt^2 + h_0$$

   where $h$ is the height of the falling object, $g$ is the acceleration due to gravity (a constant), $t$ is time, and $h_0$ is the initial height of the object.

# Chapter 11 Review

## You Should Be Able to:

### Lesson 11.1

- graph a parabola given the focus and directrix.
- write an equation of a parabola when the distance from the vertex to the focus is known.
- identify the vertex and axis of symmetry of a parabola.
- use an equation of a parabola to model a real-world situation.

### Lesson 11.2

- identify the mathematical properties of a model of a suspension bridge cable.
- find an equation of a parabola that passes through the origin given a point on the graph and the other $x$-intercept.

### Lesson 11.3

- find the coordinates of the vertex of a graph of a quadratic function.
- sketch the graph of a quadratic function.
- identify whether a parabola opens upward or downward by examining the function.
- identify the range and domain of a given quadratic function.

### Lesson 11.4

- solve problems that require previously learned concepts and skills.

### Lesson 11.5

- add and subtract polynomials.
- multiply a polynomial by a monomial.
- multiply two binomials.

### Lesson 11.6

- use graphs to solve quadratic equations.
- solve quadratic equations by factoring.
- make connections between the roots of a quadratic equation and the zeros of the graph of the related quadratic function.

### Lesson 11.7

- use the quadratic formula to solve quadratic equations.
- select and defend a method of solving a quadratic equation.

### Lesson 11.8

- use a quadratic function to model a real-world situation.

## Key Vocabulary

parabola (p. 375)

directrix (p. 375)

focus (p. 375)

axis of symmetry (p. 376)

vertex (of a parabola) (p. 376)

quadratic function (p. 383)

standard form (of a quadratic function) (p. 386)

polynomial (p. 392)

binomial (p. 392)

trinomial (p. 392)

## Chapter 11 Test Review Answers

1. directrix, focus
2. parabola
3. downward
4. discriminant
5. vertex: $(0, 0)$; focus: $(0, -3)$; directrix: $y = 3$
6. B
7. B
8. Sample graph:

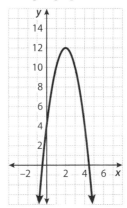

9. $\left(-\dfrac{1}{2}, 0\right)$; The vertex is a minimum.
10a. It opens downward because $a < 0$.
10b. $(1, -2)$; It is a maximum since the graph opens downward.
10c. the vertical line $x = 1$
10d. The domain is all real numbers. The range is all real numbers less than or equal to $-2$.

---

quadratic equation (p. 398)     Zero Product Property (p. 400)
roots (p. 398)                   quadratic formula (p. 404)
zeros (p. 398)                   discriminant (p. 405)

## Chapter 11 Test Review

**Fill in the blank.**

1. A parabola can be defined as the set of points in a plane that is equidistant from a given line called the _____ and a given point called the _____.

2. The graph of a quadratic function is called a(n) _____.

3. When a quadratic function is written in standard form and $a$ is negative, the parabola opens _____.

4. The value of the number under the radical sign in the quadratic formula is called the _____.

5. Consider the graph of $x^2 = -12y$. Find the vertex, the focus, and the equation of the directrix for the parabola.

6. How many real solutions does the equation $x^2 - 6x + 9 = 0$ have?

   **A.** 0      **B.** 1      **C.** 2      **D.** infinitely many

7. A parabola crosses the $x$-axis at $(0, 0)$ and $(22, 0)$, and it opens upward. Which of these points could be the vertex?

   **A.** $(0, 22)$    **B.** $(11, -15)$    **C.** $(8, 11)$    **D.** $(11, 18)$

8. Sketch the graph of $y = -2x^2 + 8x + 4$.

9. Find the vertex of $y = 4x^2 + 4x + 1$. Is this vertex a maximum or a minimum?

10. Consider the graph of $y = -3x^2 + 6x - 5$. Without graphing the function, answer the following questions.

    **a.** Does the graph open upward or downward? Explain how you know.

    **b.** What are the coordinates of the vertex of the graph? Is it a maximum or a minimum?

    **c.** What is the equation of the axis of symmetry of the graph?

    **d.** What is the domain of the function? What is the range?

**11.** Write an expression to represent the area of the shaded region.

**12.** The Gateway Arch in St. Louis, Missouri is 630 feet high. The distance between the legs of the arch at ground level is 630 feet. Its shape is actually a curve called a *catenary*, but it can be approximated by a parabola.

   **a.** Assume the origin of a coordinate system is located at the top of the arch. What are the coordinates of the point at the lower-right edge of the right leg?

   **b.** Find an equation for a parabola that approximates the arch. (Hint: Recall that a parabola with its vertex at the origin can be modeled with the function $y = ax^2$.)

**13.** Solve $2x^2 - x = 15$ by graphing.

**14.** Factor the polynomial.

   **a.** $t^2 + 5t - 24$       **b.** $3m^2 - 27m + 60$

**15.** Solve $x^2 - x = 30$ by factoring.

**16.** A penny is dropped from the top of the Tower of the Americas in San Antonio, Texas. The function $h = -16t^2 + 750$ can be used to model the height of the penny ($h$) after $t$ seconds. About how long will it take for the penny to reach the ground?

**17.** Use the quadratic formula to solve $3x^2 - 2x = 8$.

**18.** State the value of the discriminant of $5x^2 - 2x = 8$. How many real roots does the equation have?

**19.** A toy rocket is fired in the middle of a field. The relationship between the height of the rocket and time can be modeled by the function $h = -16t^2 + 256t$, where $h$ represents the height of the rocket in feet after $t$ seconds. When is the rocket 540 feet above the ground?

**11.** $(2x)(4y) - xy = 7xy$
**12a.** $(315, -630)$
**12b.** Substituting the coordinates $(315, -630)$ for $x$ and $y$ in the equation gives you $-630 = a(315)^2$, so $a = -0.00635$. The equation is $y = -0.00635x^2$.
**13.** $-2.5, 3$
**14a.** $(t + 8)(t - 3)$
**14b.** $3(m - 4)(m - 5)$
**15.** $-5, 6$
**16.** $-16t^2 + 750 = 0$; about 6.8 seconds
**17.** $2, -\dfrac{4}{3}$
**18.** 164; 2 real roots
**19.** The rocket is 540 feet above the ground at 2.5 seconds and again at 13.5 seconds after launch.

## Lesson Objectives

- investigate distance-versus-time graphs.
- use first and second differences to identify quadratic functions.

## Vocabulary

- first difference
- second difference

## Materials List

- motion detector (optional)

## Description

In the first section of this Extension, students should work in small groups as they explore the graphs of data collected by a motion detector. They will interpret distance-vs-time graphs, answering questions about increasing or decreasing rates.

In the second section of this lesson, students use first and second differences to explore linear and quadratic functions.

### TEACHING TIP

If a motion detector is available for students or classroom demonstrations, it will be both helpful and exciting for students to use it to collect data and recreate Graphs A, B, and C before answering **Questions 4–6**. Also have them collect data and create distance-vs-time graphs for **Questions 7 and 8**.

## Chapter 11 Extension Answers

1. The distance increases.
2. Sample answer: If the student walks at a constant rate, it will be a straight line. It will be curved if the student speeds up or slows down.
3. Sample answer: The graph should increase from left to right because as time increases, the distance from the motion detector increases.

---

# Chapter Extension
## Exploring Quadratic Data

In this Extension you will look at distance-versus-time graphs. For these graphs, consider time as the independent variable and distance as the dependent variable.

A motion detector can track a person walking toward or away from it. The motion detector along with a graphing calculator can be used to create a distance-versus-time graph of a person's walk.

### INTERPRETING DISTANCE-VERSUS-TIME GRAPHS

1. Imagine a person walking away from a motion detector. As time increases, what happens to the person's distance from the motion detector?

2. Would you expect the distance $d$ versus time $t$ graph to be a straight line or a curved line? Explain your answer.

3. Would you expect the graph to increase or decrease from left to right? Explain your answer.

Consider Graphs A, B, and C below. Each is a distance-versus-time graph of a person's walk.

**Graph A**                **Graph B**                **Graph C**

4. In which graph(s) was the person walking away from the motion detector? Explain your answer.

5. In which graph(s) was the person walking at a constant rate for at least part of the time? Explain your answer.

6. Look at Graph A. Explain the short horizontal segments on the graph.

---

4. A, B, and C; As time increased, the person's distance from the detector increased.
5. A and B; The graph shows a straight line which means that for every second, the same amount of distance was covered.
6. Sample answer. The horizontal segments indicate that the person's distance from the motion detector was not changing during those periods of time. This means that the person paused before beginning the walk and then stopped walking at the end.

7. A person walked in front of a motion detector. His graph of distance versus time is shown below. Describe his walk.

8. The graph below shows a person who walked in a straight line in front of the motion detector while the detector recorded her distance from it every 0.1 seconds for 6 seconds.

    a. Based on the graph, did this person walk toward or away from the motion detector? Explain your answer.

    b. After she began moving, did she walk at a constant rate or did she speed up or slow down? Explain your answer.

    c. What rules could you give to a walker so that he or she could walk a graph like the one in the figure?

## DISTINGUISHING BETWEEN LINEAR AND QUADRATIC DATA IN TABLES

Two people walked in front of motion detectors at different times. Table A on the next page shows some of the data from the first person's walk. Table B on the next page shows some of the data from the second person's walk.

7. Sample answer: He began walking as soon as the motion detector started collecting data and then walked at a constant rate. He walked toward the motion detector because the graph shows that as time increased, distance decreased.

8a. Sample answer: At first the person walked toward the detector, then walked away. Distance was decreasing for 3 seconds and then began to increase.

8b. Sample answer: At first, she walked at a fairly constant rate, then slowed down to change direction. After changing direction, she increased her rate.

8c. Sample answer: Start about 20 feet from the motion detector. Walk toward the detector at a rate of about 5 feet per second. Gradually slow down and then begin walking away from the device. When walking away, gradually increase your rate to 5 feet per second.

## TEACHING TIP

Using first and second differences can help determine a function for quadratic data. This lesson can be extended by providing students with the following information.

- If the $x$-interval is equal to 1 in a table of values and the second differences are constant, the value for $a$ in the standard form of a quadratic function, $y = ax^2 + bx + c$, is half of the constant second differences.
- If the first $x$-value is 0, then the first first-difference is equal to $a + b$.
- The $y$-value when $x = 0$ is the value of $c$.

After discussing these points, challenge students to use first and second differences to find a function that fits the data in the table below.

| x | y |
|---|---|
| 0 | 2 |
| 1 | 9 |
| 2 | 20 |
| 3 | 35 |
| 4 | 54 |
| 5 | 77 |

If students have difficulty, point out that the column of second differences is a constant 4, therefore $a = 2$. The value for $c$ is 2 (by inspecting the table where $x = 0$). The first number in the first difference column is 7, and $7 - 2 = 5$. So the equation is $y = 2x^2 + 5x + 2$.

| Table A (first person's walk) | | Table B (second person's walk) | |
|---|---|---|---|
| Time (seconds) | Distance (feet) | Time (seconds) | Distance (feet) |
| 0 | 2 | 0 | 25 |
| 1 | 5 | 1 | 15 |
| 2 | 8 | 2 | 9 |
| 3 | 11 | 3 | 7 |
| 4 | 14 | 4 | 9 |
| 5 | 17 | 5 | 15 |

9. Use your graphing calculator to create a distance-versus-time scatter plot of the first person's data. Record your window and sketch your graph.

10. Use your graphing calculator to create a distance-versus-time scatter plot of the second person's data. Record your window and sketch your graph.

11. Describe the shape of the graphs for the two walks.

12. What do you think might be a cause of the differences in the shapes of the graphs?

As you have seen in previous chapters, it is often helpful to look at the differences in consecutive table values and also examine successive ratios.

13. Add a third column to Table A and label it "First Differences." Determine the differences in the dependent variable from one table value to the next and enter them in the third column. These differences are often referred to as **first differences**.

| Table A (first person's walk) | | |
|---|---|---|
| Time (seconds) | Distance (feet) | First Differences |
| 0 | 2 | — |
| 1 | 5 | $5 - 2 = 3$ |
| 2 | 8 | |
| 3 | 11 | |
| 4 | 14 | |
| 5 | 17 | |

9.

```
WINDOW
 Xmin=0
 Xmax=6
 Xscl=1
 Ymin=0
 Ymax=20
 Yscl=1
 Xres=■
```

10.

```
WINDOW
 Xmin=0
 Xmax=6
 Xscl=1
 Ymin=0
 Ymax=25
 Yscl=1
 Xres=■
```

11. Sample answer: The first graph appears to be linear. The second graph appears to be shaped like a parabola.

12. Sample answer: The first person walked away from the motion detector at a constant rate. The second person did not walk at a constant rate and changed directions, first walking toward the detector and then away from it.

13.

| Table A (first person's walk) | | |
|---|---|---|
| Time (seconds) | Distance (feet) | First Differences |
| 0 | 2 | — |
| 1 | 5 | $5 - 2 = 3$ |
| 2 | 8 | $8 - 5 = 3$ |
| 3 | 11 | $11 - 8 = 3$ |
| 4 | 14 | $14 - 11 = 3$ |
| 5 | 17 | $17 - 14 = 3$ |

14. What do you notice about the first differences in Table A in Question 13? What does this tell you?

15. Add a third column to Table B and label it "First Differences." Determine the differences in the dependent variable from one table value to the next and enter them into the third column.

Table B
(second person's walk)

| Time (seconds) | Distance (feet) | First Differences |
|---|---|---|
| 0 | 25 | — |
| 1 | 15 | $15 - 25 = -10$ |
| 2 | 9 | |
| 3 | 7 | |
| 4 | 9 | |
| 5 | 15 | |

16. What do you notice about the first differences in Table B in Question 15? What does this tell you?

17. Now add a fourth column to Table B and label it "Second Differences." The **second difference** is the change from one first difference to the next.

Table B
(second person's walk)

| Time (seconds) | Distance (feet) | First Differences | Second Differences |
|---|---|---|---|
| 0 | 25 | — | — |
| 1 | 15 | $-10$ | — |
| 2 | 9 | $-6$ | $-6 - (-10) = +4$ |
| 3 | 7 | $-2$ | |
| 4 | 9 | $+2$ | |
| 5 | 15 | $+6$ | |

CHAPTER 11
EXTENSION

14. The first differences are constant and equal to 3. This means that the function is linear and the slope of the graph (rate of change) is 3.

15.

Table B
(second person's walk)

| Time (seconds) | Distance (feet) | First Differences |
|---|---|---|
| 0 | 25 | |
| 1 | 15 | $15 - 25 = -10$ |
| 2 | 9 | $9 - 15 = -6$ |
| 3 | 7 | $7 - 9 = -2$ |
| 4 | 9 | $9 - 7 = +2$ |
| 5 | 15 | $15 - 9 = +6$ |

16. The first differences are not constant. This means that the function is not linear.

17.

Table B
(second person's walk)

| Time (seconds) | Distance (feet) | First Differences | Second Differences |
|---|---|---|---|
| 0 | 25 | — | — |
| 1 | 15 | $-10$ | — |
| 2 | 9 | $-6$ | $-6 - (-10) = +4$ |
| 3 | 7 | $-2$ | $-2 - (-6) = +4$ |
| 4 | 9 | $+2$ | $2 - (-2) = +4$ |
| 5 | 15 | $+6$ | $6 - 2 = +4$ |

**18.** The second differences are constant and equal to +4.

**19.** Table 1 represents a quadratic function since the second differences are constant. Table 2 shows neither linear nor quadratic data since neither the first nor the second differences are constant. Table 3 represents a linear function since the first differences are constant.

**18.** What do you notice about the second differences in Table B in Question 17?

Using differences can help you determine whether a function is linear or quadratic. Assume that the differences between consecutive $x$-values in a table are constant.

- If the relationship is linear, then the first differences in the $y$ values will be constant, indicating a constant rate of change.
- If the first differences in the $y$-values are not constant, then there is not a constant rate of change and the relationship is nonlinear.
- If the second differences are constant and nonzero, then the relationship is quadratic.

**19.** Examine the three tables below. Using first and second differences, determine whether the data are linear, quadratic, or neither.

| Table 1 | | | Table 2 | | | Table 3 | |
|---|---|---|---|---|---|---|---|
| $x$ | $y$ | | $x$ | $y$ | | $x$ | $y$ |
| 0 | 0 | | 0 | 0 | | 0 | 0 |
| 1 | 2 | | 1 | 2 | | 1 | 2 |
| 2 | 8 | | 2 | 5 | | 2 | 4 |
| 3 | 18 | | 3 | 8 | | 3 | 6 |
| 4 | 32 | | 4 | 10 | | 4 | 8 |
| 5 | 50 | | 5 | 12 | | 5 | 10 |
| 6 | 72 | | 6 | 15 | | 6 | 12 |

# Chapter 12
# Indirect Measurement

## Mathematical Overview

In this chapter, students explore the relationships between the sides and the angles in right triangles. The Pythagorean theorem, its converse, 45°-45°-90° and 30°-60°-90° right triangles, the distance formula, and the midpoint formula are examined for their applications to the real world. Students draw on knowledge gained about similar polygons from Chapter 1 to explore similar triangles and the relationship between their sides. They also investigate methods for finding the height or length of objects they cannot measure directly. Various aspects of the branch of mathematics known as trigonometry are used to solve right triangles. This chapter concludes with an Extension centering on building and using a simple clinometer.

## Lesson Summaries

**Lesson 12.1** *Investigation: Right Triangles*

In this Investigation, students review the Pythagorean theorem and its converse. Then they use it to find the length of one side of a right triangle, to determine if a triangle actually is a right triangle, and to explore the relationships among the sides of two different types of special right triangles (45°-45°-90° and the 30°-60°-90°). If time permits, students are encouraged to research one of the proofs of the Pythagorean theorem.

**Lessons 12.2** *Investigation: Distance and Midpoint Formulas and* **12.3** *Activity: Similar Triangles as Models*

In Lesson 12.2, students investigate a particular use for the Pythagorean theorem, i.e., finding the distance between any two points in the coordinate plane. This variation of the theorem is called the *distance formula.* The midpoint formula is also presented. Then, in the Activity in Lesson 12.3, students explore using the *shadow method* and properties of similar triangles to determine the height of an object they cannot measure directly. They also use similar triangles and the *ruler method* to calculate the unknown height of an object as well as the unknown distance between two objects. One other method for finding the height of an object indirectly, the *mirror method,* is examined.

**Lesson 12.4** *Investigation: Trigonometric Ratios*

In this Investigation, students are introduced to trigonometry. They explore the relationships between the sides and angles of right triangles. They also distinguish the legs of a right triangle as either the adjacent leg or opposite leg according to their relationship to a reference angle. During the Investigation, students discover that the ratio of the length of the opposite leg to the length of the hypotenuse (as well as for the ratios of the adjacent leg to

the hypotenuse and the opposite leg to the adjacent leg) should be the same for similar right triangles. At this point, the trigonometric ratios for acute angles (sine, cosine, and tangent) are introduced.

**Lesson 12.5** *Using Trigonometric Ratios*

In this lesson, students use the trigonometric ratios they learned about in Lesson 12.4 to solve problems involving right triangles. Students learn that trigonometry allows them to do something the Pythagorean theorem would not—to find the sides of a right triangle when the measures of only one side and an acute angle are known. Students solve problems involving the angle of elevation and the angle of depression.

**Lesson 12.6** *R.A.P.*

In this lesson, students **R**eview **A**nd **P**ractice solving problems that require the use of skills and concepts taught in previous math levels. The skills reviewed in this lesson are skills that are needed as a basis for solving problems throughout this course.

**Lesson 12.7** *Investigation: Finding Acute Angles*

In this Investigation, students use the trigonometric ratios they learned about in Lesson 12.4 to find the measure of an acute angle of a right triangle when the measures of at least two sides of the triangle are known. Students learn about the inverse sine, inverse cosine, and inverse tangent. They also use what they have learned to solve right triangles.

**Chapter 12** *Extension: Measuring Angles of Elevation*

In this Extension, students build a simple clinometer and use it to find the height of an object they cannot measure directly.

# Lesson Guide

| Lesson/Objectives | Materials | |
|---|---|---|
| **Chapter 12 Opener: How Can You Determine the Height of a Model Rocket?**<br>• recognize that there are times that you may want to know a length or distance that cannot be measured directly. | | *Optional:*<br>• watch the movie *October Sky* (1999) as a class |
| **12.1 Investigation: Right Triangles**<br>• use the Pythagorean theorem to solve problems.<br>• use the converse of the Pythagorean theorem to solve problems.<br>• use the relationships in special right triangles (45°-45°-90° and 30°-60°-90°) to solve problems. | *Per group:*<br>• scissors<br>• 1-centimeter grid paper | *Optional:*<br>• TRM figures on a grid for Question 1<br>• TRM table shells for Exercises 10 and 11<br>• ropes and stakes to model a 3-4-5 right triangle |
| **12.2 Investigation: Distance and Midpoint Formulas**<br>• find the distance between two points in the coordinate plane.<br>• find the midpoint of a line segment in the coordinate plane. | | *Optional:*<br>• grid paper |
| **12.3 Activity: Similar Triangles as Models**<br>• use similar triangles to find distances and heights indirectly | *Per group:*<br>• ruler<br>• tape measure or meter stick | *Optional:*<br>• mirror<br>• marker |
| **12.4 Investigation: Trigonometric Ratios**<br>• find the sine, cosine, and tangent of a given angle shown in a figure.<br>• use a calculator to find the sine, cosine, and tangent of a given angle. | *Per pair:*<br>• protractor<br>• ruler | *Optional:*<br>• TRM table shells for Questions 3, 4, 6, 11<br>• TRM table shell for Exercise12 Part (a) |
| **12.5 Using Trigonometric Ratios**<br>• use trigonometric ratios to find the unknown lengths of the sides of right triangles. | | |
| **12.6 R.A.P.**<br>• solve problems that require previously learned concepts and skills. | | *Optional:*<br>• TRM table shells for Exercises 11–16 |
| **12.7 Investigation: Finding Acute Angles**<br>• use trigonometric ratios to find the unknown measures of angles in right triangles.<br>• use trigonometry to model and solve real-world problems. | | |
| **Chapter 12 Extension: Measuring Angles of Elevation**<br>• use a clinometer to determine angles of elevation.<br>• use a clinometer and trigonometry to find the height of an object that cannot be measured directly. | *Per clinometer:*<br>• protractor<br>• drinking straw<br>• tape measure or meter stick<br>• string<br>• tape<br>• a weight such as a washer or fishing weight | *Optional:*<br>• TRM table shell for Question 1 |

# Pacing Guide

| | Day 1 | Day 2 | Day 3 | Day 4 | Day 5 | Day 6 | Day 7 | Day 8 | Day 9 | Day 10 | Day 11 |
|---|---|---|---|---|---|---|---|---|---|---|---|
| **Basic** | p. 426, 12.1 | 12.2 | 12.3 | 12.3, 12.4 | 12.4 | 12.5 | 12.6 | 12.7 | project | project, review | review |
| **Standard** | p. 426, 12.1 | 12.2 | 12.3 | 12.3, 12.4 | 12.4 | 12.5 | 12.6 | 12.7 | project | review | extension |
| **Block** | p. 426, 12.1, 12.2 | 12.3 | 12.4 | 12.5, 12.6 | 12.6, 12.7 | project | review, extension | | | | |

## Supplement Support

See the Book Companion Website at www.highschool.bfwpub.com/ModelingwithMathematics and the Teacher's Resource Materials (TRM) for additional resources.

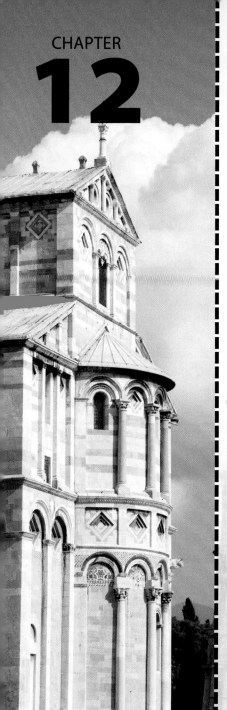

# Indirect Measurement

## CONTENTS

# CHAPTER 12 OPENER

**5e** Engage

## Lesson Objective

- recognize that there are times that you may want to know a length or distance that cannot be measured directly.

## Vocabulary

## Description

This reading helps students see that mathematics can be involved in hobbies and other recreational activities.

---

### TEACHING TIP

After students have read the Chapter Opener, lead a class discussion by first asking if anyone in the class has ever launched a rocket or if they know anyone who is a rocketeer. Also, ask students to think of something they cannot measure directly.

---

### CONNECTION

You may want to watch the movie *October Sky* (1999) as a class. It is the true story of Homer Hickman, a coal miner's son, who was inspired by the first Sputnik launch to take up rocketry.

---

## How Can You Determine the Height of a Model Rocket?

You may have seen rockets launched into space on TV, but have you ever watched the launch of a model rocket? How big are these rockets, who launches them, and how high do they go?

Model rockets became popular in the 1950s with the beginning of space travel. At that point, the sport of rocketry was rather unsafe. In fact, it was not until safe and reliable motors could be purchased commercially and safety standards were developed that the sport of model rocketry got its strong start.

Flight of a Model Rocket

Coasting Flight
Ejection Charge
Powered Ascent
Slow Descent
Launch
Recovery

According to the National Association of Rocketry (NAR), over 90,000 serious rocket modelers of all ages have joined their organization since 1957. In addition, there are many more "casual" rocketeers who participate in the sport but do not belong to the NAR.

In 1926 Robert Goddard, who is referred to as the father of American rocketry, launched a rocket that reached a height of nearly 50 feet. Many of today's NAR-sanctioned rockets weigh no more than a pound (including motor and propellant). The beginner rockets reach heights of 300 to 1,000 feet, while advanced models reach altitudes of more than a mile.

Problems that involve finding a height, length, or distance that cannot be measured directly are posed daily by architects, engineers, artists, astronomers, surveyors and rocketeers. In this chapter, you will explore similar triangles and the relationships between their sides. Your study will then turn to a branch of mathematics known as *trigonometry*, and you will develop the tools necessary to solve problems, such as the rocket-height problem.

One of the best-known theorems in mathematics is the Pythagorean theorem. This theorem, named after the Greek mathematician Pythagoras, states the relationship between the lengths of the legs and the hypotenuse in any right triangle. In this lesson, you will review the theorem and use it to explore the relationships among the sides of two different types of special right triangles.

One of the first tasks in building a house is pouring the concrete for the house's foundation. For most houses, corners are "square." That is, the walls of the house meet at right angles.

Building contractors must ensure that the corners of a foundation are square before proceeding to build the walls. In this Investigation, you will see how they can be sure.

1. Examine the figures on the grid to the left. If the grid lines are one centimeter apart, what are the lengths of the sides of the three squares?

2. Find the area of each of the three squares.

3. What relationship do you see among the areas of the three squares?

4. Now examine the triangle. Is it a right triangle? Explain.

5. Using 1-centimeter grid paper, make a copy of the figure to the left. Cut out the four figures. Arrange the squares around the triangle so that each side of the triangle is matched to a side of one of the squares.

6. What does this construction tell you about the relationship among the lengths of the sides of this triangle?

In Questions 1–6, you demonstrated a specific case of the **Pythagorean theorem**. It turns out that *for any right triangle,* the sum of the squares of the lengths of the two shorter sides is equal to the square of the length of the longest side.

It is also true that *if* the sum of the squares of the lengths of the two shorter sides of a triangle is equal to the square of the length of the

RIGHT TRIANGLES    **Lesson 12.1**    **427**

## Lesson 12.1 Investigation Answers

1. 3 cm, 4 cm, 5 cm
2. $9\ cm^2$, $16\ cm^2$, $25\ cm^2$
3. The sum of the areas of the smaller two squares $(9\ cm^2 + 16\ cm^2)$ is equal to the area of the largest square $(25\ cm^2)$.
4. Sample answer: Yes, because two of the sides are perpendicular.

5.

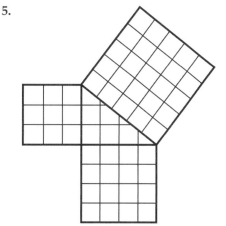

6. Sample answer: The sum of the squares of the lengths of the two shorter sides is equal to the square of the length of the longest side.

## Lesson Objectives
- use the Pythagorean theorem to solve problems.
- use the converse of the Pythagorean theorem to solve problems.
- use the relationships in special right triangles (45°-45°-90° and 30°-60°-90°) to solve problems.

## Vocabulary
- hypotenuse
- legs (of a right triangle)
- Pythagorean theorem

## Materials List
- scissors
- 1-centimeter grid paper (optional)

## Description
Most students are familiar with the Pythagorean theorem from previous courses but may remember it only as the formula $a^2 + b^2 = c^2$. The Investigation in this lesson is designed to review what these variables represent, as well as point out the relationships among the three sides of any right triangle.

This lesson works best as a whole class/small group Investigation (2-4 students). Have students read the information in the paragraphs preceding the first question of the Investigation.

Have students work in groups to complete **Questions 1–9**.

*Wrapping Up the Investigation:*

Once all groups have completed the Investigation, have them share their answers to **Question 9**. Their answers will provide insight as to the students' understanding into the usefulness of the Pythagorean theorem and its converse.

7. 5 meters; For the angle to be a right angle, the square of the distance between stake 2 and stake 3 must be $3^2 + 4^2 = 25$. The distance must equal $\sqrt{25} = 5$ meters.

8. acute; The distance is less than 5 meters, so the angle must be less than 90°.

9. Sample answers: checking whether a wall meets a floor at a right angle; checking a picture frame for squareness; ensuring that a door frame is squared off

---

longest side, then the triangle must be a right triangle. Construction workers often use this fact to test the "squareness" of a corner (a corner with a 90° angle).

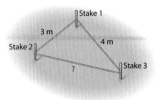

One way to get a square corner is to drive a stake at the desired corner and another stake 3 meters from the corner along the line where one wall is to be. Then a third stake is placed so that its distance from the corner is 4 meters.

7. If the corner at Stake 1 is square, what is the distance between Stake 2 and Stake 3? Explain.

8. If the distance between Stake 2 and Stake 3 is 4.5 meters, is the angle at Stake 1 an obtuse angle or an acute angle? Explain.

9. Describe some other workplace situations in which a similar technique for checking "squareness" might be useful.

The longest side of a right triangle is called the **hypotenuse**. It is also the side opposite the right angle. In the figure to the left, it is labeled $c$. The other two sides of the triangle, $a$ and $b$, are called **legs**.

The Pythagorean theorem states a relationship that has been known for thousands of years. It can be expressed concisely in terms of the labels $a$, $b$, and $c$.

> **Pythagorean Theorem**
>
> In a right triangle, the sum of the squares of the lengths of the legs is equal to the square of the length of the hypotenuse.
>
> $$a^2 + b^2 = c^2$$

Also, if the sides of a triangle satisfy the relationship $a^2 + b^2 = c^2$, then the triangle must be a right triangle.

> **Converse of the Pythagorean Theorem**
>
> If the sum of the squares of the lengths of the legs is equal to the square of the length of the hypotenuse, then the triangle is a right triangle.

It is this converse of the Pythagorean theorem that a builder uses to check a foundation. Most construction workers probably do not actually think about the Pythagorean theorem when they check foundations for squareness. But their "3-4-5" method is based on the theorem.

**1**

The size of a television screen is usually described by the length of its diagonal. Suppose a large TV screen in the shape of a rectangle is 57 inches wide by 32 inches high. How would the size of this screen be described in an advertisement?

57 in.

32 in.

**Solution:**

The diagonal of the screen forms a right triangle with two of the sides of the screen.

Use the Pythagorean theorem to find the hypotenuse $c$, which is the diagonal.

$$c^2 = a^2 + b^2$$
$$c^2 = 32^2 + 57^2$$
$$c^2 = 1,024 + 3,249$$
$$c^2 = 4,273$$
$$c = \sqrt{4,273} \qquad \leftarrow \text{This is the exact answer.}$$
$$= 65.368... \qquad \leftarrow \text{This is the calculated result.}$$
$$\approx 65 \qquad \leftarrow \text{This is an approximation.}$$

The length of the diagonal is approximately 65 inches. So, the TV should be advertised as having a 65-inch screen.

 **2**

The sides of a triangle are 6 cm, 9 cm, and 11 cm long. Is the triangle a right triangle?

**Solution:**

Check to see if the sides of the triangle satisfy the relationship $a^2 + b^2 = c^2$.

| | |
|---|---|
| Pythagorean theorem | $a^2 + b^2 = c^2$ |
| Since the length of the longest side of the triangle is 11 cm, substitute 11 for $c$. | $6^2 + 9^2 \stackrel{?}{=} 11^2$ |
| Simplify. | $36 + 81 \stackrel{?}{=} 121$ |
| Simplify. | $117 \neq 121$ |

So, the triangle is not a right triangle.

**ADDITIONAL EXAMPLE**  **1**

How high up the wall will a 12-foot ladder reach if the bottom of the ladder is 6 feet from the wall? Round your answer to the nearest tenth of a foot.

10.4 feet

**TEACHING TIP**

Unless students are directed otherwise, have students give exact answers in simplest radical form. If students need to review simplifying radicals, refer them to **Appendix M**.

**ADDITIONAL EXAMPLE**  **2**

The lengths of the sides of a triangle are 4, 2.4 and 3.2 mm. Is the triangle a right triangle?

Yes; $2.4^2 + 3.2^2 = 4^2$

### ADDITIONAL EXAMPLE

The length of the hypotenuse of an isosceles right triangle is 16 mm. Find the lengths of the legs.

$8\sqrt{2}$ mm

## SPECIAL RIGHT TRIANGLES

Two right triangles, the 45°-45°-90° triangle and the 30°-60°-90° triangle, have special relationships among their sides.

Because all 45°-45°-90° triangles have two sides of equal length and a right angle, they can also be called *isosceles right triangles*.

> **45°-45°-90° Triangles**
>
> In a 45°-45°-90° triangle, the two legs are equal in length, and the length of the hypotenuse is the length of a leg times $\sqrt{2}$.
>
> $$\text{hypotenuse} = \text{leg} \cdot \sqrt{2}$$

**E X A M P L E  3**

Find the missing lengths. Write your answers in simplest radical form.

**a.**    **b.**

4 m

*x*

*y*

45°

4 m    12 in.

**Solution:**

Both triangles are 45°-45°-90° triangles.

**a.**  hypotenuse = leg · $\sqrt{2}$

$$x = 4\sqrt{2} \text{ m}$$

**b.**  hypotenuse = leg · $\sqrt{2}$

$$12 = y \cdot \sqrt{2}$$

$$\frac{12}{\sqrt{2}} = y$$

$$\frac{12}{\sqrt{2}} \cdot \frac{\sqrt{2}}{\sqrt{2}} = y$$

$$\frac{12\sqrt{2}}{2} = y$$

$$6\sqrt{2} \text{ in.} = y$$

### 30°-60°-90° Triangles

In a 30°-60°-90° triangle, the length of the hypotenuse is 2 times the length of the shorter leg. The longer leg is the length of the shorter leg times $\sqrt{3}$.

$$\text{hypotenuse} = 2 \cdot \text{shorter leg}$$
$$\text{longer leg} = \text{shorter leg} \cdot \sqrt{3}$$

 **E X A M P L E** ❹

The figure below shows a side view of a skateboard ramp. Find the length of the base $l$ and the height $h$ of the ramp.

18 feet

30°

$h$

$l$

**Solution:**

The triangle is a 30°-60°-90° triangle.

First find the height of the ramp, which is the shorter leg of the triangle.

$$\text{hypotenuse} = 2 \cdot \text{shorter leg}$$

$$18 = 2h$$
$$\frac{18}{2} = h$$
$$9 \text{ feet} = h$$

Then use this measurement to find the length of the base of the ramp. Round to the nearest tenth.

$$\text{longer leg} = \text{shorter leg} \cdot \sqrt{3}$$
$$l = h \cdot \sqrt{3}$$
$$l = 9\sqrt{3} \text{ feet}$$
$$l \approx 15.6 \text{ feet}$$

## ADDITIONAL EXAMPLE ❹

The figure below shows a rectangular garden with a length of 6 feet. Find the length of the diagonal. Round your answer to the nearest tenth of a foot.

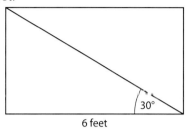

30°

6 feet

6.9 feet

## Practice for Lesson 12.1 Answers

1. $\sqrt{(4\text{ m})^2 - (2\text{ m})^2} = \sqrt{12} = 2\sqrt{3}$; $h \approx 3.5$ m

2. $\sqrt{4^2 + 7^2} = \sqrt{65}$; about 8.1 miles

3a. $\dfrac{\text{distance}}{2.5\text{ ft}} = \dfrac{12}{1}$; 30 ft

3b. $\sqrt{30^2 + 2.5^2} = \sqrt{906.25} \approx$ 30.1 ft or 30 ft 1 in.

4a. Length $\overline{BC} = \sqrt{10^2 + 14^2} = \sqrt{296} \approx 17.2$ ft; The length of the pipe $= 25$ ft $+ 17.2$ ft $= 42.2$ ft.

4b. A straight run would be the hypotenuse of a right triangle with legs of 35 ft and 14 ft, or $\sqrt{35^2 + 14^2} = \sqrt{1{,}421} \approx 37.7$ ft. The savings would be 42.2 ft – 37.7 ft = 4.5 ft.

5. $90\sqrt{2} \approx 127$ feet

---

**For Exercises 1–4, round answers to the nearest tenth.**

1. A 4-meter-long pole leans against a wall with its lower end 2 meters from the wall. How high up on the wall is the upper end?

2. If you hike 4 miles north and then 7 miles east, about how many miles are you from your starting point?

3. The Americans with Disabilities Act (ADA) requires that all public buildings be accessible. Ramps are often used to satisfy the act's requirements.
   a. A ramp cannot rise more than 2 feet 6 inches without a landing, and the ratio of horizontal distance to height must be at least 12 to 1. If a ramp rises 2 feet 6 inches, how great a horizontal distance must it cover to maintain the 12 to 1 ratio?
   b. How long is the ramp, to the nearest inch?

4. The figure below represents a top view of a drain line.

   a. How much pipe is needed to construct the drain line?
   b. If it were possible to connect $A$ to $C$ with a straight pipe, how much less pipe would be needed?

5. A baseball diamond is in the shape of a square. The distance between first and second base is 90 feet. To the nearest foot, how far is it from home plate to second base?

For Exercises 6–9, state whether a triangle with sides of the given lengths is a right triangle. If the triangle is *not* a right triangle, state whether it is acute or obtuse.

**6.** $6, 6, 6\sqrt{2}$    **7.** $4, 4\sqrt{3}, 8$    **8.** $9, 9, 15$    **9.** $5, 12, 13$

For Exercises 10–11, find the missing lengths in the table.

**10.**

|      | a    | b        | c   |
|------|------|----------|-----|
| i.   | 10 m |          |     |
| ii.  |      | $6\sqrt{2}$ m |     |
| iii. |      |          | 8 m |

**11.**

|      | x    | y        | z            |
|------|------|----------|--------------|
| i.   | 5 ft |          |              |
| ii.  |      | $2\sqrt{3}$ ft |        |
| iii. |      |          | $18\sqrt{3}$ ft |

**12.** A carpenter needs to build a truss for the roof of a building.

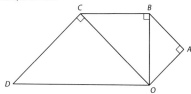

king post

If the king post is 10 feet long and $D$ is the midpoint of $\overline{AB}$, find the length of $\overline{AB}$ and $\overline{AC}$. Round to the nearest tenth.

**13.** A diagonal of a square has a length of 10 mm. What is the perimeter of the square?

**14.** The figure below shows three 45°-45°-90° triangles. If $OA = 1$, find $OB$, $OC$, and $OD$.

**15.** There have been many proofs of the Pythagorean theorem over the years. Research one of these proofs and write a short paper showing the proof.

**TEACHING TIP**

**Exercise 10** If students struggle while completing this table, suggest that they first identify the legs, and if necessary, remind them that the legs in this triangle are equal in length. Then ask them why that is so.

**TEACHING TIP**

**Exercise 11** If students are not sure where to begin with this table, suggest that in a 30°-60°-90° triangle, it is often helpful to identify the shortest side first.

**CONNECTION**

**Exercise 12** The king post truss is the simplest type of truss. The king post itself is the central vertical post that supports the weight of a heavy roof.

**COMMON ERROR**

**Exercise 13** Students sometimes forget to add the lengths of all of the sides of a figure when finding the perimeter. Suggest that they make a diagram and label each of the sides.

**TEACHING TIP**

**Exercise 15** If students struggle finding a proof that they can understand, suggest that they search for a proof by *dissection* as this proof is well within the grasp of students at this level. In this proof, students are asked to separate the square on the longer leg of a right triangle into four specified pieces. They then place the square on the shorter leg and the four parts of the square on the longer leg so that they exactly cover the square of the hypotenuse.

**10.**

|      | a           | b           | c             |
|------|-------------|-------------|---------------|
| i.   | 10 m        | 10 m        | $10\sqrt{2}$ m |
| ii.  | $6\sqrt{2}$ m | $6\sqrt{2}$ m | 12 m        |
| iii. | $4\sqrt{2}$ m | $4\sqrt{2}$ m | 8 m         |

**11.**

|      | x           | y           | z             |
|------|-------------|-------------|---------------|
| i.   | 5 ft        | $5\sqrt{3}$ ft | 10 ft      |
| ii.  | 2 ft        | $2\sqrt{3}$ ft | 4 ft       |
| iii. | $9\sqrt{3}$ ft | 27 ft     | $18\sqrt{3}$ ft |

**12.** $AC = 20$ feet; $AB = 2 \cdot 10\sqrt{3} \approx$ 34.6 feet

**13.** $20\sqrt{2}$ mm

**14.** $OB = \sqrt{2}$; $OC = 2$; $OD = 2\sqrt{2}$

**15.** Answers will vary.

**6.** yes
**7.** yes
**8.** no; acute
**9.** yes

**433**

# LESSON 12.2

## Lesson Objectives

- find the distance between two points in the coordinate plane.
- find the midpoint of a line segment in the coordinate plane.

## Vocabulary

- distance formula
- midpoint formula

## Materials List

## Description

This lesson works best as a small group Investigation (2–3 students). Begin the lesson by pointing out that this Investigation uses what they already know about the Pythagorean theorem.

In groups have students work through **Questions 1–8**.

*Wrapping Up the Investigation:*

Once all groups have completed the Investigation, ask them to find the distance between a computer located at $(x_1, y_1)$ and one that is located at $(x_2, y_2)$. Once they have found that distance, point out that they have derived what is known as the distance formula.

## Lesson 12.2 Investigation Answers

1. #1 (0, 4), #2 (5, 4); #3 (4, 8)
2. $d_{H1} = 4$ feet
3. $d_{12} = 5$ feet
4. $d_{H2} = \sqrt{41} \approx 6.4$ feet
5. $d_{23} = \sqrt{17} \approx 4.1$ feet
6. Option (b) is the least expensive. About 19.3 feet of cable are needed for Option (a) and about 14.7 feet of cable are needed for Option (b).

---

**Lesson 12.2**    **INVESTIGATION:** **Distance and Midpoint Formulas**

In Lesson 12.1, you found that both the Pythagorean theorem and its converse have many applications to the real world. In this lesson, you will use that theorem to find the distance between any two points in the coordinate plane. You will also learn to find the coordinates of the midpoint of a line segment whose endpoints are known.

### DISTANCE FORMULA

A computer network with three computers is being installed in a small study room. A technician must find the least expensive way to connect the computers to the hub $H$, which is in a corner of the room.

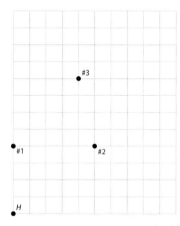

1. The 10 ft × 12 ft room is modeled in the diagram to the left. If the hub is located at the point $H(0, 0)$ on the grid, find the coordinates of computers #1, #2, and #3.

2. Find the length of cable needed to connect the hub to computer #1. That is, find the distance $d_{H1}$ from point $H$ to #1.

3. Find the distance from computer #1 to computer #2. Denote this distance from #1 to #2 as $d_{12}$.

4. Use the Pythagorean theorem to find the length of cable required to connect the hub to computer #2. Denote this distance as $d_{H2}$ and round it to the nearest tenth.

5. Find the distance between computer #3 and computer #2. Denote this distance as $d_{23}$ and round it to the nearest tenth.

6. The figures at the top of the next page show two connection options. Option (a) shows a direct connection of every computer to the hub $H$. Option (b) uses a secondary hub at computer #1.

   If there is no extra cost for a secondary hub, which option costs less? Explain.

---

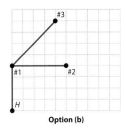

**Option (a)**        **Option (b)**

7. Suppose that the location of computer #3 has not been decided. If the coordinates of #3 are $(x_3, y_3)$, use the Pythagorean theorem to write a generalized formula for the distance $(d_{H3})$ from the hub to computer #3.

8. Assume that the hub can be moved to any location $(x_H, y_H)$ in the room. Write a generalized formula for the distance $(d_{H3})$ from the hub to the computer at $(x_3, y_3)$.

When you found a formula for the distance between the hub and computer #3, you discovered a particular use of the Pythagorean theorem that is important in many applications. This formula is generally referred to as the **distance formula**.

---

**The Distance Formula**

The distance $d$ between any two points having coordinates $(x_1, y_1)$ and $(x_2, y_2)$ is $d = \sqrt{(x_2 - x_1)^2 + (y_2 - y_1)^2}$.

---

**E X A M P L E** ❶

Find the distance between $F(8, -6)$ and $G(-2, 4)$.

**Solution:**

| | |
|---|---|
| Distance formula | $d = \sqrt{(x_2 - x_1)^2 + (y_2 - y_1)^2}$ |
| Substitute. | $d = \sqrt{(8 - (-2))^2 + (-6 - 4)^2}$ |
| Subtract. | $d = \sqrt{10^2 + (-10)^2}$ |
| Simplify. | $d = \sqrt{200}$ |
| Simplify the radical. | $d = 10\sqrt{2}$ |

The distance between $F$ and $G$ is $10\sqrt{2}$ or about 14.1 units.

7. $d_{H3} = \sqrt{(x_3)^2 + (y_3)^2}$

8. $d_{H3} = \sqrt{(x_3 - x_H)^2 + (y_3 - y_H)^2}$

**TEACHING TIP**

Ask students if it matters which $x$-coordinate is $x_1$ and which is $x_2$. Demonstrate that it does not matter because the difference between the two $x$-coordinates is squared in the distance formula, and the squared value is the same whether the difference is positive or negative. This is true for the $y$-coordinates as well.

**ADDITIONAL EXAMPLE** ❶

Find the distance between $R(4, 6)$ and $S(6, -2)$.
$2\sqrt{17}$ units

## MIDPOINT FORMULA

If you know the coordinates of the endpoints of a line segment, you can find the coordinates of its midpoint.

**The Midpoint Formula**

If the endpoints of a line segment are $A(x_1, y_1)$ and $B(x_2, y_2)$, then the midpoint of $\overline{AB}$ is

$$\left(\frac{x_1 + x_2}{2}, \frac{y_1 + y_2}{2}\right).$$

Notice that the $x$-coordinate of the midpoint is the mean (average) of the $x$-coordinates of the endpoints, and the $y$-coordinate of the midpoint is the mean (average) of the $y$-coordinates of the endpoints.

**ADDITIONAL EXAMPLE**

Find the midpoint of the segment that joins (–3, –4) and (7, –2).
$(2, -3)$

### E X A M P L E ②

Find the midpoint of the segment that joins $(-2, 6)$ and $(8, 5)$.

**Solution:**

The $x$-coordinate of the midpoint is:

$$\frac{x_1 + x_2}{2} = \frac{-2 + 8}{2}$$
$$= \frac{6}{2} \text{ or } 3$$

The $y$-coordinate of the midpoint is:

$$\frac{y_1 + y_2}{2} = \frac{6 + 5}{2}$$
$$= \frac{11}{2} \text{ or } 5.5$$

The midpoint is (3, 5.5).

**ADDITIONAL EXAMPLE** 3

The midpoint of $\overline{KL}$ is $M(1, 6)$ and one endpoint is $L(4, 7)$. Find the coordinates of $K$.
$(-2, 5)$

### E X A M P L E ③

The midpoint of $\overline{AB}$ is $M(1, 2)$ and one endpoint is $A(-3, 4)$. Find the coordinates of $B$.

**Solution:**

Let $(x, y)$ be the coordinates of $B$.

The $x$-coordinate of $B$ is:

$$\frac{x_1 + x_2}{2} = 1$$
$$\frac{-3 + x}{2} = 1$$
$$-3 + x = 2$$
$$x = 5$$

The $y$-coordinate of $B$ is:

$$\frac{y_1 + y_2}{2} = 2$$
$$\frac{4 + y}{2} = 2$$
$$4 + y = 4$$
$$y = 0$$

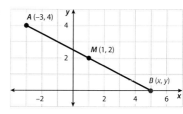

The other endpoint is $B(5, 0)$.

**For Exercises 1–6, find the distance between the two points and the midpoint of the segment that joins the two points.**

1. (6, 13) and (1, 1)    2. (−8, 2) and (−4, 1)   3. (−6, 4) and (3, −5)

4. (3, −3) and (−2, 9)   5. (1, 1) and (4, 5)    6. (2, −4) and (−3, 1)

7. Suppose you forget the distance formula. Use figures and words to explain how you can find the distance between $A(1, 5)$ and $B(5, 2)$.

8. It is important for archaeologists to keep precise records of locations of their findings. To do this, site locations are keyed to a selected point or landmark on a map. From this point, a grid of squares made of rope can be laid out over the area. The grid provides a system of coordinates for record keeping.

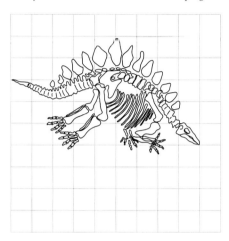

a. Assume that the origin of the grid is in the lower-left corner and that grid lines are one unit apart. What are the approximate coordinates of the tip of the tail of the dinosaur?

b. What are the approximate coordinates of the tip of the nose?

c. If the grid lines are 1 meter apart, about how far is it from the tip of the dinosaur's tail to the tip of its nose?

DISTANCE AND MIDPOINT FORMULAS    **Lesson 12.2**    **437**

---

# LESSON 12.2

## Practice for Lesson 12.2 Answers

1. 13; (3.5, 7)

2. $\sqrt{17}$; (−6, 1.5)

3. $9\sqrt{2}$; (−1.5, −0.5)

4. 13; (0.5, 3)

5. 5; (2.5, 3)

6. $5\sqrt{2}$; (−0.5, −1.5)

7. Sample answer: You can use the Pythagorean theorem to find the distance between the two points. Begin by plotting the points on a coordinate plane. Connect the points with a line segment and create a right triangle as shown. Determine the lengths of the horizontal leg and the vertical leg. Then use the Pythagorean theorem to determine the length of the hypotenuse (the distance between the two points).

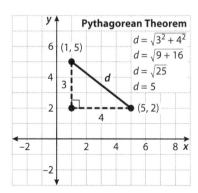

8a. (0, 7)

8b. (9, 4)

8c. Sample answer: about 9.5 meters

**9.** From *A* to *B* to *C* to *D* = 36 feet; from *A* to *D* ≈ 28 feet; the climber climbs about 8 fewer feet if he climbs directly from Hold *A* to Hold *D*.

**10.** The lengths of the sides are $\sqrt{90}$, $\sqrt{41}$, and $\sqrt{89}$, so the triangle is scalene.

**11.** Two of the sides have lengths of 5 (and the third side is $2\sqrt{5}$), so the triangle is isosceles.

> **TEACHING TIP**
>
> **Exercises 10 and 11** If necessary, remind students that scalene triangles have no sides equal in length, isosceles triangles have at least two sides of equal length, and equilateral triangles have three sides of equal length.

> **TEACHING TIP**
>
> **Exercise 14** If students struggle getting started with this problem, suggest that they make a diagram and label each of the segments.

**12.** Sample answer: To find the *x*-coordinate of the midpoint, find the average of the *x*-coordinates of the endpoints: $\frac{1+5}{2} = 3$.

To find the *y*-coordinate of the midpoint, find the average of the *y*-coordinates of the endpoints: $\frac{5+2}{2} = 3.5$.

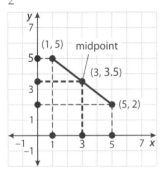

**13.** (7, 9)

**14.** The midpoint of $\overline{WX}$ is (1, −1). Since it is also the midpoint of $\overline{YZ}$, the coordinates of *Z* are (3, −4).

**15.** Sample answer: Use the distance formula to find the length of $\overline{AM}$ and $\overline{MB}$. If the distances are the same, *M* is the midpoint.

**438**

**9.** The figure below shows four holds on a rock-climbing wall. Climbers generally climb from Hold *A* to Hold *B*, then to Hold *C*, and finally to Hold *D*. About how many *fewer* feet would a climber climb if he or she climbs directly from Hold *A* to Hold *D*? (Assume that the distance between grid lines represents 2 feet.)

**10.** Triangle *ABC* has vertices *A*(7, 4), *B*(−2, 1), and *C*(2, −4). Determine whether △*ABC* is equilateral, scalene, or isosceles.

**11.** Determine whether the triangle formed by (−3, 2), (2, 2), and (−1, −2) is equilateral, isosceles, or scalene.

**12.** Suppose you forget the midpoint formula. Use figures and words to explain how you can find the midpoint of the segment that joins (1, 5) and (5, 2).

**13.** One endpoint of $\overline{CD}$ is *C*(5, 1). The midpoint of $\overline{CD}$ is *M*(6, 5). Find the other endpoint *D*.

**14.** Line segments *WX* and *YZ* intersect at their midpoints. The coordinates of *W*, *X*, and *Y* are *W*(−2, −3), *X*(4, 1), and *Y*(−1, 2). Find the coordinates of *Z*.

**15.** Explain how you can use the distance formula to verify that a point *M* on segment *AB* is the midpoint of $\overline{AB}$.

In Chapter 1, you found that two polygons are similar if their corresponding angles are equal in measure and the lengths of their corresponding sides are proportional. In this lesson, you will explore similar triangles and use that information to find measurements indirectly.

Triangles are the simplest of all of the polygons. They are also one of the most useful. Triangles can be seen everywhere. They can be seen in art, building designs, and construction. If the lengths of the sides of a triangle are fixed, its size and shape cannot change. It is the only polygon with this property. When bracing and strength are needed, triangles are used.

### Similar Triangles

Two triangles are similar if two angles of one triangle are congruent to two angles of another. Also, if two triangles are similar, the corresponding angles are congruent and the lengths of the corresponding sides form proportions.

One way to find the height of an object that you cannot measure directly is to use the *shadow method*. This method uses similar triangles.

1. Suppose that at 11:00 a.m. a flagpole casts a shadow of 3 feet 9 inches. At the same time, a 3-foot stick casts a shadow of 6 inches. Explain why $\triangle ABC \sim \triangle DEF$. (Assume that the angle between the sun's rays and the ground is the same for both shadows.)

2. Use a proportion to find the height of the flagpole.

SIMILAR TRIANGLES AS MODELS     **Lesson 12.3**     **439**

## Lesson Objective

- use similar triangles to find distances and heights indirectly.

## Vocabulary

- similar triangles

## Materials List

*Per group:*
- ruler
- tape measure or meter stick

## Description

*Preparation:*

Have students work in groups that have at least three members. Provide each group with a ruler and a tape measure or meter stick. Make sure that each group member has a specific task to accomplish within the group.

*During the Activity:*

In this lesson, students take measurements of the apparent height of a student who is several meters away. Then they use their measurements to calculate ratios that lead to an analysis using similar triangles.

Have students read the introductory paragraphs. Remind students what they know about similar polygons from **Lesson 1.2**. Also remind them that to prove triangle similarity, they only need to show that two angles of one triangle are congruent to two angles of another.

If time permits, you may want to use **Questions 1 and 2** as the framework for an outdoor student activity.

*Closing the Activity:*

Take time to talk about errors in their calculated heights (**Question 7**) and calculated distances (**Question 11**). Point out that a small error in their reading of the apparent height of the person on the ruler will make a big difference in their calculated heights and distances. Ask them what effect an error of 0.25 inch in their reading of the ruler would have on their indirect measurements.

## Lesson 12.3 Activity Answers

1. In $\triangle ABC$ and $\triangle DEF$, the flagpole and nearby stick are both perpendicular to the ground. So, $\angle C \cong \angle F$. Because the angle of elevation of the sun is the same for each shadow, $\angle B \cong \angle E$. And since two angles of one triangle are congruent to two angles of another, the triangles are similar.

2. $$\frac{\text{height of the flagpole}}{\text{length of the shadow (flagpole)}} = \frac{\text{height of the stick}}{\text{length of the shadow (stick)}};$$
$$h = 22.5 \text{ ft}$$

Other methods can be used to measure objects indirectly. In Questions 3–7, you will use similar triangles and what is often called the *ruler method* to do so.

3. Hold a ruler or meter stick in your hand, and extend your arm in front of you at eye level so that the ruler is vertical and your arm is extended fully. Have a member of your group measure the distance from your eye to the ruler. Record this distance.

4. Have another member of your group, the "stander," stand several feet away from you. Have the "measurer" use a tape measure or yardstick to measure the horizontal distance between your eye and the "stander." Record this distance.

5. Use the ruler in your extended hand to measure the apparent height of the "stander." Record this measurement.

6. Make a sketch similar to the one below that shows the lines of sight. Replace $d_r$ and $d_p$ in your sketch with your measured distances.

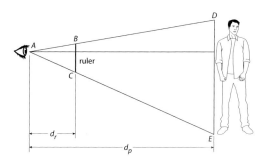

Explain why $\triangle ABC$ is similar to $\triangle ADE$. Assume that the "stander" and the ruler are both perpendicular to the ground.

7. Use the properties of similar triangles to set up a proportion and calculate the height $h$ of the stander.

8. Is your answer reasonable? Explain.

**440** Chapter 12 INDIRECT MEASUREMENT

3. Sample answer: 22 in.
4. Sample answer: 15 ft
5. Sample answer: 9.5 in.
6. Sample answer: $\overline{BC} \parallel \overline{DE}$ (If two lines in a plane are perpendicular to the same line, then the two lines are parallel.); $\angle ABC \cong \angle ADE$ and $\angle ACB \cong \angle AED$. (If two parallel lines are cut by a transversal, corresponding angles are congruent.); So, $\triangle ABC \sim \triangle ADE$. (If two angles of one triangle are congruent to two angles of another, the triangles are similar.)

7. $\dfrac{\text{distance from eye to ruler}}{\text{distance from eye to "stander"}} = \dfrac{\text{apparent height of "stander" (ruler reading)}}{h}$

$$\frac{22 \text{ in.}}{15 \text{ ft}} = \frac{9.5 \text{ in.}}{h}$$
$$h \approx 6.5 \text{ ft}$$

8. Sample answer: Yes, but there are many places errors can occur. For example, you have to measure carefully and that is not always easy.

You can also use similar reasoning to find the distance from yourself to an object if you know the height of the object.

9. Measure the height of one member of your group.

10. Now ask that person to stand at an unknown distance from you. Hold your ruler at arm's length and measure the apparent height of the person.

11. Use the properties of similar triangles and your measurements to calculate the distance $d$ from your eye to the other person.

12. Measure the actual distance. Explain why the actual distance might differ from the calculated distance.

**Practice for Lesson 12.3**

1. The figure shown is a sketch of your hand held up 2 feet in front of your eye. Suppose your hand is 7 inches long and just blocks out your view of a friend who is 5′6″ tall.

Your eye ⊢——2 ft——→ Your hand

7 in.

a. Make a sketch showing your eye, your hand, and your friend. Show all the given measurements in your figure.

b. How far from your eye is your friend standing? Explain how you found your answer.

2. The Washington Monument is 169 meters high. About how far should you stand from it to block it out with your hand? Assume your hand is 18 cm long and you hold it 50 cm from your eye.

3. To estimate the height of a building, a 5-foot-3-inch tall person measured her shadow while her friend measured the shadow of the building. The building cast a shadow of 40 feet. Her shadow is 32 inches long. To the nearest foot, how tall is the building?

SIMILAR TRIANGLES AS MODELS     Lesson 12.3     441

2. $\dfrac{\text{length of hand}}{\text{height of monument}} = \dfrac{\text{distance to hand}}{\text{distance to monument}}$;
You should stand about 470 m from the monument.

3. about 79 ft

9. Sample answer: 5 ft 9 in. or 5.75 ft
10. Sample answer: 9 in.
11. Sample answer:

$$\dfrac{\text{distance from eye to ruler}}{d} = \dfrac{\text{apparent height of person (ruler reading)}}{\text{height of person}}$$

$$\dfrac{22 \text{ in.}}{d} = \dfrac{9 \text{ in.}}{5.75 \text{ ft}}$$

$$d \approx 14.1 \text{ ft}$$

**TEACHING TIP**

**Exercise 1** Have students try this themselves to see that they can actually "block out" a person with their hand.

12. Sample answers: People may not have measured accurately or may not have measured the horizontal distance from the eye to the other person.

**TEACHING TIP**

**Exercise 2–4** Remind students that it is often helpful to draw a picture and label the dimensions when diagrams are not provided.

**Practice for Lesson 12.3 Answers**

1a. Sample sketch:

⊢ 2 ft ⊣ Your hand

Your eye

66 in.

7 in.

⊢24 in.⊣

⊢———— $x$ in. ————⊣

1b. about 226 inches or 18′10″ away; The ratio $\dfrac{\text{distance to hand}}{\text{distance to friend}}$ should be equal to the ratio $\dfrac{\text{length of hand}}{\text{height of friend}}$.

441

4. about 17.8 feet or 17′ 9″ high

5. Student *A*: The shorter leg of Triangle I is to the longer leg of Triangle I as the shorter leg of Triangle II is to the longer leg of Triangle II.

   Student *B*: The shorter leg of Triangle I is to the shorter leg of Triangle II as the longer leg of Triangle I is to the longer leg of Triangle II.

   Student *C*: The longer leg of Triangle II is to the longer leg of Triangle I as the shorter leg of Triangle II is to the shorter leg of Triangle I.

6. $\dfrac{66 \text{ in.}}{40 \text{ in.}} = \dfrac{h}{14 \text{ ft}}$ 23.1 feet

**TEACHING TIP**

**Exercise 6** If time permits, turn this exercise into an activity where students find the height of something they cannot actually measure, for example, a light pole or a tree. If students cannot leave the building, have them calculate the height of the ceiling of the gym. Students will need mirrors (with dots drawn on them with markers) and tape measures.

**TEACHING TIP**

Once students have completed this lesson and the exercises, choose an object in or around your school. Then have small groups of students choose one of the methods they have studied in this lesson and measure it indirectly. This always leads to a spirited argument over which way is best.

**442**

4. A ruler is held at arm's length, 27 inches from the viewer's eye. The viewer is 100 yards away from the goalpost on a football field. The apparent height of the goalpost is 1.6 inches. How high is the goalpost?

5. Students are told that Triangle I and Triangle II are similar.

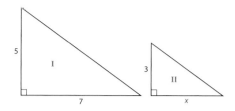

Three students set up the following proportions:

Student *A*: $\dfrac{5}{7} = \dfrac{3}{x}$     Student *B*: $\dfrac{5}{3} = \dfrac{7}{x}$     Student *C*: $\dfrac{x}{7} = \dfrac{3}{5}$

The instructor said that all three proportions are correct. Explain each student's thinking.

6. Another method that can be used to find the height of an object indirectly is often called the *mirror method*. In this method, a mirror with a dot on it is placed between a person and the object to be measured. The person looks into the mirror and walks back and forth until he can see the top of the object on the dot in the mirror.

   If the person knows his height (to his eye), his distance from the dot on the mirror, and the distance between the mirror and the object, he can use similar triangles to find the height of the object.

   Suppose your eye is 66 inches above the ground and your feet are 40 inches from the dot on the mirror. How tall is the tree if the mirror is 14 feet away from the tree?

In the first part of this chapter, you explored the relationships among the sides of right triangles. You also investigated the relationships among similar triangles and used those relationships to find lengths that could not be measured directly. In this lesson, you will explore the relationships between the sides and angles of right triangles.

**Note**

The word *trigonometry* is taken from the Greek words for "triangle" and "measure." Trigonometry was used by the ancient Greeks to estimate the distances to the moon and the sun.

The mathematical relationships among the sizes of angles and the lengths of sides in right triangles are part of a field of mathematics known as **trigonometry**. This field was first developed in ancient times to aid in navigation and surveying.

You already know that the side opposite the right angle in a triangle is the *hypotenuse*. But in order to distinguish between the other two sides, it is necessary to give names to the two legs. To do this, the legs are named according to their relationship to a **reference angle**.

The **adjacent leg** is the leg that is next to the reference angle.

The **opposite leg** is the side that is opposite the reference angle.

1. Sketch two right triangles similar to those below. For each triangle, label the hypotenuse, the leg adjacent to the marked angle, and the leg opposite the marked angle.

## Lesson Objectives

- find the sine, cosine, and tangent of a given angle shown in a figure.
- use a calculator to find the sine, cosine, and tangent of a given angle.

## Vocabulary

- adjacent leg
- cosine ratio
- opposite leg
- reference angle
- sine ratio
- tangent ratio
- trigonometric ratios
- trigonometry

## Materials List

- protractors
- rulers

## Description

As a class, read the paragraphs preceding **Question 1**. Make sure that students can identify the adjacent leg and the opposite leg in a right triangle when given a reference angle.

In groups of two, have students work through **Questions 1–13**.

## Lesson 12.4 Investigation Answers

1.

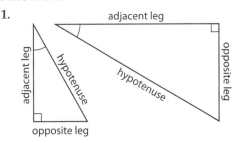

*Wrapping Up the Investigation:*

The mnemonic device SOH-CAH-TOA can be used to help students recall the ratios.

**S**ine—**O**pposite : **H**ypotenuse
**C**osine—**A**djacent : **H**ypotenuse
**T**angent—**O**pposite : **A**djacent

To help students recall this device, tell them the following story:

Prince Rahib escorted his girlfriend, Princess Rahana, as she rode her camel. The sun beat down on them as they rode through the desert. Suddenly, Rahana's camel lay down and refused to move. The sun was hot

and they were going to have to walk back home. Since the princess was barefoot, Prince Rahib insisted that she wear his shoes. They hurried, but the Prince's feet were blistered. When they arrived at the palace, Rahana cried, "My hero!" and went to give Rahib a kiss. "Get back!" he cried. "I have no time for you, I just want to SOH-CAH-TOA!"

**2.** Use a protractor to draw a 55° angle on a piece of paper. Label it ∠A and extend the rays of the angle to the edges of the paper.

**3.** In your drawing, add a small right triangle, △ABC, so that ∠C is a right angle. Use a centimeter ruler to measure the lengths of the sides of the triangle to the nearest tenth of a centimeter. Record your measurements in a table like the one shown below.

| Triangle | Hypotenuse | Opposite Leg | Adjacent Leg |
|---|---|---|---|
| △ABC | AB = | BC = | AC = |
| △ADE | | | |
| △AFG | | | |

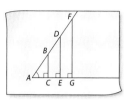

**4.** Draw $\overline{DE}$ and $\overline{FG}$ parallel to and to the right of $\overline{BC}$ on your drawing from Question 3, as shown to the left.

Measure the lengths of the sides of △ADE and △AFG. Then record the measurements in your table.

**5.** Are △ABC, △ADE, and △AFG similar to each other? Explain.

**6.** Use your measurements from Question 4 to complete the table below. Round your answers to the nearest hundredth.

| Ratio | △ABC | △ADE | △AFG |
|---|---|---|---|
| opposite leg / hypotenuse | | | |
| adjacent leg / hypotenuse | | | |
| opposite leg / adjacent leg | | | |

**7.** What patterns do you observe in your completed table?

**8.** What can you conclude?

**9.** Suppose you create another right triangle in your drawing with a hypotenuse of 10 cm. Use the ratios in your table to predict the length of the opposite leg. If possible, draw the triangle to check your prediction.

**2.** See students' papers.

**3.** Answers will vary. See the completed table in the answer to Exercise 4.

**4.** Answers will vary. Sample answer:

| Triangle | Hypotenuse | Opposite Leg | Adjacent Leg |
|---|---|---|---|
| △ABC | AB = 7.5 cm | BC = 6.1 cm | AC = 4.3 cm |
| △ADE | AD = 13.1 cm | DE = 10.7 cm | AE = 7.5 cm |
| △AFG | AF = 20.7 cm | FG = 17.0 cm | AG = 12.0 cm |

**5.** Yes, all three triangles are right triangles and each has a 55° angle. So the triangles are similar since each triangle has two angles congruent to each of the others.

**6.** Sample answers:

| Ratio | △ABC | △ADE | △AFG |
|---|---|---|---|
| opposite leg / hypotenuse | $\frac{BC}{AB} = \frac{6.1}{7.5} \approx 0.81$ | $\frac{DE}{AD} = \frac{10.7}{13.1} \approx 0.82$ | $\frac{FG}{AF} = \frac{17.0}{20.7} \approx 0.82$ |
| adjacent leg / hypotenuse | $\frac{AC}{AB} = \frac{4.3}{7.5} \approx 0.57$ | $\frac{AE}{AD} = \frac{7.5}{13.1} \approx 0.57$ | $\frac{AG}{AF} = \frac{12.0}{20.7} \approx 0.58$ |
| opposite leg / adjacent leg | $\frac{BC}{AC} = \frac{6.1}{4.3} \approx 1.42$ | $\frac{DE}{AE} = \frac{10.7}{7.5} \approx 1.43$ | $\frac{FG}{AG} = \frac{17.0}{12.0} \approx 1.42$ |

**7.** Sample answer: Each type of ratio has about the same value for all three triangles.

**8.** Sample answer: Based on the table, the ratio of any corresponding pair of sides for similar triangles should be the same. That is, the ratio of the length of the opposite leg to the length of the hypotenuse should be the same for similar triangles. The same applies to the other two ratios.

**9.** $\frac{\text{opposite leg}}{\text{hypotenuse}} = 0.82;$

$\frac{\text{opposite leg}}{10 \text{ cm}} = 0.82;$

opposite leg = 8.2 cm

These right triangle ratios that you have been investigating are called **trigonometric ratios**. Each of the trigonometric ratios that you found has a special name.

The **sine ratio** = $\dfrac{\text{length of the leg opposite the reference angle}}{\text{length of the hypotenuse}}$ or

sine ratio = $\dfrac{\text{opposite}}{\text{hypotenuse}}$

The **cosine ratio** = $\dfrac{\text{length of the leg adjacent to the reference angle}}{\text{length of the hypotenuse}}$ or

cosine ratio = $\dfrac{\text{adjacent}}{\text{hypotenuse}}$

The **tangent ratio** = $\dfrac{\text{length of the leg opposite the reference angle}}{\text{length of the leg adjacent to the reference angle}}$ or

tangent ratio = $\dfrac{\text{opposite}}{\text{adjacent}}$

To use a graphing calculator to investigate trigonometric ratios, first make sure your calculator is in **DEGREE** mode. To use your calculator to find the sine ratio for a 30° angle, press **SIN**, enter 30**)**, and press **ENTER**. You should get 0.5.

10. What does sin 30° = 0.5 tell you about the relationship between the length of the leg opposite a 30° angle and the length of the hypotenuse?

11. Use a calculator and your answers from Question 6 to complete the table.

| | Calculated Ratio from Question 6 | Calculator Value |
|---|---|---|
| sin 55° | | |
| cos 55° | | |
| tan 55° | | |

12. How do your calculated values compare to the calculator values for the sine, cosine, and tangent of 55°?

13. Consider $\triangle ABC$.
   a. Find $a$.
   b. Find sin $A$, cos $A$, and tan $A$.

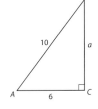

TRIGONOMETRIC RATIOS  **Lesson 12.4**  **445**

---

10. In a right triangle with one acute angle of 30°, the ratio of the length of the side opposite the 30° angle to the length of the hypotenuse is 1 : 2. In other words, the hypotenuse is twice as long as the side opposite the 30° angle.

11. Sample answers:

| | Calculated Ratio from Question 6 | Calculator Value |
|---|---|---|
| sin 55° | 0.82 | 0.82 |
| cos 55° | 0.57 | 0.57 |
| tan 55° | 1.42 | 1.43 |

**TEACHING TIP**

**Question 11** As a "rule of thumb," trigonometric ratios are rounded to the nearest hundredth when angle measurements are given to the nearest degree. If angles are given to the nearest tenth of a degree, then the ratios are rounded to the nearest thousandth.

12. Sample answer: The values are nearly the same if you round to the nearest hundredth.

13a. $6^2 + a^2 = 10^2$; $a = 8$

13b. sin $A = \dfrac{4}{5}$ or 0.8;

cos $A = \dfrac{3}{5}$ or 0.6;

tan $A = \dfrac{4}{3}$ or 1.333 . . .

**TEACHING TIP**

Have students round their answers to the nearest tenth unless the problem suggests otherwise.

**TEACHING TIP**

If students struggle with **Exercises 7 and 8**, point out that they need to find the length of $\overline{LM}$ before they can find the desired ratios.

**TEACHING TIP**

**Exercise 9** If students have difficulty drawing and labeling the figure described in the problem, ask them which side is opposite the right angle ($\overline{TS}$). Once they know that, then they know the vertex of the right angle ($R$).

## Practice for
## Lesson 12.4 Answers

1. (a)

(b)

(c)

2. $\sin A = \dfrac{\text{opposite}}{\text{hypotenuse}} = \dfrac{12}{13}$

3. $\cos A = \dfrac{\text{adjacent}}{\text{hypotenuse}} = \dfrac{5}{13}$

1. In relationship to the marked angles in the triangles below, label the hypotenuse, opposite leg, and adjacent leg.

a.   b.   c.

**For Exercises 2–4, write each ratio in both words and numbers.**

2. $\sin A = \dfrac{?}{?} = \dfrac{?}{?}$

3. $\cos A = \dfrac{?}{?} = \dfrac{?}{?}$

4. $\tan A = \dfrac{?}{?} = \dfrac{?}{?}$

**For Exercises 5–8, write each answer as a fraction and a decimal.**

5. Find sin $L$.

6. Find cos $N$.

7. Find tan $L$.

8. Find sin $N$.

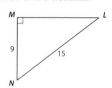

9. In right triangle $RST$, $RS = 10$ cm, $TS = 15$ cm, and $\overline{TS}$ is the hypotenuse of the triangle. (Round answers to four decimal places if necessary.)
   a. Find sin $T$.
   b. Find sin $S$.

10. Explain why neither the sine nor the cosine of an angle can be greater than 1.

11. Explain how you know that $\sin 30° = \dfrac{1}{2}$ or 0.5.

4. $\tan A = \dfrac{\text{opposite}}{\text{adjacent}} = \dfrac{12}{5}$

5. $\dfrac{9}{15} = 0.6$ ✓

6. $\dfrac{9}{15} = 0.6$

7. $\dfrac{9}{12} = 0.75$

8. $\dfrac{12}{15} = 0.8$

9a. $\sin T = \dfrac{10}{15} \approx 0.6667$

9b. Using the Pythagorean theorem, $RT = 5\sqrt{5}$. So, $\sin S = \dfrac{5\sqrt{5}}{15} \approx 0.7454$.

10. Sample answer: The ratio of the length of one leg to the length of the hypotenuse will always be less than 1 because the hypotenuse is longer than either of the legs since it is the longest side of a right triangle.

11. Sample answer: In a 30°-60°-90° triangle, the hypotenuse is twice the length of the shorter leg (the leg opposite the 30° angle).

So, the ratio $\dfrac{\text{opposite}}{\text{hypotenuse}} = \dfrac{1}{2}$.

**12 a.** Complete the following table:

| ∠A | sin A | cos A |
|-----|-------|-------|
| 10° | | |
| 20° | | |
| 30° | | |
| 40° | | |
| 50° | | |
| 60° | | |
| 70° | | |
| 80° | | |

**b.** What patterns do you notice in the table when you compare the sine and cosine of ∠A?

**c.** Find the value of $x$ in sin 25° = cos $x$.

**d.** Use your observations to complete this statement.
sin A = cos B if ∠A and ∠B are _____ angles.

**12a.**

| ∠A | sin A | cos A |
|-----|-------|-------|
| 10° | 0.1736 | 0.9848 |
| 20° | 0.3420 | 0.9397 |
| 30° | 0.5 | 0.8660 |
| 40° | 0.6428 | 0.7660 |
| 50° | 0.7660 | 0.6428 |
| 60° | 0.8660 | 0.5 |
| 70° | 0.9397 | 0.3420 |
| 80° | 0.9848 | 0.1736 |

**12b.** Sample answer:
sin $A$ = cos $(90° - A)$

**12c.** $x = 90° - 25° = 65°$

**12d.** complementary

**5e** Explain

## Lesson Objective

- use trigonometric ratios to find the unknown lengths of the sides of right triangles.

## Vocabulary

- angle of depression
- angle of elevation

## Description

In this lesson, students use what they learned about trigonometric ratios (Lesson 12.4) to solve right triangle problems in which one angle and one side are given.

## ADDITIONAL EXAMPLE

A right triangle has a 22° angle and a hypotenuse of 10 cm. Find the length of each leg.

about 3.7 cm and about 9.3 cm

> **TEACHING TIP**
>
> Calculator skills should be closely monitored if students are unfamiliar with using the **SIN**, **COS**, and **TAN** features of a graphing calculator.

---

In Lesson 12.4, you were introduced to the branch of mathematics called trigonometry. You also investigated three trigonometric ratios for acute angles in right triangles. In this lesson, you will use these ratios to solve problems.

### USING TRIGONOMETRIC RATIOS TO FIND SIDE LENGTHS

The trigonometric ratios that you studied in Lesson 12.4 allow you to do something that the Pythagorean theorem did not. They allow you to find the lengths of the sides of a right triangle when the length of only one side is known. If you know the measure of an acute angle and the length of one side of a right triangle, you can use trigonometric ratios to find the lengths of the other two sides.

Use trigonometric ratios to find $f$ and $g$.

**Solution:**

Find $f$:

$$\sin 27° = \frac{\text{opposite}}{\text{hypotenuse}}$$

$$\sin 27° = \frac{37}{f}$$

$$f \cdot \sin 27° = 37$$

$$f = \frac{37}{\sin 27°}$$

$$f \approx \frac{37}{0.4540}$$

$$f \approx 81.5 \text{ in.}$$

Find $g$:

$$\tan 27° = \frac{\text{opposite}}{\text{adjacent}}$$

$$\tan 27° = \frac{37}{g}$$

$$g \cdot \tan 27° = 37$$

$$g = \frac{37}{\tan 27°}$$

$$g \approx \frac{37}{0.5095}$$

$$g \approx 72.6 \text{ in.}$$

---

**Note**

The values of trigonometric ratios are often rounded to the nearest ten-thousandth. However, to get more precise answers when solving problems, use the ratio instead of a decimal approximation. For example, use "sin 27°" instead of 0.4540.

If an object is located above the horizontal, the angle your line of sight makes with the horizontal is called the **angle of elevation**.

**E X A M P L E 2**

A person is holding a kite on a string that is 150 yards long. The angle of elevation is 35°, and the person's eye is 1.5 yards above the ground. How high is the kite?

**Solution:**

First, create a sketch that represents the situation.

Let $h$ = the height of the kite above eye level.

$$\sin 35° = \frac{\text{opposite}}{\text{hypotenuse}}$$

$$\sin 35° = \frac{h}{150}$$

$$150 \cdot \sin 35° = h$$

$$150(0.5736) = h$$

$$h \approx 86 \text{ yards}$$

150 yards

35°

1.5 yards

### ADDITIONAL EXAMPLE 2

A person is holding a kite string about 3 feet off the ground. The angle of elevation is 55° when the kite is directly over a streetlight. If the streetlight is 50 feet from the person, how high is the kite?
about 74 feet

The kite is about 86 yards above eye level. So the kite is about $86 + 1.5 = 87.5$ yards high.

3 feet 9 inches

1. One acute angle of a right triangle is 57°, and the hypotenuse is 38.5 mm. Find the lengths of the two legs.

2. One acute angle of a right triangle is 32°, and the leg opposite it is 15 ft. Find the lengths of the adjacent leg and the hypotenuse.

3. Return to the flagpole problem that you solved in the Activity in Lesson 12.3. See the figure to the left. You can now solve this problem without having to use a stick. Suppose the angle between the sun's rays and the ground is 80.5°. Find the height of the flagpole.

4. A 22-foot ladder is leaning against a wall so that the end of the ladder extends 2 feet above the edge of the wall. If the ladder makes an angle of 75° with the ground, how far is the base of the ladder from the house?

5. The Leaning Tower of Pisa is known both for its beauty and its incline. The tower is 185 feet tall and makes an angle of approximately 84.5° with the ground. If the sun were shining directly overhead, how long a shadow would the tower cast?

6. A person is standing 50 meters from a lamp pole. If the angle of elevation is 11.2° and the person's eye is 2 meters above the ground, how tall is the lamp pole?

7. If an object is located below the horizontal, the angle your line of sight makes with the horizontal is called the **angle of depression**. Suppose the angle of depression from the top of a 210–foot cliff to an object on the ground is 34°. How far is the object from the base of the cliff?

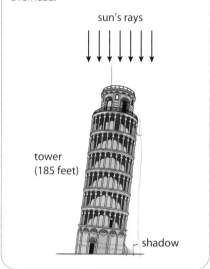
## Practice for Lesson 12.5 Answers

1. 32.3 mm and 21.0 mm
2. leg ≈ 24.0 ft; hypotenuse ≈ 28.3 ft
3. $\tan 80.5° = \dfrac{h}{3.75 \text{ feet}}$; $h ≈ 22.4$ feet
4. about 5.2 feet
5. about 17.7 feet
6. $9.9 + 2 = 11.9$ meters
7. $\tan 34° = \dfrac{210}{d} ≈ 311$ feet

8. *Hypsometers* are instruments used by the U.S. Forestry Service to measure the heights of trees. They also provide information about slopes of roads and pieces of land. There are many different types of hypsometers, but all operate on the principle illustrated in the figure below.

Suppose a forester standing 20 meters from a tree finds $\angle 1 = 47°$ and $\angle 2 = 5.5°$. Find the height of the tree.

9. Find the approximate perimeter of the figure below.

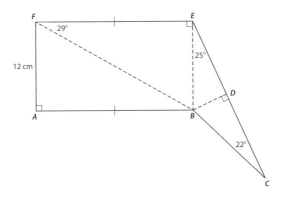

10. The Ferris wheel at Chicago's Navy Pier is modeled after the one that was built for the 1893 Chicago World Columbian Exposition. The attraction can hold up to 240 passengers and offers a fantastic view of Chicago's skyline and lakefront. About how tall is the Ferris wheel if there is a 70° angle of depression from the top of the ride to an object located on the ground 55 feet from the bottom of the ride?

## CONNECTION

**Exercise 8** In actuality, when using a hypsometer, all a forester has to do is measure a desired distance from the base of an object such as a tree. Then he selects an appropriate distance scale on the hypsometer, sights the top of the object, pulls the trigger on the meter, reads the height from the scale, sites the base of the object, reads the height from the scale, and adds the two heights together.

## COMMON ERROR

**Exercise 9** Some students may answer the question based on how the figure looks. Remind them that they cannot make assumptions about length or angle measures just from "looking at" the diagram.

8. $21.4 + 1.9 \approx 23.3$ meters

9. Answers may vary depending on rounding and the order in which the lengths are found. $AB \approx 21.6$; $BC \approx 13.6$; $CD \approx 12.6$; $DE \approx 10.9$; $EF \approx 21.6$; $FA = 12$; $P \approx 21.6 + 13.6 + 12.6 + 10.9 + 21.6 + 12 = 92.3$ cm

10. $\tan(70°) = \dfrac{h}{55}$; $h \approx 151$ feet

# LESSON 12.6

**5e** Evaluate

## Lesson Objective

- solve problems that require previously learned concepts and skills.

## Exercise Reference

Exercises 1–3: Lesson 12.1

Exercise 4: Appendix O

Exercises 5–10: Appendix B

Exercises 11–16: Appendices B and E

Exercises 17–22: Appendix I

Exercises 23–24: Lesson 5.6

Exercise 25: Lesson 5.1

Exercise 26: Lessons 8.2 and 8.3

Exercise 27: Lesson 8.5

Exercises 28–30: Lesson 6.3

## Lesson 12.6 R.A.P. Answers

1. hypotenuse
2. shorter leg
3. C
4. D
5. 13.653
6. 14.94
7. 10.39
8. 0.0028
9. 1.8
10. $4.\overline{6}$ or approximately 4.7
11. $\frac{1}{2}$, 0.5
12. $\frac{1}{4}$, 25%
13. 0.3, 30%
14. $\frac{1}{25}$, 0.04
15. $1\frac{1}{5}$, 120%
16. 0.875, 87.5%

---

**Lesson 12.6** **R.A.P.**

**Fill in the blank.**

1. In a right triangle, the side opposite the right angle is called the _____.

2. In a 30°-60°-90° triangle, the length of the hypotenuse is equal to two times the length of the _____ _____.

**Choose the correct answer.**

3. In △LMN, what is the length of the hypotenuse?

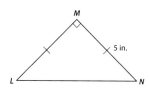

   **A.** 5 in.    **B.** 10 in.    **C.** $5\sqrt{2}$ in.    **D.** $5\sqrt{3}$ in.

4. Which point lies in Quadrant IV of the coordinate plane?
   **A.** (2, 3)    **B.** (−2, −3)   **C.** (−2, 3)    **D.** (2, −3)

**Add, subtract, multiply, or divide.**

5. 12.3 + 1.23 + 0.123    **6.** 15 − 0.06    **7.** 11.09 − 0.7

8. 0.07 × 0.04    **9.** 0.054 ÷ 0.03    **10.** 14 ÷ 3

**Complete the table below.**

| | Fraction | Decimal | Percent |
|---|---|---|---|
| **11.** | | | 50% |
| **12.** | | 0.25 | |
| **13.** | $\frac{3}{10}$ | | |
| **14.** | | | 4% |
| **15.** | | 1.2 | |
| **16.** | $\frac{7}{8}$ | | |

**Evaluate.**

**17.** $4 + (-3) - 6$

**18.** $-5(-2 - 6)$

**19.** $-9 + 6 \div 3 - 4$

**20.** $(-9 + 6) \div 3 - 4$

**21.** $-(-2)^3 + 8$

**22.** $\dfrac{4 - 6}{-6 - 4}$

**23.** Write an equation for the line that has a slope of $-3$ and passes through the point $(2, -1)$.

**24.** Write an equation for the line that passes through the points $(-4, 7)$ and $(-2, 1)$.

**25.** Is the relationship between $x$ and $y$ that is shown in the table a function? Explain.

| x | 1 | 2 | 3 | 4 | 5 |
|---|---|---|---|---|---|
| y | 1 | 2 | 3 | 2 | 1 |

**26.** Solve the system of equations.

$2x - 3y = 21$

$4x + \ y = \ 7$

**27.** Graph $2x - y \geq 8$ on a coordinate plane.

**The stem-and-leaf diagram below shows the total number of points scored in each of a team's basketball games.**

**Total Number of Points Scored**

```
4 | 9
5 | 5 7
6 | 2 4 5 7 7
7 | 1 2
8 | 2
```

Key: 4|9 represents 49 points.

**28.** How many games did the team play?

**29.** What is the median number of points scored?

**30.** What is the range of the number of points scored?

**17.** $-5$

**18.** 40

**19.** $-11$

**20.** $-5$

**21.** 16

**22.** $\dfrac{1}{5}$

**23.** $y = -3x + 5$

**24.** $y = -3x - 5$

**25.** Yes, for each input value ($x$), there is exactly one output value ($y$).

**26.** $(3, -5)$

**27.**

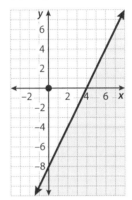

**28.** 11

**29.** 65

**30.** $82 - 49 = 33$

# LESSON 12.7

## Lesson Objectives

- use trigonometric ratios to find the unknown measures of angles in right triangles.
- use trigonometry to model and solve real-world problems.

## Vocabulary

- inverse cosine
- inverse sine
- inverse tangent

## Materials List

## Description

In this lesson, students apply their knowledge of trigonometric ratios to solve trigonometric equations for angle values.

In groups of two, have students work through **Questions 1–8**.

*Wrapping Up the Investigation:*

Emphasize the use of inverse operations in this section. Just as students "add the opposite" or "take the square root" when solving other types of equations, they will use the inverse sine, inverse cosine, and inverse tangent to solve equations.

## Lesson 12.7 Investigation Answers

1.

2.

3. Sample answer: In the drawing, the angle of elevation of the ski lift is $\angle A$.

---

## Lesson 12.7 | INVESTIGATION: Finding Acute Angles

In previous lessons, you explored methods of determining the heights of objects that could not be measured directly. In some methods, you used the properties of similar triangles. In others, you used trigonometric ratios. In this lesson, you will use what you have learned to "solve right triangles." You will also apply these techniques to solving a variety of real-world problems.

In Lesson 12.5, you used trigonometric ratios to find a missing side of a right triangle when at least one side and one acute angle were known. In this lesson, you will use these ratios to find the measure of an acute angle of a right triangle when the lengths of at least two sides are known.

Consider the following problem:

A ski lift rides a 250-meter track up the side of a mountain to the top, which is 160 meters above ground level. What is the ski lift's angle of elevation?

1. Make a sketch to model the situation. Label the known information.
2. Relative to the angle of elevation, label the hypotenuse, adjacent leg, and opposite leg.
3. Where in your sketch is the angle of elevation that you are being asked to find?
4. How does this problem differ from those found in Lesson 12.5?
5. What ratio can be formed using the lengths of the two known sides?
6. What is the sine ratio for the angle that you want to find?

---

4. In Lesson 12.5, we knew the measure of one of the acute angles and the length of one side, and were asked to find the length of another side. In this situation we know the lengths of two sides of the right triangle and are asked to find the measure of an acute angle.

5. the sine ratio

6. $\sin A = \dfrac{\text{opposite}}{\text{hypotenuse}} = \dfrac{160}{250} = 0.64$

**7.** Use the table below to approximate the angle of elevation of the ski lift.

| Angle | Sine | Cosine | Tangent |
|---|---|---|---|
| **38°** | 0.616 | 0.788 | 0.781 |
| **39°** | 0.629 | 0.777 | 0.810 |
| **40°** | 0.643 | 0.766 | 0.839 |
| **41°** | 0.656 | 0.755 | 0.869 |
| **42°** | 0.669 | 0.743 | 0.900 |

The process of working backwards to find an angle measure whose sine ratio is known is called finding the **inverse sine**. Likewise, you can find the **inverse cosine** or **inverse tangent** if you know an angle's cosine ratio or tangent ratio. For example, if you know that the sine ratio of an angle is 0.957, then you can write this equation.

$$\sin B = 0.957$$

Most scientific and graphing calculators have built-in features that allow you to compute the inverses of trigonometric ratios. To find the angle whose sine ratio is 0.957, you can use the $\sin^{-1}$ key on your calculator.

$$\sin B = 0.957$$
$$B = \sin^{-1}(0.957)$$
$$B \approx 73.1°$$

You can read "$B = \sin^{-1}(0.957)$" as "$B$ is the angle whose sine is 0.957."

**8.** Use a calculator to find the ski lift's angle of elevation. (Hint: Find the angle whose sine ratio is 0.64.)

If $\tan M = \frac{8}{7}$, find $M$.

**Solution:**

You can use a calculator to find $M$.

$$M = \tan^{-1}\left(\frac{8}{7}\right)$$
$$M \approx 48.8°$$

**7.** Sample answer: It appears to be close to 40°.

**8.** $\sin^{-1}(0.64) = 39.7918\ldots$; So, the angle of elevation is about 39.8°.

**ADDITIONAL EXAMPLE**

If $\sin N = \frac{2}{3}$, find $N$.

$N \approx 41.8°$

**Note**

To use a calculator's inverse trigonometry features, you generally have to press the **2ND** or **Shift** key before pressing the **SIN**, **COS**, or **TAN** key.

## ADDITIONAL EXAMPLE ❷

Solve the right triangle.

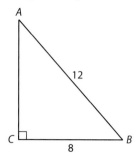

$\angle A \approx 41.8°$; $\angle B \approx 48.2°$; $AC \approx 8.9$

## SOLVING RIGHT TRIANGLES

To *solve a right triangle* means to calculate the lengths of each of the sides and the measures of each of the angles of the triangle. You now have the background to find both missing sides and angles of right triangles.

The diagram shows a metal block with holes drilled at $R$, $S$, and $T$. Find the measures of the acute angles and the distance between the centers of holes $R$ and $S$.

**Solution:**

Find $\angle R$:

$$\sin R = \frac{89}{95}$$

$$\angle R = \sin^{-1}\left(\frac{89}{95}\right)$$

$$\angle R \approx 69.53°$$

Find $\angle T$:

$$\cos T = \frac{89}{95}$$

$$\angle T = \cos^{-1}\left(\frac{89}{95}\right)$$

$$\angle T \approx 20.47°$$

To find the length of $t$, use either trigonometric ratios or the Pythagorean theorem.

Trigonometric ratios:

$$\sin 20.47° = \frac{t}{95}$$

$$t = (95)(\sin 20.47°)$$

$$t \approx 33.2 \text{ mm}$$

Pythagorean theorem:

$$t^2 + 89^2 = 95^2$$

$$t^2 = 95^2 - 89^2$$

$$t^2 = 1{,}104$$

$$t \approx 33.2 \text{ mm}$$

**Practice** for Lesson 12.7

1. Solve an isosceles right triangle with a hypotenuse of 8 inches.

2. Solve △ABC for AB, BC, and ∠B.

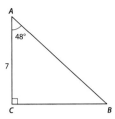

3. What are the acute angle measures of a 3-4-5 right triangle? (Round your answers to the nearest degree.)

4. A staircase, which takes up 12.5 feet of horizontal floor space, connects two floors that are 10 feet apart. What is the angle of elevation of the staircase?

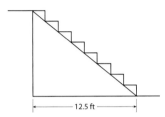

5. One end of a cable is attached to the top of a tower, 180 feet above the ground. The other end of the cable is secured to the ground at a point 80 feet from the base of the tower.

   a. Assume that the cable is stretched tight. About what angle does the cable make with the ground?

   b. About what angle does the cable make with the tower?

   c. How long is the cable?

## Practice for Lesson 12.7 Answers

1. legs ≈ 5.7 inches; acute angles = 45°
2. $AB ≈ 10.5$; $BC ≈ 7.8$; $∠B = 42°$
3. 37° and 53°
4. about 38.7°
5a. about 66°
5b. about 24°
5c. about 197 feet

**6.** $x \approx 4.8°$

**7.** C

**8.** The radius of the pile is 7.5 feet.
So, $\tan \theta = \dfrac{4.5}{7.5}$ and $\theta$ is about 31°.

**9.** $AD = 5.9$ cm; $BD = 2.7$ cm;
$BC = 4.9$ cm

**6.** The Americans with Disabilities Act (ADA) of 1990 states that the slope of any ramp must be no greater than 1 : 12.

What is the maximum angle of elevation $x$ for a ramp that meets these specifications?

**7.** Which information would *not* be enough to solve a right triangle?
   **A.** the length of the hypotenuse and the length of a leg
   **B.** the length of a leg and the measure of one acute angle
   **C.** the measure of two acute angles
   **D.** the length of the hypotenuse and the measure of one acute angle

**8.** When a truck full of gravel is dumped on a flat surface such as a parking lot, it forms a pile similar to that shown in the figure below. The angle that the gravel makes with the surface is called the *angle of repose*, and it is denoted by the symbol theta, $\theta$. Note that if more gravel is dumped on the pile, the pile just spreads out and the angle of repose does not change.

Find the angle of repose for gravel if the pile on the flat surface is 4.5 feet high and 15 feet in diameter.

**9.** In order to drill holes at $A$, $B$, $C$, and $D$, the distances $AD$, $BD$, and $BC$ must be determined. Find these distances to the nearest tenth.

**10.** A carpenter's square is a tool used by people to mark off right angles. It is more than an L-shaped metal ruler. With skill it can also be used to construct other angles.

For example, suppose a carpenter draws a line along one side of the square and places a mark at 12 inches. A second mark is placed at 7 inches along the other side of the square. Then the two marks are connected to form angle $x$, opposite the 7-inch side. What is the measure of this angle?

**11.** By observing the sun and a half-full moon when they are both visible at the same time and estimating the measure of the angle $x$ between them, you can calculate the ratio of the earth-moon distance to the earth-sun distance.

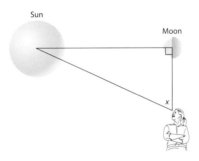

**a.** Suppose you estimate the angle to be 89 degrees. What is the ratio of the earth-moon distance to the earth-sun distance?
**b.** The distance from the earth to the moon is about 239,000 miles. Use your ratio from Part (a) to find the distance from the earth to the sun.

**10.**

7 in.

12 in.

$\tan x = \frac{7}{12}; x = 30°$

**11a.** The desired ratio is cos $x$ or about 0.01745.

**11b.** $\cos x = \frac{239{,}000}{s}$; For $x = 89°$, the distance from the earth to the sun is found to be about 13,694,000 miles.

## Materials List

- drinking straw
- piece of cardboard (at least 6" × 8")
- string
- a weight such as a washer or fishing weight
- ruler

## Description

In this project, students use simple materials to construct a hypsometer. Then they use the hypsometer and what they know about indirect measurement to calculate the height of a tall object. This project can be done in pairs or as individual students.

## Sample Answers

This sample answer is based on the following:

- the hypsometer reading shown in the first figure in the text,
- the figure being measured is the tree in the second figure in the text,
- the eye of the person in the figure is about 6 feet from the ground, and
- the distance from the tree to the person is 24 feet.

The markings on the hypsometer give two sides (opposite and adjacent) of a right triangle. The triangle on the hypsometer is similar to the right triangle whose leg is part of the unknown height of the second figure in the text.

The following proportion can be used to find the height of the object being measured that is above eye level.

$$\frac{4.5}{h} = \frac{10}{24}$$
$$h \approx 11 \text{ feet}$$

So, the height of the object is about 11 ft + 6 ft = 17 feet.

## What's Your Angle?

A *scale hypsometer* is an instrument that is used to measure heights or altitudes. This device is used in both the surveying and construction industries. It is also one of the tools used by forest management personnel.

Build a simple hypsometer using a straw, a piece of cardboard, a piece of string, and a weight. See the figure below.

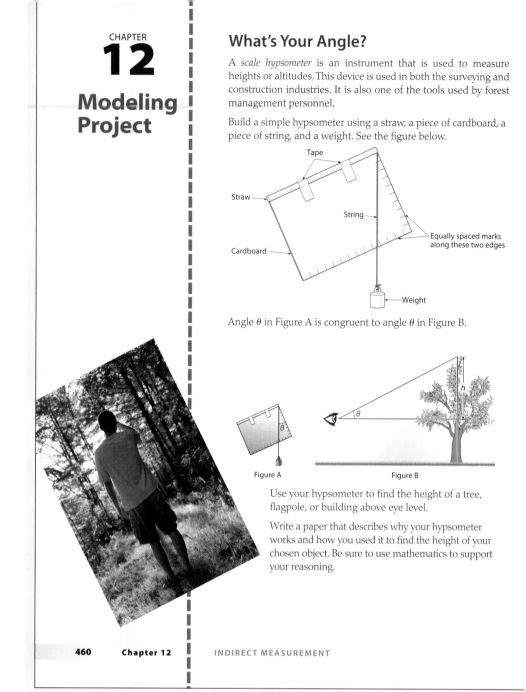

Angle $\theta$ in Figure A is congruent to angle $\theta$ in Figure B.

Use your hypsometer to find the height of a tree, flagpole, or building above eye level.

Write a paper that describes why your hypsometer works and how you used it to find the height of your chosen object. Be sure to use mathematics to support your reasoning.

# Chapter 12 Review

## You Should Be Able to:

### Lesson 12.1

- use the Pythagorean theorem to solve problems.
- use the converse of the Pythagorean theorem to solve problems.
- use the relationships in special right triangles (45°-45°-90° and 30°-60°-90°) to solve problems.

### Lesson 12.2

- find the distance between two points in the coordinate plane.
- find the midpoint of a line segment in the coordinate plane.

### Lesson 12.3

- use similar triangles to find distances and heights indirectly.

### Lesson 12.4

- find the sine, cosine, and tangent of a given angle shown in a figure.
- use a calculator to find the sine, cosine, and tangent of a given angle.

### Lesson 12.5

- use trigonometric ratios to find the unknown lengths of the sides of right triangles.

### Lesson 12.6

- solve problems that require previously learned concepts and skills.

### Lesson 12.7

- use trigonometric ratios to find the unknown measures of angles in right triangles.
- use trigonometry to model and solve real-world problems.

## Key Vocabulary

Pythagorean theorem (p. 427)

hypotenuse (p. 428)

legs (of a right triangle) (p. 428)

distance formula (p. 435)

midpoint formula (p. 436)

similar triangles (p. 439)

trigonometry (p. 443)

reference angle (p. 443)

adjacent leg (p. 443)

opposite leg (p. 443)

trigonometric ratios (p. 445)

sine ratio (p. 445)

cosine ratio (p. 445)

tangent ratio (p. 445)

angle of elevation (p. 449)

angle of depression (p. 450)

inverse sine (p. 455)

inverse cosine (p. 455)

inverse tangent (p. 455)

# CHAPTER REVIEW

## Chapter 12 Test Review Answers

1. hypotenuse
2. isosceles right triangle
3. $45°$
4. $\sqrt{58^2 + 79^2} = \sqrt{9605} \approx 98.0$ ft
5. No, the diagonal of the doorway is $\sqrt{(76 \text{ in.})^2 + (30 \text{ in.})^2} \approx 82$ in., too short for the 7-foot (84-inch) dimension.
6. $r = 16$, $s = 8$, $t = 8\sqrt{3}$
7a. $5\sqrt{2}$ units
7b. $(7.5, 0.5)$

---

## Chapter 12  Test Review

**Fill in the blank.**

1. The longest side of a right triangle is called the _____ .

2. A triangle with two sides of equal measure and a right angle is called a(n) _____ _____ _____.

3. The acute angles of an isosceles right triangle always measure _____.

4. Find the missing length. Round your answer to the nearest tenth.

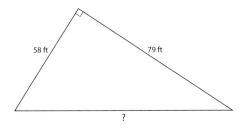

5. A doorway is 76 inches high and 30 inches wide. Will a 7 ft × 7 ft plywood panel fit through the doorway? Explain.

6. Find $r$, $s$, and $t$.

7. A line segment has endpoints at $S(5, -2)$ and $T(10, 3)$.

   a. Find the length of the segment.

   b. Find the midpoint of the segment.

**8  a.** Find the midpoint $M$ of $\overline{PQ}$.

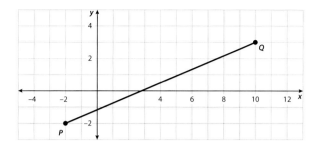

**b.** Use the distance formula to show that $M$ is the midpoint of $\overline{PQ}$.

**9.** If you stand 132 feet from a tree, you can block it out with your hand. Assume your hand is 8 inches long and you hold it 22 inches from your eye. How tall is the tree?

**10.** Find the distance $d$ across the pond.

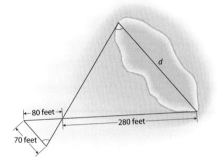

**11.** For the figure below, find sin $E$, cos $E$, and tan $E$. Write each answer as a fraction and a decimal. (Round decimals to four places, if necessary.)

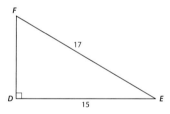

---

**8a.** $(4, 0.5)$

**8b.**
$$PM = \sqrt{(4 - (-2))^2 + (0.5 - (-2))^2}$$
$$= \sqrt{42.25};$$
$$MQ = \sqrt{(4 - 10)^2 + (0.5 - 3)^2}$$
$$= \sqrt{42.25};$$ Since $M$ is a point on $\overline{PQ}$ and $PM = MQ$, $M$ is the midpoint of $\overline{PQ}$.

**9.** $\dfrac{\text{length of hand}}{\text{height of tree}} = \dfrac{\text{distance to hand}}{\text{distance to tree}}$;
The tree is 48 feet tall.

**10.** $\dfrac{80}{280} = \dfrac{70}{d}$; $d = 245$ feet

**11.** $\sin E = \dfrac{8}{17} \approx 0.4706$,

$\cos E = \dfrac{15}{17} \approx 0.8824$, and

$\tan E = \dfrac{8}{15} \approx 0.5333$

**12.** $\sin A = \dfrac{\sqrt{2}}{2}$; $\cos A = \dfrac{\sqrt{2}}{2}$;
 $\tan A = 1$

**13.** $\sin 48° = \dfrac{100}{x}$; $x \approx 134.6$ feet

**14.** about 111.5 meters

**15.** about 4.6 feet

**16.** $\text{leg}_1 \approx 26.5$ ft; $\text{leg}_2 \approx 14.1$ ft;
 acute angle $= 28°$

**17.** 20.7 cm$^2$

**12.** Give the exact value of sin A, cos A, and tan A, where ∠A is one of the acute angles of a 45°-45°-90° triangle.

**13.** The stairs of the Kukulcan Pyramid in Mexico rise at a 48° angle. When you get to the top of the stairway, you are 100 feet above the ground (about ten stories). How long is the stairway?

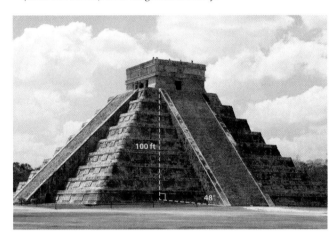

**14.** The angle of elevation from a person in a kayak to the top of a 52-meter lighthouse is 25°. About how far is the person from the lighthouse? (Assume that the lighthouse is vertical and the horizontal line of sight of the person meets the bottom of the lighthouse.)

**15.** Suppose you want to use an 8-foot long ramp to move objects from ground level into the bed of a truck. It is difficult to move objects up a ramp if the ramp makes an angle of more than 35° with the ground. What is the maximum height for the bed of the truck, given the ramp restriction of 35°?

**16.** A right triangle has an acute angle of 62° and a hypotenuse of 30 feet. Solve the right triangle.

**17.** A right triangle has a hypotenuse of 10 cm and one angle that measures 28°. What is the area of the triangle?

# Chapter Extension
## Measuring Angles of Elevation

In this lesson, you will build a device called a *clinometer* and use it to find the height of something that you are unable to measure directly.

### BUILDING AND USING A CLINOMETER

With a partner, begin constructing your clinometer by taping a weighted string to the vertex point of a protractor. Then tape a drinking straw to the straight edge of the protractor as shown in the figure.

### USING YOUR CLINOMETER

To use the device, hold it so that when you look through the straw you see the top of the object you want to measure. Be careful when you read the angle measure from your clinometer, because the angle formed by the straw and the weighted string is the complement of the desired angle of elevation. In the diagram above, the angle of elevation is $90° − 70° = 20°$.

CHAPTER EXTENSION    **Chapter 12**    **465**

## Lesson Objectives
- use a clinometer to determine angles of elevation.
- use a clinometer and trigonometry to find the height of an object that cannot be measured directly.

## Vocabulary

## Materials List

*Per clinometer:*
- drinking straw
- measuring tape or meter stick
- protractor
- string
- tape
- weight such as a washer or fishing weight

## Description

In this lesson, students will use protractors and straws to build simple clinometers.

Working in groups of two or three, they will then use their clinometers to measure angles of elevation. Once the angles have been determined and specified distances measured, they will use what they have learned in the chapter to determine the height of an object that cannot be measured directly.

**TEACHING TIP**

If students wonder why the complement of the angle shown on their protractor is the actual angle of elevation, show them the following figure:

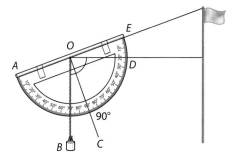

Then have them use the figure to explain why the complement of the angle read on the protractor, ∠BOC, is congruent to the angle of elevation, ∠DOE.

**TEACHING TIP**

It may be helpful to have students estimate the height of the object they have chosen. This might help them avoid large errors, such as failing to use the complement of the angle shown on their protractors as the angle of elevation.

Begin by choosing a tall object to measure. To find the height of the object,

- measure the distance of your eye to the ground,
- measure the distance between where you are standing and the object you want to measure,
- use the clinometer to find the desired angle of elevation, and then
- calculate the approximate height of the object.

**1.** Record the measurements in a table like the one shown below.

| Object | Ground-to-Eye Height | Distance to the Object | Reading on the Clinometer | Angle of Elevation | Calculated Height of the Object |
|---|---|---|---|---|---|
| | | | | | |
| | | | | | |

**2.** Suppose you did not read your clinometer carefully and made an error of 1°. How would this error affect the calculation of the height of your object?

**3.** How can you improve the accuracy of your results?

## Chapter 12 Extension Answers

**1.** Sample answers:

| Object | Ground-to-Eye Height | Distance to the Object | Reading on the Clinometer | Angle of Elevation | Calculated Height of the Object |
|---|---|---|---|---|---|
| Building | 5.5 feet | 15 feet | 20° | 70° | 41.2 + 5.5 = 46.7 feet |

**2.** Sample answer: Using 70° and 71° for the angles of elevation and a distance of 15 feet from the observer to the object, the error would be about 2.4 feet.

**3.** Sample answers: Measure more carefully. Use a protractor with a more precise scale.

# Chapter 13
# Periodic Functions and Sound

## Mathematical Overview

Repetitive behaviors, such as oscillations and periodic motion, all have common mathematical characteristics. Students begin this chapter with a study of how mathematical models for music and repeated motion share some basic similarities. In the remainder of the chapter, students examine frequency, pitch, loudness, and amplitude while exploring the mathematics of musical sounds. This chapter concludes with an Extension in which the graphs of the functions $y = \sin(x)$ and $y = \cos(x)$, known as *sinusoidal wave patterns*, are found to be periodic. A wide variety of real-world situations that involve circular motions, oscillations, musical tones, and other wave behavior can be modeled with sinusoidal functions.

## Lesson Summaries

### Lesson 13.1   *Activity: Periodic Motion*

In this Activity, students use a CBR™ to collect height-vs-time data to illustrate periodic motion. During the Activity, students investigate the movements made by bouncing a ball attached at the end of a Slinky™. They identify the amplitude, period, and frequency of the motion. They then draw and examine a graph of their data to understand periodic motion and how a translation can extend the data.

### Lesson 13.2   *Activity: Frequency and Pitch*

In this Activity, students examine properties of sound waves. Students working in groups blow across the top of a bottle containing water to produce a musical tone and use a CBL 2™ and a microphone probe to produce a pressure-vs-time graph of the different tones produced. Then they repeat the Activity after adding more water to their bottles. They discover that there is a relationship between frequency of sound pressure oscillations and the pitch of sound. The data collected from all the groups are combined for use in the Investigation in Lesson 13.3. Students complete this lesson with an understanding of how our ears perceive a pressure wave as a sound wave. The pitch corresponds to the frequency of our eardrums' vibration. The loudness of the sound depends on the amplitude of the pressure wave.

### Lesson 13.3   *Investigation: Modeling with Sound Waves*

In this Investigation, students explore in more depth the relationship between the frequency of the tone produced by blowing across a bottle and the water level of the bottle. Students use the data they collected in Lesson 13.2 to construct a table. Then they use the data in their tables to make and analyze four different scatter plots involving water height, frequency, length of air column, and period to find appropriate models wherever possible.

### Lesson 13.4   *R.A.P.*

In this lesson, students **R**eview **A**nd **P**ractice solving problems that require the use of skills and concepts taught in previous math levels. The skills reviewed in this lesson are skills that are needed as a basis for solving problems throughout this course.

### Chapter 13   *Extension: Sinusoidal Functions*

In this Extension, students collect data by placing a sticker on a hula hoop (or similar wheel), rolling the hoop along a tape measure, and then stopping every 12 inches to record the height of the sticker placed on the hoop. Students use a graphing calculator to make a scatter plot of height vs distance. The graph of the data is compared to that of a cosine function. Students learn that simple periodic functions can be modeled by sinusoids.

# Lesson Guide

| Lesson/Objectives | Materials | |
|---|---|---|
| **Chapter 13 Opener: How Are Music and Repeated Motion Related?**<br>• identify processes that repeat at regular intervals. | | |
| **13.1 Activity: Periodic Motion**<br>• observe periodic motion.<br>• describe the characteristics of periodic motion. | *Per group:*<br>• Slinky™<br>• baseball or similar ball<br>• tape<br>• meter stick<br>• grid paper<br>• CBR™ and unit-to-unit link cable | *Optional:*<br>• CBL 2™ and motion detector |
| **13.2 Activity: Frequency and Pitch**<br>• observe how the pressure of a musical sound wave varies with time.<br>• recognize the connection between the frequency of a sound wave and the pitch of the sound. | *Per group:*<br>• CBL 2™ with unit-to-unit link cable<br>• microphone probe<br>• glass bottle, such as a soda bottle (all identical)<br>• water<br>• ruler<br>• rubber band | *Optional:*<br>• set of tuning forks<br>• musical instruments used by students in the class<br>• alcohol wipes<br>• a computer program such as Vernier's *Logger Lite* |
| **13.3 Investigation: Modeling with Sound Waves**<br>• choose appropriate models for data. | *Per group:*<br>• class data from the Activity in Lesson 13.2<br>• graphing calculator | *Optional:*<br>• TRM table shell for Questions 1 and 2 |
| **13.4 R.A.P.**<br>• solve problems that require previously learned concepts and skills. | • grid paper | |
| **Chapter 13 Extension: Sinusoidal Functions**<br>• use sine and cosine functions to model periodic functions. | *Per group:*<br>• hula hoop or bicycle wheel<br>• 25-ft tape measure<br>• masking tape<br>• yardstick<br>• graphing calculator | *Optional:*<br>• round stickers<br>• TRM table shells for Questions 2, 17<br>• grid paper<br>• This activity could also be done with a smaller circular object rolled across a tabletop. |

# Pacing Guide

| | Day 1 | Day 2 | Day 3 | Day 4 | Day 5 | Day 6 | Day 7 | Day 8 | Day 9 |
|---|---|---|---|---|---|---|---|---|---|
| **Basic** | p. 468, 13.1 | 13.1 | 13.2 | 13.2 | 13.3 | 13.4 | project | project, review | review |
| **Standard** | p. 468, 13.1 | 13.1 | 13.2 | 13.2 | 13.3 | 13.4 | project | review | extension |
| **Block** | p. 468, 13.1 | 13.2 | 13.3, 13.4 | project, review | review, extension | | | | |

**Supplement Support**

See the Book Companion Website at www.highschool.bfwpub.com/ModelingwithMathematics and the Teacher's Resource Materials (TRM) for additional resources.

# Periodic Functions and Sound

CHAPTER 13
## Periodic Functions and Sound

## CONTENTS

**5e** Engage

## Lesson Objective

- identify processes that repeat at regular intervals.

## Vocabulary

## Description

The preliminary reading gives examples of periodic motion and makes a connection between periodic motion and music.

---

### TEACHING TIP

Ask students to name other situations that involve periodic motion. Examples might include such things as certain amusement park rides, a basketball bouncing up and down, etc. Then, to find out if students are familiar with the terms *frequency*, *period*, and *amplitude*, ask them to describe the characteristics of periodic motion.

---

## How Are Music and Repeated Motion Related?

All around us there are processes that occur over and over again.

- Your heart beats repeatedly during your entire life.
- Ocean waves hit the shore every few seconds.
- A child swings back and forth on a swing.
- The Earth spins on its axis once a day.
- Many clocks keep time through regular motion of a pendulum or spring.

These and many other situations involve motion that repeats more or less at regular intervals.

When you hear music or other sounds, it is not obvious that they are based on repetitive motion. But consider how music is produced. A string of a guitar is plucked or strummed, the reed of a clarinet vibrates rapidly, and the lips of a trumpet player buzz. In fact, in order for you to hear such sounds, your eardrum must also vibrate. These vibrations are normally so fast that you cannot sense them individually. But for the notes with the lowest pitch, like those made by pressing the keys at the left end of a piano, the vibrations may be slow enough to be noticed separately.

The mathematical models for music and repeated motion share some basic similarities that you will study in the first lesson of this chapter. In the remainder of the chapter, you will explore the mathematics of musical sounds.

Things that repeat over and over all have common mathematical characteristics. In this lesson, you will examine repetitive behavior and learn how to describe its properties.

The spinning of a disk and the back-and-forth motion of a pendulum are examples of *cyclic behavior*. In this type of behavior, every repetition is identical to the one before and after it. Each repetition is called a **cycle**. Cycles that involve back-and-forth or up-and-down motion are often called **oscillations**.

1. Attach a solid object, such as a baseball, to one end of a Slinky. Suspend the Slinky directly above a Calculator-Based Ranger (CBR™) or other motion detector so that the CBR can record up and down motion of the ball. Practice releasing the ball so that the minimum height of a bounce is about 0.5 meter and the maximum height is about 1 meter above the CBR.

2. Set up the CBR for data collection as follows:
   * Connect the CBR to the calculator using the link cable.
   * Press the APPS key on the calculator. Then choose **CBL/CBR**.
   * Press any key. Then choose **RANGER**.
   * Choose **SET UP/SAMPLE**.
   * Adjust settings in the **MAIN MENU** window as shown below. (Use the ENTER key to toggle the settings if necessary.)

```
MAIN MENU        START NOW

REALTIME: ▶NO
   TIME(S): 5
  DISPLAY: DIST
 BEGIN ON: [ENTER]
SMOOTHING: LIGHT
    UNITS: METERS
```

   * Choose **START NOW**.

3. Pull the ball down and release it. While it is bouncing steadily, press ENTER on the calculator. Observe the graph that is automatically produced after the data are collected.

4. What quantities, including units, are represented on the horizontal and vertical axes?

PERIODIC MOTION    **Lesson 13.1**    **469**

## LESSON 13.1

**5e** Engage

### Lesson Objectives
* observe periodic motion.
* describe the characteristics of periodic motion.

### Vocabulary
* amplitude
* cycle
* frequency
* oscillations
* period
* periodic motion

### Materials List
* Slinky
* baseball, tennis ball, or similar-size ball
* tape
* meter stick
* CBR and unit-to-unit link cable
* grid paper

### Description
*Preparation:*

Have students work in groups of 3 or 4. A baseball can be attached to the end of a Slinky using tape. Other objects and springs can be used, provided they can be sensed by the CBR. A CBL 2 and motion detector may also work, but the motion detector will not correctly operate at distances as close as the CBR can.

Depending on the calculator used, there may be variations in the programs that must be used for data collection, so be sure to check this out in advance. Students should follow the data collection instructions that are provided.

If there is not enough equipment for group work, perform the experiment as a class demonstration.

*During the Activity:*

In this Activity, students use a CBR to collect distance-versus-time data to illustrate periodic motion. They investigate the graph of vertical oscillations of a ball bouncing at the end of a Slinky and identify characteristics of the motion.

*Closing the Activity:*

Debrief the Activity by going over the answers to the questions with the students. Make sure that students have correctly identified the *period, frequency,*

### TEACHING TIP

Examine the graphical output for each group and make sure the shape is sinusoidal. If the shape of the graph is not correct, the ball may be bouncing too close to the CBR, which will not measure objects that are closer than about 15 centimeters.

### TEACHING TIP

As the ball bounces on the Slinky, the oscillations will eventually *damp out*, or gradually reduce in amplitude, since the Slinky is not perfectly elastic. Students should focus on the first few bounces, for which the amplitude should be approximately constant.

*axis of oscillation,* and *amplitude* of the motion on their graphs in **Question 11**. Then discuss these terms and their relationship to the graphs with the class.

### Lesson 13.1 Activity Answers

3. Sample graph:

```
D(M)                    P1
```
```
X=0          Y=.153
```

**[0, 5] × [−0.2, 1.0]**

4. horizontal: time in seconds; vertical: height of the bottom of the ball above the CBR in meters

**5.** How many cycles are shown on the graph? (Each cycle is a complete up-and-down bounce, but the graph may begin at any point in a cycle.)

**6.** Using the TRACE function of your calculator, explore the points on the graph with the right and left arrow keys. Identify the minimum and maximum heights to the nearest 0.01 meter.

**7.** The **amplitude** of the oscillations is the greatest distance, up or down, that the ball moves from its central position. It can be found by computing half the difference of the maximum and minimum heights.

$$\text{amplitude} = \frac{\text{maximum height} - \text{minimum height}}{2}$$

What is the amplitude for your experiment?

**8.** The **period** of the oscillations is the time for one complete cycle. Find the period for your experiment. Measure to the nearest 0.01 second.

**9.** The **frequency** of the oscillations is a count of the number of cycles per unit time. Explain the relationship between frequency and period.

**10.** Find the frequency for your experiment.

**11.** On grid paper, draw a graph of height vs time for your experiment. On the graph, label the amplitude and the period.

**Note**

The period can be measured between any two corresponding points in consecutive cycles.

## PERIOD AND FREQUENCY

Notice that your graph in Question 11 shows a transformation. If you isolate one period of the motion on the graph and shift it to the right or to the left, you generate additional periods on the graph. As you saw in Chapter 9, this kind of transformation is called a *translation*. Using translations, you can extend the graph indefinitely based on the graph of a single period.

Cyclic behavior is also called *periodic behavior*. The bouncing of the ball connected to the Slinky is an example of **periodic motion**.

The frequency counts the number of cycles in a unit time period and is the reciprocal of the period.

$$\text{frequency} = \frac{1}{\text{period}}$$

### TEACHING TIP

In **Question 8**, make sure that students understand that the period can be measured between any pair of identical points in adjacent cycles. The time between adjacent maxima or minima may be easiest to measure.

### TEACHING TIP

You may wish to point out that the graph from **Question 11** also contains a glide reflection, with the axis being the centerline of the graph.

**5.** Sample answer: a little more than 3 cycles

**6.** Sample answer: minimum height: 0.13 m; maximum height: 0.83 m

**7.** Sample answer:
$$\frac{0.83 - 0.13}{2} = 0.35 \text{ m}$$

**8.** Sample answer:
2.78 s – 1.18 s = 1.60 seconds

**9.** Sample answer: Since period measures time for a cycle, and frequency measures cycles per unit time, the frequency is the reciprocal of the period.

**10.** Sample answer:
$$\frac{1}{1.60 \text{ s}} = 0.625 \text{ cycle per second}$$

**11.** Sample answer:

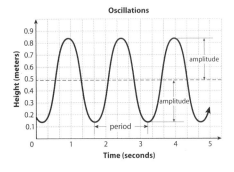

# E X A M P L E

A graph of the motion of the bit on the end of a jackhammer is shown.

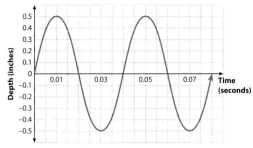

Find (a) the amplitude, (b) the period, and (c) the frequency of the motion.

**Solution.**

**a.** The minimum depth is $-0.5$ in. and the maximum is 0.5 in. So, the amplitude is $\dfrac{0.5 - (-0.5)}{2} = 0.5$ in.

**b.** The motion completes a cycle in 0.04 s, which is the period.

**c.** The frequency is the reciprocal of the period, $\dfrac{1}{0.04} = 25$ cycles per second.

## Practice for Lesson 13.1

**For Exercises 1–4, use the following information.**

The table below shows the position $x$ (in centimeters) of a pendulum at various times $t$ (in seconds), measured from the middle (center) of its swing. Positive values of $x$ represent positions to the right of center, and negative values represent positions to the left.

| $t$ (s) | 0 | 0.2 | 0.4 | 0.6 | 0.8 | 1.0 | 1.2 | 1.4 | 1.6 | 1.8 | 2.0 | 2.2 | 2.4 |
|---|---|---|---|---|---|---|---|---|---|---|---|---|---|
| $x$ (cm) | 25 | 21 | 12 | 0 | $-12$ | $-21$ | $-25$ | $-21$ | $-12$ | 0 | 12 | 21 | 25 |

| $t$ (s) | 2.6 | 2.8 | 3.0 | 3.2 | 3.4 | 3.6 | 3.8 | 4.0 | 4.2 | 4.4 | 4.6 | 4.8 | 5.0 |
|---|---|---|---|---|---|---|---|---|---|---|---|---|---|
| $x$ (cm) | 21 | 12 | 0 | $-12$ | $-21$ | $-25$ | $-21$ | $-12$ | 0 | 12 | 21 | 25 | 21 |

**1.** Make a scatter plot of the data. Then connect the points with a smooth curve.

**2.** Find the amplitude of the pendulum's swings.

PERIODIC MOTION    **Lesson 13.1**    **471**

## CONNECTION

In the **Example**, you may need to explain to students that a jackhammer is a machine that is used to break up pavement or concrete. It works by causing a chisel to move rapidly up and down.

## ADDITIONAL EXAMPLE

Find (a) the amplitude, (b) the period, and (c) the frequency of the motion for the graph below.

**a.** 4 cm

**b.** 3 seconds

**c.** $\dfrac{1}{3}$ cycle per second

## Practice for Lesson 13.1 Answers

**1.** Sample answer:

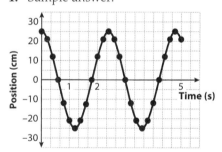

**2.** $\dfrac{25 \text{ cm} - (-25 \text{ cm})}{2} = 25$ cm

3. 2.4 seconds

4. $\frac{1}{2.4} \approx 0.42$ cycle per second

3. Find the period of the pendulum's swings.

4. Find the frequency of the pendulum's swings.

**For Exercises 5–7, use the following information.**

During the year, the length of daylight changes. The table below shows the number of hours of daylight in Boston every 30 days from December 31 to March 26 more than a year later.

| Daylight in Boston | | |
|---|---|---|
| Date | Day Number | Length of Daylight (hours) |
| 12/31 | 0 | 9.1 |
| 1/30 | 30 | 9.9 |
| 3/1 | 60 | 11.2 |
| 3/31 | 90 | 12.7 |
| 4/30 | 120 | 14.0 |
| 5/30 | 150 | 15.0 |
| 6/29 | 180 | 15.3 |
| 7/29 | 210 | 14.6 |
| 8/28 | 240 | 13.3 |
| 9/27 | 270 | 11.9 |
| 10/27 | 300 | 10.6 |
| 11/26 | 330 | 9.5 |
| 12/26 | 360 | 9.1 |
| 1/25 | 390 | 9.7 |
| 2/24 | 420 | 11.0 |
| 3/26 | 450 | 12.4 |

5. Plot the data from the table. Draw a smooth curve through the points and extend the graph to show how it should look over 720 days, almost two years.

6. Find the period and frequency of the graph.

7. Find the amplitude.

5. Sample graph:

**Daylight in Boston**

As the Earth orbits the sun, the amount of daylight fluctuates periodically and should follow a cyclic pattern.

6. The period appears to be about one year (365 days). The frequency is one cycle per year or $\frac{1}{365}$ cycle per day.

7. $\frac{15.3\ \text{h} - 9.1\ \text{h}}{2} = 3.1$ hours

**For Exercises 8–10, use the following information.**

Suppose you are pushing your sister on a swing. If you sketch a graph of her distance from you over time, it might look like this.

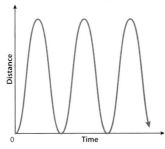

8. What happens to the distance between you and your sister over time if you push with the same force each time?

9. What do the maximum values in the graph represent? What do the minimum values in the graph represent?

10. Where in the graph are the swing's chains perpendicular to the ground? Explain.

11. The figure shows graphs of three periodic functions. Each function's graph repeats some basic shape. The horizontal axis measures time in seconds.

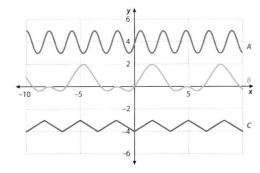

Find an approximate period and frequency for each graph.

**CONNECTION**

**Exercise 11** presents three periodic graphs. The motion in the first is often referred to as *simple harmonic motion*. Periodic behavior often has this pattern, but many types of periodic motion do not.

8. Sample answer: The distance oscillates between two values, a maximum distance away from you and a minimum distance right next to you.

9. Sample answer: The maximum value is your sister's distance from you when she is farthest away, and the minimum value is her distance from you when she is closest.

10. Sample answer: The chains are perpendicular to the ground at a distance exactly halfway between the endpoints of each swing. On the graph, these halfway points are at a height that is midway between the minimum and maximum heights of the graph.

11. Sample answers:
    Graph A: period ≈ 2 s;
    frequency ≈ $\frac{1}{2}$ cycle per second
    Graph B: period ≈ 6.3 s;
    frequency ≈ 0.16 cycle per second
    Graph C: period ≈ 3 s;
    frequency ≈ $\frac{1}{3}$ cycle per second

# LESSON 13.2

## Lesson Objectives

- observe how the pressure of a musical sound wave varies with time.
- recognize the connection between the frequency of a sound wave and the pitch of the sound.

## Vocabulary

- pitch
- sound wave
- wave

## Materials List

*Per group:*

- glass or plastic bottle, such as a soda bottle (identical for all groups)
- water
- ruler
- rubber band
- CBL 2 with unit-to-unit link cable
- microphone probe

## Description

*Preparation:*

Have students work in groups of 3 or 4. All groups should have bottles of the same size and shape, as data from this Activity will be aggregated for the Investigation in Lesson 13.3. Students should be told to save their data for that lesson. You may want to experiment with a variety of bottles to find one that is appropriate. (Either glass or plastic bottles can be used.) The height units used here may be either centimeters or inches, but all students should use the same units for comparison purposes.

Demonstrate the method of data collection for the class before students begin the Activity on their own. Have a volunteer produce a musical tone by blowing across the opening of a bottle that has a small amount of water in it. It may take some trial-and-error for students to produce a recognizable tone. Have alcohol wipes available for sanitation purposes, since several students may use the same bottle.

The **Datamate** program on a TI-83/84 calculator's **APPS** menu

will automatically recognize a microphone probe attached to the CBL 2. (Some calculators may have different programs to accomplish the data analysis.) Have another student hold the microphone to the side of the first student's airstream as the tone is produced and have a third student press **Choice 2** to begin data collection. A graph of the tone's pressure variation with time will be produced.

As an alternative to using a CBL, a computer program such as Vernier's *Logger Lite* can be used with the microphone probe.

---

## Lesson 13.2    ACTIVITY: Frequency and Pitch

Periodic motion can sometimes produce waves that travel through space, or even through solids and liquids. In this lesson, you will examine properties of sound waves.

Your ears can hear many types of sounds. One property of a sound is its **pitch**. High-pitched sounds can be produced by pressing the keys on the right side of a piano, while pressing the keys on the left side produces low-pitched sounds.

1. Put some water in a bottle so that the bottle is less than one-fourth full. Record the height of the water level.
2. Blow across the top of the bottle to produce a musical tone. You may have to experiment a little in order to get a sound with a well-defined pitch. Describe what you hear.
3. Use a Calculator-Based Laboratory 2 (CBL 2™) and a microphone probe to measure the sound pressure while you blow across the top of the bottle. Your teacher will demonstrate how to collect sound pressure data. Record the sound pressure graph.
4. It may be surprising to see that the pressure oscillates up and down at a rapid rate. The pressure varies by only a small amount above and below atmospheric pressure. It is this variation that is measured by the microphone.
   a. Find the period of the pressure oscillations.
   b. If a period is measured in seconds, as in Part (a), then the frequency is measured in cycles per second, or *hertz* (Hz). Determine the frequency of the pressure oscillations. Explain the meaning of this value.
5. Add more water to the bottle so that it is between one-fourth and three-fourths full. Record the new height.
6. Blow across the top of the bottle. Describe what you hear.
7. Use the microphone to collect sound pressure data, and record the graph.
8. Determine the period and frequency of this graph.
9. Summarize what you have discovered about the relationship between frequency of sound pressure oscillations and the pitch of the sound.

---

*During the Activity:*

In this Activity, students use a CBL 2 and microphone probe to produce a pressure-vs-time graph of the two different tones produced by blowing across the opening of a bottle. By tracing the graph, they can directly find the period of each tone, and then calculate the tone's frequency.

*Closing the Activity:*

Make sure that all students see that the pitch of a musical tone is related to the frequency of its pressure variation. The pitch is higher for greater frequencies, and lower for lesser frequencies. Discuss these terms with the class.

## SOUND WAVES

When you pluck a violin or guitar string, it vibrates back and forth. To see this effect, try plucking a stretched rubber band. The blur you see is the rubber band vibrating.

The vibrations of a violin string push on nearby air particles. These air particles push on other nearby air particles. This push increases the air pressure in a very small region of space. Behind this, a region of lower pressure is created. Alternating regions of increased and decreased pressure form a pressure wave. Your ears perceive the pressure wave as a **sound wave**.

**Note**
A **wave** is a disturbance that moves from one place to another. Waves can carry energy or information without a transfer of material.

When the pressure wave hits your ear, your eardrum begins to vibrate at the same rate as the vibrating string. The pitch of the note you hear corresponds to the frequency of the vibration.

## LOUDNESS AND AMPLITUDE

A pure tone has a simple pressure-vs-time graph.

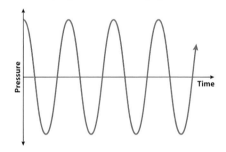

FREQUENCY AND PITCH    **Lesson 13.2**    475

As an alternative to using bottles for the Activity, a set of tuning forks can be used (which may be available in your school's physics department). However, since they usually have their frequencies labeled, a significant feature of the data analysis is lost. Another option is to have students who play musical instruments provide the tones. This could lead to an interesting comparison of waveforms for different instruments, although a synthesizer keyboard can be made to produce almost pure sinusoidal waveforms. However, either of these alternatives would render the data analysis of Lesson 13.3 impossible. In such a case, if either of these alternatives is used, students will not have the data necessary to answer the questions in the Investigation of Lesson 13.3. Sample data for that lesson can be found in the answer to Question 2 of Lesson 13.3.

**TEACHING TIP**

The data from all groups will be combined for use in the Investigation in Lesson 13.3. You may want to assign each group two heights to use in this Activity so that the class data contain a uniform range of heights. Depending on the type of bottle used, students may find it difficult to produce a well-defined tone when the bottle approaches $\frac{3}{4}$-full. You may want to experiment with different amounts of water before presenting this Activity to your class.

**TEACHING TIP**

The heights for this experiment can be measured either in inches or in centimeters, as long as all groups use the same units.

**TEACHING TIP**

For **Question 4**, frequencies could also be determined by inspection of the raw data in lists **L1** and **L2** of the calculator upon exiting the **Datamate** program.

**CONNECTION**

**Question 4** You may wish to point out to students that the abbreviation for hertz is Hz. When a unit is named after a person (in this case the German physicist Heinrich Hertz, who discovered electromagnetic waves), the name of the unit is not capitalized, but the abbreviation is.

## Lesson 13.2 Activity Answers

1.  Sample answer: $1\frac{3}{4}$ inches

2.  Sample answer: The sound is a low-pitched steady note.

3.  Sample answer:

[−0.002, 0.022] × [−0.2588, 0.3175]

4a.–9.  See answers beginning on page 623.

The loudness of the sound depends on the amplitude. When the pressure amplitude increases, the sound is louder.

Pressure-vs-time graphs for musical sounds have a regular pattern. A flute produces tones with simple wave patterns, while other instruments' patterns are more complex. For example, the pattern shown below was produced by a note played on a trombone.

*Noise* contains many unrelated sound frequencies and does not show a regular pattern. You may have heard of singers who can break a glass with their voices. By singing a sustained pure note under very controlled conditions, a singer's voice may cause the glass to vibrate so much that the glass shatters from the pressure.

Different instruments produce sound waves in different ways.

- The harp is one of the oldest stringed instruments. Each string vibrates to produce a different note.
- Some string instruments use a few strings to produce many notes. For example, violins and guitars produce different notes by using only parts of strings.
- Wind instruments such as trombones, flutes, and clarinets play different notes when the length of the air column inside the instrument is changed.
- Percussion instruments, such as marimbas and steel drums, create vibrations that ring at precise pitches when struck.

## Practice for Lesson 13.2

For Exercises 1–3, use the scatter plot below. The plot represents data collected from a tuning fork with a CBL.

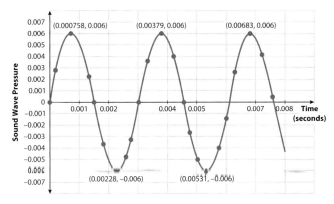

1. Find the period of the sound wave.
2. Find the frequency of the sound wave.
3. Find the amplitude of the sound wave.

**For Exercises 4–9, match each term with its description.**

4. large amplitude
5. small amplitude
6. period
7. frequency
8. low-pitched note
9. high-pitched note

A. a sound wave with a short period
B. the number of cycles of a sound wave in one second
C. a loudly played note
D. a sound wave with a low frequency
E. the length of time for one complete cycle of a periodic function
F. a softly played note

### Practice for Lesson 13.2 Answers

1. Sample answer: about 0.00303 second
2. Sample answer: about 330 cycles per second, or 330 Hz
3. 0.006
4. C
5. F
6. E
7. B
8. D
9. A

**CONNECTION**

The data used in **Exercises 10–13** are based on the modern *equally-tempered* scale, in which the frequency ratios for successive half-notes equal $\sqrt[12]{2}$. This results in an exact doubling of frequency for an octave containing 12 half-notes, while providing constant ratios for musical intervals in all keys. Equal-tempering became common around the time of Bach, who wrote *The Well-tempered Clavier* in the 17th century. It made it easier for ensembles of different instruments to play in tune in all keys.

**TEACHING TIP**

For **Exercise 12**, you may need to remind students of methods for identifying functions from a table of data. If necessary, review the ways in which linear, quadratic, and exponential functions can be identified. (See Chapters 3, 5, 10, and 11.)

**10.** Sample answer:

**11.** Yes, for each value in the domain, there is one value in the range.

**12.** Successive frequency ratios are all approximately equal to 1.0595. So, the data are exponential. Using the frequency of $C_4$ as the initial value, the function $f = 261.63(1.0595)^n$ models the relationship.

**13.** Since the frequency was 330 hertz, the note is close to $E_4$.

**For Exercises 10–13, use the following information.**

Instead of identifying notes by their frequencies, musicians have given them names. The table below displays the frequencies for the notes in the middle octave of a well-tuned piano.

| Name of the Note | Note Number | Frequency |
|---|---|---|
| $C_4$ | 0 | 261.63 |
| $C_4^{\#}$ | 1 | 277.18 |
| $D_4$ | 2 | 293.66 |
| $D_4^{\#}$ | 3 | 311.13 |
| $E_4$ | 4 | 329.63 |
| $F_4$ | 5 | 349.23 |
| $F_4^{\#}$ | 6 | 369.99 |
| $G_4$ | 7 | 392.00 |
| $G_4^{\#}$ | 8 | 415.30 |
| $A_4$ | 9 | 440.00 |
| $A_4^{\#}$ | 10 | 466.16 |
| $B_4$ | 11 | 493.88 |
| $C_5$ | 12 | 523.25 |

**10.** Make a scatter plot of frequency vs note number.

**11.** Do these data represent a function?

**12.** Find an equation that models the relationship between frequency and note number.

**13.** What note do you think was played by the tuning fork in Exercises 1−3?

**14.** The figure below shows graphs of sound pressure waves collected from two sources.

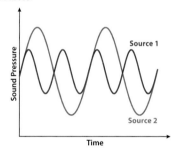

**a.** Which source is louder? How do you know?
**b.** Which source has the higher pitch? How do you know?

**14a.** Source 2 is louder because its graph has the larger amplitude.
**14b.** Source 1 has the higher pitch because it has the smaller period (and therefore, the greater frequency).

The Activity in Lesson 13.2 demonstrated that the frequency of the tone produced by blowing across a bottle varies with the water level in the bottle. In this lesson, you will explore this relationship in more detail.

A pipe organ like those found in many churches contains many pipes of different lengths to produce the notes played by the organist. A flute relies on a similar length variation, but the change is produced by opening or closing holes along the flute's cylindrical body.

By examining data from Lesson 13.2, you can find a way to predict the note that a pipe will produce from the length of the pipe.

1. Use the class data from the Activity in Lesson 13.2 to construct a table similar to the one below. Include enough rows to hold all of the class data. Leave the last two columns blank for now.

| Water Height | Frequency (Hz) | | |
|---|---|---|---|
| | | | |
| | | | |
| | | | |

2. Label the third column "Length of Air Column" and the fourth "Period (s)." Then complete the table. The length of the air column is the measured difference between the height of the bottle and the height of the water. The period can be calculated from the frequency value in the second column.

| Water Height | Frequency (Hz) | Length of Air Column | Period (s) |
|---|---|---|---|
| | | | |
| | | | |
| | | | |

3. From the data in your table, make the following four scatter plots:
   a. frequency $f$ vs water height $h$
   b. period $P$ vs water height $h$
   c. frequency $f$ vs length of air column $L$
   d. period $P$ vs length of air column $L$

can tell them that the equation $f = \dfrac{1,600}{B - h}$ is appropriate, based on the given sample data, where $B$ is the height of the bottle (8.75 inches in the sample data found in the table in the answer to Question 2.).

*Wrapping Up the Investigation:*

Lead a whole-class discussion that considers the various models that students have proposed. Discuss evidence suggesting direct and inverse variation as well as linear models of the form $y = mx + b$.

**TEACHING TIP**

**Question 2** Make sure students indicate in their tables the units used to measure the height of the water. Either inches or centimeters are appropriate.

## Lesson 13.3 Investigation Answers

1.–3. See answers beginning on page 623.

## Lesson Objective

- choose appropriate models for data.

## Vocabulary

## Materials List

- Class data from the Activity in Lesson 13.2

## Description

Students should work in groups of 3 or 4 on this Investigation. Class data from the Activity in Lesson 13.2 form the basis for modeling the frequency and period of the tones produced in that Activity as functions of either the height of the water column or the length of the air column in the bottle. (As an alternative, provide data similar to the sample answer to Question 2.) This is meant to be an open-ended exploration of functional relations, and can serve as a culminating exercise for the modeling course.

In theory, the frequency of a sound wave in a cylindrical pipe that is closed at one end only is given by the equation $f = \dfrac{v}{4L}$, where $v$ is the speed of sound (a constant) and $L$ is the length of the air column. But the exact relationship between $f$ and $L$ for a bottle, as used here, depends strongly on the shape of the bottle, and is difficult to predict theoretically.

Students should be able to identify an inverse variation between frequency $f$ and length $L$. And since period is the reciprocal of frequency, the graph of *period* vs *length of the air column* should be a direct variation function.

*Period* vs *height* of water will be a linear function with negative slope. The important thing here is that students analyze the scatter plots and make informed conjectures regarding appropriate models, then try to confirm those models.

The relationship between frequency and height of water is a rational function, which students have not yet studied. If students are curious, you

4.  Sample answer:
    The scatter plots of period vs water height (Question 3, Part (b)) and period vs length of air column (Question 3, Part (d)) both appear to have linear trends.
    *   The plot of period vs length of air column (Question 3, Part (d)) suggests a line passing very close to the origin, which would describe a direct variation function. To test this conjecture, the ratios of period to length of air column were calculated, and all were just over 0.0006. The equation $P = 0.0006L$ models the data well.
    *   Assuming that the length of the bottle is 8.75 inches, the height of the water is $h = 8.75 - L$, and the equation $P = 0.0006(8.75 - L)$ should model the $P$ vs $h$ relationship, and it does.

Both of the frequency scatter plots (Question 3, Parts (a) and (c)) appear to be curved.
    *   For Question 3, Part (c), the products of frequency and length of air column are all approximately 1,600, which suggests an inverse variation. The equation $f = \dfrac{1,600}{L}$ models the data well. This makes sense, since frequency is the reciprocal of period, and 1,600 is close to the reciprocal of 0.0006.
    *   For Question 3, Part (a), none of the models studied in this course (direct variation, linear, quadratic, or exponential) fit the data.

4.  Using what you know about various kinds of functions, analyze the four relationships. Based on the scatter plots and their related data sets, find appropriate models whenever possible.

## Practice for Lesson 13.3

1.  Explain how you could tune a bottle to play the note F above middle C on a piano ($F_4$ in the table preceding Exercise 10 in Lesson 13.2).

2.  A group wanted to use a bottle to produce a tone with a frequency of 300 Hz. They collected data from a CBL and used the **TRACE** feature of a calculator to find the two sets of coordinates shown below.

Should they add or remove water to get closer to the desired frequency?

3.  Another group wanted to use a bottle to produce a tone with a frequency of 400 Hz. They collected data from a CBL and used the **TRACE** feature of a calculator to find the two sets of coordinates shown below.

Should they add or remove water to get closer to the desired frequency?

## Practice for Lesson 13.3 Answers

1.  Sample answer: Put a little water in the bottle, then use a CBL to record the wave pattern when you blow across the top of the bottle. Find the frequency of the wave by measuring the period on the graph and computing the reciprocal of the period. If the result is less than 349 Hz, add water gradually until that frequency is produced.

2.  They should add a small amount of water. The current period is $0.0128 - 0.0092 = 0.0036$ second, so the current frequency is $\dfrac{1}{0.0036 \text{ s}}$, or about 278 Hz.

3.  They should remove some water. The current period is $0.0106 - 0.0088 = 0.0018$ second, so the current frequency is $\dfrac{1}{0.0018s}$, or about 556 Hz.

**Fill in the blank.**

1. In periodic motion, each repetition is called a(n) _____.

2. The reciprocal of the period in periodic motion is called the _____.

**Choose the correct answer.**

3. A parabola with a vertical axis opens upward and has $x$-intercepts $(-2, 0)$ and $(8, 0)$. Which of the following points could be the vertex of the parabola?

   **A.** $(-2, 3)$     **B.** $(3, 0)$     **C.** $(3, 5)$     **D.** $(3, -8)$

4. Which of these is a factor of the expression $x^2 + 2x - 48$?

   **A.** $(x - 2)$     **B.** $(x + 8)$     **C.** $(x + 6)$     **D.** $(x - 4)$

**Perform the indicated operations. Write answers in simplest form.**

5. $\frac{3}{5} + \frac{2}{3}$

6. $\frac{3}{4} \div 2\frac{1}{2}$

7. $\frac{5}{32} \cdot \frac{4}{25}$

8. $\frac{9}{10} \div \frac{3}{5}$

9. $3\frac{1}{8} - 1\frac{3}{16}$

10. $\frac{5}{6} + \frac{1}{3} - \frac{3}{4}$

**Solve.**

11. What is 5% of 18?

12. What is 48% of 80?

13. What percent of 60 is 12?

14. What percent of 200 is 300?

15. 15% of what number is 18?

16. 200% of what number is 50?

**Write in scientific notation.**

17. 452,000

18. 0.0032

19. 0.163

**Write in standard form.**

20. $1.96 \times 10^{-4}$

21. $5.7 \times 10^{1}$

22. $8 \times 10^{9}$

## Lesson Objective

- solve problems that require previously learned concepts and skills.

## Exercise Reference

Exercises 1–2: Lesson 13.1

Exercise 3: Lesson 11.3

Exercise 4: Lesson 11.6

Exercises 5–10: Appendix A

Exercises 11–16: Appendix F

Exercises 17–22: Appendix K

Exercises 23–24: Lesson 2.3

Exercise 25: Lesson 3.5

Exercise 26: Lesson 3.6

Exercise 27: Lesson 3.7

Exercise 28: Lesson 4.3

Exercise 29: Lesson 4.7

Exercise 30: Lesson 7.2

## Lesson 13.4 R.A.P. Answers

1. cycle
2. frequency
3. D
4. B
5. $1\frac{4}{15}$
6. $\frac{3}{10}$
7. $\frac{1}{40}$
8. $\frac{3}{2}$ or $1\frac{1}{2}$
9. $1\frac{15}{16}$
10. $\frac{5}{12}$
11. 0.9
12. 38.4
13. 20%
14. 150%
15. 120
16. 25
17. $4.52 \times 10^{5}$
18. $3.2 \times 10^{-3}$
19. $1.63 \times 10^{-1}$
20. 0.000196
21. 57
22. 8,000,000,000

**23.** The relationship is not a direct variation function. Sample explanation: The ratios of volume to height are not constant.

**24a.** The relationship is a direct variation function. Sample explanation: The ratios of volume to height are all very close to 210.

**24b.** Sample answer: $V = 210h$

**25.** $t = 18$

**26.** $p > -6$

**27.** $1 \le y < 4$

**28.** 1,133 in.$^2$

**29.** 600,000 ft$^3$

**30.** Sample answer: $y = 63 - \dfrac{4}{3}x$

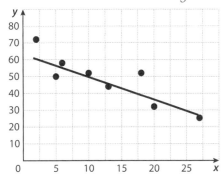

---

**For Exercises 23–24, use the given table that shows the height and volume of liquid in a storage tank.**

  **a.** Determine whether the relationship is a direct variation function. Explain how you know.

  **h.** If it is a direct variation function, write an equation expressing volume $V$ as a function of height $h$.

**23.**

| Height (ft) | Volume (ft³) |
|---|---|
| 1 | 4 |
| 2 | 150 |
| 3 | 570 |
| 4 | 1,200 |
| 5 | 1,950 |

**24.**

| Height (ft) | Volume (ft³) |
|---|---|
| 1 | 209 |
| 2 | 419 |
| 3 | 630 |
| 4 | 845 |
| 5 | 1,052 |

**25.** Solve the equation $8t - 5(4 - t) = 2(6t - 1)$ for $t$.

**26.** Solve the inequality $3 - 4p < 27$ for $p$.

**27.** Write a compound inequality and draw a graph that represents the following statement:

$y$ is at least 1 and less than 4

**28.** A *Norman window* has the shape of a semicircle placed above a rectangle. Find the area of the Norman window shown below. Round to the nearest square inch.

**29.** A model of a ship is constructed at a scale of 1 : 100. The volume of the model's hull is 0.6 ft$^3$. What is the volume of the ship's hull?

**30.** Make a scatter plot of the data in the table below. Then draw a line that models the trend in the data, and find its equation.

| x | 2 | 5 | 6 | 10 | 13 | 18 | 20 | 27 |
|---|---|---|---|---|---|---|---|---|
| y | 72 | 50 | 58 | 52 | 44 | 52 | 32 | 25 |

## Bottle Harmony

When different musical tones are played together, the result is sometimes pleasing to the ear. But other combinations of tones can sound *dissonant* (that is, they do not seem to "go together").

In Lessons 13.2 and 13.3, you created musical tones and measured their frequencies. In this project, you will investigate properties of pleasing sound combinations.

Begin by putting a small amount of water in a bottle. Have a partner use an identical bottle, but with more water in it.

1. If you blow across the tops of your bottles at the same time, do the notes produced make a pleasant-sounding combination?

2. Add water to the second bottle until the notes produced by both bottles sound pleasant together. Use a CBL-2 and a microphone probe to determine their frequencies.

3. Continue adding water to the second bottle to find additional frequencies that make pleasant-sounding combinations with the first bottle.

4. The Pythagoreans long ago discovered that pairs of tones whose frequencies form ratios of small whole numbers, such as 2 to 1, 3 to 2, and so on, tend to sound pleasant together. Are the frequency ratios for any of your pleasant-sounding tone pairs approximately equivalent to ratios of small whole numbers?

# MODELING PROJECT

**5e** Elaborate

## Materials List

- two identical bottles
- water
- ruler
- CBL-2 and microphone probe

## Description

In this project, students investigate frequency ratios for pairs of musical tones. They can work in pairs, although groups of 3 could extend the project to explore three-note chords.

People may not agree on what tones constitute pleasing combinations. A sound that pleases one person may sound dissonant to another. But, at least in the Western musical tradition, tone intervals such as those listed here are often pleasing to the ear and are common in tonal music.

| Interval Name | Example | Frequency Ratio |
|---|---|---|
| Third | C–E | 5 : 4 |
| Fourth | C–F | 4 : 3 |
| Fifth | C–G | 3 : 2 |
| Octave | C–C | 2 : 1 |

The determination of whether two tones sound pleasing together (*consonant*) is of course somewhat subjective. But most people identify the notes in a major chord as a pleasing combination. Students will need to use the microphone/CBL equipment to measure frequencies. This would also be a particularly good place to substitute musical instruments for bottles. A guitar or piano, either of which can play two notes at once, would be especially helpful.

## Sample Answers

1. No.
2. 208 Hz and 250 Hz
3. 278 Hz, 303 Hz, 400 Hz
4. $\frac{250}{208} \approx 1.2$ or 6 to 5;

   $\frac{278}{208} \approx 1.33$ or 4 to 3;

   $\frac{303}{208} \approx 1.46$, which is close to 3 to 2;

   $\frac{400}{208} \approx 1.92$, which is close to 2 to 1

## Chapter 13 Test Review Answers

1. frequency
2. amplitude
3. period

# Chapter 13  Review

## You Should Be Able to:

### Lesson 13.1
- observe periodic motion.
- describe the characteristics of periodic motion.

### Lesson 13.2
- observe how the pressure of a musical sound wave varies with time.
- recognize the connection between the frequency of a sound wave and the pitch of the sound.

### Lesson 13.3
- choose appropriate models for data.

### Lesson 13.4
- solve problems that require previously learned concepts and skills.

## Key Vocabulary

cycle (p. 469)

oscillations (p. 469)

amplitude (p. 470)

period (p. 470)

frequency (p. 470)

periodic motion (p. 470)

pitch (p. 474)

wave (p. 475)

sound wave (p. 475)

## Chapter 13  Test Review

**For Exercises 1–3, fill in the blank with a property of a periodic function.**

1. The number of cycles per unit of time is called the _____.

2. Half of the difference between the maximum point and the minimum point is called the _____.

3. The time for one complete cycle is called the _____.

**For Exercises 4–6, use the following situation.**

The height of a carousel horse's stirrup changes periodically over time as the carousel spins. The graph of this motion is shown below.

4. What is the period in seconds?

5. What are the maximum and minimum heights of the stirrup in feet?

6. What is the amplitude in feet?

**For Exercises 7–8, use the following situation.**

The graph below shows how the force of impact of a runner's shoes with the ground varies with time.

SOURCE: DANIEL LIEBERMAN/HARVARD UNIVERSITY VIA THE BOSTON GLOBE

7. What is the period of the graph in seconds?

8. What is the frequency of the runner's steps?

**For Exercises 9–11, use the following situation.**

A population of gray wolves in Yellowstone Park varies periodically over a year (365 days). A graph of a function that models the relationship between wolf population and time is shown below.

4. about 10 seconds
5. maximum: 5 feet; minimum: 1 foot
6. 2 feet
7. a little less than 0.4 second
8. about 2.7 cycles per second

9. Sample answer: The period is
365 days, the time it takes for the
population to return to a low of
1,200 or a high of 1,600.

10. Sample answer: The amplitude
is 200, which is the amount the
population increases or decreases
from its middle value of 1,400.

11. Sample answer: There are 1,600
wolves at about mid-year (July 1).

12. increases

13. decreases

14. Remove water from the bottle.

15. Sample answer: period =
0.0081 − 0.0028 = 0.0053 second;
frequency $= \dfrac{1}{0.0053} \approx 189 \dfrac{\text{cycles}}{\text{second}}$
$= 189$ Hz

9. State the graph's period and discuss what it means in this situation.

10. Give the graph's amplitude and discuss what it means in this situation.

11. When is the wolf population largest, and how many wolves are there at
that time?

**For Exercises 12–13, complete the statement.**

12. If the period of a sound pressure-vs-time graph decreases, the
frequency _____.

13. If the period of a sound pressure-vs-time graph increases, the
frequency _____.

14. Would you add or remove water to decrease the frequency of the tone
produced by blowing across the top of a bottle?

15. Find the period and frequency of the sound wave
from the graph and data.

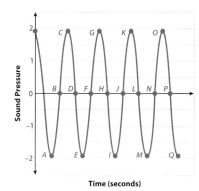

| Point | Time (seconds) | Sound Pressure |
|-------|----------------|----------------|
| A | 0.0028 | −1.917 |
| B | 0.0042 | 0 |
| C | 0.0056 | 1.917 |
| D | 0.0069 | 0 |
| E | 0.0081 | −1.917 |
| F | 0.0095 | 0 |
| G | 0.0109 | 1.917 |
| H | 0.012 | 0 |
| I | 0.013 | −1.917 |
| J | 0.0148 | 0 |
| K | 0.0159 | 1.917 |
| L | 0.0174 | 0 |
| M | 0.0187 | −1.917 |
| N | 0.02 | 0 |
| O | 0.0212 | 1.917 |
| P | 0.0227 | 0 |
| Q | 0.0239 | −1.917 |

**16.** The graphs below are of different tones. Which one represents the tone with the lower pitch? Justify your answer.

Graph A

Graph B

**17.** Suppose the period of a tone is 0.0048 second. Find the frequency.

**18.** Suppose the frequency of a tone is 154 cycles per second. Find the period.

**19.** A group of students are trying to tune a bottle to a note that has a frequency of 311 Hz. They put water in the bottle and blow across it while collecting sound pressure data with a CBL. They estimate the period of the scatter plot to be 0.003 second. Should they add or remove water from their bottle?

**16.** Sample answer: Graph A represents the lower tone. Lower tones have longer periods and generate fewer cycles per second than higher tones. Graph A has fewer cycles per second than Graph B.

**17.** 208 cycles per second

**18.** 0.0065 second

**19.** The current frequency is
$$\frac{1}{0.003} \approx 333 \text{ cycles per second,}$$
which is too high. Therefore, they should remove some water.

**CHAPTER**
**13**

**Chapter Extension**
Sinusoidal Functions

## Lesson Objective

• use sine and cosine functions to model periodic functions.

## Vocabulary

• sinusoidal

## Materials List

• hula hoop, bicycle wheel, or other thin, circular object
• 25-ft tape measure
• masking tape
• yardstick

## Description

Students collect data on the height of a point on a circular object such as a wheel or hula hoop as the wheel rolls on the floor. A graph of the data is compared to that of a cosine function. Students can then see that simple periodic functions are modeled by sinusoids.

This activity could also be done with a smaller circular object rolled across a tabletop.

## Chapter 13 Extension Answers

1. Sample answers:
   diameter = 26 inches;
   circumference = $26\pi \approx 81.7$ inches
2. Sample data:

In 1893, George W. Ferris built the world's first Ferris wheel for the World's Fair in Chicago. In 1985, the Texas Star® opened at the Fair Park in Dallas. Today, the Texas Star is one of the world's largest Ferris wheels. From its maximum height of 212 feet, a rider gets a great view of the Dallas skyline.

One Texas Star rider wondered how he could find his height above ground at any given time.

To help answer this question, first consider a simpler situation. You will need something smaller than a Ferris wheel to model the motion of a rider. Instead of an actual Ferris wheel, you will collect data from a Hula-Hoop® or some other circular object.

1. What is the diameter of your "wheel?" What is its circumference?

2. Collect data as follows:
   • Extend a tape measure and tape it to the floor.
   • Place a piece of masking tape on the floor at one end of the tape measure. Place the wheel directly on top of this masking tape. The wheel should touch the tape measure, with its center directly above the tape measure.
   • Place a dot (or a sticker) on the wheel at the point where the wheel sits on the masking tape you placed at the end of the tape measure.
   • Roll the wheel forward alongside the tape measure. Stop the wheel every 12 inches.

| Distance Wheel Moves (in.) | 0 | 12 | 24 | 36 | 48 | 60 | 72 | 84 | 96 | 108 | 120 |
|---|---|---|---|---|---|---|---|---|---|---|---|
| Height of Dot Above the Floor (in.) | 0 | 5.25 | 16.5 | 25.125 | 24.125 | 14.25 | 3.375 | 0.25 | 7.125 | 18.75 | 25.75 |

| Distance Wheel Moves (in.) | 132 | 144 | 156 | 168 | 180 | 192 | 204 | 216 | 228 | 240 | 252 |
|---|---|---|---|---|---|---|---|---|---|---|---|
| Height of Dot Above the Floor (in.) | 22.75 | 11.875 | 2.0 | 0.75 | 9.25 | 20.75 | 26.0 | 21.0 | 9.75 | 1.0 | 1.75 |

3.

**[0, 260] × [–5, 30]**

- Each time you stop, measure and record the total distance the wheel has traveled and the height of the dot above the floor in a table like the one below.

| Distance Wheel Moves (in.) | 0 | 12 | 24 | 36 | 48 | etc. |
|---|---|---|---|---|---|---|
| Height of Dot Above the Floor (in.) | 0 | | | | | |

3. Use a graphing calculator to make a scatter plot of *height* vs *distance*. Be sure to state your window.

4. Sketch your scatter plot on paper. On your plot, sketch a smooth curve that you think best represents the relationship between height and distance.

5. Do you think the relationship between the height of a marked spot on the wheel and the distance rolled is periodic? Explain.

6. Does your scatter plot appear to be periodic? Explain.

7. What is the height of the center of your wheel above the ground?

8. Based on the height of the center of your wheel above the ground and the diameter of the wheel, what would you expect the maximum and minimum heights of your marked spot to be? Explain.

9. From your data, what are the maximum and minimum heights? How does this compare with what you expected? Explain any differences.

10. How far did your wheel move before the pattern of heights for your marked spot began repeating?

11. What is the horizontal length of one repetition on your graph?

12. How do your answers in Questions 10 and 11 compare?

13. On your calculator's function screen $\boxed{Y=}$, enter the function $y = A - A\cos(360x/d)$ using the cosine key $\boxed{COS}$. Use your answer to Question 7 for $A$ and your answer to Question 10 for $d$.

14. Use your calculator to graph your function from Question 13 along with the scatter plot of your data.

15. Does your function model the data well?

16. Use your function to predict the height of the marked spot if the wheel were to roll 300 inches.

CHAPTER EXTENSION    **Chapter 13**    **489**

**TEACHING TIP**

For **Question 4**, encourage students to use grid paper to generate a large scatter plot of their data. The scatter plot will help them see the critical features of the resulting function more easily.

**TEACHING TIP**

In **Question 11**, remind students that the **TRACE** feature of the calculator can be used to determine an approximate horizontal length from the graph.

**TEACHING TIP**

In **Question 13**, tell students to make sure their calculators are set to degree mode.

**TEACHING TIP**

**Question 14** Some students may have difficulty seeing their graphs. If necessary, suggest that they use a window that corresponds to $[0, \text{at least } 2A] \times [-5, \text{at least } 10d]$.

3. See answer on page 488.
4. Sample answer:

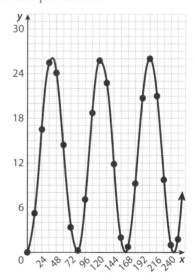

5. Sample answer: Yes, a wheel can roll any number of times. The height of the marked spot rises and falls as the wheel rolls in the same pattern for every turn of the wheel.

6. Sample answer: Yes; there are three "waves" that appear to have the same width and height.

7. Sample answer: 13 inches (for a 26-inch-diameter wheel)

8. Sample answer: The minimum height of the marked spot is the ground, with a height of 0 inches. The maximum height should be equal to the diameter of the wheel, 26 inches.

9. Sample answer: The maximum height is 26 inches and the minimum height is 0 inches, which matches expectations.

10. Sample answer: about 82 inches

11. Sample answer: about 82 inches

12. Sample answer: They are the same.

13. Sample answer:

14.

$[0, 260] \times [-5, 30]$

15. Sample answer: Yes, the match is almost perfect.

16. Sample answer: 20.1 inches

## SINUSOIDAL GRAPHS

The graph you made in Question 14 describes the height of a point on the wheel as a function of the distance the wheel traveled. If you knew how fast the wheel rolled, a similar graph might show the height of the point as a function of time.

The graphs of the functions $y = \sin(x)$ and $y = \cos(x)$ are **sinusoidal** wave patterns. These and other functions based on them are periodic. They can be used to model a wide variety of situations that involve circular motions, oscillations, musical tones, and other wave behavior. In Chapter 12, specific values of these trigonometric functions were used to solve problems in geometry.

17. Use a calculator to complete a table, like the one shown below, of sine values (rounded to two decimal places) for angles from 0° to 360° in 15-degree increments.

| Angle Measure | 0° | 15° | 30° | 45° | 60° | etc. |
|---|---|---|---|---|---|---|
| Sine Value | | | | | | |

18. Make a scatter plot of *sine value* vs *angle measure*. Describe the shape of the scatter plot.

19. Create a graph of the function $y = \sin(x)$ on your calculator. How does it compare to your scatter plot?

20. What would you expect to happen if you continued the graph to 720°?

21. Create a graph of the function $y = \cos(x)$ on your calculator. How does it compare to your graph of $y = \sin(x)$?

### COMMON ERROR

In **Question 19**, if students' graphs do not match their scatter plots, remind them to set their calculators to degree mode.

**17.**

| Angle Measure | 0° | 15° | 30° | 45° | 60° | 75° | 90° | 105° | 120° |
|---|---|---|---|---|---|---|---|---|---|
| Sine Value | 0 | 0.26 | 0.5 | 0.71 | 0.87 | 0.97 | 1 | 0.97 | 0.87 |

| Angle Measure | 135° | 150° | 165° | 180° | 195° | 210° | 225° | 240° | 255° |
|---|---|---|---|---|---|---|---|---|---|
| Sine Value | 0.71 | 0.5 | 0.26 | 0 | −0.26 | −0.5 | −0.71 | −0.87 | −0.97 |

| Angle Measure | 270° | 285° | 300° | 315° | 330° | 345° | 360° |
|---|---|---|---|---|---|---|---|
| Sine Value | −1 | −0.97 | −0.87 | −0.71 | −0.5 | −0.26 | 0 |

**18.** The plot has a sinusoidal shape.

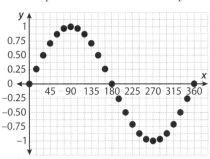

**19.** The graph describes the scatter plot perfectly.

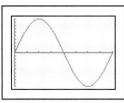

[0, 360] × [−1, 1]

**20.** The graph would repeat the same pattern.

**21.** The graph of $y = \cos(x)$ is the same shape as the graph of $y = \sin(x)$, except that it is shifted horizontally.

[0, 360] × [−1, 1]

490

# Chapter 14
# Probability

## Mathematical Overview

Probability is a measure of how likely it is that some event will occur. In this chapter, students investigate various ways to answer questions about the likelihood that some given event will occur, as well as various real-world applications of probability. Students use a formula to find the theoretical probabilities of simple events and collect data to calculate experimental probabilities. They also explore and calculate conditional probabilities, complements of events, and joint probabilities, including those involving independent, dependent, and mutually exclusive events. Binomial experiments are defined and then conducted. Using the collected data, experimental probabilities are compared to their theoretical probabilities using binomial expansions. Geometric probability is examined in the exercises throughout the chapter. By the end of this chapter, students see why some people call probability the "language of uncertainty."

## Lesson Summaries

### Lesson 14.1  Activity: Determining Probability

In this Activity, students determine the number of ways a particular event can occur and divide it by the total number of possible outcomes to find the theoretical probability of the event. They learn that probability is a number between 0 and 1, inclusive, and it can be expressed in the form of a fraction, decimal, or percent. As a method for gaining a better understanding of experimental probability, students conduct an experiment and collect data involving "defective" paper clips. To wrap up this lesson, the *Law of Large Numbers* that links theoretical and experimental probabilities is discussed.

### Lesson 14.2  Activity: Conditional Probability

In this Activity, students examine situations in which the probability of an event depends on whether or not another event happens. To explore conditional probability, students perform a flexibility test on pieces of pasta, some that are directly out of the box and others that have been wet and allowed to dry. Students learn to symbolically represent conditional probability. In the last section of this lesson students learn that if two events $A$ and $B$ are complementary, then one or the other is certain to occur, and $P(A) + P(B) = 1$. Given the probability of an event, students solve for the probability of the complement.

### Lesson 14.3  Investigation: Joint Probabilities

In this Investigation, students investigate the probability of two events both occurring. Students draw area models to help them understand joint probabilities. The Investigation includes a study of two types of probability:

- the probability of independent events—if two events, $A$ and $B$, are independent, then the probability that both occur is $P(A \text{ and } B) = P(A) \cdot P(B)$, and

- the probability of dependent events—If two events, $A$ and $B$, are dependent, then the probability that both occur is $P(A \text{ and } B) = P(A) \cdot P(B|A)$.

Independent and dependent events are explained symbolically as well as through real-world examples. This lesson concludes with students investigating two events that are mutually exclusive. The probability that either of these two events occurs can be found by adding their probabilities.

### Lesson 14.4  R.A.P.

In this lesson, students **R**eview **A**nd **P**ractice solving problems that require the use of skills and concepts taught in previous math levels. The skills reviewed in this lesson are skills that are needed as a basis for solving problems throughout this course.

### Lesson 14.5  Activity: Binomial Experiments

In this Activity, students explore the conditions that must be met for a situation to be a binomial experiment. In the Activity students record the results for 20 tosses, then 50 tosses, and finally for 100 tosses of a coin. They compare the experimental probabilities to their theoretical probabilities using binomial expansions. Then they use their results to predict what would happen if they tossed the coin 1,000 times. Since the expansions of binomials are not the focus of this lesson, binomial expansions beyond $(a + b)^3$ are provided for the students to use when calculating theoretical probabilities.

## Lesson Guide

| Lesson/Objectives | Materials | |
|---|---|---|
| **Chapter 14 Opener: What Are the Chances?**<br>• recognize that probability is often used to evaluate risk in the real world. | | |
| **14.1 Activity: Determining Probability**<br>• find the theoretical probability of an event.<br>• find the experimental probability of an event by conducting an experiment. | *Per group:*<br>• two different brands of jumbo paper clips (at least 50 of each brand)<br>• box of thumbtacks<br>• graphing calculator | *Optional:*<br>• coin<br>• clear plastic box to hold thumbtacks being shaken<br>• TRM table shell for Question 3<br>• TRM table shell for Exercise 15, Part (a)<br>• standard deck of cards |
| **14.2 Activity: Conditional Probability**<br>• find conditional probabilities.<br>• find the probability of the complement of an event. | *Per group:*<br>• pasta (preferably fettuccini): 50–60 dry pieces and 50–60 pieces that have gotten wet and have been allowed to dry<br>• rulers<br>• water | |
| **14.3 Investigation: Joint Probabilities**<br>• find the probability that two independent events both occur.<br>• find the probability that two dependent events both occur.<br>• find the probability that either of two mutually exclusive events occurs. | *Per pair:*<br>• rulers | *Optional:*<br>• TRM table shell for Questions 4, 6<br>• paper clip<br>• pencil<br>• paper circles to make Spinners A and B shown in Exercise 14 |
| **14.4 R.A.P.**<br>• solve problems that require previously learned concepts and skills. | | |
| **14.5 Activity: Binomial Experiments**<br>• identify binomial experiments.<br>• find probabilities for binomial experiments.<br>• use binomial expansions to find probabilities. | *Per group:*<br>• two coins | *Optional:*<br>• TRM table shell for Questions 1, 4, Part (a), 5 |

## Pacing Guide

| | Day 1 | Day 2 | Day 3 | Day 4 | Day 5 | Day 6 | Day 7 | Day 8 | Day 9 | Day 10 |
|---|---|---|---|---|---|---|---|---|---|---|
| **Basic** | p. 492, 14.1 | 14.1 | 14.2 | 14.2 | 14.3 | 14.3 | 14.4 | 14.5 | project | review |
| **Standard** | p. 492, 14.1 | 14.1 | 14.2 | 14.2 | 14.3 | 14.3 | 14.4 | 14.5 | project | review |
| **Block** | p. 492, 14.1 | 14.2 | 14.3 | 14.4, 14.5 | 14.5, project | project, review | | | | |

### Supplement Support

See the Book Companion Website at www.highschool.bfwpub.com/ModelingwithMathematics and the Teacher's Resource Materials (TRM) for additional resources.

CHAPTER

# 14

# Probability

## CONTENTS

# CHAPTER 14 OPENER

**5e** Engage

## Lesson Objective

- recognize that probability is often used to evaluate risk in the real world.

## Vocabulary

- probability

## Description

Probability is introduced in the context of defective fuel pumps that were discovered in 2002 on Boeing aircraft. This reading sets up the scenario and is then revisited in Lesson 14.3 as students gain skills in using probability to solve problems.

### CONNECTION

The defective pumps discussed in this reading were made by Hydro-Aire Inc. of California. The discovery initially necessitated the testing of 1,440 aircraft, but ultimately 30,000 planes had to be inspected.

### TEACHING TIP

To guide instruction in this chapter, it might be helpful to ask students what they remember about their previous studies of probability. Specifically, you might ask if they remember doing any experiments. If they do, question them about what they discovered.

## What Are the Chances?

Several years ago, the Boeing Corporation discovered that fuel pumps on some of their airplanes were faulty. The defective pumps, which were made by a company in California, had been installed during a four-month period. No serious incidents resulted from the faulty pumps, but all the planes that had pumps installed during those months had to be inspected.

The problem was that the wires in some pumps were placed too close to a rotor. Friction with the rotor might cause a spark that could cause a fuel explosion. Only a small percent of the pumps were actually faulty. So, most planes that had these pumps were not at risk. But how much risk was there for any particular plane? There are several important questions that could be asked.

- What is the chance that a particular pump had the misplaced wiring?
- If a pump had misplaced wiring, what was the chance of an explosion?
- Some large planes had several fuel tanks and pumps. What was the chance that one of the pumps on such a plane was faulty?

Answers to questions like these are based on **probability**, a measure of how likely it is that some event will occur. In this chapter, you will investigate various ways to answer questions such as these. You will also investigate various applications of probability. By the end of this chapter, you will see why some people call probability the "language of uncertainty."

492     **Chapter 14**     PROBABILITY

### TEACHING TIP

Vocabulary organizers, such as the one below, are particularly helpful for this chapter.

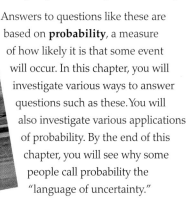

| Formal Definition | Informal Definition |
|---|---|
| the total number of ways the event can occur divided by the total number of equally likely outcomes | the chance of something happening |

**Probability**

| | |
|---|---|
| The probability of rolling a 5 on a number cube, labeled 1 through 6, is $\frac{1}{6}$. | No probability can be greater than 1. The probability of rain tomorrow cannot be 150%. |
| Example | Non-example |

The probability of rain tomorrow is 90%. This statement and others like it are used to indicate how likely it is for an event to happen. In this lesson, you will find the theoretical probability of a simple event. You will also investigate how experiments can be used to find experimental probabilities.

### Connection

Gerolamo Cardano, a 16th-century Italian mathematician, was the first person to use a mathematical model to predict what happens in the long run in a game of chance. It took mathematicians over 300 years to agree on a formal definition for probability. Since that time, probability has spread to other areas, such as the insurance industry and the field of genetics, where measuring uncertainty is important.

Any company that sells a product or service must be concerned about quality. Many companies have *quality control* departments. Items produced on assembly lines are inspected regularly by quality control inspectors or machines.

A manufacturing operation cannot produce perfect items 100% of the time. The inspection process determines what fraction of the total is defective and what fraction is not defective (nondefective). These fractions also describe the probabilities that a single item is defective or nondefective.

### THEORETICAL PROBABILITY

You already know that probability can sometimes be easily predicted. On the spinner below, you could spin a 1, 2, 3, or 4. These are all of the possible outcomes. Because the area represented by each number is the same, each outcome is equally likely. So, the probability of spinning the number 3 or any other number on this spinner is $\frac{1}{4}$. This means that, on the average, we expect one-fourth of all spins to result in the spinner landing on the number 3. The probability can also be expressed as a decimal, 0.25, and as a percent, 25%. This type of probability is called **theoretical probability**.

### Note

An **event** is a particular outcome or collection of outcomes of an experiment or process.

**Theoretical Probability**

The probability that a particular event will occur is found by counting all the different possible outcomes.

$$\text{Probability of an event} = \frac{\text{total number of ways the event can occur}}{\text{total number of equally likely outcomes}}$$

The probability of an event is always a number between 0 and 1, inclusive. A probability of 1 means that an event is certain to occur. A probability of 0 means that an event cannot occur.

DETERMINING PROBABILITY     **Lesson 14.1**     **493**

### Lesson Objectives
- find the theoretical probability of an event.
- find the experimental probability of an event by conducting an experiment.

### Vocabulary
- event
- experimental probability
- Law of Large Numbers
- theoretical probability

### Materials List
*Per group:*
- two different brands of *jumbo* paper clips (at least 50 of each brand)
- box of thumbtacks

### Description
*Preparation:*

Have students work in small groups of two or three. Provide each group with the materials needed for the Activity. Jumbo paper clips are suggested here because they are more brittle than the small (#1) size paper clips.

Note: As an alternative to using paper clips for this experiment, students can perform the Activity by first flipping a coin and collecting the indicated data and then spinning a coin and collecting data.

*During the Activity:*

Before beginning this Activity, have students read the material preceding the actual Activity as this sets up the quality control context of the Activity and introduces the concept of a defective item.

Even though this is a somewhat contrived experiment to test for defects, it is an easy and inexpensive way to perform a test.

*Closing the Activity:*

After students have finished the Activity, point out that the type of quality control discussed here is often referred to in the industry as *inspection for attributes,* which usually involves a comparison to some standard. In

this case, the properties are classified as either defective or nondefective. Ask them if they can think of any other situations in which this type of inspection is done. For example, students might mention inspections in the clothing industry that make sure that the colors of materials are uniform and logos are put on items properly.

### CONNECTION

*Inspection for variables* is another type of quality control that involves measurement of some value, such as strength of a metal or time to failure such as in a light bulb.

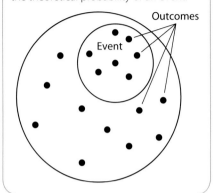
A shorthand notation is often used to denote probabilities. The symbol $P(A)$ stands for "the probability of event $A$" or "the probability that event $A$ occurs." For example, the probability that the spinner on page 493 will land on 3 can be written as $P(3)$. So you can write $P(3) = \frac{1}{4}$.

## EXPERIMENTAL PROBABILITY

Sometimes theory and logic are unable to provide probabilities for events. In such cases, only the collection of data can provide the information needed to determine probabilities. In this Activity, you will collect data that involves the opening of paper clips.

1. Hold a paper clip, and open it up as shown below. Did it break?

Paper clips are not intended to be opened all the way. But suppose that is their purpose. If one breaks, we could say that it is defective.

2. A common sample size for inspection is *five*. Test five clips, and record the number of defective ones.

3. Now repeat your test on 10 more samples of size five. Record your results in a table similar to the one below. The third column should contain the total number of defective clips found in all samples up to that point. The fourth column should contain the percent of defective clips up to that point.

| Sample Number | Number of Defects in Sample | Cumulative Number of Defects | Cumulative Percent of Defects |
|---|---|---|---|
| 1 | | | |
| 2 | | | |
| 3 | | | |
| 4 | | | |
| 5 | | | |
| 6 | | | |
| 7 | | | |
| 8 | | | |
| 9 | | | |
| 10 | | | |

## Lesson 14.1 Activity Answers

1. Sample answer: no
2. Sample answer: 1

3. Sample answer:

| Sample Number | Number of Defects in Sample | Cumulative Number of Defects | Cumulative Percent of Defects |
|---|---|---|---|
| 1 | 1 | 1 | $1 \div 5 = 20\%$ |
| 2 | 0 | $1 + 0 = 1$ | $1 \div 10 = 10\%$ |
| 3 | 1 | $1 + 1 = 2$ | $2 \div 15 = 13\%$ |
| 4 | 1 | $2 + 1 = 3$ | $3 \div 20 = 15\%$ |
| 5 | 0 | $3 + 0 = 3$ | $3 \div 25 = 12\%$ |
| 6 | 2 | $3 + 2 = 5$ | $5 \div 30 = 17\%$ |
| 7 | 0 | $5 + 0 = 5$ | $5 \div 35 = 14\%$ |
| 8 | 0 | $5 + 0 = 5$ | $5 \div 40 = 13\%$ |
| 9 | 1 | $5 + 1 = 6$ | $6 \div 45 = 13\%$ |
| 10 | 0 | $6 + 0 = 6$ | $6 \div 50 = 12\%$ |

**4.** Construct a line graph of the percent of defects versus the total number of clips tested.

As the number of paper clips tested increases, your graph should begin to level off. The height of the graph as it levels off provides an approximate value for the probability that a given clip is defective. This type of probability is called an **experimental probability**.

### Experimental Probability

The experimental probability that a particular event will occur is found by collecting data.

$$\text{Probability of an event} = \frac{\text{number of times the event occurs}}{\text{total number of trials}}$$

**5.** Estimate the probability of a defective paper clip. Express your answer as a percent, a decimal, and a fraction.

**6.** Now repeat Questions 2–5 for a different brand of paper clip.

The graph below shows the results of an experiment in which a coin was tossed 200 times.

**Coin Toss Experiment**

Notice that the fraction of the tosses that are heads tends to level off to a fairly stable value of $\frac{1}{2}$. If more samples are taken, this value will be even more evident. That is, the fraction would approach $\frac{1}{2}$, the theoretical probability of tossing heads when tossing a coin. This is an example of the **Law of Large Numbers** that links theoretical and experimental probabilities. This law states that if an experiment is repeated many times, the experimental probability of an event will tend to be close to the theoretical probability of that event.

DETERMINING PROBABILITY    **Lesson 14.1**    **495**

**4.** Sample graph:

**Number of Paper Clips Tested**

**5.** Sample answer: 12%, 0.12, $\frac{12}{100}$

**6.** Sample answer:

| Sample Number | Number of Defects in Sample | Cumulative Number of Defects | Cumulative Percent of Defects |
|---|---|---|---|
| 1 | 2 | 2 | 40% |
| 2 | 4 | 6 | 60% |
| 3 | 2 | 8 | 53% |
| 4 | 3 | 11 | 55% |
| 5 | 1 | 12 | 48% |
| 6 | 3 | 15 | 50% |
| 7 | 2 | 17 | 49% |
| 8 | 3 | 20 | 50% |
| 9 | 4 | 24 | 53% |
| 10 | 3 | 27 | 54% |

**Number of Paper Clips Tested**

The probability of a defective paper clip is about 54%, or 0.54, or $\frac{27}{50}$.

For Exercises 1–6, a tile is randomly drawn from a bag containing twenty tiles numbered 1 through 20. Find the probability of the given event.

1. A 12 is drawn.

2. An even number is drawn.

3. A number that is a perfect square is drawn.

4. A prime number is drawn.

5. A number greater than 15 is drawn.

6. A single-digit number is drawn.

7. A number cube, with faces labeled 1–6, is rolled 25 times.

   a. If a 3 were rolled 4 times, what is the experimental probability of rolling a 3?

   b. How does your answer to Part (a) compare to the theoretical probability of rolling a 3?

8. A probability that involves a geometric measure such as a length or an area is sometimes referred to as a *geometric probability*. Assuming that a dart is equally likely to hit any point on the target, find the probability that the dart thrown at the target will land in the shaded region. Write your answers in terms of $\pi$.

a.

8 cm

b.

5

5   10 in.

## TEACHING TIP

**Exercise 7** Explain to students that in the text, a "number cube" refers to a small cube with faces numbered 1–6.

## Practice for Lesson 14.1 Answers

1. $\dfrac{1}{20}$

2. $\dfrac{10}{20} = \dfrac{1}{2}$

3. $\dfrac{4}{20} = \dfrac{1}{5}$

4. $\dfrac{8}{20} = \dfrac{2}{5}$

5. $\dfrac{5}{20} = \dfrac{1}{4}$

6. $\dfrac{9}{20}$

7a. $\dfrac{4}{25} = 0.16$

7b. The theoretical probability of rolling a 3 is $\dfrac{1}{6}$. So, the experimental probability is slightly less than the theoretical probability.

8a. $\dfrac{16\pi}{64} = \dfrac{\pi}{4}$

8b. $\dfrac{\frac{1}{2}(10)(5)}{25\pi} = \dfrac{1}{\pi}$

**9.** Design and conduct an experiment to determine the experimental probability that an ordinary thumbtack will land with its point facing up when dropped on a horizontal surface. Write an explanation of what you did and what conclusions you can draw from your experiment.

**10.** Of the 366 birthdates, what is the probability that a March date will be randomly chosen in a lottery?   *31/366*

**11.** In a large data set, what is the approximate probability of randomly choosing a value that is below the median?   *50*

**12.** According to a NASA space scientist, a city could be destroyed once every 30,000 years by an asteroid hitting the Earth. If he is correct, what is the probability of a city being destroyed by an asteroid in any year?

**13.** When the euro coin was issued, a German newspaper reported that a coin-flipping experiment with the Belgian one-euro coin showed that heads came up 140 times out of 250. Because of this, a ban on using euros at the start of soccer matches was considered. According to the experiment, what is the probability that a flipped euro results in heads?   *14/25 = 56%*

**14.** The term *odds* is used to describe a ratio that is often used in connection with the chance of winning (or losing) a game or competition. When all outcomes are equally likely, the odds *in favor* of an event *A* are

$$\text{Odds in favor of } A = \frac{\text{number of outcomes in } A}{\text{number of outcomes not in } A}$$

The odds *against* event *A* are

$$\text{Odds against event } A = \frac{\text{number of outcomes not in } A}{\text{number of outcomes in } A}$$

*odds*
*1 to 3 : 4*

**a.** If the odds in favor of a runner winning a gold medal in a race are 1 to 3, what are the odds against the runner winning a gold medal? What is the probability that the runner will win a gold medal?

**b.** A company has bid on a contract to write a new probability book. The company estimates that it has a 0.4 probability of winning the contract. What are the odds in favor of winning the contract?   *4 to 6 = 2 to 3*

**c.** What are the odds in favor of drawing a 2 from a standard deck of 52 cards?   *4 to 48 = 1 to 12*

**14a.** $\frac{3}{1}; \frac{1}{4}$

**14b.** The probability of winning is $\frac{2}{5}$.

So, the odds of winning are $\frac{2}{3}$.

**14c.** $\frac{4}{48} = \frac{1}{12}$

---

**Exercise 9** To help prevent students from dropping loose tacks in the classroom, place a group of tacks in a sealed, clear, plastic box and have students shake the box to conduct their sampling.

**TEACHING TIP**

**Exercise 9** You may want to encourage students to include a graph of relative frequency for increasing numbers of 10- or 20-tack samples as this provides students with a visual model of what is happening with the experimental probability.

**TEACHING TIP**

**Exercise 14 , Part (c)** If students are not familiar with a standard deck of cards, show them a standard deck and point out the following characteristics:

• A "standard" deck has 52 cards.
• Half are red and half are black.

Of the 52 cards,

• 13 are red diamonds (Ace, King, Queen, Jack, and 10-2).
• 13 are red hearts (Ace, King, Queen, Jack, and 10-2).
• 13 are black clubs (Ace, King, Queen, Jack, and 10-2).
• 13 are black spades (Ace, King, Queen, Jack, and 10-2).
• There are 4 Aces, 4 Kings, 4 Queens, etc.

**9.** Sample answer: 100 thumbtacks are dropped, and 62 landed point up.

So, *P*(tack lands up) = 0.62, or 62%. This means that on average, 62% of the thumbtacks that are dropped will land point up.

**10.** $\frac{31}{366} \approx 0.085$ or 8.5%

**11.** $\frac{1}{2} = 0.5 = 50\%$ since half the numbers are below the median.

**12.** $\frac{1}{30,000} \approx 0.00003$

**13.** $\frac{140}{250} = \frac{14}{25}$ or 56%

**Exercise 15** If you do not have the Probability Simulation (**Prob Sim**) App on your graphing calculator, you may download it from the TI website http://education.ti.com/.

15. Probability simulations can be performed on a calculator. For example, follow these steps to make the calculator simulate rolling a number cube, with faces labeled 1–6.

| Step 1: | Press the **APPS** key. | |
| Step 2: | Scroll down to **Prob Sim**. Press **ENTER**. | |
| Step 3: | Press **ENTER**. | |
| Step 4: | Choose **2. Roll Dice**. Press **ENTER**. | |
| Step 5. | Press the **ZOOM** key to select **SET**. | |

| Step 6: | This screen tells you that you are rolling one six-sided number cube. The calculator rolls the cube one time, and the data will be displayed as a frequency graph. Press the **GRAPH** key to select **OK**. | 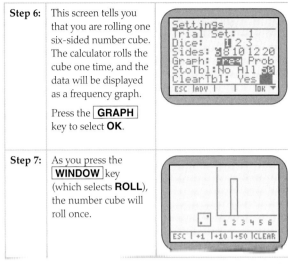 |
|---|---|---|
| Step 7: | As you press the **WINDOW** key (which selects **ROLL**), the number cube will roll once. | |

a. As you simulate each roll, record the information in a table like the one shown below. After you have rolled the number cube 24 times and recorded the frequencies, calculate each frequency as a fraction, decimal, and percent.

| | | Frequency Written as a | | |
|---|---|---|---|---|
| Number | Frequency | Fraction | Decimal | Percent |
| 1 | | | | |
| 2 | | | | |
| 3 | | | | |
| 4 | | | | |
| 5 | | | | |
| 6 | | | | |
| Totals | | | | |

b. Press the **TRACE** key to select **+50**. What do you think is happening?

c. What do you think will happen if you roll the number cube at least 1,000 times?

**15a.** Sample table:

| | | Frequency Written as a | | |
|---|---|---|---|---|
| Number Rolled | Frequency | Fraction | Decimal | Percent |
| 1 | 6 | $\frac{1}{4}$ | 0.25 | 25% |
| 2 | 4 | $\frac{1}{6}$ | 0.1667 | 16.67% |
| 3 | 5 | $\frac{5}{24}$ | 0.2083 | 20.83% |
| 4 | 5 | $\frac{5}{24}$ | 0.2083 | 20.83% |
| 5 | 3 | $\frac{1}{8}$ | 0.125 | 12.5% |
| 6 | 1 | $\frac{1}{24}$ | 0.0417 | 4.17% |
| Totals | 24 | 1 | 1 | 100% |

**15b.** The calculator simulates 50 additional rolls of the number cube very quickly.

**15c.** The frequency graph would become more and more level, meaning the frequencies are close to equal.

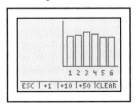

# LESSON 14.2

## Lesson Objectives

- find conditional probabilities.
- find the probability of the complement of an event.

## Vocabulary

- complement of an event
- conditional probability

## Materials List

- pasta (preferably fettuccini)
- rulers

## Description

*Preparation:*

Have students work in groups that have three or four members. Provide each group with 50–60 pieces of each type of pasta.

Fettuccini is suggested for this Activity because it tends to be more brittle and breaks more cleanly than other pasta, such as spaghetti. The pasta for the second part of the experiment needs to be prepared ahead of time. To prepare the pasta, simply submerge it in water for less than 5 minutes and then let it dry. It helps to hold down the ends as the pasta tends to curl as it dries. It may be wise to experiment with different types and brands of pasta ahead of time.

*During the Activity:*

This Activity provides students with a good simulation of a conditional probability experiment. Encourage students to be consistent as they bend the pasta downward.

*Closing the Activity:*

Focus attention on **Question 6** because this question has students compare the two probabilities: *P*(pasta bending) and *P*(pasta bending | gotten wet).

Work through **Example 1** as a group, paying special attention to the notation used for conditional probability.

---

**Lesson 14.2**  **ACTIVITY:  Conditional Probability**

In Lesson 14.1, you reviewed theoretical probability and conducted an experiment to determine an experimental probability. In this lesson, you explore situations in which the probability of an event depends on whether or not another event happens.

In the Activity in Lesson 14.1, you may have found that the probability of a defective paper clip was different for the two brands that you tested. If so, then it is not meaningful to try to identify a single value for *P*(paper clip is defective). The probability in this case depends on the brand.

> **Conditional Probability**
>
> A **conditional probability** measures the likelihood of an event based on whether another event occurs.
>
> The probability of event *A*, given that another event *B* occurs, is symbolized by $P(A|B)$.

Some materials must be flexible in order to perform correctly under normal use. For example, the plastic clasp on the battery compartment of a calculator must be flexible enough to bend, but not break, when pressed down.

1. You can perform a flexibility test on a piece of pasta that comes directly from the box. One piece at a time, hold the pasta firmly onto a tabletop so that 4 inches of the pasta hangs over the edge of the table. Press the free end of the pasta down until it is about 3 inches below the table. Did it break?

2. Repeat the experiment for as many pieces of pasta as you have. How many pieces of pasta can be bent downward 3 inches without breaking?

3. What is *P*(pasta bending), the probability that a piece of pasta can be bent downward 3 inches without breaking?

4. Now repeat the experiment for similar pasta that has gotten wet but has been allowed to dry out.

5. What is *P*(pasta bending|gotten wet), the conditional probability that a piece of pasta can be bent downward 3 inches without breaking if it has gotten wet?

6. Are the two probabilities the same? Explain.

## Lesson 14.2 Activity Answers

1. Sample answer: no
2. Sample answer: 46 out of 50 bent without breaking.
3. Sample answer: $\frac{23}{25} = 0.92 = 92\%$
4. Sample answer: 9 out of 50 bent without breaking.
5. Sample answer: $\frac{9}{50} = 0.18 = 18\%$
6. Sample answer: No, the pasta that has been wet seems to be less flexible than the pasta that came directly from the box.

The probability calculation in Question 3 is also a conditional probability because it is the probability that a piece of pasta can be bent downward 3 inches without breaking if it has *not* gotten wet. So, the probability in that question is more correctly symbolized by *P*(pasta bending | not gotten wet).

Two machines produce optical lenses for cameras.

Of 200 lenses made by Machine 1, six are defective. Five of the 250 lenses produced by Machine 2 are defective.

**a.** Explain what is meant by *P*(defective lens | Machine 1). Then find its value.

**b.** Explain what is meant by *P*(defective lens | Machine 2). Then find its value.

**Solution:**

**a.** *P*(defective lens | Machine 1) means the probability that a lens is defective if it is made by Machine 1.

$P(\text{defective lens} | \text{Machine 1}) = \frac{6}{200} = 0.03 = 3\%$.

**b.** *P*(defective lens | Machine 2) means the probability that a lens is defective if it is made by Machine 2.

$P(\text{defective lens} | \text{Machine 2}) = \frac{5}{250} = 0.02 = 2\%$.

### THE COMPLEMENT OF AN EVENT

Recall that an event is a particular outcome or collection of outcomes of an experiment or process. The **complement** of the event includes all *other* possible outcomes. Here are a few examples:

The complement of "heads" is "tails" for the tossing of a coin.

The complement of "winning" is "tying or losing" a game.

The complement of "the door is open" is "the door is closed."

The complement of "red" is "green or yellow" for a traffic light.

The complement of "even" is "odd" for the rolling of a number cube.

If two events *A* and *B* are complementary, then one or the other is certain to occur, and $P(A) + P(B) = 1$. If you know the probability of one event, then you can solve for the probability of the complement.

**ADDITIONAL EXAMPLE 1**

Company A says that 1 out of every 4 cars manufactured at their plants is gray. Explain what is meant by *P*(gray | Company A). Then find its value.

*P*(gray | Company A) means the probability that a car is gray if it was made by Company A.;

$\frac{1}{4} = 0.25 = 25\%$

**TEACHING TIP**

Some students may struggle with the examples of events and their complements. Have them look carefully at the fourth example and point out that the complement of red on a traffic light is "not red," which means it can be either "green" or "yellow."

# LESSON 14.2

## ADDITIONAL EXAMPLE 2

The probability of drawing a red marble from a bag of marbles is $\frac{2}{7}$.

What is the probability of drawing a marble that is not red?

$\frac{5}{7}$

A manufacturing process makes circuit boards for smartphones. The probability that a circuit board made by this process is defective is 0.002. What is the probability that a circuit board is *not* defective?

$$P(\text{nondefective}) + P(\text{defective}) = 1$$
$$P(\text{nondefective}) = 1 - P(\text{defective})$$
$$= 1 - 0.002$$
$$= 0.998$$

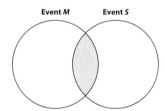

## Practice for Lesson 14.2

For Exercises 1–6, a card is randomly drawn from a deck of 15 cards numbered 1 through 15. Find the probability of the given event.

1. A 1 is drawn given that the number on the card is less than 10.
2. A 3 is drawn given that the number on the card is odd.
3. An odd number is drawn given that the number on the card has two digits.
4. An even number is drawn given that the number on the card is greater than 10.
5. A multiple of 5 is drawn given that the number on the card is between 4 and 13.
6. A 4 is drawn given that the number on the card is prime.
7. Venn diagrams can be used to help find conditional probabilities. In the Venn diagram below, the shaded area is the location of the results that are in both Event *M* and Event *S*.

Event *M*    Event *S*

## Practice for Lesson 14.2
## Answers

1. $\frac{1}{9}$

2. $\frac{1}{8}$

3. $\frac{3}{6} = \frac{1}{2}$

4. $\frac{2}{5}$

5. $\frac{2}{8} = \frac{1}{4}$

6. 0; This cannot happen because 4 is not a prime number.

**a.** Draw the Venn diagram and use the following information to place numbers of students in each of the three regions of the diagram.

  Event *M* represents an *A* grade in mathematics.
  Event *S* represents an *A* in science.
  12 students received an *A* in math but not in science.
  10 students received an *A* in science but not in math.
  2 students received an *A* in math and science.

**b.** What is the probability that a particular randomly chosen student received an *A* in math? 7/12

**c.** What is the probability that a particular randomly chosen student received an *A* in math, given that the student received an *A* in science? Explain. 2/12 = 1/6

**8.** A number cube, labeled 1–6, is rolled and the result is a 3. If a second cube with the same labels is rolled, what is the probability that the sum of the two cubes is 7? 1/6

**9.** A diamond is drawn from a standard deck of 52 cards and placed face down on the table.

  **a.** How many diamonds remain in the deck? 12
  **b.** How many cards are left in the deck? 51
  **c.** What is the probability of drawing another diamond from the deck? 12/51
  **d.** Was the second draw affected by the first draw? Explain. yes

**10.** A weather forecaster said that the probability of rain tomorrow is 60%. What is the probability that it will not rain? complement 40%

**11.** If the probability of a defective snap on a newly manufactured pair of jeans is 0.11, what is the probability that a snap is not defective? .89

**12.** The figure below shows a target. Assume that a dart is equally likely to hit any point on the target. Find the probability that a dart thrown at the target will land in the unshaded region. Use 3.14 for $\pi$. complement

20 cm
80 cm

**7a.** Sample diagram:

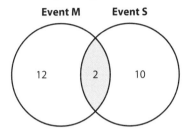

Event M    Event S

12    2    10

**7b.** There are 24 students altogether, and 14 are in the Event *M* circle, so the probability that a particular student received an *A* in math is $\frac{14}{24} = \frac{7}{12}$.

**7c.** There are 12 students in the Event *S* circle, and 2 of those are also in the Event *M* circle, so the conditional probability is $\frac{2}{12} = \frac{1}{6}$.

**8.** $P(\text{sum of } 7 \mid 3 \text{ on the first roll}) = \frac{1}{6}$

**9a.** 12

**9b.** 51

**9c.** $\frac{12}{51} = \frac{4}{17}$

**9d.** Yes, the second draw was affected by the first draw. Without replacing the diamond back in the deck, there is one less card in the deck and one less diamond in the deck.

**10.** $100\% - 60\% = 40\%$

**11.** $1 - 0.11 = 0.89$ or 89%

**12.** $P(\text{shaded}) = \frac{\pi(20)^2}{80^2} = \frac{\pi}{16}$; So, $P(\text{unshaded}) = 1 - \frac{\pi}{16} = \frac{16 - \pi}{16} \approx 0.804$ or 80.4%.

# LESSON 14.3

5e   Explore

## Lesson Objectives

- find the probability that two independent events both occur.
- find the probability that two dependent events both occur.
- find the probability that either of two mutually exclusive events occurs.

## Vocabulary

- dependent events
- independent events
- mutually exclusive events

## Materials List

- rulers

## Description

This lesson works best if students work in pairs.

In this Investigation, students use an area model to examine joint probabilities for two independent events. In the area model, the probabilities are proportional to the rectangular areas. Many students are helped by visualizing joint probabilities in this way.

Note: The defect rates used here are unrealistically high in order to make the area models legible. The actual Boeing pump data are addressed in **Exercise 12**.

As students use their model, they are led to discover the multiplication rule for the probability that two independent events both occur. The Investigation ends with a brief look at the addition rule for mutually exclusive events.

*Wrapping Up the Investigation:*

Have students summarize the major points of the Investigation. Use the two sections and the Examples that follow the Investigation to reinforce what the students learned about joint probability.

### TEACHING TIP

After students have completed the table in **Question 4**, ask them to add the probabilities for all possible events and point out that the sum equals 1.

---

## Lesson 14.3   INVESTIGATION:   Joint Probabilities

In Lesson 14.2, you learned to find conditional probabilities. In this lesson, you will use what you learned to investigate the probability of two events occurring together.

Suppose that the pump manufacturer referred to in the Chapter Opener on page 492 has such poor quality control that one-fourth of its pumps are defective. If each airplane has two pumps, you can use what you know about probability to determine the probability that both of these pumps are defective, exactly one pump is defective, or both pumps are nondefective.

1. Draw a square to represent a total probability of 1 or 100%. Probabilities for all possible pump combinations will be represented in the square. Draw a vertical line that divides the square into two rectangles. One rectangle should contain $\frac{1}{4}$ of the total area. These rectangles represent the probabilities that Pump #1 is either defective or nondefective.

    Write appropriate labels along the top side of the square. Be sure to include the probability values on your area models.

2. Now draw a horizontal line that divides the left side of the square in a similar way. Write labels along the left side to show the probabilities that Pump #2 is either defective or nondefective.

3. The square is now divided into four regions. The smallest region represents the event that both pumps are defective. Label each region according to the combination of pump conditions it represents.

4. Complete the table below by computing the areas of the regions to find the probability of each state of the system.

| State of the System | Probability |
|---|---|
| Both pumps defective | |
| Pump #1 defective, Pump #2 nondefective | |
| Pump #1 nondefective, Pump #2 defective | |
| Both pumps nondefective | |

---

## Lesson 14.3 Investigation Answers

1. Sample answer:

Pump #1
Defective   Nondefective
$\frac{1}{4}$          $\frac{3}{4}$

2. Sample answer:

Pump #1
Defective   Nondefective
$\frac{1}{4}$          $\frac{3}{4}$

Pump #2

Defective $\frac{1}{4}$

Nondefective $\frac{3}{4}$

**3.–4.** See answers on page 505.

5. The probabilities in the table are called *joint probabilities* since each of them is a combination of the probabilities of two events. Whether the system works or not depends on two separate events *both* occurring. Examine how you computed each probability. Then write a rule for finding the probability that two events both occur.

6. Suppose an airline has 80 aircraft of this type. Use your answer to Question 4 to help you complete the table below. Fill in the expected number of airplanes in each category.

|  |  | Fuel Pump #1 | |
|---|---|---|---|
|  |  | Defective | Nondefective |
| Fuel Pump #2 | Defective |  |  |
|  | Nondefective |  |  |

7. How many of the 80 planes have exactly 1 defective fuel pump?

8. What is the probability that a plane has exactly 1 defective pump?

9. Explain how you could use your answer to Question 4 to find the probability that a plane has exactly 1 defective pump.

## INDEPENDENT AND DEPENDENT EVENTS

In the Investigation, you found that the joint probability that both fuel pumps fail could be found by multiplying the failure probabilities for the individual pumps. This assumes that fuel pump failures are **independent** events. That is, the occurrence of one event does not depend on the occurrence of the other event. In this case, the probability that one of the pumps fails does not depend on whether the other pump fails.

> **Probability of Independent Events**
>
> If two events, A and B, are independent, then the probability that both occur is the product of the probability of A and the probability of B.
>
> $$P(A \text{ and } B) = P(A) \cdot P(B)$$

What if the events are not independent? That is, what if the failure of Pump #1 made Pump #2 more (or less) likely to fail? In this case, the events are **dependent**. That is, the occurrence of one event affects the occurrence of the other. In such a case, a conditional probability would have to be used for the failure probability of Pump #2. And the probability that both pumps fail would be found from

$$P(\text{both pumps fail}) = P(\text{Pump \#1 fails}) \cdot P(\text{Pump \#2 fails} | \text{Pump \#1 fails}).$$

JOINT PROBABILITIES    **Lesson 14.3**    505

4.

| State of the System | Probability |
|---|---|
| Both pumps defective | $\frac{1}{16}$ |
| Pump #1 defective, Pump #2 nondefective | $\frac{3}{16}$ |
| Pump #1 nondefective, Pump #2 defective | $\frac{3}{16}$ |
| Both pumps nondefective | $\frac{9}{16}$ |

5. Sample answer: To find the probability that two events both occur, multiply the probabilities of the individual events.

6.

|  |  | Fuel Pump #1 | |
|---|---|---|---|
|  |  | Defective | Nondefective |
| Fuel Pump #2 | Defective | 5 | 15 |
|  | Nondefective | 15 | 45 |

7. 30

8. $\frac{30}{80} = \frac{3}{8}$

9. Sample answer: Add the probabilities for the two situations that have one defective pump and one nondefective pump.

3. Sample answer:

Pump #1

|  |  | Defective $\frac{1}{4}$ | Nondefective $\frac{3}{4}$ |
|---|---|---|---|
| Pump #2 | Defective $\frac{1}{4}$ | Both pumps defective | Pump #1 nondefective Pump #2 defective |
|  | Nondefective $\frac{3}{4}$ | Pump #1 defective Pump #2 nondefective | Both pumps nondefective |

## Probability of Dependent Events

If two events, $A$ and $B$, are dependent, then the probability that both occur is the product of the probability of $A$ and the probability of $B$ given that $A$ also occurs.

$$P(A \text{ and } B) = P(A) \cdot P(B|A)$$

### ADDITIONAL EXAMPLE

One-fifth of all Americans have allergies. But if both parents of a child have allergies, the probability that the child has allergies is 70%. What is the probability that a mother, a father, and their child have allergies?

$(0.2)(0.2)(0.7) = 0.028$

### E X A M P L E ①

According to the Asthma and Allergy Foundation of America, one-fifth of all Americans have allergies of some kind. But if a person has one parent with allergies, that person has a one-third chance of having allergies.

**a.** What is the probability that two randomly selected Americans both have allergies?

**b.** What is the probability that four randomly selected Americans all have allergies?

**c.** What is the probability that a mother and her child both have allergies?

**Solution:**

**a.** If the two people are randomly selected, then we can assume that whether each has allergies or not are independent events. That is, the probability that one person is allergic does not depend on whether the other is allergic. So, the joint probability that they both have allergies is

$$P(\text{first person has allergies}) \cdot P(\text{second person has allergies}) = \frac{1}{5} \cdot \frac{1}{5}$$
$$= \frac{1}{25} \text{ or } 4\%$$

**b.** Assume independent events:

$$P(\text{four people have allergies}) = \frac{1}{5} \cdot \frac{1}{5} \cdot \frac{1}{5} \cdot \frac{1}{5}$$
$$= \frac{1}{625} \text{ or } 0.16\%$$

**c.** These are dependent events:

$P(\text{mother and child have allergies})$

$$= P(\text{mother has allergies}) \cdot P(\text{child has allergies}\,|\,\text{mother has allergies})$$
$$= \frac{1}{5} \cdot \frac{1}{3}$$
$$= \frac{1}{15} \text{ or about } 6.7\%$$

## E X A M P L E  2

A bag contains 2 red, 5 white, and 8 blue marbles.

**a.** What is the probability of drawing a red marble randomly from the bag?

**b.** A marble is drawn randomly from the bag. Then it is placed back in the bag and a second marble is drawn. What is the probability of drawing a white marble, followed by a blue marble?

**c.** Two marbles are drawn successively from the bag and not replaced. Find the probability of drawing a white marble, followed by a blue marble.

**Solution:**

**a.** $P(\text{red}) = \dfrac{2}{15}$

**b.** The selection of the first marble does not affect the selection of the second. So, the events are *independent*.

$$P(\text{white then blue}) = P(\text{white}) \cdot P(\text{blue})$$
$$= \frac{5}{15} \cdot \frac{8}{15}$$
$$= \frac{8}{45}$$

**c.** Since the first marble is not placed back in the bag after it is drawn, its selection affects the selection of the second marble. The events are *dependent*.

$$P(\text{white then blue}) = P(\text{white}) \cdot P(\text{blue following white})$$
$$= P(\text{white}) \cdot P(\text{blue} \mid \text{white})$$
$$= \frac{5}{15} \cdot \frac{8}{14}$$
$$= \frac{4}{21}$$

## ADDITIONAL EXAMPLE  2

A box contains 5 purple chips, 7 yellow chips, and 8 green chips.

**a.** What is the probability of drawing a green chip randomly from the bag?

**a.** $\dfrac{2}{5}$

**b.** A chip is drawn from the bag and not replaced. Then a second chip is drawn. Find the probability of drawing two purple chips.

**b.** $\dfrac{1}{19}$

**c.** A chip is drawn from the bag and then replaced in the bag. A second chip is drawn. Find the probability of drawing two purple chips.

**c.** $\dfrac{1}{16}$

# LESSON 14.3

## ADDITIONAL EXAMPLE 3

An MD-11 airplane has 17 fuel pumps. If each pump has a 3% probability of being defective, what is the probability that at least one of the pumps is defective?

$1 - P(\text{all 17 nondefective}) =$
$1 - (0.97)^{17} \approx 0.404$ or about 40%

## E X A M P L E 3

Studies have been made of human error rates for simple tasks. For example, a technician will insert a circuit board incorrectly about 0.4% of the time. If she has to insert 20 circuit boards, what is the probability that at least one of the 20 will be inserted incorrectly?

**Solution:**

Assuming that correct insertions of the 20 circuit boards are independent, the events "at least one of the 20 incorrectly inserted" and "all 20 correctly inserted" are complementary. Also, if there is a 0.4% chance of an incorrect insertion, there is a 99.6% chance of a correct insertion.

$$P(\text{all 20 correctly inserted}) = 0.996^{20}$$
$$\approx 0.923$$

Therefore,

$$P(\text{at least 1 of 20 inserted incorrectly}) = 1 - P(\text{all 20 correctly inserted})$$
$$= 0.077 \text{ or about } 7.7\%$$

### ADDING PROBABILITIES

In Question 9 of the Investigation, you found that the chance of only one pump being defective is equal to the sum of two probabilities. In many cases, the joint probability that one or the other of two events occurs is equal to the sum of their individual probabilities. But this is only true if the events *cannot both occur*. Such events are **mutually exclusive** events.

> **Mutually Exclusive Events**
>
> If two events, $A$ and $B$, are mutually exclusive, then the probability that either $A$ or $B$ occurs is the sum of their probabilities.
>
> $$P(A \text{ or } B) = P(A) + P(B)$$

**E X A M P L E 4**

The table below shows the percent of traffic fatalities by age group during the past year for a major metropolitan area.

| Age Group | Percent of Fatalities |
|-----------|----------------------|
| Under 16  | 6                    |
| 16–24     | 25                   |
| 25–54     | 45                   |
| Over 54   | 24                   |

**a.** What is the probability that a randomly selected traffic fatality involved a person who was either under 16 or over 54 years old?

**b.** Are the events "person is under 16" and "person is over 54" mutually exclusive? Explain.

**c.** Are the events "person is under 25 years old" and "person is from 16 to 24 years old" mutually exclusive? Explain.

**Solution:**

**a.** P(under 16) + P(over 54) = 6% + 24% = 30%

**b.** Yes. The events are mutually exclusive because no one can be both under 16 and over 54 years old.

**c.** No. The events are not mutually exclusive because it is possible for someone to be in both categories.

**Practice for Lesson 14.3**

**1.** In Lesson 14.1 you compared the quality of two brands of paper clips. For that type of test, suppose 20% of Brand A clips and 45% of Brand B are defective. Also suppose 100 Brand A clips and 150 Brand B clips are mixed together and a randomly selected clip is tested.
   **a.** What is the probability that the selected clip is Brand A and it breaks?
   **b.** What is the probability that the selected clip is Brand B and it breaks?
   **c.** What is the total probability that the selected paper clip breaks?

**ADDITIONAL EXAMPLE 4**

Use the table in Example 4 in the text.

**a.** What is the probability that a randomly selected traffic fatality was either "under 16" or in the "16–24" age group?

**a.** 6% + 25% = 31%

**b.** Are the events "under 16" and "16–24" mutually exclusive? Explain.

**b.** Yes. The events are mutually exclusive because no one can be both "under 16" and "16–24" years old.

**c.** Are the events "over 24" and "25–64" mutually exclusive? Explain.

**c.** No. The events are not mutually exclusive because anyone who is 25–64 years old is also over 24.

**Practice for Lesson 14.3 Answers**

**1a.** P(Brand A and breaks) = P(A) · P(breaks if Brand A)

$$= \frac{100}{250} \cdot 0.2$$

$$= 0.08$$

**1b.** P(Brand B and breaks) = P(B) · P(breaks if Brand B)

$$= \frac{150}{250} \cdot 0.45$$

$$= 0.27$$

**1c.** P(breaks) = P(Brand A and breaks) + P(Brand B and breaks)

$$= 0.08 + 0.27$$

$$= 0.35$$

2. dependent; $\frac{2}{9} \cdot \frac{3}{8} \cdot \frac{4}{7} = \frac{1}{21}$

3. independent; $\left(\frac{1}{6}\right)^4 = \frac{1}{1,296}$

4a. $\frac{5}{50} \cdot \frac{5}{50} = \frac{1}{100}$

4b. $\frac{5}{50} \cdot \frac{4}{49} = \frac{2}{245}$

4c. $\frac{2}{50} \cdot \frac{3}{50} = \frac{3}{1,250}$

4d. $\frac{2}{50} \cdot \frac{3}{49} = \frac{3}{1,225}$

5. $\frac{1}{6}$; The events are independent, so the probability of rolling a 6 is $\frac{1}{6}$. It does not depend on the outcomes of previous rolls.

6. $P(3 \text{ or even}) = P(3) + P(\text{even}) = \frac{1}{20} + \frac{1}{2} = \frac{11}{20}$

7. The events are independent. So, $P(1) \cdot P(2 \text{ if the first spinner is a 1}) + P(2) \cdot P(1 \text{ if the first spinner is a 2}) = \frac{1}{2} \cdot \frac{1}{4} + \frac{1}{2} \cdot \frac{1}{4} = \frac{2}{8} = \frac{1}{4}$.

**For Exercises 2 and 3, determine whether the two events are independent or dependent and then find the probability.**

2. A coin purse contains 3 dimes, 2 pennies, and 4 quarters. What is the probability of selecting a penny, then a dime, and then a quarter, if the coins are not replaced?

3. What is the probability of rolling a number cube, labeled 1–6, four times and rolling a 3 each time?

4. A box contains 50 tiles with shapes drawn on them. In addition to other shapes, there are 2 squares, 5 circles, and 3 triangles in the box.
   a. Find the probability of drawing two circles if you replace the first before drawing the second.
   b. Find the probability of drawing two circles without replacing the first circle.
   c. Find the probability of drawing a square followed by a triangle with replacement.
   d. Find the probability of drawing a square followed by a triangle without replacement.

5. A number cube, labeled 1–6, is rolled 4 times, and it lands on 6 each time. What is the probability that the next roll will be a 6? Explain.

6. In a deck of 20 cards, numbered 1–20, what is the probability of drawing a 3 or an even number?

7. Two spinners are spun at the same time.

What is the probability that the sum of the numbers on the spinners will be 3?

8. A quality control inspector checks flat-panel televisions for defects. The table below shows the probabilities of different numbers of defects.

| Number of Defects Observed | 0 | 1 | 2 | 3 | 4 | 5 | 6 | 7 | 8 | 9 or more |
|---|---|---|---|---|---|---|---|---|---|---|
| Probability | 0.11 | 0.03 | 0.07 | 0.18 | 0.23 | 0.16 | 0.09 | 0.06 | 0.04 | 0.03 |

   a. What is the probability that a television has fewer than three defects?
   b. What is the probability that a television has at least five and no more than eight defects?

9. The probabilities of a randomly selected blood sample in the New York Blood Center being type O, type A, type B, or type AB are 0.45, 0.40, 0.10, and 0.05, respectively. What is the probability that a sample is either type A or type B?

10. A student takes a ten-question, multiple-choice test. Each question has five answer choices.
   a. If the student guesses each answer, what is the probability that the student will get all of the questions wrong?
   b. What is the probability that the student will get all of the questions correct?

11. A dart is thrown at the target shown below.

   a. If the dart hits the target at a random location, what is the probability that it will land in a red triangle?
   b. What is the probability that it will land in a green or a purple region?

8a. $0.11 + 0.03 + 0.07 = 0.21$
8b. $0.16 + 0.09 + 0.06 + 0.04 = 0.35$
9. Blood types are mutually exclusive.
$$P(\text{type A or type B}) = P(\text{type A}) + P(\text{type B})$$
$$= 0.40 + 0.10$$
$$= 0.50$$

10a. The probability of getting one question wrong is $\frac{4}{5}$. So, the probability of getting all 10 questions incorrect is $\left(\frac{4}{5}\right)^{10} \approx 0.107$.

10b. $\left(\frac{1}{5}\right)^{10} \approx 0.000000102$

11a. $\frac{8}{40} = \frac{1}{5}$

11b. $\frac{10}{40} + \frac{12}{40} = \frac{22}{40} = \frac{11}{20}$

12. The fuel pumps used by Boeing were thought to have a 3% chance of having faulty wiring. Consider an airplane with two such pumps.
    a. What is the probability that both pumps are faulty?
    b. What is the probability that neither pump is faulty?
    c. What is the probability that exactly one of the pumps is faulty?

13. A company that makes refrigerator ice-making units has a 4% defect rate. What is the probability that an inspector might examine a sample of five randomly selected units and find no defects in the sample?

14. Shown below are two spinners that were used in an experiment.

Spinner A                    Spinner B

The results of that experiment are as follows:

Spinner A landed on a shaded area in 11 of 40 spins.

Spinner B landed on a shaded area in 12 out of 50 spins.

a. Use the results of the experiment to complete the table below. (Write your probabilities as percents.)

|  |  | Spinner A | |
|---|---|---|---|
|  |  | Shaded | Unshaded |
| **Spinner B** | Shaded |  |  |
|  | Unshaded |  |  |

**12a.** $(0.03)(0.03) = 0.0009$

**12b.** $(0.97)(0.97) = 0.9409$

**12c.** $1 - (0.0009 + 0.9409) = 0.0582$

**13.** The probability of a nondefective unit is $1 - 0.04 = 0.96$. So the probability of finding 5 nondefective units in a sample of 5 is $(0.96)^5 \approx 0.815$.

**14a.** Sample answer:

|  |  | Spinner A | |
|---|---|---|---|
|  |  | **Shaded** | **Unshaded** |
| **Spinner B** | **Shaded** | 6.6% | 17.4% |
|  | **Unshaded** | 20.9% | 55.1% |

**b.** What is the probability of both spinners landing in a shaded area?

**c.** What is the probability of both spinners landing in an unshaded area?

**d.** What is the probability of Spinner A landing in a shaded area and Spinner B landing in an unshaded area?

**e.** What is the probability of Spinner A landing in an unshaded area and Spinner B landing in a shaded area?

**f.** What is the probability of one of the spinners landing in a shaded area and the other landing in an unshaded area?

**g.** What is the sum of all of the probabilities in the table?

**14b.** 6.6%
**14c.** 55.1%
**14d.** 20.9%
**14e.** 17.4%
**14f.** 17.4% + 20.9% = 38.3%
**14g.** 1

# LESSON 14.4

## Lesson Objective

- solve problems that require previously learned concepts and skills.

## Exercise Reference

Exercise 1: Lesson 14.1

Exercises 2–3: Lesson 14.3

Exercise 4: Lesson 4.3

Exercises 5–10: Appendix A

Exercises 11–16: Appendix E

Exercises 17–19: Lesson 3.5

Exercises 20–22: Lesson 2.5

Exercises 23–25: Lesson 11.5

Exercise 26: Appendix H

Exercise 27: Appendix F

Exercises 28–29: Lesson 12.1

Exercise 30: Lesson 1.2

Exercise 31: Lesson 11.3

Exercise 32: Lesson 12.2

## Lesson 14.4 R.A.P. Answers

1. experimental
2. independent
3. B
4. C
5. $\dfrac{2}{3}$
6. $\dfrac{25}{24}$ or $1\dfrac{1}{24}$
7. $\dfrac{1}{2}$
8. $\dfrac{5}{33}$
9. $\dfrac{3}{208}$
10. $\dfrac{5}{72}$
11. 16.7%
12. 21.2%
13. 69.4%
14. $\dfrac{8}{25}$
15. $\dfrac{7}{8}$
16. $\dfrac{13}{25}$
17. $-2$
18. 18
19. $-22$
20. 1
21. $\dfrac{3}{4}$

22. undefined
23. $12t^4 - 18t^3 + 24t$
24. $3m^2 - 2m - 16$
25. $4b^2 + 48b + 144$

---

## Lesson 14.4 | R.A.P.

**Fill in the blank.**

1. Probability that is based on repeated trials of an experiment is called _____ probability.

2. Two events are called _____ events if the occurrence of one does not depend on the occurrence of the other event.

**Choose the correct answer.**

3. A coin is flipped and a number cube, labeled 1–6, is rolled. What is the probability of getting tails and an odd number?

   **A.** $\dfrac{1}{12}$   **B.** $\dfrac{1}{4}$   **C.** $\dfrac{1}{3}$   **D.** $\dfrac{1}{2}$

4. The _____ of a figure is measured in units such as square centimeters (cm²).

   **A.** perimeter   **B.** circumference   **C.** area   **D.** volume

**Add. Write your answer in simplest form.**

5. $\dfrac{1}{6} + \dfrac{1}{2}$   6. $\dfrac{3}{8} + \dfrac{2}{3}$   7. $\dfrac{13}{52} + \dfrac{1}{4}$

**Multiply. Write your answer in simplest form.**

8. $\dfrac{5}{12} \cdot \dfrac{4}{11}$   9. $\dfrac{13}{52} \cdot \dfrac{3}{52}$   10. $\dfrac{5}{6} \cdot \dfrac{1}{6} \cdot \dfrac{3}{6}$

**Write the fraction as a percent. Round to the nearest tenth.**

11. $\dfrac{1}{6}$   12. $\dfrac{11}{52}$   13. $\dfrac{25}{36}$

**Write the percent as a fraction in simplest form.**

14. 32%   15. 87.5%   16. 52%

**Solve.**

17. $-2(t + 4) = 8t + 12$   18. $6 + \dfrac{n}{3} = 12$   19. $8y + 55 = 5y - 11$

**Find the slope of the line that passes through the given points.**

20. $(-1, 3), (3, 7)$   21. $(-3, 9), (-7, 6)$   22. $(4, 2), (4, 8)$

**Find the product.**

23. $3t(4t^3 - 6t^2 + 8)$   24. $(3m - 8)(m + 2)$   25. $4(b + 6)^2$

**26.** What is the value of the expression $(1 + 4)^2 - 8 \times \sqrt{16 + 9} \div \sqrt{16}$?

**27.** A $400 telescope is on sale for 20% off. What is the sale price of the item?

**28.** Find the missing lengths. Write your answers in simplest radical form.

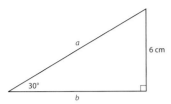

**29.** Find the length of a diagonal of a 9-inch by 9-inch square picture frame. Round your answer to the nearest tenth.

**30.** Triangle $ABC$ and triangle $RST$ are similar. Find the value of $x$.

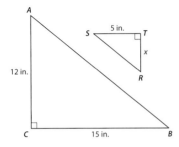

**31.** Consider the function $y = x^2 + 4x - 5$. Without graphing the function, answer the following questions:

**a.** Does the graph open upward or downward? Explain how you know.

**b.** What are the coordinates of the vertex of the graph?

**c.** What is the equation of the axis of symmetry of the graph?

**d.** What are the zeros of the graph?

**32.** A segment has endpoints at $M(5, 6)$ and $N(-3, 2)$. Find the midpoint of the segment.

**26.** 15
**27.** $320
**28.** $a = 12$ cm; $b = 6\sqrt{3}$ cm
**29.** 12.7 in.
**30.** 4 in.
**31a.** upward; The coefficient of $a$ is greater than 0.
**31b.** $(-2, -9)$
**31c.** the vertical line $x = -2$
**31d.** $-5$ and 1
**32.** $(1, 4)$

## Lesson Objectives

- identify binomial experiments.
- find probabilities for binomial experiments.
- use binomial expansions to find probabilities.

## Vocabulary

- binomial experiment

## Materials List

*Per group:*

- two coins

## Description

*Preparation:*

Have students work in pairs. Give each group two coins to flip.

*During the Activity:*

Before beginning the Activity, have students read the material preceding it, because students should realize that they are looking at a binomial experiment as they collect their data.

*Closing the Activity:*

It might be helpful to collect all group data from **Question 4** and examine them. As results are accumulated, the experimental probabilities based on the totals should be even closer to the theoretical values that were calculated by the binomial expansion (0.25, 0.5, and 0.25).

Bring closure to the Activity by having students work through Example 2.

## ADDITIONAL EXAMPLE

Consider the situation in which a marble is drawn from a bag 6 times, checked each time to see if it is blue, and then put back in the bag. Is this a binomial experiment? Explain.

Yes, there are a fixed number of trials (6), the trials are independent, there are exactly two outcomes for each trial, and the probability of drawing a blue marble is constant.

---

In Lesson 14.3, you used an area model to examine the four ways that a system consisting of two pumps could contain defective or nondefective pumps. Unfortunately, area diagrams such as those are only helpful for two pumps. What happens when there are three or more pumps? In this lesson, you will explore ways to determine such probabilities.

**Note**

The meaning of "success" depends on the particular context under study. A "success" always represents one of the two outcomes of a binomial experiment.

Consider a situation in which a coin is tossed twice and you count the number of heads. This is an example of a **binomial experiment** because it meets the following conditions:

- There is a fixed number of trials. (In this case, a coin is tossed twice.)
- Each trial is independent of the others. (That is, getting heads on one trial does not affect the other trial.)
- There are exactly two outcomes for each trial. (Only heads or tails can be tossed.)
- The probability of success is constant. (The probability of tossing heads is the same on each trial, $\frac{1}{2}$.)

Consider the following situations:

> A number cube, labeled 1–6, is rolled 10 times to see how many 3s are rolled.
> A number cube, labeled 1–6, is rolled until a 3 appears.

Are these binomial experiments? Explain.

**Solution:**

The first situation is a binomial experiment. There is a fixed number of trials (10), the trials are independent, there are exactly two outcomes for each trial (rolling a 3 and not rolling a 3), and the probability of success is constant ($\frac{1}{6}$ on every trial).

The second is not a binomial experiment because the number of trials is not fixed.

## BINOMIAL EXPANSIONS AND PROBABILITIES

In this Activity, you will compare the experimental probabilities of tossing two coins to the theoretical probabilities found by using the expansion of the binomial $(H + T)^2$.

1. Toss two coins 20 times and record the results in the table below.

|  | 0 Heads | 1 Head | 2 Heads |
|---|---|---|---|
| 20 Tosses |  |  |  |

2. Calculate the experimental probability of each of the following:

   $P(0$ heads$)$      $P(1$ head$)$      $P(2$ heads$)$

3. When you expand the binomial $(H + T)^2$, you get $H^2 + 2HT + T^2$ or $HH + 2\,HT + TT$. In this expansion, you can see a count of the number of ways each event can occur.

number of ways a head and a tail can occur: head first, tail second or tail first, head second

$$(H + T)^2 = 1H^2 \;+\; 2\,HT \;+\; 1T^2$$

number of ways two heads can occur      number of ways two tails can occur

You can also use this binomial expansion to calculate the theoretical probabilities of tossing two coins. If you replace $H$ with the probability of getting heads and replace $T$ with the probability of getting tails, you get

$$= \left(\tfrac{1}{2}\right)\left(\tfrac{1}{2}\right) + 2\left(\tfrac{1}{2}\right)\left(\tfrac{1}{2}\right) + \left(\tfrac{1}{2}\right)\left(\tfrac{1}{2}\right)$$

$$= \tfrac{1}{4} \;+\; \tfrac{1}{2} \;+\; \tfrac{1}{4}$$

probability of tossing two coins and getting two heads    probability of tossing two coins and getting a head and a tail    probability of tossing two coins and getting two tails

Compare the probabilities in the binomial expansion to your experimental probability results in Question 2. What do you notice?

4  a. Repeat Question 1 for 50 tosses.
   b. Recalculate the experimental probability of 0 heads, 1 head, and 2 heads. Then compare your experimental probabilities to the binomial expansion in Question 3.

### TEACHING TIP

**Question 3** A review of the sample space for tossing two coins {HH, HT, TH, TT} might be helpful in clearing up the confusion that is likely to occur about the 2HT in the expression. To help clarify the outcomes of tossing two coins, show students a table such as the one below.

|  |  | Second Coin | |
|---|---|---|---|
|  |  | **H** | **T** |
| **First Coin** | **H** | HH | HT |
|  | **T** | TH | TT |

## Lesson 14.5 Activity Answers

1. Sample answer:

|  | 0 Heads | 1 Head | 2 Heads |
|---|---|---|---|
| **20 Tosses** | 4 | 11 | 5 |

2. Sample answer: $P(0$ heads$) = 0.20$; $P(1$ head$) = 0.55$; $P(2$ heads$) = 0.25$

3. Sample answer: The experimental probability for 2 heads is equal to the value of $HH$. The other values are close but not exact.

4a. Sample answer:

|  | 0 Heads | 1 Head | 2 Heads |
|---|---|---|---|
| **50 Tosses** | 15 | 25 | 10 |

4b. Sample answer: $P(0$ heads$) = 0.3$; $P(1$ head$) = 0.5$; $P(2$ heads$) = 0.2$; The experimental probability of getting a head and a tail is equal to $2HT$. The other values are close but not exact.

**5a.** Sample answer:

| | 0 Heads | 1 Head | 2 Heads |
|---|---|---|---|
| **100 Tosses** | 27 | 51 | 22 |

**5b.** Sample answer: $P(0 \text{ heads}) = 0.27$; $P(1 \text{ head}) = 0.51$; $P(2 \text{ heads}) = 0.22$; None of the values are exact, but all are close to the theoretical values calculated by expanding the binomial.

**6.** Sample answer: The experimental probabilities will get closer to the theoretical values calculated by expanding the binomial.

## ADDITIONAL EXAMPLE

Four number cubes, each labeled 1–6, are rolled. Use the binomial expansion for $(R + N)^4$ to find the probability that a 3 is rolled exactly 1 time.

$$4RN^3 = 4\left(\frac{1}{6}\right)\left(\frac{5}{6}\right)^3 = \frac{500}{1,296} \approx 0.386$$

---

**5 a.** Repeat Question 1 for 100 tosses.

**b.** Recalculate the experimental probability of 0 heads, 1 head, and 2 heads. Then compare your experimental probabilities to the binomial expansion in Question 3.

**6.** What do you think will happen if you repeat for 1,000 tosses?

A number cube, labeled 1–6, is rolled four times. What is the probability of rolling a 5 exactly three of those times?

**Solution:**

Let $R$ represent rolling a 5.

Let $N$ represent not rolling a 5.

This situation represents a binomial experiment since all four criteria are met. So expanding the binomial $(R + N)^4$ gives the probabilities of rolling a 5 exactly four times, exactly three times, exactly two times, exactly one time, and exactly 0 times.

Expand the binomial:

$$(R + N)^4 = R^4 + 4R^3N + 6R^2N^2 + 4RN^3 + N^4$$

The term in red represents rolling a 5 exactly three times and not rolling a 5 once. There are four ways this can occur depending on which of the four rolls is *not* a 5.

To find the probability, substitute the probability of rolling a 5 on a number cube $\left(\frac{1}{6}\right)$ for $R$, and substitute the probability of not rolling a 5 on the number cube $\left(\frac{5}{6}\right)$ for $N$.

$$\begin{aligned} 4R^3N &= 4\left(\frac{1}{6}\right)^3\left(\frac{5}{6}\right) \\ &= \frac{5}{324} \\ &\approx 0.015 \text{ or about } 1.5\% \end{aligned}$$

So, the probability of rolling a 5 exactly three times out of four rolls is about 1.5%.

For Exercises 1–4, determine whether each situation is a binomial experiment. If not, explain why.

**1.** spinning a spinner until it lands on red

**2.** spinning four spinners 100 times and determining how many times 3 of them land on red

**3.** removing three 3 cards from a standard deck of 52 cards without replacement and recording whether they are red diamonds or not

**4.** asking 20 people their favorite color

**5.** A couple plans to have three children. Assuming that boys and girls have an equal chance of being born, what is the probability that the couple will have 3 boys? 2 boys? 1 boy? 0 boys?

**6.** Three coins are tossed. Find $P$(2 or 3 tails).

For Exercises 7–10, use the following binomial expansions when needed.

$$(a + b)^4 = a^4 + 4a^3b + 6a^2b^2 + 4ab^3 + b^4$$

$$(a + b)^5 = a^5 + 5a^4b + 10a^3b^2 + 10a^2b^3 + 5ab^4 + b^5$$

$$(a + b)^6 = a^6 + 6a^5b + 15a^4b^2 + 20a^3b^3 + 15a^2b^4 + 6ab^5 + b^6$$

**7.** The star player on the basketball team has a $\frac{7}{8}$ probability of making a basket when he shoots a free throw. He shoots 5 free throws in the first ten minutes of the game. What is the probability that he makes exactly 4 of the free throws?

**8.** The spinner shown to the left is spun 6 times.

   **a.** What is the probability that the spinner lands on yellow exactly 2 times?

   **b.** What is the probability that the spinner lands on yellow at least 5 times?

**9.** What is the probability of guessing exactly 4 out of 5 questions correctly on a multiple-choice test if there are 3 possible choices for each question?

**10.** A coin is spun (rather than flipped). If the probability of it landing tails is 52%, what is the probability of spinning a coin 5 times and having it land on tails exactly 2 times?

BINOMIAL EXPERIMENTS    Lesson 14.5    **519**

**6.** $(H + T)^3 = H^3 + 3H^2T + \underline{3HT^2} + \underline{T^3}$; $P$(2 or 3 tails) $= 3HT^2 + T^3 = 3\left(\frac{1}{2}\right)\left(\frac{1}{2}\right)^2 + \left(\frac{1}{2}\right)^3 = \frac{4}{8} = \frac{1}{2}$

**7.** $(B + N)^5 = B^5 + \underline{5B^4N} + 10B^3N^2 + 10B^2N^3 + 5BN^4 + N^5$; $5B^4N = 5\left(\frac{7}{8}\right)^4\left(\frac{1}{8}\right) = \frac{12,005}{32,768} \approx 0.37$

**8a.** $(Y + N)^6 = Y^6 + 6Y^5N + 15Y^4N^2 + 20Y^3N^3 + \underline{15Y^2N^4} + 6YN^5 + N^6$; $15Y^2N^4 = 15\left(\frac{1}{4}\right)^2\left(\frac{3}{4}\right)^4 = \frac{1,215}{4,096} \approx 0.297$

**8b.** $(Y + N)^6 = \underline{Y^6} + \underline{6Y^5N} + 15Y^4N^2 + 20Y^3N^3 + 15Y^2N^4 + 6YN^5 + N^6$; $Y^6 + 6Y^5N = \left(\frac{1}{4}\right)^6 + 6\left(\frac{1}{4}\right)^5\left(\frac{3}{4}\right) = \frac{19}{4,096} \approx 0.0046$

**9.** $(C + W)^5 = C^5 + \underline{5C^4W} + 10C^3W^2 + 10C^2W^3 + 5CW^4 + W^5$; $5C^4W = 5\left(\frac{1}{3}\right)^4\left(\frac{2}{3}\right) = \frac{10}{243} \approx 0.041$ or about 4%

**10.** $(H + T)^5 = H^5 + 5H^4T + \underline{10H^3T^2} + 10H^2T^3 + 5HT^4 + T^5$; $10H^3T^2 = 10(0.48)^3(0.52)^2 \approx 0.30$

**Practice for Lesson 14.5 Answers**

**1.** No, the number of trials is not fixed.

**2.** Yes, it is a binomial experiment.

**3.** No, the trials are not independent.

**4.** No, there are more than two outcomes.

**5.** $(B + G)^3 = B^3 + 3B^2G + 3BG^2 + G^3 = \left(\frac{1}{2}\right)^3 + 3\left(\frac{1}{2}\right)^2\left(\frac{1}{2}\right) + 3\left(\frac{1}{2}\right)\left(\frac{1}{2}\right)^2 + \left(\frac{1}{2}\right)^3$; $P(3) = \left(\frac{1}{2}\right)^3 = \frac{1}{8}$; $P(2) = 3\left(\frac{1}{2}\right)^3 = \frac{3}{8}$; $P(1) = 3\left(\frac{1}{2}\right)^3 = \frac{3}{8}$; $P(0) = \left(\frac{1}{2}\right)^3 = \frac{1}{8}$

**519**

## Materials List

- two number cubes, each labeled 1–6, per group

## Description

Students are asked to develop and implement a plan for collecting and analyzing data. Once the data have been gathered and analyzed, they write papers communicating what they have learned from their experiment. This project works best when students work individually.

## Sample Answer

Answers will vary depending on the data collected.

If a calculator simulation is used to perform this experiment, suggest that each student perform at least 1,000 rolls.

To use a calculator to perform a simulation for this experiment, press the **APPS** key, scroll down to **Prob Sim,** and press **ENTER**. Press **ENTER** again.

Choose **Roll Dice** and press **ENTER**

Press the **ZOOM** key to select **SET**. Then choose two dice. Press the **GRAPH** key to select **OK**.

As you press the **WINDOW** key the calculator will roll two dice and calculate the sum.

---

## Let the Good Times Roll

- Conduct an experiment or calculator simulation that uses two number cubes, each labeled 1–6, to determine the experimental probability of rolling a sum that is less than or equal to 4.

- Determine the theoretical probability of rolling a sum that is less than or equal to 4.

- Write a paper that addresses each of the following points:

  ✓ Describe your experiment.

  ✓ Display the results of your experiment in an appropriate way.

  ✓ Analyze the results of your experiment by comparing the results of the experimental and theoretical probabilities.

  ✓ Address the question: How could you alter your experiment so that the experimental probability is likely to be closer to the theoretical probability?

# Chapter 14 Review

## You Should Be Able to:

### Lesson 14.1
- find the theoretical probability of an event.
- find the experimental probability of an event by conducting an experiment.

### Lesson 14.2
- find conditional probabilities.
- find the probability of the complement of an event.

### Lesson 14.3
- find the probability that two independent events both occur.

- find the probability that two dependent events both occur.
- find the probability that either of two mutually exclusive events occurs.

### Lesson 14.4
- solve problems that require previously learned concepts and skills.

### Lesson 14.5
- identify binomial experiments.
- find probabilities for binomial experiments.
- use binomial expansions to find probabilities.

## Key Vocabulary

probability (p. 492)

theoretical probability (p. 493)

event (p. 493)

experimental probability (p. 495)

Law of Large Numbers (p. 495)

conditional probability (p. 500)

complement of an event (p. 501)

independent events (p. 505)

dependent events (p. 505)

mutually exclusive events (p. 508)

binomial experiment (p. 516)

## Chapter 14  Test Review

**Fill in the blank.**

1. _____ probability is determined using mathematical methods and the fairness of coins, spinners, number cubes, etc.

2. _____ probability is determined by performing experiments and making observations about their outcomes.

3. Two events are _____ if the occurrence of one does not affect the occurrence of the other.

## Chapter 14 Test Review Answers

1. Theoretical
2. Experimental
3. independent

**4.** conditional

**5.** $\dfrac{16}{120} = \dfrac{2}{15}$

**6.** $\dfrac{2}{7} \approx 0.286 = 28.6\%$

**7a.** $\dfrac{3}{800}$

**7b.** $500,000 \times \dfrac{3}{800} = 1,875$

**8.** $\dfrac{22}{50} = \dfrac{11}{25}$ or $44\%$

---

**4.** The probability that an event *M* will occur given that some other event *N* also occurs is called the _____ probability of *M* given *N*.

**5.** A dart is thrown at the target shown below.

What is the probability it will land in region C?

**6.** Veteran's Day is celebrated on its original date (November 11), rather than always on a Monday. In any arbitrary year, what is the probability that Veteran's Day will be on a weekend?

**7.** A quality control engineer for a toy company tested 800 computer games and found 3 to be defective.
  **a.** Based on these findings, what is the probability that a computer game manufactured by this company will be defective?
  **b.** The company plans to make 500,000 computer games this year. Based on these findings, how many computer games can be expected to be defective?

**8.** A group of students designed a board game with a spinner that is divided into four equal sections: 1, 2, 3, and "Lose a Turn." To help them determine the number of times a player would spin "Lose a Turn" in 10 spins, they conducted an experiment. In the experiment, one trial consisted of 10 spins.

Look at the table. The third row, for example, shows that students spun "Lose a Turn" 2 times in 11 of their 50 trials. Based on the results of the experiment, what is the probability that a player will spin "Lose a Turn" 3 or more times in a trial?

| Number of Times a "Lose a Turn" Was Spun in a Trial of 10 Spins | Number of Trials |
| --- | --- |
| 0 | 5 |
| 1 | 12 |
| 2 | 11 |
| 3 | 15 |
| 4 | 4 |
| 5 | 2 |
| 6 | 0 |
| 7 | 1 |
| 8 | 0 |
| 9 | 0 |
| 10 | 0 |
| Total number of trials | 50 |

9. If you randomly guess at the answer to a multiple-choice test question for which there are five answer choices, what is the probability that you will guess correctly? What is the probability that you will guess incorrectly?

10. What is the complement of rolling a 5 on a number cube that is labeled 1–6?

11. A card is drawn from a standard deck of 52 cards. What is $P(\text{even-numbered card}|\text{spade})$?

12. A coin is flipped 3 times.

    a. Are these events independent or dependent?

    b. Find the probability of getting tails each time.

13. A large jar is filled with bills of different denominations. If a person draws two $100 bills in succession without looking, he will receive the entire jar of bills. The jar contains the following number of bills.

| Bill Value | Number of Bills |
|---|---|
| $100 | ? |
| $20 | 10 |
| $10 | 20 |
| $5 | 50 |
| $1 | 100 |

What is the probability of drawing two $100 dollar bills in succession without replacement?

14. Two jeeps are used on a humanitarian mission that is expected to take 150 hours. The motor in each jeep has a 0.94 probability of lasting 150 hours. The mission can succeed if at least one of the jeeps completes the mission. What is the probability that the motor in at least one of the two jeeps lasts for the entire mission?

9. $\frac{1}{5}$; $1 - \frac{1}{5} = \frac{4}{5}$

10. rolling a 1, 2, 3, 4, or 6

11. $\frac{5}{13}$

12a. independent

12b. $\left(\frac{1}{2}\right)^3 = \frac{1}{8}$

13. $\frac{2}{182} \cdot \frac{1}{181} = \frac{2}{32{,}942}$ or about 0.00006

14. $P(\text{at least one motor lasts}) = 1 - P(\text{both motors fail}) = 1 - (0.06)^2 = 0.9964$

**15a.** $\frac{1}{2}$

**15b.** $\left(\frac{1}{2}\right)\left(\frac{1}{4}\right) = \frac{1}{8}$

**15c.** $\frac{3}{4}$

**16a.** $(a + b)^6 = a^6 + 6a^5b + 15a^4b^2 + 20a^3b^3 + 15a^2b^4 + 6ab^5 + b^6$

**16b.** $6a^5b$

**16c.** $6a^5b = 6(0.9)^5 (0.1) \approx 0.354$ or about 35%

**17.** $(H + M)^3 = H^3 + 3H^2M + 3HM^2 + M^3 = \left(\frac{2}{5}\right)^3 + 3\left(\frac{2}{5}\right)^2 \left(\frac{3}{5}\right) + 3\left(\frac{2}{5}\right)\left(\frac{3}{5}\right)^2 + \left(\frac{3}{5}\right)^3$;

$3\left(\frac{2}{5}\right)^2\left(\frac{3}{5}\right) = \frac{36}{125} = 0.288$

---

**15.** Graduate students are selected for grants from a group of people who have applied. Half of the students in the group are selected and half are rejected. Because some students decline the grants, the students who are rejected have a second chance. The probabilities of being selected and rejected are shown in the diagram below.

a. What is the probability that a student will be selected in the first round?

b. What is the probability that a student will be rejected in the first round and selected in the second?

c. Find $P$(grant accepted|selected in first round).

**16.** A doctor tells you that 90% of the time a certain type of surgery is successful. You want to know the probability that exactly 5 out of 6 surgeries will be successful.

a. Which of these binomial expansions could be used to solve this problem?

$$(a + b)^2 = a^2 + 2ab + b^2$$

$$(a + b)^5 = a^5 + 5a^4b + 10a^3b^2 + 10a^2b^3 + 5ab^4 + b^5$$

$$(a + b)^6 = a^6 + 6a^5b + 15a^4b^2 + 20a^3b^3 + 15a^2b^4 + 6ab^5 + b^6$$

b. Which term of the binomial expansion could be used to solve the problem?

c. If this surgery is performed 6 times, what is the probability that exactly 5 surgeries will be successful?

**17.** The probability that an archery student hits the small center circle on a target is $\frac{2}{5}$. She shoots 3 arrows. What is the probability that she will hit the center circle exactly 2 times?

# Chapter 15
## The Mathematics of Personal Finance

## Mathematical Overview

In this chapter, students learn that financial literacy and mathematical knowledge work hand-in-hand to promote good decision making about money—earning, spending, saving, and borrowing. Spreadsheets are used throughout the chapter as a tool for keeping track of expenses, as well as money earned. Through a discussion of how taxes and other deductions affect income, students understand why their gross income does not equal their net income. Once income and expenses are determined, students complete a budget and see how a budget is fundamental to making decisions about finances. Students learn about setting financial goals. They also learn that modifying a budget is sometimes necessary in order to make the goals realistic. Students examine the effect of simple interest on savings and then proceed to derive a formula for future value when interest is compounded. They also create a spreadsheet to calculate the interest owed on a loan and the number of monthly payments needed to pay back what is owed on a loan.

## Lesson Summaries

### Lesson 15.1  *Investigation: Budgeting Expenses*

In this Investigation, students work in groups/pairs that they will be a part of throughout Lessons 15.1, 15.2, and 15.3. Students use a spreadsheet program or grid paper and a calculator to organize given data about a student's expenses. They use what they have learned about functions to write an equation that best models the total expenses paid as a function of time. Students are asked to save their spreadsheets for use in Lesson 15.3.

### Lesson 15.2  *Investigation: Income and Taxes*

In this Investigation, students investigate what happens to their gross income once they are earning a steady paycheck that shows their net income. Students calculate the amount of withholding tax using a mathematical formula or a tax-withholding table. The exercises in this lesson focus on calculating net income after deductions and allowances are considered. Students use what they have learned about mathematical models to describe the total Social Security plus Medicare taxes as a function of a yearly base salary.

### Lesson 15.3  *Investigation: Implementing a Budget*

For this Investigation, students return to the spreadsheet they made in Lesson 15.1. Using what they learned about taxes in Lesson 15.2, students update their spreadsheet to include salary, withholding taxes, Social Security, and Medicare taxes. They analyze the spreadsheet to determine if the total net income is more or less than the total expenses. Financial goals (long-, medium-, and short-range) are discussed. Once the goals are established, students see that a budget can be initiated or modified so that the goals are realistic.

### Lesson 15.4  *Investigation: Saving*

In this Investigation, students examine the effect that interest has on building savings. Students calculate simple interest for given principals and interest rates to determine

future value. Students then calculate the future value with annual compounding of interest and compare the results to the future value with simple interest. After seeing the results of calculations for finding the future value with quarterly compounding, students use the compound interest formula to find the future value for any number of years under various compounding methods. In order to find the option best suited for their needs, students are advised on what to look for when comparison shopping for an institution in which to build their savings. The Rule of 72 is introduced and used as a way for students to approximate the time it takes money to double at a given interest rate.

### Lesson 15.5  *R.A.P.*

In this lesson, students **R**eview **A**nd **P**ractice solving problems that require the use of skills and concepts taught in previous math levels. The skills reviewed in this lesson are skills that are needed as a basis for solving problems throughout this course.

### Lesson 15.6  *Investigation: Borrowing*

In this Investigation, students expand upon what they learned about compounding in Lesson 15.4 to include calculating payment amounts when paying back money that was borrowed. Students use a spreadsheet and the remaining balance method to calculate the interest on a loan. They also use a monthly payment formula to determine a monthly payment for a loan. A section comparing buying a car vs leasing a car is provided in this lesson as an optional study section.

### Chapter 15  *Extension: Annuities*

In this Extension, students learn about savings plans, such as IRAs and annuities. They use a formula to find the future value of an ordinary annuity.

## Lesson Guide

| Lesson/Objectives | Materials | |
|---|---|---|
| **Chapter 15 Opener: How Much Income Do I Need to Cover My Expenses?**<br>• understand the importance of financial planning. | | |
| **15.1 Investigation: Budgeting Expenses**<br>• use a computer spreadsheet to record and summarize expenses for a budget. | *Per pair:*<br>• computer spreadsheet program such as Microsoft® Excel® | *Optional:*<br>• grid paper<br>• TI-Nspire™ |
| **15.2 Investigation: Income and Taxes**<br>• find income equivalents for different time periods.<br>• use federal tax tables to find withholding amounts for various income levels.<br>• use formulas to determine Social Security and Medicare taxes.<br>• identify functions that model tax calculations. | *Per pair:*<br>• grid paper<br>• computer spreadsheet program such as Excel<br>• federal tax withholding table excerpt from IRS Publication 15 or Handout 15A | *Optional:*<br>• TRM table shells for Questions 1, 4, 6 and 10<br>• TRM table shells for Exercises 6 and 9 |
| **15.3 Investigation: Implementing a Budget**<br>• include income data in a complete budget spreadsheet.<br>• determine whether a budget is balanced. | *Per pair:*<br>• computer spreadsheet program such as Excel<br>• spreadsheet files from Lesson 15.1.<br>• federal tax withholding table excerpt from IRS Publication 15 or Handout 15A | |
| **15.4 Investigation: Saving**<br>• distinguish between simple and compound interest.<br>• determine the future value of savings under various compounding methods. | *Per pair:*<br>• computer spreadsheet program such as Excel | *Optional:*<br>• TRM table shell for Questions 1, 4, 6<br>• TRM table shell for Exercise 6<br>• grid paper |
| **15.5 R.A.P.**<br>• solve problems that require previously learned concepts and skills. | | *Optional:*<br>• TRM table shell for Exercises 17–22 |
| **15.6 Investigation: Borrowing**<br>• construct and interpret an amortization schedule.<br>• compare the relative costs of buying and leasing (optional). | *Per pair:*<br>• computer spreadsheet program such as Excel | *Optional:*<br>• graphing calculator |
| **Chapter 15 Annuities**<br>• determine the future value of an annuity. | | |

## Pacing Guide

| | Day 1 | Day 2 | Day 3 | Day 4 | Day 5 | Day 6 | Day 7 | Day 8 | Day 9 | Day 10 | Day 11 | Day 12 |
|---|---|---|---|---|---|---|---|---|---|---|---|---|
| **Basic** | p. 526, 15.1 | 15.1 | 15.2 | 15.2 | 15.3 | 15.3 | 15.4 | 15.4 | 15.5 | 15.6 | project | review |
| **Standard** | p. 526, 15.1 | 15.1 | 15.2 | 15.2 | 15.3 | 15.3 | 15.4 | 15.5 | 15.6 | project | review | extension |
| **Block** | p. 526, 15.1 | 15.2 | 15.3 | 15.4, 15.5 | 15.6, project | review, extension | | | | | | |

### Supplement Support

See the Book Companion Website at www.highschool.bfwpub.com/ModelingwithMathematics and the Teacher's Resource Materials (TRM) for additional resources.

# The Mathematics of Personal Finance

## CONTENTS

## Lesson Objective

- understand the importance of financial planning.

## Vocabulary

## Description

The preliminary reading describes some fundamental aspects of financial literacy, as well as consequences that result from financial illiteracy.

### TEACHING TIP

If students ask what is meant by "disposable personal income," tell them that it is equal to total income minus taxes.

### TEACHING TIP

Ask students to describe what they think is involved in financial planning. Ask them to be specific about steps they might take to create a budget.

## How Much Income Do I Need to Cover My Expenses?

In order to make good decisions about money, it helps to be both financially literate and mathematically knowledgeable. According to Alan Greenspan, economist and former chairman of the United States Federal Reserve Board:

> It has been my experience that competency in mathematics, both in numerical manipulations and in understanding its conceptual foundations, enhances a person's ability to handle the more ambiguous and qualitative relationships that dominate our day-to-day financial decision-making.

Financial literacy involves

- understanding basic financial concepts,
- reading and communicating about the financial conditions that affect us,
- having the skills necessary to complete financial tasks, and
- making appropriate financial decisions.

The overall costs of financial *illiteracy* to society and individuals are huge. Consider the following:

- At the beginning of 2008, the personal savings rate (savings as a percentage of disposable personal income) was near zero. This means that people spent all of the money they had left after paying taxes.
- Currently, the typical family's credit card balance is equal to almost 5 percent of their annual income.
- Each year from 2006 to 2009, the number of Americans filing for consumer bankruptcy increased by more than 30%.

Mathematical knowledge and financial literacy go hand-in-hand. As you proceed through this chapter, the relevance of mathematics in all aspects of your personal finances should become apparent to you. In fact, many of the mathematical topics you have already studied in this course will be used in helping you understand and improve the management of your own money.

People may avoid making decisions about their personal finances because they do not know where to begin. The goal of this chapter is to help you find the place to begin, starting with the budgeting process.

## Lesson 15.1

### INVESTIGATION: Budgeting Expenses

A first step in gaining an understanding of your finances is to know where your money goes after you earn it. A spreadsheet is a useful tool for keeping track of your expenses.

In simple terms, a **budget** is a summary of money coming in and going out. It is an organized list of your income and expenses and can be used to help you make financial decisions. A realistic budget can only be developed if you know exactly how you spend your money. So, for a couple of months before creating an actual budget, you must collect data that represent your true expenses. These data include every expense paid by cash, check, and credit card. Even the smallest expenses, like the cost of a slice of pizza, should be recorded.

Expenses can be divided into two types:

- **fixed expenses**—expenses that cannot be changed. These expenses are essentially the same each month, for example, rent or car payments.
- **variable expenses**—expenses over which you have some control, for example, food, clothing, savings, and entertainment.

The table below lists a college student's average monthly expenses. She is attending a Midwestern university. She has a part-time job and shares an apartment with a friend. She has kept track of what she spent each day for several months and now wants to set up a budget.

| Fixed Expenses | | Variable Expenses | |
| --- | --- | --- | --- |
| Rent | $350 | Food | $280 |
| Tuition | $1,400 | Utilities | $150 |
| | | Books | $165 |
| | | Credit Card | $100 |
| | | Clothing | $50 |
| | | Personal Items | $30 |
| | | Entertainment | $50 |
| | | Pocket Money | $50 |

BUDGETING EXPENSES    **Lesson 15.1**    **527**

# LESSON 15.1

**5e**  Engage

## Lesson Objective

- use a computer spreadsheet to record and summarize expenses for a budget.

## Vocabulary

- budget
- fixed expenses
- variable expenses

## Materials List

- computer spreadsheet program such as Microsoft® Excel®

## Description

Students should work in pairs on this Investigation if possible. Group size may depend upon the number of computers available. If the class does not have access to an electronic spreadsheet program, have them create the spreadsheet on grid paper and use a calculator for computations.

Students who have never used a spreadsheet will need additional guidance during this Investigation.

As an alternative to using a computer spreadsheet program, calculators that can emulate spreadsheets could be used. TI-83/84 calculators may include a **CelSheet APP** that has spreadsheet functionality, although the size of the screen limits what can be viewed at one time. The TI-Nspire™ is better suited to emulate a spreadsheet.

*Wrapping Up the Investigation:*

Make sure all groups have accurately completed their spreadsheets. If their yearly expenses total $31,500, they have probably done so.

Remind students to save their spreadsheet files, as they will use them during the Investigation in Lesson 15.3, where they will develop a complete budget.

## Lesson 15.1 Investigation Answers

1. Students' spreadsheets should look like the one shown in the text preceding Question 1.

To organize this information, you can use a computer spreadsheet program, such as in the Microsoft® Excel® examples shown here. Once the data are entered into the spreadsheet, calculations can be performed on the numbers that are entered.

|  | A | B |
|---|---|---|
| 1 | **Fixed Expenses** | |
| 2 | Rent | $350 |
| 3 | Tuition | $1,400 |
| 4 | | |
| 5 | | |
| 6 | **Variable Expenses** | |
| 7 | Food | $280 |
| 8 | Utilities | $150 |
| 9 | Books | $165 |
| 10 | Credit Card | $100 |
| 11 | Clothing | $50 |
| 12 | Personal Items | $30 |
| 13 | Entertainment | $50 |
| 14 | Pocket Money | $50 |
| 15 | | |

1. To create your own spreadsheet of this student's expenses, start a computer spreadsheet program. Open a blank worksheet. It will contain many *cells* arranged in rows and columns. The rows are labeled with numbers and the columns are labeled with letters. Save your worksheet as "Lesson 15.1 Inv".

   - Click on cell A1 and type the words "Fixed Expenses".
   - Rent is the first fixed expense, so type "Rent" in cell A2. Then enter $350 in cell B2.
   - Type "Tuition" in cell A3 and enter $1,400 in cell B3.
   - For now, leave the cells in rows 4 and 5 blank. Type "Variable Expenses" in cell A6.
   - Continue down the A column, listing the names of the variable expenses. Enter the corresponding amounts in the B column until you have included all of the student's expenses from the table.

2. Next, use your spreadsheet to find subtotals for the two expense categories. Type "Subtotal" in cell A4. Right-justify this text (that is, click the toolbar icon that places the text on the right-hand side of the cell). Then follow these steps to enter a formula in cell B4 that computes the sum of the two fixed expenses.

   - Type an equal sign. An equal sign indicates that the cell contains a formula that must be evaluated.
   - Click on cell B2.

2. Entry for the formula is shown below on the left. The result of the formula evaluation is shown below on the right.

|  | A | B |
|---|---|---|
| 1 | **Fixed Expenses** | |
| 2 | Rent | $350 |
| 3 | Tuition | $1,400 |
| 4 | Subtotal | =B2+B3 |
| 5 | | |
| 6 | **Variable Expenses** | |
| 7 | Food | $280 |
| 8 | Utilities | $150 |
| 9 | Books | $165 |
| 10 | Credit Card | $100 |
| 11 | Clothing | $50 |
| 12 | Personal Items | $30 |
| 13 | Entertainment | $50 |
| 14 | Pocket Money | $50 |

|  | A | B |
|---|---|---|
| 1 | **Fixed Expenses** | |
| 2 | Rent | $350 |
| 3 | Tuition | $1,400 |
| 4 | Subtotal | $1,750 |
| 5 | | |
| 6 | **Variable Expenses** | |
| 7 | Food | $280 |
| 8 | Utilities | $150 |
| 9 | Books | $165 |
| 10 | Credit Card | $100 |
| 11 | Clothing | $50 |
| 12 | Personal Items | $30 |
| 13 | Entertainment | $50 |
| 14 | Pocket Money | $50 |

**Note**

You may want to increase the column widths to fit the text. For example, to change the width of column A, place the cursor on the vertical line between the cells labeled A and B. The cursor will change to back-to-back arrows. Click and drag to change the column width.

- Type a + sign. A plus sign indicates that the contents of the cell you just clicked on must be added to the next thing you type.
- Click on cell B3. Then click the save button or press "Enter" to have the formula evaluated.

3. In a similar manner, type "Subtotal" in cell A15 and enter a formula in cell B15 that will compute the sum of the eight variable expenses. When you finish, your spreadsheet should look similar to the one shown below.

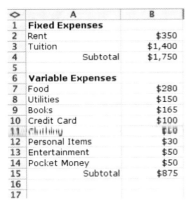

| ◇ | A | B |
|---|---|---|
| 1 | **Fixed Expenses** | |
| 2 | Rent | $350 |
| 3 | Tuition | $1,400 |
| 4 | Subtotal | $1,750 |
| 5 | | |
| 6 | **Variable Expenses** | |
| 7 | Food | $280 |
| 8 | Utilities | $150 |
| 9 | Books | $165 |
| 10 | Credit Card | $100 |
| 11 | Clothing | $50 |
| 12 | Personal Items | $30 |
| 13 | Entertainment | $50 |
| 14 | Pocket Money | $50 |
| 15 | Subtotal | $875 |
| 16 | | |
| 17 | | |

4. Now determine the total monthly expenses. In cell A17, type "Total Expenses." Then, in cell B17, enter a formula that computes the sum of the subtotals for the fixed and variable expenses.

5. Put your spreadsheet aside for now. Consider the rent expense of $350 per month. Make a table and a graph that show the total rent paid for any number of months from 0 to 12.

6. What kind of function best models this situation? Write an equation that gives total rent paid $R$ as a function of the number of months $n$.

7. Instead of calculating the yearly expenses for each item in this manner, you can use your spreadsheet. Of course, this assumes that all months have the same expenses. In cell C1, type "Yearly Expenses." Then in cell C2 enter a formula that reflects your answer to Question 6. Use * to indicate multiplication.

8. The formula you entered in cell C2 can be applied to other cells. Highlight cell C2. Then click on the little box in the lower right-hand corner of that cell. Drag your cursor down to cell C17. Describe what this does to your spreadsheet.

**TEACHING TIP**

For **Question 3**, you may wish to point out two more efficient alternatives for finding the sum of a range of values. One is the SUM function, which will compute the sum of the values in cells B7 through B14 using the following syntax: =SUM(B7:B14). The cells B7 and B14 can be typed in, or clicked on with the mouse.

The second way is to use the "Autosum" feature. Highlight the range of cells to be added (in this case, cells B7 through B14). Then click on the "Σ" icon in the toolbar. The sum of the cell entries in the highlighted range will be displayed in the first open cell below the range.

3. The formula in cell B15 should be "=B7+B8+B9+B10+B11+B12+B13+B14". Alternatively, the formula "=SUM(B7:B14)" will produce the same result.

**TEACHING TIP**

For **Question 8**, you may wish to explain the concept of a "relative cell address," in which the spreadsheet program automatically changes cell references in a formula when the formula is copied to other cells. In this case, the formula "=12*B2" is adjusted to reflect the appropriate row. Explain that there are times when such an adjustment is not desirable, and a copied formula must refer to the same location as the cell from which it was copied. In such a case, a dollar sign $ is inserted before the cell's column letter or row number, or both, to lock in an "absolute cell address."

5.–8. See answers beginning on page 624.

---

4. Entry for the formula is shown below on the left. The result of the formula evaluation is shown below on the right.

| | A | B |
|---|---|---|
| 1 | **Fixed Expenses** | |
| 2 | Rent | $350 |
| 3 | Tuition | $1,400 |
| 4 | Subtotal | $1,750 |
| 5 | | |
| 6 | **Variable Expenses** | |
| 7 | Food | $280 |
| 8 | Utilities | $150 |
| 9 | Books | $165 |
| 10 | Credit Card | $100 |
| 11 | Clothing | $50 |
| 12 | Personal Items | $30 |
| 13 | Entertainment | $50 |
| 14 | Pocket Money | $50 |
| 15 | Subtotal | $875 |
| 16 | | |
| 17 | **Total Expenses** | =B4+B15 |

| | A | B |
|---|---|---|
| 1 | **Fixed Expenses** | |
| 2 | Rent | $350 |
| 3 | Tuition | $1,400 |
| 4 | Subtotal | $1,750 |
| 5 | | |
| 6 | **Variable Expenses** | |
| 7 | Food | $280 |
| 8 | Utilities | $150 |
| 9 | Books | $165 |
| 10 | Credit Card | $100 |
| 11 | Clothing | $50 |
| 12 | Personal Items | $30 |
| 13 | Entertainment | $50 |
| 14 | Pocket Money | $50 |
| 15 | Subtotal | $875 |
| 16 | | |
| 17 | **Total Expenses** | $2,625 |

**9.** Sample answer: The formulas in the cells are adjusted so that they refer to the monthly expense cell in the same row.

## Practice for Lesson 15.1 Answers

**1.** Sample answer: Entries showing formulas and the results of formula evaluations are shown in the spreadsheets below.

| | A | B |
|---|---|---|
| 1 | **Fixed Expenses** | |
| 2 | Savings | $690 |
| 3 | Mortgage | $1,460 |
| 4 | Student Loans | $345 |
| 5 | Auto Loan | $313 |
| 6 | Taxes | $815 |
| 7 | Property Taxes | $168 |
| 8 | Health Insurance | $348 |
| 9 | Homeowner's Insurance | $147 |
| 10 | Auto Insurance | $86 |
| 11 | Subtotal | =sum(B2:B10) |
| 12 | | |
| 13 | **Variable Expenses** | |
| 14 | Food | $480 |
| 15 | Utilities | $435 |
| 16 | Home Repair | $80 |
| 17 | Gas/Oil/Car Repairs | $215 |
| 18 | Credit Cards | $275 |
| 19 | Personal Items | $60 |
| 20 | New Clothing | $125 |
| 21 | Gifts | $50 |
| 22 | Vacation Savings | $100 |
| 23 | Emergency Savings | $325 |
| 24 | Entertainment | $380 |
| 25 | Pocket Money | $350 |
| 26 | Subtotal | =sum(B14:B25) |
| 27 | | |
| 28 | **Total Expenses** | =B11+B26 |

| | A | B |
|---|---|---|
| 1 | **Fixed Expenses** | |
| 2 | Savings | $690 |
| 3 | Mortgage | $1,460 |
| 4 | Student Loans | $345 |
| 5 | Auto Loan | $313 |
| 6 | Taxes | $815 |
| 7 | Property Taxes | $168 |
| 8 | Health Insurance | $348 |
| 9 | Homeowner's Insurance | $147 |
| 10 | Auto Insurance | $86 |
| 11 | Subtotal | $4,372 |
| 12 | | |
| 13 | **Variable Expenses** | |
| 14 | Food | $480 |
| 15 | Utilities | $435 |
| 16 | Home Repair | $80 |
| 17 | Gas/Oil/Car Repairs | $215 |
| 18 | Credit Cards | $275 |
| 19 | Personal Items | $60 |
| 20 | New Clothing | $125 |
| 21 | Gifts | $50 |
| 22 | Vacation Savings | $100 |
| 23 | Emergency Savings | $325 |
| 24 | Entertainment | $380 |
| 25 | Pocket Money | $350 |
| 26 | Subtotal | $2,875 |
| 27 | | |
| 28 | **Total Expenses** | $7,247 |

**9.** Click on individual cells in your Yearly Expenses column and examine the formulas in those cells. Describe what you see.

Save your spreadsheet for use in Lesson 15.3.

Variable expenses can rarely be predicted precisely. Because they are variable, they may not be exactly the same from month to month. For these expenses, it is helpful to estimate an average value for each of the various expense categories, and then to try not to spend more than those estimates.

## Practice for Lesson 15.1

**For Exercises 1–4, use the table below.**

A young married couple has monthly expenses as shown.

| Fixed Expenses | | Variable Expenses | |
|---|---|---|---|
| Savings | $690 | Food | $480 |
| Mortgage | $1,460 | Utilities | $435 |
| Student Loans | $345 | Home Repair | $80 |
| Auto Loan | $313 | Gas/Oil/Car Repairs | $215 |
| Taxes | $815 | Credit Cards | $275 |
| Property Taxes | $168 | Personal Items | $60 |
| Health Insurance | $348 | New Clothing | $125 |
| Homeowner's Insurance | $147 | Gifts | $50 |
| Auto Insurance | $86 | Vacation Savings | $100 |
| | | Emergency Savings | $325 |
| | | Entertainment | $380 |
| | | Pocket Money | $350 |

**1.** Use a computer spreadsheet to record the couple's expenses. Save your worksheet as "Lesson 15.1 Prac." Include an automatic calculation of subtotals for fixed and variable expenses, as well as total expenses.

**2.** In column C of your spreadsheet, show total expenses for a year in each category, assuming that every month's expenses are the same. Then save your spreadsheet for use in Lesson 15.3.

**3.** The costs of many goods and services often increase from year to year. The average percent change in cost is called the *inflation rate*.

**2.** Sample answer:

| | A | B | C |
|---|---|---|---|
| 1 | **Fixed Expenses** | | Yearly Expenses |
| 2 | Savings | $690 | $8,280 |
| 3 | Mortgage | $1,460 | $17,520 |
| 4 | Student Loans | $345 | $4,140 |
| 5 | Auto Loan | $313 | $3,756 |
| 6 | Taxes | $815 | $9,780 |
| 7 | Property Taxes | $168 | $2,016 |
| 8 | Health Insurance | $348 | $4,176 |
| 9 | Homeowner's Insurance | $147 | $1,764 |
| 10 | Auto Insurance | $86 | $1,032 |
| 11 | Subtotal | $4,372 | $52,464 |
| 12 | | | $0 |

| | | B | |
|---|---|---|---|
| 13 | **Variable Expenses** | | $0 |
| 14 | Food | $480 | $5,760 |
| 15 | Utilities | $435 | $5,220 |
| 16 | Home Repair | $80 | $960 |
| 17 | Gas/Oil/Car Repairs | $215 | $2,580 |
| 18 | Credit Cards | $275 | $3,300 |
| 19 | Personal Items | $60 | $720 |
| 20 | New Clothing | $125 | $1,500 |
| 21 | Gifts | $50 | $600 |
| 22 | Vacation Savings | $100 | $1,200 |
| 23 | Emergency Savings | $325 | $3,900 |
| 24 | Entertainment | $380 | $4,560 |
| 25 | Pocket Money | $350 | $4,200 |
| 26 | Subtotal | $2,875 | $34,500 |
| 27 | | | $0 |
| 28 | **Total Expenses** | $7,247 | $86,964 |

If the inflation rate is 3%, determine how much the couple will have to spend on food during the second year. Base your answer on the *total* food expense for the first year.

4. Add columns to your spreadsheet that show an additional 4 years of expenses. For each year, *change the variable expenses only* to reflect an annual inflation rate of 3%.

5. Examine your answer to Exercise 3 and the calculations in the Food row of your spreadsheet. Make a scatter plot of the yearly food expense for years 1 through 5.

6. What kind of function best models their food expense as a function of year number? Justify your answer.

7. Write an equation that models the relationship between food expense $F$ and year number $n$.

3. $(1.03)(\$5,760) = \$5,932.80$

4. See answers beginning on page 625.

5. Sample graph:

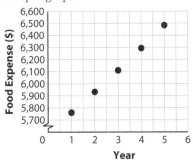

6. Sample answer: Since the ratios of food expenses in successive years are constant and equal to 1.03, an exponential function is the best model.

7. Sample answer: An exponential function has the form $y = ab^x$. Since the value $y$ for food expense in year 1 is $5,760, and $b^1 = 1.03$, then $a = \dfrac{\$5,760}{1.03} = \$5,592.23$. So, the equation $F = \$5,592.23(1.03)^n$ models the data. Alternatively, the equation $F = \$5,760(1.03)^{n-1}$ could be used.

## Lesson Objectives

- find income equivalents for different time periods.
- use federal tax tables to find withholding amounts for various income levels.
- use formulas to determine Social Security and Medicare taxes.
- identify functions that model tax calculations.

## Vocabulary

- gross income
- net income
- tax withholding table

## Materials List

- computer spreadsheet program such as Excel
- Federal tax withholding table excerpt from IRS Publication 15 (Handout 15A)
- grid paper

## Description

This is a particularly long lesson, which may take two days for students to complete.

Students should work in pairs on this Investigation. Groups should be the same as for Lesson 15.1. Each group should be given a copy of the 3-page excerpt from IRS Publication 15. The first page describes the Percentage Method for finding the amount of income that is subject to withholding, which depends on the number of allowances claimed. The remaining two pages contain tables that describe how to calculate the amount of tax withheld from a paycheck for various income levels.

Note: Sample answers for this lesson are based on 2011 withholding tables. If you choose to base this lesson on your current year, you will have to generate new answers for the Questions and Exercises in this lesson.

*Wrapping Up the Investigation:*

Lead a group discussion of the effect of taxes on gross vs net income. If students are surprised by the fact that a larger percent of income is devoted to taxes for higher incomes, explain that the United States has a *graduated income tax,* meaning that people with higher incomes pay a larger share of their incomes to support the operation of the federal government.

**532**

---

## Lesson 15.2    INVESTIGATION:   Income and Taxes

Identifying income is equally as important as identifying expenses. But first you must know what will be deducted from your pay before you can make use of it. This lesson discusses how taxes and other deductions can affect your income.

You may have already earned money for performing odd jobs, such as babysitting, mowing lawns, or shoveling snow. When you agree to do a job like one of these, you know in advance exactly how much money you will make. That amount is what you are paid when you finish the job.

When you take on a job, even a summer job, that provides a steady income, you may get a weekly or monthly company paycheck. Some people are surprised when they find out that the amount of their first check is less than the wages they have earned. Money is deducted (subtracted) from your earnings before you get your paycheck.

1. Complete the table at the top of page 533 to see how earnings translate to different time periods. You may want to use a computer spreadsheet program. Use these conversions:

   40 hours = 1 work week
   52 weeks = 1 year
   12 months = 1 year

   A useful method for making conversions is based on ratios. For example, to change weekly earnings of $500 to hourly earnings, form a ratio based on the equivalence of 40 hours in 1 work week.

   $$\frac{500 \text{ dollars}}{1 \text{ work week}} \cdot \frac{1 \text{ work week}}{40 \text{ hours}} = \frac{500 \text{ dollars}}{40 \text{ hours}}$$

   $$= 12.5 \text{ dollars per hour or } \$12.50 \text{ per hour}$$

## Lesson 15.2 Investigation Answers

1. See answer on page 533.

| Hourly Earnings | Weekly Earnings | Monthly Earnings | Yearly Earnings |
|---|---|---|---|
| $6.50 | | | |
| $10.75 | | | |
| $17.50 | | | |
| | $350.00 | | |
| | $715.00 | | |
| | $1,400.00 | | |
| | | $1,250.00 | |
| | | $1,855.00 | |
| | | $2,000.00 | |
| | | $3,333.33 | |
| | | | $15,000.00 |
| | | | $23,000.00 |
| | | | $32,000.00 |
| | | | $54,000.00 |

2. What is the mean of the hourly earnings?

3. Are the above hourly earnings a good indicator of how much the average worker makes in the United States? Why or why not?

4. The 2010 yearly earnings for some well-known people are listed in the table below. Complete the table to find their hourly wages (to the nearest dollar) if you assume a 40-hour work week.

| Person | 2010 Yearly Earnings | Hourly Wages |
|---|---|---|
| Oprah Winfrey | $315 million | |
| James Cameron | $210 million | |
| Tyler Perry | $125 million | |
| Steven Spielberg | $100 million | |
| George Lucas | $95 million | |
| Beyoncé Knowles | $87 million | |
| Johnny Depp | $75 million | |
| Michael Jordan | $55 million | |
| Taylor Swift | $45 million | |

SOURCE: FORBES MAGAZINE ON-LINE WWW.FORBES.COM

INCOME AND TAXES    Lesson 15.2    533

2. $14.62

3. Sample answer: Two of the hourly figures are significantly greater than the others, and the mean is sensitive to outliers. The median ($11.30) may be a better measure of a typical worker's earnings.

1.

| Hourly Earnings | Weekly Earnings | Monthly Earnings | Yearly Earnings |
|---|---|---|---|
| $6.50 | $260.00 | $1,126.67 | $13,520.00 |
| $10.75 | $430.00 | $1,863.33 | $22,360.00 |
| $17.50 | $700.00 | $3,033.33 | $36,400.00 |
| $8.75 | $350.00 | $1,516.67 | $18,200.00 |
| $17.88 | $715.00 | $3,098.33 | $37,180.00 |
| $35.00 | $1,400.00 | $6,066.67 | $72,800.00 |
| $7.21 | $288.46 | $1,250.00 | $15,000.00 |
| $10.70 | $428.08 | $1,855.00 | $22,260.00 |
| $11.54 | $461.54 | $2,000.00 | $24,000.00 |
| $19.23 | $769.23 | $3,333.33 | $39,999.96 |
| $7.21 | $288.46 | $1,250.00 | $15,000.00 |
| $11.06 | $442.31 | $1,916.67 | $23,000.00 |
| $15.38 | $615.38 | $2,666.67 | $32,000.00 |
| $25.96 | $1,038.46 | $4,500.00 | $54,000.00 |

4.

| Person | 2010 Yearly Earnings | Hourly Wages |
|---|---|---|
| Oprah Winfrey | $315 million | $151,442 |
| James Cameron | $210 million | $100,962 |
| Tyler Perry | $125 million | $60,096 |
| Steven Spielberg | $100 million | $48,077 |
| George Lucas | $95 million | $45,673 |
| Beyoncé Knowles | $87 million | $41,827 |
| Johnny Depp | $75 million | $36,058 |
| Michael Jordan | $55 million | $26,442 |
| Taylor Swift | $45 million | $21,635 |

5. $59,135
6. See the answer for Question 10 on page 535 for the completed table for 2011 withholding tables.
7. Sample answer for 2011 withholding tables: Yes, it appears to have at least two straight-line segments with different slopes (linear functions).

5. What is the mean hourly wage for the people in the table in Question 4?

According to the Internal Revenue Service (IRS), about 40% of the income for the United States government comes from personal income taxes. The amount of income tax that a person pays depends on the amount of money that person earns in a year.

It is difficult for some people to save the money needed to pay their annual taxes all at one time. Therefore, the IRS requires employers to withhold money from each paycheck in order to spread the tax burden over time. The amount of *withholding*, the money that an employer takes out of an employee's paycheck, can be found using a mathematical formula or a **tax withholding table**.

6. Use the federal income tax withholding tables, along with the Percentage Method, to find the amount withheld each month from a single person's paycheck for each monthly income listed in the table below. Use a *withholding allowance* of 1, which means the person has no other dependents and claims an allowance only for himself or herself.

| Monthly Income | Withholding | | | |
|---|---|---|---|---|
| $500 | | | | |
| $1,000 | | | | |
| $1,500 | | | | |
| $2,000 | | | | |
| $2,500 | | | | |
| $3,000 | | | | |
| $3,500 | | | | |
| $4,000 | | | | |
| $4,500 | | | | |

7. Make a scatter plot of withholding versus monthly income. Does the scatter plot appear to have the form of any of the functions you have studied in this course (direct or inverse variation, linear, quadratic, exponential)? Explain.

When you work for someone, 4.2% of your wages is withheld as Social Security tax, as of 2011. Your employer also pays an amount equal to 6.2% of your wages for Social Security programs. In 2011 there was no Social Security tax on either the employee or employer for wages over $106,800.

Also, 1.45% of your wages is withheld, and the employer pays a matching 1.45% amount, to the Medicare program. All wages are subject to Medicare tax; there is no upper limit.

8.  Label the third column in your table "Social Security Tax" and the fourth column "Medicare Tax." Then complete the table to include the amount the employee pays for each of these two taxes for each listed income.

9.  On the same set of axes, make a scatter plot of Social Security tax versus monthly income and a scatter plot of Medicare tax versus monthly income. Do the scatter plots appear to have the form of any of the functions you have studied in this course (direct or inverse variation, linear, quadratic, exponential)? Explain.

10. Label the fifth column "Money Remaining." In this column, list the amounts that would appear in a monthly paycheck for each income level after all taxes have been deducted.

The total amount of salary or wages before deductions is often referred to as **gross income**. The money remaining *after* taxes and any other deductions is called **net income**. Examples of other items that may be deducted from someone's pay are health insurance and life insurance premiums, retirement plan payments, and union dues.

## E X A M P L E

Find mathematical models for (a) Social Security tax and (b) Medicare tax as functions of yearly income for 2011. Indicate the problem domain of each function.

**Solution:**

a.  In 2011, Social Security tax $S$ is equal to 4.2% of earnings until yearly income $I$ reaches \$106,800. So, the equation $S = 0.042I$ describes the Social Security tax up to that limit. For incomes above \$106,800, the Social Security tax stays constant at \$4,485.60. So, a model for Social Security tax is

$$S = 0.042I \text{ if } I \text{ is from } \$0 \text{ to } \$106,800$$
and
$$S = \$4,485.60 \text{ if } I \text{ is greater than } \$106,800.$$

The problem domain for this function is all non-negative values of $I$.

b.  In 2011, Medicare tax is equal to 1.45% of earnings for all income levels, without limit. So, a model for Medicare tax is $M = 0.0145I$. The problem domain of this function is all non-negative values of $I$.

INCOME AND TAXES    **Lesson 15.2**    535

8.  See answer to Question 10 for the completed table for 2011 withholding tables.

9.  Sample answer for 2011 withholding tables: Both plots are of direct variation (linear) functions. The ratios of Social Security tax to income and of Medicare tax to income are both constant.

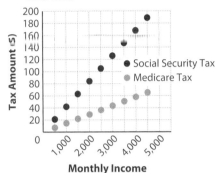

**ADDITIONAL EXAMPLE**

As of 2012, Illinois has a state income tax rate of 5% on all levels of income. Find a function that models Illinois income tax $T$ as a function of total income $I$. Indicate the problem domain of the function.

$T = 0.05I$; non-negative values of $I$

10. Sample answer for 2011 withholding tables:

| Monthly Income | Withholding | Social Security Tax | Medicare Tax | Money Remaining |
|---|---|---|---|---|
| \$500 | \$1.67 | \$21 | \$7.25 | \$470.08 |
| \$1,000 | \$51.67 | \$42 | \$14.50 | \$891.83 |
| \$1,500 | \$117.10 | \$63 | \$21.75 | \$1,298.15 |
| \$2,000 | \$192.10 | \$84 | \$29.00 | \$1,694.90 |
| \$2,500 | \$267.10 | \$105 | \$36.25 | \$2,091.65 |
| \$3,000 | \$342.10 | \$126 | \$43.50 | \$2,488.40 |
| \$3,500 | \$431.27 | \$147 | \$50.75 | \$2,870.98 |
| \$4,000 | \$556.27 | \$168 | \$58.00 | \$3,217.73 |
| \$4,500 | \$681.27 | \$189 | \$65.25 | \$3,564.48 |

## Practice for Lesson 15.2
## Answers

**1a.** $904.40
**1b.** $47,028.80
**1c.** $3,919.07

**TEACHING TIP**

**Exercises 3 and 4** You may need to remind students that the tax withholding table excerpt from IRS Publication 15 (Handout 15A) will be necessary for these exercises.

**2.** Sample answer: Multiply monthly earnings by 12 months in a year. Divide the result by 52 to get weekly earnings. Divide weekly earnings by 40 hours in a week to get hourly earnings.

**3a.** $2,708.33

**3b.** One allowance for a monthly pay period is $308.33, so the amount subject to withholding is $2,708.33 − $308.33 = $2,400.00. The amount of income tax withheld is $70.80 + 0.15($2,400.00 − $883) = $298.35.

**4.** The amount subject to withholding is $5,234.00 − $308.33 − $87 = $4,838.67. The amount of income tax withheld is $395.85 + 0.25($4,838.67 − $3,050) = $843.02; SS tax = 0.042($5,234.00 − $87) = $216.17; Medicare tax = 0.0145($5,234.00 − $87) = $74.63; Net pay = $5,234.00 − ($87 + $843.02 + $216.17 + $74.63) = $4,013.18.

**5.** gross income − [$243.10 + 0.042(gross income) + 0.0145(gross income) + $26] = $1,938.69. Solving for gross income gives a value of $2,340.

**6.** Sample answer for 2011 withholding tables:

| Yearly Base Salary ($) | SS + Medicare Taxes ($) |
| --- | --- |
| 10,000 | 565 |
| 20,000 | 1,130 |
| 30,000 | 1,695 |
| 40,000 | 2,260 |
| 50,000 | 2,825 |
| 60,000 | 3,390 |
| 70,000 | 3,955 |
| 80,000 | 4,520 |
| 90,000 | 5,085 |
| 100,000 | 5,650 |
| 106,800 | 6,034.20 |

**536**

**1.** According to the U.S. Bureau of Labor Statistics, the average hourly wage in the United States for 2010 was $22.61. Use this hourly wage to find each of the following earnings.
  **a.** weekly     **b.** yearly     **c.** monthly

**2.** Explain how you can find hourly earnings when you are given monthly earnings.

**3.** A single woman earned a total of $32,500 in 2011.
  **a.** What was her monthly salary?
  **b.** If she claims one allowance, what is the amount withheld each month according to the tax tables for single persons?

**4.** Assume you are single and claim one allowance, and your gross income for one month is $5,234.00. The cost of your health insurance is $87.00 per month and is deducted from your earnings before taxes are calculated. Federal withholding, Social Security, and Medicare taxes are also deducted. Use your knowledge of these deductions to calculate your net income.

**5.** Assume you are single and claim one allowance. Your net income for one month is $1,938.69. The cost of your health insurance is $26 per month and is deducted from your earnings after taxes are calculated. Federal withholding tax is $243.10, and Social Security and Medicare taxes are also deducted. What is your gross income?

**6.** Complete a table like the one to the left to find the total of Social Security (SS) and Medicare taxes that are deducted from the given yearly base salary for 2011.

**7.** Make a scatter plot of Social Security plus Medicare taxes vs yearly base salary for the data in Exercise 6.

**8 a.** What kind of function is represented by your graph in Exercise 7?

  **b.** Find a mathematical model that describes the total of Social Security plus Medicare taxes $T$ as a function of yearly base salary $S$ for 2011.

  **c.** State the problem domain for your function.

| Yearly Base Salary ($) | SS + Medicare Taxes ($) |
| --- | --- |
| 10,000 | |
| 20,000 | |
| 30,000 | |
| 40,000 | |
| 50,000 | |
| 60,000 | |
| 70,000 | |
| 80,000 | |
| 90,000 | |
| 100,000 | |
| 106,800 | |

**7.** Sample answer for 2011 withholding tables:

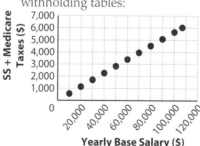

**8a.** a direct variation function (or a linear function)

**8b.** $T = 0.0565S$

**8c.** $0 \leq S \leq 106,800$

9. For people who make more than $106,800 per year in 2011, $4,485.60 is withheld for Social Security, plus 1.45% of the yearly base salary is withheld for Medicare.

Complete a table like the one below based on the information given above.

| Yearly Base Salary ($) | Social Security Tax ($) | Medicare Tax ($) | SS + Medicare Taxes ($) |
|---|---|---|---|
| 150,000 | | | |
| 200,000 | | | |
| 250,000 | | | |
| 300,000 | | | |
| 350,000 | | | |
| 400,000 | | | |
| 450,000 | | | |

10. Make a scatter plot of Social Security plus Medicare taxes vs yearly base salary for the situation in Exercise 9.

11 a. What kind of function is represented by your graph in Exercise 10?
   b. Find a mathematical model that describes total Social Security plus Medicare taxes $T$ as a function of yearly base salary $S$ for 2011.
   c. State the problem domain for your function.

9. Sample answer for 2011 withholding tables:

| Yearly Base Salary ($) | Social Security Tax ($) | Medicare Tax ($) | SS + Medicare Taxes ($) |
|---|---|---|---|
| 150,000 | 4,485.60 | 2,175.00 | 6,660.60 |
| 200,000 | 4,485.60 | 2,900.00 | 7,385.60 |
| 250,000 | 4,485.60 | 3,625.00 | 8,110.60 |
| 300,000 | 4,485.60 | 4,350.00 | 8,835.60 |
| 350,000 | 4,485.60 | 5,075.00 | 9,560.60 |
| 400,000 | 4,485.60 | 5,800.00 | 10,285.60 |
| 450,000 | 4,485.60 | 6,525.00 | 11,010.60 |

10. Sample answer for 2011 withholding tables:

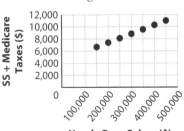

**Yearly Base Salary ($)**

11a. a linear function
11b. $T = 0.0145S + 4,485.60$
11c. $S > 106,800$

# LESSON 15.3

**5e** Explore

## Lesson Objectives

- include income data in a complete budget spreadsheet.
- determine whether a budget is balanced.

## Vocabulary

- balanced budget

## Materials List

- computer spreadsheet program such as Excel, and spreadsheet files from Lesson 15.1.
- Federal tax withholding table excerpt from IRS Publication 15 (Handout 15A)

## Description

Students should work in pairs on this Investigation. Groups should be the same as for Lessons 15.1 and 15.2. Each group should be given a copy of the three-page excerpt from IRS Publication 15 or Handout 15A.

Students use what they learned about taxes in Lesson 15.2 to include income and deductions in their original spreadsheets from Lesson 15.1, and then determine whether the completed budget is balanced.

Note: If students want to keep their original spreadsheets, suggest that they copy columns A and B of their originals into a new spreadsheet for this Investigation.

*Wrapping Up the Investigation:*

Make sure that each group has found that the budget is initially balanced but contains a surplus of $101.31 after additional income is included.

## Lesson 15.3

## INVESTIGATION: Implementing a Budget

Once your income and expenses have been accounted for, a budget can be completed. In this lesson, you will see how a completed budget can form the basis for decisions that can give you control over your finances.

A good budget allows you to compare your income and expenses and to determine whether you need to change the amounts in any of the categories. When your income exceeds your expenses, you gain flexibility in your budget. You can choose to increase the amount devoted to a particular type of expense or to include another category. On the other hand, you could choose to save the surplus amount.

However, if your total expenses are greater than your net income, you will probably have to decrease one or more of the expense amounts. Otherwise you will have to seek other sources of income.

Consider again the situation of the college student from the Investigation in Lesson 15.1. In addition to income from her part-time job, she has a scholarship and student loans that are not taxed, as well as support in the form of gifts from her family. The table below lists these monthly sources of income as well as the expenses previously examined.

| Income | | Fixed Expenses | | Variable Expenses | |
|---|---|---|---|---|---|
| Salary | $960 | Rent | $350 | Food | $280 |
| Scholarship | $617 | Tuition | $1,400 | Utilities | $150 |
| Student Loans | $650 | | | Books | $165 |
| Gifts | $500 | | | Credit Card | $100 |
| | | | | Clothing | $50 |
| | | | | Personal Items | $30 |
| | | | | Entertainment | $50 |
| | | | | Pocket Money | $50 |

1. Open your spreadsheet "Lesson 15.1 Inv." The student's monthly expenses are listed in columns A and B. Delete all entries in the cells of any of the other columns. Leave column C blank. Type "Income" in cell D1. In cells D2 through D5, type "Salary", "Withholding", "Social Security", and "Medicare" as shown in the spreadsheet below.

| | A | B | C | D |
|---|---|---|---|---|
| 1 | **Fixed Expenses** | | | **Income** |
| 2 | Rent | $350 | | Salary |
| 3 | Tuition | $1,400 | | Withholding |
| 4 | Subtotal | $1,750 | | Social Security |
| 5 | | | | Medicare |
| 6 | **Variable Expenses** | | | |
| 7 | Food | $280 | | |
| 8 | Utilities | $150 | | |
| 9 | Books | $165 | | |
| 10 | Credit Card | $100 | | |
| 11 | Clothing | $50 | | |
| 12 | Personal Items | $30 | | |
| 13 | Entertainment | $50 | | |
| 14 | Pocket Money | $50 | | |
| 15 | Subtotal | $875 | | |
| 16 | | | | |
| 17 | **Total Expenses** | $2,625 | | |

**Note**

Assume the student is filing her own tax return as a single person and is not being claimed as a dependent on her parents' return.

2. Using what you learned about taxes in Lesson 15.2, enter the appropriate amounts for Salary, Withholding, Social Security, and Medicare taxes in cells E2 through E5. Use the tax withholding handout to calculate the amount of income tax withheld. For the last two taxes, enter formulas.

3. Type "Salary after Deductions" in cell D6. Then enter a formula in cell E6 that computes the amount of the student's monthly paycheck.

4. Leave cell D7 blank. Then enter the other income categories in cells D8–D10. Enter the corresponding amounts in column E, cells E8–E10.

5. Leave the next cell, D11, blank. Then type "Total Net Income" in cell D12. Enter a formula in the cell E12 that computes the total net income in column E beginning with cell E6.

For **Question 1**, you may need to remind students that they can change the column widths by dragging the divider between column headings so that all cell entries can be seen.

**Question 1** Since income is treated differently in this Investigation than it was in Lesson 15.1, make sure students do not copy the income categories from their earlier spreadsheets.

## Lesson 15.3 Investigation Answers

1.–5. See answers beginning on page 625.

6. See answer on page 541.

7. Yes

8. Sample answer: The amounts in the Total Expenses and Difference cells change. The difference for 2011 is now negative because expenses exceed net income.

9. The cells containing the Salary and Withholding (Income Tax) must be changed. Everything else changes automatically.

6. By comparing the cells containing the Total Expenses and the Total Net Income, you can determine whether or not the college student's income is enough to cover her expenses. But you can also have the difference between income and expenses computed automatically. Type "Difference" in cell D15, and enter a formula in cell E15 that computes the difference. A positive result should indicate that income exceeds expenses, while a negative result means the opposite.

7. A budget is **balanced** if income and expenses are equal. To the nearest dollar, is the college student's budget balanced?

8. Suppose the student spends more than her budgeted amount of $50 for clothing in a particular month. Observe what happens to the spreadsheet if you change the clothing amount to a larger number. Explain.

9. Return the clothing expense to its original $50 amount. Now suppose that the student gets a raise at work so that her monthly salary is increased by $120. What cells do you have to change in order to make the spreadsheet reflect this increase?

10. What amount now appears in the cell showing the difference? Explain its meaning.

## EVALUATING A BUDGET

Once a tentative budget is created, you must put it to work. You should keep accurate records of actual expenses and income. At the end of each month, calculate the difference between income and expenses to see if you are living within your budget.

If you are living within your budget,

$$(Income - deductions) - (fixed\ expenses + variable\ expenses) \geq 0.$$

Extra income may be available to use. Generally, it is wise to place this income into short-term savings for unexpected expenses such as gifts, medical expenses, and household repairs.

However, if

$$(income - deductions) - (fixed\ expenses + variable\ expenses) < 0,$$

overspending has occurred. Either more income must be earned or expenses must be cut in order to balance your budget.

10. Sample answer for 2011: $101.31; She now has a monthly surplus of $101.31.

| | A | B | C | D | E |
|---|---|---|---|---|---|
| 1 | **Fixed Expenses** | | | **Income** | |
| 2 | Rent | $350 | | Salary | $1,080 |
| 3 | Tuition | $1,400 | | Withholding | $59.67 |
| 4 | Subtotal | $1,750 | | Social Security | $45.36 |
| 5 | | | | Medicare | $15.66 |
| 6 | **Variable Expenses** | | | **Salary after Deductions** | $959.31 |
| 7 | Food | $280 | | | |
| 8 | Utilities | $150 | | Scholarship | $617 |
| 9 | Books | $165 | | Student Loans | $650 |
| 10 | Credit Card | $100 | | Gifts | $500 |
| 11 | Clothing | $50 | | | |
| 12 | Personal Items | $30 | | **Total Net Income** | $2,726.31 |
| 13 | Entertainment | $50 | | | |
| 14 | Pocket Money | $50 | | | |
| 15 | Subtotal | $875 | | **Difference** | $101.31 |
| 16 | | | | | |
| 17 | **Total Expenses** | $2,625 | | | |

A budget is usually used in the context of a person's financial goals. Goals can be long-range, medium-range, or short-range.

- *Long-range goals* take time and require planning. Saving $20,000 within the next five years in order to attend graduate school or to make a down payment on a home are examples of long-range goals.
- *Medium-range goals* such as buying a used car are goals that can be achieved in a year or two.
- *Short-range goals*, goals that can be achieved within a few months, can be set to help you achieve your medium- and long-range goals, or they may simply be goals that can be achieved quickly. For example, a short-range goal might be to pay off the balance on a credit card by the end of the year.

Once goals are established, a budget can be initiated or modified so that the goals are realistic.

## Practice for Lesson 15.3

1. Assume that a monthly budget shows the following:

    total income = $7,980

    total expenses = $7,840

    Which of the following best describes this situation?
    - I. The person is overspending.
    - II. The person has extra money to spend.
    - III. The budget can be balanced by increasing income.
    - IV. The budget can be balanced by increasing savings.
    - A. I and III
    - B. II and IV
    - C. II and III

2. In a balanced budget, which of the following is *not* true?
    - A. total income − total expenses = 0
    - B. total income = total expenses
    - C. total income + total expenses = 0

### Practice for Lesson 15.3 Answers

1. B
2. C

6. Sample entries showing the formula and the result of the formula evaluation are shown in the spreadsheets below, for 2011 withholding tables.

|  | A | B | C | D | E |
|---|---|---|---|---|---|
| 1 | **Fixed Expenses** | | | Income | |
| 2 | Rent | $350 | | Salary | $960 |
| 3 | Tuition | $1,400 | | Withholding | $47.67 |
| 4 | Subtotal | $1,750 | | Social Security | $40.32 |
| 5 | | | | Medicare | $13.92 |
| 6 | **Variable Expenses** | | | **Salary after Deductions** | $858.09 |
| 7 | Food | $280 | | | |
| 8 | Utilities | $150 | | Scholarship | $617 |
| 9 | Books | $165 | | Student Loans | $650 |
| 10 | Credit Card | $100 | | Gifts | $500 |
| 11 | Clothing | $50 | | | |
| 12 | Personal Items | $30 | | **Total Net Income** | $2,625.09 |
| 13 | Entertainment | $50 | | | |
| 14 | Pocket Money | $50 | | | |
| 15 | Subtotal | $875 | | Difference | =E12-B17 |
| 16 | | | | | |
| 17 | **Total Expenses** | $2,625 | | | |

|  | A | B | C | D | E |
|---|---|---|---|---|---|
| 1 | **Fixed Expenses** | | | Income | |
| 2 | Rent | $350 | | Salary | $960 |
| 3 | Tuition | $1,400 | | Withholding | $47.67 |
| 4 | Subtotal | $1,750 | | Social Security | $40.32 |
| 5 | | | | Medicare | $13.92 |
| 6 | **Variable Expenses** | | | **Salary after Deductions** | $858.09 |
| 7 | Food | $280 | | | |
| 8 | Utilities | $150 | | Scholarship | $617 |
| 9 | Books | $165 | | Student Loans | $650 |
| 10 | Credit Card | $100 | | Gifts | $500 |
| 11 | Clothing | $50 | | | |
| 12 | Personal Items | $30 | | **Total Net Income** | $2,625.09 |
| 13 | Entertainment | $50 | | | |
| 14 | Pocket Money | $50 | | | |
| 15 | Subtotal | $875 | | Difference | $0.09 |
| 16 | | | | | |
| 17 | **Total Expenses** | $2,625 | | | |

For Exercises 3–5, use the following budget.

### BUDGET

| | |
|---|---|
| Wages (minus taxes) | $3,760 |
| Miscellaneous Income | $  80 |
| TOTAL INCOME | |
| | |
| Rent | $1,500 |
| Insurance | $ 450 |
| Utilities | $ 750 |
| Savings | $ 300 |
| Food | $ 420 |
| Personal | $  80 |
| Other | $ 340 |
| TOTAL EXPENSES | |

**3.** What is the total income?

**4.** What are the total expenses?

**5.** Is the budget balanced? Explain.

**6.** Classify each of the following goals as
   **I.** short-range
   **II.** medium-range
   **III.** long-range
   **a.** buying a new pair of sneakers next month
   **b.** saving for a child's education
   **c.** taking a family vacation to Disney World next year

**For Exercises 7–9, refer back to columns A and B of the spreadsheet for the young married couple you saved as "Lesson 15.1 Prac." The couple has net monthly salaries totaling $6,850, interest and dividend income of $47, and miscellaneous income of $100.**

**7.** Complete the spreadsheet to reflect the couple's income. Include a calculation of the difference between income and expenses.

**8.** Is the couple's budget balanced? Explain.

**9.** What suggestions can you make that would balance their budget?

**3.** $3,840
**4.** $3,840
**5.** Yes;
   total income − total expenses = 0
**6a.** I
**6b.** III
**6c.** II
**7.** See answers beginning on page 626.
**8.** Sample answer: No; expenses exceed income by $250.
**9.** Sample answer: They could reduce spending in one or more of the variable expenses, such as food, credit cards, savings, entertainment, or pocket money. Otherwise, they might take on an extra job to provide more money for expenses.

In the previous lesson, you learned how to prepare a budget and determine whether it is balanced. You will now examine the effect interest has on building your savings.

If your budget shows a positive balance, then each month you have money that you could put into a savings account. Savings institutions such as banks, credit unions, savings and loan associations, and mutual fund investment companies provide several different ways to store your money safely. In most banks and credit unions, deposits of amounts up to $250,000 per depositor are insured by the Federal Deposit Insurance Corporation (FDIC) or the National Credit Union Administration (NCUA).

In addition to storing your money safely, these institutions pay you a fee, called **interest**, for the use of your money. The more money you deposit, and the longer you keep it deposited, the more interest you earn. Different institutions have different ways of computing the interest that they pay. So when you look for a place to invest your savings, it is worth the time and effort to do some comparison shopping.

1. The money you deposit in a savings account is called the **principal**. The amount of interest you are paid for the use of your money depends on the principal, the **interest rate** (given as a percent), and the time for which the money is in the account. The interest paid on some short-term loans is called **simple interest**. This means that the amount of interest is calculated *only* on the principal.

### Simple Interest Formula

$$I = Prt$$

where
$I$ = simple interest
$P$ = principal
$r$ = annual rate of interest (as a decimal)
$t$ = time (in years)

Consider a situation where $1,000 is deposited in a saving institution at a simple interest rate of 4%.

Create a five-column table as shown on the next page. Complete the first two columns to show the simple interest at the end of the first 5 years.

---

## LESSON 15.4

**5e**   Explore

## Lesson Objectives

- distinguish between simple and compound interest.
- determine the future value of savings under various compounding methods.

## Vocabulary

- compound interest
- compounding period
- future value
- interest
- interest rate
- nominal rate
- principal
- simple interest

## Materials List

- computer spreadsheet program such as Excel

## Description

Students should work in pairs or individually on this Investigation. Groups should be the same as for Lessons 15.1 and 15.2. They begin this lesson by examining the effect of simple interest on savings and then proceed to derive a formula for future value when interest is compounded annually.

*Wrapping Up the Investigation:*

Make sure that each group has identified the pattern that results from compounding interest (**Questions 7 and 8**). Discuss the formula from **Question 10**, and ask what might happen if interest were compounded semiannually. Lead them to the expression $\left(1 + \frac{r}{2}\right)^2$ for the accumulation after one year, which leads to the formula $A = \left(1 + \frac{r}{2}\right)^{2t}$ for the future value after $t$ years under semiannual compounding.

## Lesson 15.4 Investigation Answers

1. See the completed table in the answer to Question 6 on page 545.

2. Sample answer: $A = P + Prt$
3. $A = P(1 + rt)$
4. See the completed table in the answer to Question 6 on page 545.
5. $A = P(1 + rt) = (\$1,040)(1.04) = \$1,081.60$

| Time (years) | Interest | | | |
|---|---|---|---|---|
| 0 | $0 | | | |
| 1 | | | | |
| 2 | | | | |
| 3 | | | | |
| 4 | | | | |
| 5 | | | | |

2. The total amount $A$ that accumulates in an account is called **future value**. In the case of simple interest, the future value is the sum of the principal and the interest. Write a formula for future value as a function of time $t$.

3. Use factoring to write your formula as a product of two factors.

4. Label the third column of your table "Future Value with Simple Interest." Then complete the column.

| Time (years) | Interest | Future Value with Simple Interest | | |
|---|---|---|---|---|
| 0 | $0 | $1,000 | | |
| 1 | $40 | $1,040 | | |
| 2 | | | | |
| 3 | | | | |
| 4 | | | | |
| 5 | | | | |

5. Few investments actually earn simple interest. Most earn **compound interest**, interest that is paid on both the principal *and* on the accumulated interest. How often interest is calculated and deposited depends on the **compounding period**.

When compounded annually, interest is calculated at the end of each year. However, at the end of the second year, the interest is based on the total amount $A$ that was in the account at the end of the first year, instead of on the original principal $P$. At the end of the second year, the interest is based on the total amount that was in the account at the end of the second year, and so on.

Find the future value at the end of the second year using annual compounding.

**Note**

Interest may be compounded annually (once per year), semiannually (twice per year), quarterly (four times per year), monthly, or daily.

6. Label the fourth column of your table "Computing Process" and the fifth column "Future Value with Annual Compounding." Complete the table. In the fourth column, show how each amount in the fifth column is found. (Round each amount to the nearest cent.)

| Time (years) | Interest | Future Value with Simple Interest | Computing Process | Future Value with Annual Compounding |
|---|---|---|---|---|
| 0 | $0 | $1,000 | — | — |
| 1 | $40 | $1,040 | ($1,000)(1.04) | $1,040 |
| 2 | | | ($1,040)(1.04) | |
| 3 | | | | |
| 4 | | | | |
| 5 | | | | |

7. Use your answers from Question 6. Look at the computing process for Year 2. Rewrite the process to show how the future value in the fifth column could be found directly from the original $1,000 principal.

8. Repeat Question 7 for the remaining years in the table.

9. Look for a pattern in your expressions in Questions 7 and 8. Write an equation that gives the future value $A$ as a function of time $t$.

10. Now generalize your result. Write a formula that gives the future value $A$ using annual compounding for any principal $P$ and any annual interest rate $r$.

## COMPOUND INTEREST MODELS

In practice, interest is usually compounded more than once a year. Before the 1960s, savings accounts were often based on *quarterly compounding*. Under quarterly compounding, interest is calculated 4 times per year, or every 3 months. But the rate for each quarter is $\frac{1}{4}$ of the stated nominal rate, which is the interest rate for annual compounding.

If the **nominal rate** is 4%, then 1% interest is calculated each quarter. In such a case, the future value at the end of the first year would be ($1,000)(1.01)$^4$ = $1,040.60. The table on the next page shows results for the first 5 years using quarterly compounding.

6. Sample answer:

| Time (years) | Interest | Future Value with Simple Interest | Computing Process | Future Value with Annual Compounding |
|---|---|---|---|---|
| 0 | $0 | $1,000 | — | — |
| 1 | $40 | $1,040 | ($1,000)(1.04) | $1,040 |
| 2 | $80 | $1,080 | ($1,040)(1.04) | $1,081.60 |
| 3 | $120 | $1,120 | ($1,081.60)(1.04) | $1,124.86 |
| 4 | $160 | $1,160 | ($1,124.86)(1.04) | $1,169.85 |
| 5 | $200 | $1,200 | ($1,169.85)(1.04) | $1,216.64 |

7. Sample answer: ($1,000)(1.04)(1.04) or ($1,000)(1.04)$^2$

8. Sample answer: Year 3: ($1,000)(1.04)(1.04)(1.04) or ($1,000)(1.04)$^3$; Year 4: ($1,000)(1.04)(1.04)(1.04)(1.04) or ($1,000)(1.04)$^4$; Year 5: ($1,000)(1.04)(1.04)(1.04)(1.04)(1.04) or ($1,000)(1.04)$^5$

9. Sample answer: $A = ($1,000)(1.04)^t$

10. Sample answer: $A = P(1 + r)^t$

| Time (years) | Computing Process | Future Value with Quarterly Compounding |
|:---:|:---|:---:|
| 1 | $(\$1,000)(1.01)^4 = (\$1,000)(1.01)^{4 \cdot 1}$ | $1,040.60 |
| 2 | $(\$1,000)(1.01)^4 (1.01)^4 = (\$1,000)(1.01)^{4 \cdot 2}$ | $1,082.86 |
| 3 | $(\$1,000)(1.01)^4 (1.01)^4 (1.01)^4 = (\$1,000)(1.01)^{4 \cdot 3}$ | $1,126.83 |
| 4 | $(\$1,000)(1.01)^4 (1.01)^4 (1.01)^4 (1.01)^4 = (\$1,000)(1.01)^{4 \cdot 4}$ | $1,172.58 |
| 5 | $(\$1,000)(1.01)^4 (1.01)^4 (1.01)^4 (1.01)^4 (1.01)^4 = (\$1,000)(1.01)^{4 \cdot 5}$ | $1,220.19 |

The pattern suggests that the future value after any time $t$ measured in years can be modeled by this expression:

$$(\$1,000)(1.01)^{4t}$$

And just as you did in Question 9 of the Investigation, this result can be generalized into a formula for the future value after *any* number of years under *any* compounding method.

### Compound Interest Formula

$$A = P\left(1 + \frac{r}{n}\right)^{nt}$$

where

$A$ = future value
$P$ = principal
$r$ = nominal yearly interest rate (as a decimal)
$n$ = number of compounding periods per year
$t$ = time (in years)

### E X A M P L E

Find the future value of $500 placed in a savings account that pays 6% interest compounded monthly after 8 years. Assume there are no other deposits or withdrawals made.

**Solution:**

In decimal form, the nominal yearly rate is 0.06. For monthly compounding, interest is computed 12 times per year. For any number of years, the compound interest formula becomes

$$A = \$500\left(1 + \frac{0.06}{12}\right)^{12t}$$

$$= \$500(1.005)^{12t}$$

After 8 years, the value of the account is $\$500(1.005)^{12 \cdot 8} = \$807.07$.

## ADDITIONAL EXAMPLE

Find the value after 12 years of $2,000 placed in a savings account that pays 8% interest compounded quarterly. $5,174.14

## SAVING WISELY

When looking for an institution in which to build their savings, wise consumers keep the following in mind:

- Check the type of interest (simple or compound) and the interest rates.
- In order to open some "levels" of savings accounts, a minimum deposit is required. A minimum balance may also be needed in order to maintain them. Beware, as some institutions charge a hefty fee when the balance drops below the minimum.
- Depending on the institution, accounts can start to earn interest at different times. For example, the interest on some accounts is based on an *average daily balance*, which is the average amount that exists in an account during the interest period. Other institutions pay interest compounded daily for every day your money is in one of their accounts.

In other words, when comparison shopping, compare the terms of the institutions where you will be doing business and the accounts that you will be opening in order to find the option best suited to your needs.

### Practice for Lesson 15.4

1. A savings account earns 3.65% interest compounded yearly. Find the future value of a deposit of $4,000 after 12 years.

2. Suppose the annual interest rate on a savings account is 4.5%. Calculate $i$, the interest rate per compounding period, when interest is compounded semiannually.

**For Exercises 3–5, use the following information.**

An amount of $1,000 is deposited in a savings account that earns 5% interest.

3. What is the future value after 1 year if the interest is compounded quarterly?

4. What is the future value after 10 years if the interest is compounded quarterly?

5. What is the future value after 10 years if the interest is compounded monthly?

4. The number of periods $n$ in 10 years is $4 \times 10 = 40$.

$$A = P\left(1 + \frac{r}{n}\right)^{nt}$$
$$= \$1,000\left(1 + \frac{0.05}{4}\right)^{4 \cdot 10}$$
$$= \$1,643.62$$

5. The number of periods $n$ in 10 years is $12 \times 10 = 120$.

$$A = P\left(1 + \frac{r}{n}\right)^{nt}$$
$$= \$1,000\left(1 + \frac{0.05}{12}\right)^{12 \cdot 10}$$
$$= \$1,647.01$$

**COMMON ERROR**

**Exercise 3** Remind students that the nominal yearly interest rate must be divided by the number of compounding periods.

### Practice for Lesson 15.4 Answers

1. $A = P(1 + r)^t$
$= \$4,000(1 + 0.0365)^{12}$
$= \$6,150.23$

2. $i = \dfrac{r}{n}$
$= \dfrac{0.045}{2}$
$= 0.0225$

3. The interest is compounded 4 times per year. So, the number of compounding periods $n$ in one year is 4.
$$A = P\left(1 + \frac{r}{n}\right)^{nt}$$
$$= \$1,000\left(1 + \frac{0.05}{4}\right)^{4 \cdot 1}$$
$$= \$1,050.95$$

**6a.** For daily compounding, the number of periods $n$ in 1 year is $365 \times 1 = 365$.

$$A = P\left(1 + \frac{r}{n}\right)^{nt}$$

$$= \$10,000\left(1 + \frac{0.05}{365}\right)^{365 \cdot 1}$$

$$= \$10,512.67$$

| Compounding Interval | Value after One Year |
|---|---|
| Annually | $10,500.00 |
| Semiannually | $10,506.25 |
| Quarterly | $10,509.45 |
| Monthly | $10,511.62 |
| Weekly | $10,512.46 |
| Daily | $10,512.67 |

**6b.** $A = P\left(1 + \frac{r}{n}\right)^{nt}$

$$= \$10,000\left(1 + \frac{0.05}{360}\right)^{360 \cdot 1}$$

$$= \$10,512.67$$

To the nearest penny, the amount of interest is the same for both methods.

**6.** Many financial institutions use daily compounding of interest.

a. Complete the table to show how daily compounding affects the future value after one year of $10,000 at 5% interest. Assume 52 weeks and 365 days in a year.

| Compounding Interval | Value After One Year |
|---|---|
| Annually | |
| Semiannually | |
| Quarterly | |
| Monthly | |
| Weekly | |
| Daily | |

b. Instead of using a 365-day year, daily interest is sometimes calculated as if a year contained only 360 days. What difference would this method make in the amount of interest earned in one year on $10,000 at 5%?

**For Exercises 7–9, consider your table from Question 6 of the Investigation on page 545. Make a scatter plot of each indicated relationship. Then identify each function as either direct variation, linear, or exponential. Explain.**

**7.** amount of simple interest vs time

**8.** future value with simple interest vs time

**9.** future value with annual compound interest vs time

**For Exercises 10–13, use the following information.**

As you have seen, when interest is compounded at intervals of less than a year, the yearly interest amount is greater than the simple interest amount would be. The nominal interest rate is therefore not an accurate measure of compound interest. Financial institutions are required to disclose the actual yearly percent interest earned in an account. This interest rate is called the *annual percentage yield* (APY) or the *effective rate*.

**10.** Examine the compound interest formula. Then write a formula for the future value $A$ after one year for any principal $P$ at a nominal interest rate $r$ and having $n$ compounding periods per year.

**11.** Use your answer to Exercise 10 to find a formula for the total amount of interest $I$ earned after one year.

**7.** Sample answer: This is a direct variation (linear) function, since the graph is a straight line passing through the origin. The data show that the ratio of interest amount to time is constant.

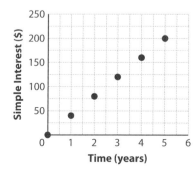

**8.** Sample answer: This is a linear function as the rates of change are constant and its vertical intercept is non-zero.

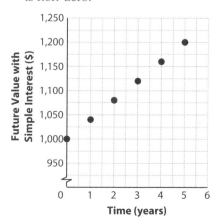

12. The APY is equal to the total yearly interest as a fraction of the principal. That is, it equals the ratio $\frac{I}{P}$. Use this fact to find a formula for APY in terms of $r$ and $n$.

13. Use your formula to find the APY for a savings account with a nominal interest rate of 4% compounded (a) quarterly, (b) monthly, and (c) daily. (Round to the nearest hundredth of a percent.)

**For Exercises 14–15, use the following information.**

It is sometimes helpful to know how much money you need to deposit in a savings account in order for it to grow to a given amount in the future. This principal amount is called *present value*.

14. Use the compound interest formula from page 546 to derive a formula for the present value $P$ in terms of the future value $A$, interest rate $r$, and number of compounding periods per year $n$.

15. How much should be deposited in an account today that earns 4.8% compounded semiannually so that in 8 years it will have a balance of $30,000?

**For Exercises 16–17, use the following information.**

Often credited to Albert Einstein, the *Rule of 72* is a rule of thumb that provides a quick way to approximate the time it takes for money to double at a given interest rate (assuming that the interest is compounded annually). For example, if money is invested at an interest rate of 6% compounded annually, the amount invested will double in about 12 years ($72 \div 6 = 12$).

16. Use the Rule of 72 to find how many years it would take for $5,000 to grow to $10,000 at a rate of 4% compounded annually.

17. Suppose a 20-year-old person invests $1,000 at an interest rate of 8% compounded annually. Use the Rule of 72 to find the future amount when the person's age is 29, 38, and 47.

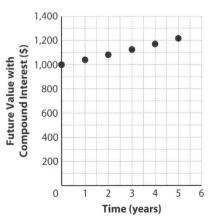

**CONNECTION**

**Exercises 16–17** Although the Rule of 72 is discussed in terms of annual compounding, suggest that students find out whether the rule is adequate for other compounding periods. They will find that the rule is still a good approximation, with an error of less than a month.

12. $APY = \dfrac{I}{P}$

$$= \dfrac{P\left(1 + \frac{r}{n}\right)^n - P}{P}$$

$$APY = \left(1 + \frac{r}{n}\right)^n - 1$$

13a. $\left(1 + \dfrac{0.04}{4}\right)^4 - 1 \approx 0.0406$
or 4.06%

13b. $\left(1 + \dfrac{0.04}{12}\right)^{12} - 1 \approx 0.0407$
or 4.07%

13c. $\left(1 + \dfrac{0.04}{365}\right)^{365} - 1 \approx 0.0408$
or 4.08%

14. Compound interest formula
$$A = P\left(1 + \frac{r}{n}\right)^{nt}$$
Divide by $\left(1 + \frac{r}{n}\right)^{nt}$
$$\dfrac{A}{\left(1 + \frac{r}{n}\right)^{nt}} = P$$
Use a negative exponent.
$$P = A\left(1 + \frac{r}{n}\right)^{-nt}$$

15. The interest is compounded 2 times per year.
$$P = \$30{,}000\left(1 + \frac{0.048}{2}\right)^{-8\cdot2}$$
$$= \$20{,}526.83$$

16. $\dfrac{72}{4} = 18$ years

17. $2,000; $4,000; $8,000

9. Sample answer: This is an exponential function, since its equation has the form $y = ab^x$. The data show that, as the independent variable increases by constant amounts, the ratios of successive function values are constant.

**Time (years)**

10. $A = P\left(1 + \dfrac{r}{n}\right)^n$

11. $I = P\left(1 + \dfrac{r}{n}\right)^n - P$

# LESSON 15.5

## Lesson Objective

- solve problems that require previously learned concepts and skills.

## Exercise Reference

Exercise 1: Lesson 15.3

Exercises 2–3: Lesson 15.4

Exercise 4: Lesson 15.2

Exercises 5–12: Appendix B

Exercises 13–16: Appendix D

Exercises 17–22: Appendices B and E

Exercises 23–28: Appendix F

Exercise 29: Lessons 4.6 and 4.7

Exercise 30: Lesson 5.6

Exercise 31: Lesson 8.3

Exercise 32: Lesson 10.3

Exercise 33: Lesson 15.4

## Lesson 15.5 R.A.P. Answers

1. balanced
2. simple interest
3. D
4. C
5. 14.765
6. 16.821
7. 13.76
8. 21.55
9. 1.75
10. 0.00455
11. 12.03
12. 800
13. 8
14. 15
15. 25.2
16. 25

**Fill in the blank.**

1. If total income and total expenses are equal, a budget is _____.

2. When the amount of interest on a savings account is calculated based on the principal only, the interest is called _____ interest.

**Choose the correct answer.**

3. The future value of a savings account based on compound interest is described by which type of function?
   - **A.** direct variation
   - **B.** linear
   - **C.** quadratic
   - **D.** exponential

4. An hourly wage of $11 is equivalent to what amount for a 40-hour work week?
   - **A.** $3.64
   - **B.** $51
   - **C.** $440
   - **D.** $4,400

**Add, subtract, multiply, or divide. Write your answer in simplest form.**

5. $6.44 + 8.325$
6. $2.32 + 14.501$
7. $16.45 - 2.69$
8. $35.8 - 14.25$
9. $2.5 \times 0.7$
10. $1.3 \times 0.0035$
11. $96.24 \div 8$
12. $7.2 \div 0.009$

**Solve the proportion.**

13. $\frac{4}{5} = \frac{a}{10}$
14. $\frac{x}{10} = \frac{3}{2}$
15. $\frac{14}{5} = \frac{y}{9}$
16. $\frac{6}{5} = \frac{30}{t}$

**Complete the table below.**

|     | Fraction | Decimal | Percent |
|-----|----------|---------|---------|
| 17. | $\frac{1}{4}$ |     |     |
| 18. |          | 1.5     |     |
| 19. |          |         | 60% |
| 20. | $\frac{3}{8}$ |     |     |
| 21. |          | 0.875   |     |
| 22. |          |         | 7.5% |

**Solve.**

**23.** 5% of 60 is what number?    **24.** What percent of 12 is 48?

**25.** 39 is 150% of what number?    **26.** What percent of 48 is 12?

**27.** 63 is 75% of what number?    **28.** What number is 2% of 1,440?

**29.** The wedge shown here is in the shape of a triangular prism.

5 cm

12 cm    10 cm

    **a.** Find the surface area of the wedge.
    **b.** Find the volume of the wedge.

**30.** A line passes through the points (–1, 5) and (3, –1). Find an equation of the line in slope-intercept form.

**31.** Solve.

$$3x - 7y = 1$$
$$2x + 4y = 5$$

**32.** Simplify $\left( \dfrac{2a^2b^5}{6a^4b^4} \right)^{-3}$.

**33.** Find the future value after 2 years of $1,000 placed in a savings account that pays 5% interest compounded annually.

**17.** 0.25, 25%

**18.** $\frac{3}{2}$ or $1\frac{1}{2}$, 150%

**19.** $\frac{3}{5}$, 0.6

**20.** 0.375, 37.5%

**21.** $\frac{7}{8}$, 87.5%

**22.** $\frac{3}{40}$, 0.075

**23.** 3

**24.** 400%

**25.** 26

**26.** 25%

**27.** 84

**28.** 28.8

**29a.** 360 cm$^2$

**29b.** 300 cm$^3$

**30.** $y = -\frac{3}{2}x + \frac{7}{2}$

**31.** $\left( \frac{3}{2}, \frac{1}{2} \right)$

**32.** $\frac{27a^6}{b^3}$

**33.** $1,102.50

**5e** Explore

## Lesson Objectives

- construct and interpret an amortization schedule.
- compare the relative costs of buying and leasing (optional).

## Vocabulary

- amortization
- amortization schedule
- finance a loan
- interest-only loan
- loan principal
- loan term
- remaining-balance method

*Optional:*

- adjusted capitalized cost
- capitalized cost
- depreciation
- money factor
- residual value

## Materials List

- computer spreadsheet program such as Excel

## Description

Students should work in pairs on this Investigation. They explore the remaining-balance method for repaying a loan, and use a computer spreadsheet program to construct an amortization schedule for a car loan. This lesson may take more than one day depending on whether you choose to do the optional section, *Buying Versus Leasing*.

*Wrapping Up the Investigation:*

Check the work of each group to ensure that they arrive at a total interest of $2,399.54 in **Question 13**, which will confirm that their spreadsheet was correctly developed. Students should observe that the first few payments for this type of loan consist mainly of interest, and that successive payments increasingly serve to pay back loan principal.

---

## Lesson 15.6   INVESTIGATION: Borrowing

Lesson 15.4 explained how compounding can increase the rate at which money in a savings account grows. Compounding is also used to calculate payment amounts when you pay back money you borrowed.

At some point in their lives, most people have a reason to borrow money. Long-term loans are often taken out to pay college costs, buy a car, or buy a house. In order to borrow money, you usually pay interest. Interest on a loan may be computed in a way that has some similarity to the method for computing compound interest on savings.

1. Suppose you decide to buy a car with a selling price of $17,000. You might begin by making a down payment of $2,000. Then you would have to **finance a loan** for the remaining $15,000. Your first payment would probably be due one month after purchase. So, you will have borrowed $15,000 for one month.

   If your loan has an interest rate of 6%, how much interest would you owe after the first month?

2. If this were all you paid, you would still owe $15,000. Your second month's interest would be the same as your first month's interest. If this process were to continue, you would never pay off the loan. Such a loan is an **interest-only loan**. It is unwise to take out an interest-only loan because you would forever be in debt.

   Instead, your monthly payment would probably be higher than just the interest. If the payment were $200, you would also be paying off part of the **loan principal**, or the total amount borrowed. Find (a) how much principal would be paid off, and (b) how much would still be owed (remaining balance) after the first payment.

3. After the second month, you would pay 0.5% interest on the remaining balance. Such a process is called the **remaining balance method** for computing interest on a loan. Find (a) the interest amount, (b) the principal payment, and (c) the remaining balance after your second $200 payment.

### Connection

Regular equal payments on a loan are often called *installments*. The loan may be called an *installment loan*.

---

### TEACHING TIP

The time that it takes to complete this lesson depends on many factors. As you plan, take into account that **Exercises 2, 3, 5, 6, and 14** require the use of a computer spreadsheet. If home computers are not available to all of your students, you may want to arrange an extra day for this lesson so that students can do these exercises in class.

## Lesson 15.6 Investigation Answers

1. The monthly interest rate is $\frac{1}{12}$ of 6%, or 0.5%. The interest owed is ($15,000)(0.005) = $75.
2a. $200 − $75 = $125
2b. $15,000 − $125 = $14,875
3a. ($14,875)(0.005) = $74.38
3b. $200 − $74.38 = $125.62
3c. $14,875 − $125.62 = $14,749.38
4. See the answer to Question 7 on page 553.

**4.** Under the remaining balance method, each successive payment includes less interest and more paid principal. So, the loan is eventually paid off completely. But computing the interest, principal paid, and remaining balance for all the payments of the loan would be very tedious if done one month at a time. A computer spreadsheet program can make the process much more efficient.

Open a spreadsheet program and enter information as shown below. Adjust column widths as necessary. Save your worksheet as "Lesson 15.6 Inv."

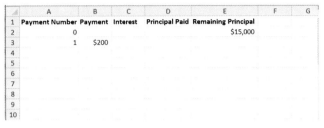

| | A | B | C | D | E | F | G |
|---|---|---|---|---|---|---|---|
| 1 | Payment Number | Payment | Interest | Principal Paid | Remaining Principal | | |
| 2 | 0 | | | | $15,000 | | |
| 3 | 1 | $200 | | | | | |
| 4 | | | | | | | |
| 5 | | | | | | | |
| 6 | | | | | | | |
| 7 | | | | | | | |
| 8 | | | | | | | |
| 9 | | | | | | | |
| 10 | | | | | | | |

**5.** Highlight cells A2 and A3 in the "Payment Number" column. Then click on the little box in the lower right-hand corner of the highlighted area and drag it downward to cell A26. Describe what happens.

**6.** Highlight cell B3 that contains the $200 monthly payment. Then click on the lower right-hand corner of that cell and drag. Describe what happens.

**7.** Complete the row for Payment Number 1 by entering formulas to calculate Interest, Principal Paid, and Remaining Principal. Use your calculations from Questions 1 and 2 as a guide. But instead of entering dollar amounts, leave each cell showing the appropriate cell addresses. (Remember that each formula you enter must begin with an equal sign.)

**8.** Now highlight cells C3 through E3. Drag the formulas in these cells down as far as row 26 to produce two years' worth of payment information.

**9.** Continue your table until the loan is paid off, at which point you would actually own the car. First extend the Payment Number and Payment columns, then copy the three formula cells downward until the Remaining Principal amount becomes negative. After how many payments will the loan be paid off?

**10.** The amount of the last payment is usually different from the regular monthly payment. What is the amount of your last payment?

BORROWING    **Lesson 15.6**    **553**

**7.** Sample answer:

| | A | B | C | D | E |
|---|---|---|---|---|---|
| 1 | Payment Number | Payment | Interest | Principal Paid | Remaining Principal |
| 2 | 0 | | | | $15,000 |
| 3 | 1 | $200 | =0.005*E2 | =B3-C3 | =E2-D3 |
| 4 | | | | | |

**8.** See answers beginning on page 627.

**9.** The Remaining Principal becomes negative after the 95th payment, so the 95th payment should be the last one.

**10.** Sample answer: The 95th payment is only $46.96 plus $0.23 interest, or $47.19.

**5.** The number pattern is extended, ending with "24" in cell A26.

**6.** All the cells in the column are filled with the $200 amount.

11. $R = \dfrac{(\$15{,}000)(0.005)}{1-(1 + 0.005)^{-60}} = \$289.99$

12. Sample answer: If the 60th payment is $290.13, the loan will be exactly paid off.

13. $2,399.54

---

11. Remaining balance loans are usually written for a fixed number of months or years, called the **loan term**. The monthly payment is then determined from the principal, interest rate, and number of months in the loan term.

**Monthly Payment Calculation**

$$R = \frac{Pi}{1 - (1 + i)^{-n}}$$

where

$R$ = regular loan payment
$P$ = principal
$i$ = interest rate per month (as a decimal)
$n$ = number of months

A common loan term for a car loan is 5 years. Determine the monthly payment $R$ for the $15,000 loan at 6% with a 5-year term.

12. Replace the original $200 payment amounts in column B of your spreadsheet with the payment amount you found in Question 11. The Interest, Principal Paid, and Remaining Balance columns will adjust automatically. What is the amount of the last payment?

13. What is the total amount of interest that is paid during the term of the loan?

This process of repaying a loan through regular payments of principal and interest is known as **amortization**. A table that shows the breakdown of each payment into interest and principal for the life of a loan is referred to as an **amortization schedule**.

## HIGH-COST LOANS

Payday loans are very expensive, small cash-advance loans that are generally used to cover a borrower's expenses until the next payday. At the end of the term of the loan (usually about two weeks), the loan plus finance charges must be repaid. These loans can be obtained with little effort by applying in person at a payday store location or by applying online.

Loan amounts range from $100 to $1,000 depending on state law, and interest rates average over 400% APR. If borrowers are unable to repay loans when they are due, they can often be renewed at an even higher rate. For example, suppose a payday loan company provides a cash advance of $300 for up to 15 days for a fee of $90, and up to four 15-day extensions can be obtained for $90 each. If the loan were rolled over three times and kept for 60 days (or about 2 months), the borrower would be expected to pay back $300 + (4 × $90) or $660!

The United States Federal Trade Commission recommends that consumers think twice and try to avoid payday lenders. They suggest alternatives such as local credit unions, credit card cash advances, and pay advances from family or employers. They also suggest that if people must use a payday lender, they should *not* borrow more than they can afford to pay back with their next paycheck.

## BUYING VERSUS LEASING (OPTIONAL)

In recent years, leasing a car has become a popular alternative to buying a car. Leasing is like having a long-term rental agreement. The consumer pays a fixed amount each month to the leasing company, who owns the car. Insurance and operating costs must also be paid. At the end of the lease agreement, the company gets the car back.

Because leasing a car is different from purchasing one, a new set of terms is used to describe the factors that influence the cost of the lease.

- **Capitalized cost** is the selling price agreed upon by the consumer and the leasing company.
- **Adjusted capitalized cost** $C$ is the final lease price of the car. It equals the capitalized cost plus additional up-front costs, minus such things as trade-in allowance, rebates, and other discounts.
- **Residual value** $R$ is the value of the car at the end of the lease period. It is often expressed as a percent of the Manufacturer's Suggested Retail Price (MSRP), although it may sometimes be based on the capitalized cost.
- **Depreciation** is the decrease in value of the car during the lease period. It equals the difference between the adjusted capitalized cost and the residual value $(C - R)$.
- **Money factor** (or *lease factor*) is half of the monthly interest rate $i$. The money factor is used to calculate the average interest amount paid per month, which equals $(C + R) \cdot$ (money factor).

Sales tax must usually be paid each month on the sum of the monthly depreciation and the monthly interest charge.

> The monthly lease payment is the sum of the monthly depreciation, the monthly interest, and the monthly sales tax.

### Note

Interest is based on the value of the car in any month. The average value of the car equals $\frac{C + R}{2}$. And the average monthly interest amount equals $\left(\frac{C + R}{2}\right)i$. This expression is therefore equivalent to $(C + R) \cdot$ (money factor).

## ADDITIONAL EXAMPLE

A car dealer offers a trade-in of $4,000 on the lease of a $30,000 SUV. The car will be leased for 5 years at 4.8% interest compounded monthly after a down payment of $2,500. The state sales tax rate is 3%.

**a.** Find the monthly payment, if the residual value is 40% of the $30,000 cost.
monthly depreciation + monthly interest + monthly sales tax = $191.67 + $71.00 + $7.88 = $270.55

**b.** Find the total amount paid during the term of the lease.
60($270.55) + $4,000 + $2,500 = $22,733.00

**c.** Find the total amount that would be paid if the car were purchased for the same price, down payment, trade-in allowance, and interest rate.

The sales tax on $30,000 is $900, so the total amount financed is $23,500 + $900 = $24,400. The monthly payment on $24,400 is $458.23. So, the total cost is $4,000 + $2,500 + 60($458.23) − $12,000 = $21,993.80.

**d.** Is it less expensive to buy and finance the car or to lease the car?
$22,733.00 − $21,993.80 = $739.20. It is less expensive to buy than to lease.

## E X A M P L E

Suppose you see the following ad while shopping for a car:

> Lease a new Ford Edge with automatic transmission, 4-cylinder engine, antilock brakes, AM/FM radio/CD/MP3 player, air conditioning, and power steering. MSRP is $25,810, and financing is available at a special APR rate of 0.9% for 48 months with a mileage allowance of 45,000 miles. $1,000 down payment and $800 security deposit due on lease signing.

You respond to the ad and agree with the car dealer on a value of $25,000. In addition, the dealer agrees to allow $5,000 off the price for trading in your old car. The dealer thinks the car will depreciate to 48.43% of MSRP over the term of the lease. Assume a state sales tax rate of 6.25%.

**a.** Find the monthly payment.
**b.** Find the total amount paid during the 4-year term of the lease.
**c.** Find the amount you would pay for the car if you were to buy the car at the same selling price, down payment, trade-in allowance, and interest rate.

**Solution:**

**a.** The capitalized cost is the agreed-upon price of $25,000. Subtract the $1,000 down payment and the $5,000 trade-in allowance to get an adjusted capitalized cost $C$ of $19,000.

- The estimated residual value $R$ is 48.43% of $25,810 (MSRP), or $12,499.78. So, the total expected depreciation over the 48-month lease period is calculated as shown below.

$$C - R = \$19,000 - \$12,499.78$$
$$= \$6,500.22$$

Therefore, the monthly depreciation over 4 years is
$$\frac{\$6,500.22}{48} = \$135.42.$$

- The interest rate for one month, expressed as a decimal, is $\frac{0.009}{12} = 0.00075$. The money factor is half of 0.00075, or 0.000375. So, the monthly interest amount is

$$
\begin{aligned}
(C + R)(\text{money factor}) &= (C + R)(0.000375) \\
&= (\$19{,}000 + \$12{,}499.78)(0.000375) \\
&= \$11.81
\end{aligned}
$$

- The sales tax paid each month is the product of the sales tax rate and the sum of the monthly depreciation and the monthly interest.

$$
\text{Monthly sales tax} = (0.0625)(\$135.42 + \$11.81) = \$9.20
$$

- Finally, the total monthly payment is the sum of the monthly depreciation, the monthly interest, and the monthly sales tax.

$$
\begin{aligned}
\text{Monthly payment} &= \$135.42 + \$11.81 + \$9.20 \\
&= \$156.43
\end{aligned}
$$

**b.** The total amount paid for the car includes the down payment plus the trade-in allowance plus the 48 monthly payments.

$$
\begin{aligned}
\text{Total amount paid to lease the car} &= \$1{,}000 + \$5{,}000 + 48(\$156.43) \\
&= \$13{,}508.64
\end{aligned}
$$

**c.** The sales tax on the car's capitalized price is $(0.0625)(\$25{,}000) = \$1{,}562.50$. After the down payment and trade-in, $\$19{,}000 + \$1{,}562.50 = \$20{,}562.50$ must be financed at 0.9%. The monthly interest rate is 0.00075, as determined in Part (a), and the monthly payment is

$$
\frac{Pi}{1 - (1 + i)^{-n}} = \frac{(\$20{,}562.50)(0.00075)}{1 - (1 + 0.00075)^{-48}}
$$

$$
= \$436.30
$$

Over the four-year life of the loan, monthly payments will total $48(\$436.30) = \$20{,}942.40$. You can then expect to sell the car for the residual value of $12,499.78.

The total cost of owning the car includes the down payment plus the trade-in allowance plus the 48 monthly payments minus the residual value.

Total amount paid to own the car

$$
\begin{aligned}
&= \$1{,}000 + \$5{,}000 + \$20{,}942.40 - \$12{,}499.78 \\
&= \$14{,}442.62
\end{aligned}
$$

The total cost of owning the car is $933.98 more than the total cost of leasing the car. Of course, this assumes that there are no extra mileage charges for the lease option and that you get your security deposit back.

# LESSON 15.6

## Practice for Lesson 15.6 Answers

1. The monthly interest rate is $\frac{0.12}{12} = 0.01$.

$$R = \frac{Pi}{1 - (1 + i)^{-n}}$$
$$= \frac{(\$1,850)(0.01)}{1-(1+0.01)^{-4}} = \$474.12$$

2. See answers beginning on page 627.

3. $46.47

4. $\frac{Pi}{1 - (1 + i)^{-n}} = \frac{(\$15,000)(0.005)}{1-(1+0.005)^{-48}}$
= \$352.28

5. $352.03

6. The total is $1,909.19, which is $490.35 less than for the 5-year loan.

7. Option A: 360 months at $\frac{0.0675}{12} = $
0.005625 monthly interest rate;

$$\frac{Pi}{1 - (1 + i)^{-n}} =$$
$$\frac{(\$15,000)(0.005625)}{1-(1+0.005625)^{-360}} = \$972.90$$

Option B: 180 months at $\frac{0.06}{12} = $
0.005 monthly interest rate;
$$\frac{Pi}{1 - (1 + i)^{-n}} = \frac{(\$150,000)(0.005)}{1-(1+0.005)^{-180}}$$
= \$1,265.79

8. $292.89

9. $150,000 is 80% of $187,500, and the 20% down payment is $37,500. The total cost is $37,500 + 360($972.90) = $387,744.

10. The total cost is $37,500 + 180($1,265.79) = $265,342.20.

11. Sample answer: The monthly payments are higher, so the principal balance is paid off more quickly. So, if someone wants to pay off the loan and build up equity (the difference between market value and unpaid mortgage balance) in the home more quickly, a 15-year loan would be good.

12. Sample answer: The monthly payments are lower with a longer loan term. So, if someone wants lower monthly payments, a 30-year loan is a better option.

13a. $P = \frac{R(1 - (1 + i)^{-n})}{i}$

13b. $21,839.38

14. See answers beginning on page 627.

15. $C = \$20,000 - \$2,000 - \$2,500 = \$15,500$

16. $R = (0.50)(\$20,000) = \$10,000$

17. total depreciation = $C - R = \$15,500 - \$10,000 = \$5,500$;
monthly depreciation $= \frac{\$5,500}{24} = \$229.17$

18. $(C + R)\left(\frac{i}{2}\right) = (\$15,500 + \$10,000)$
$\left(\frac{0.001658}{2}\right) = \$21.14$

---

**Practice** for Lesson 15.6

**For Exercises 1–3, use the following information.**

A 4-month loan is taken out to buy a new laptop computer that costs $1,850. The annual interest rate is 12%, and payments are made at the end of each month to amortize the loan.

1. Find the monthly payment amount.

2. Use a computer spreadsheet to create an amortization schedule for the loan.

3. How much interest is paid during the life of the loan?

**For Exercises 4–6, change the term of the $15,000 car loan in the Investigation in this lesson to 4 years instead of 5 years.**

4. Find the amount of the monthly payment.

5. Use your answer to Exercise 4 to revise your spreadsheet for the loan amortization. What will be the amount of the final payment?

6. Compute the total interest paid for a 4-year loan. Then compare it to the total interest paid for the 5-year loan.

**For Exercises 7–12, use the following information.**

Homes are often purchased with amortized loans, as with car loans. A conventional fixed-rate loan uses the same interest rate for the entire life of the loan.

A family is considering a fixed-rate loan to buy a new home. After a 20% down payment, they need to finance $150,000. They consider these two options:

Option A: A 30-year home loan for $150,000 at 6.75% interest
Option B: A 15-year home loan for $150,000 at 6.00% interest

7. Find the monthly payment for each option.

8. What is the difference between the monthly payment for the 30-year loan and the monthly payment for the 15-year loan?

9. How much money does the house cost, including down payment, principal, and interest, with the 30-year loan?

10. How much money does the house cost, including down payment, principal, and interest, with the 15-year loan?

11. Why might someone want to use a 15-year conventional loan?

12. Why might someone want to use a 30-year conventional loan?

13. You have used the formula $R = \dfrac{Pi}{1 - (1+i)^{-n}}$ to determine the monthly payment $R$ that will amortize a principal (or present value) amount $P$ in $n$ payments with periodic interest rate $i$.

    **a.** Solve the formula for $P$.

    **b.** Use your answer from Part (a) to find the amount that can be borrowed for a monthly payment of \$525 if the loan is amortized over 4 years at an annual interest rate of 7.2%.

14. Consider two options for buying a \$2,400 home theater system if you have \$100 a month to put toward this purchase.

    Option A: Place \$100 a month into a savings account that pays 5% annual interest compounded monthly and purchase the system when you have saved \$2,400.

    Option B: Use a credit card to purchase the system now. The credit card charges 13.5% annual interest compounded monthly. You pay \$100 a month until the theater system is paid off. (This would be similar to amortization of a car or home loan, provided that you charge no further purchases to the credit card.)

    Determine which will happen first: will you save enough money to buy the system with money in your savings account, or will you be able to pay the credit card balance entirely?

**For Exercises 15–22 (optional), use the following information.**

Suppose you want to lease a new car. You and the dealer agree on a price of \$20,000. You pay \$2,000 down and receive a trade-in allowance of \$2,500 for your old car. The car will be leased for 2 years at 1.99% interest. You live in a state that has a 5% sales tax. The dealer estimates that the car's value will depreciate to 50% of its original capitalized cost.

15. Find the adjusted capitalized cost.

16. Find the residual value.

17. Find the monthly depreciation.

18. Find the monthly interest amount.

19. Find the monthly sales tax.

20. Find the total monthly payment.

21. As an alternative, you can finance the purchase of the car for the same price, down payment, trade-in allowance, and interest rate. What is the monthly payment?

22. Compare the total amount paid for the lease option and for the purchase option. Assume that if you buy the car, you sell it for the same residual value as for the lease option.

BORROWING    Lesson 15.6    559

**TEACHING TIP**

**Exercise 14 Option A** Students have not encountered this type of calculation before. Suggest they try a variation on the amortization schedule. Instead of an initial loan value, begin with a balance of \$0, increase the balance by systematically adding monthly payments and compounded interest until \$2,400 is accumulated. The Extension in this chapter discusses annuities, of which this is an example.

**TEACHING TIP**

**Exercise 14** If students find that a cell in a spreadsheet shows ##### instead of an expected calculation result, suggest that they increase the column width to accommodate a larger value.

**TEACHING TIP**

**Exercise 18** Remind students that the monthly interest rate is divided by 2 to find the money factor used in lease calculations. But in reality, this is equivalent to using the actual monthly interest rate and applying it to the average of the adjusted capitalized cost and the residual value.

**COMMON ERROR**

**Exercise 19** Remind students that the sales tax rate is *not* divided by 12 when applied to the monthly payment. The 5% rate is applied to each payment.

**TEACHING TIP**

**Exercise 22** Point out to students that when they compare the total cost of purchasing a car to that of leasing a car, it assumes that the car can be sold for the residual value that was estimated by the dealer. This may or may not be what actually happens if the owner tries to sell the car.

19. Since the sales tax is based on the sum of the monthly depreciation and monthly interest charge, sales tax = $(0.05)(\$229.17 + \$21.14) = \$12.52$.

20. monthly payment = monthly depreciation + monthly interest + monthly sales tax = $\$229.17 + \$21.14 + \$12.52 = \$262.83$

21. the amount financed = purchase price – down payment – trade-in + sales tax = $\$20,000 - \$2,000 - \$2500 + 0.05(20,000) = \$16,500$

The monthly interest rate is $\dfrac{0.0199}{12} \approx 0.001658$. The payment is $\dfrac{Pi}{1 - (1+i)^{-n}} = \dfrac{(\$16,500)(0.001658)}{1 - (1 + 0.001658)^{-24}} = \$701.84$.

22. Lease option: $\$2,000 + \$2,500 + 24(\$262.83) = \$10,807.92$

Buy option: $\$2,000 + \$2,500 + 24(\$701.84) - \$10,000 = \$11,344.16$

The total cost of buying the car is \$536.24 more than the lease option.

## Materials List

- computer spreadsheet program such as Excel

## Description

Students are asked to research and develop a comprehensive plan for a hypothetical financial future, including projected income and expenses.

### TEACHING TIP

Encourage students to talk with a parent and/or a financial adviser regarding aspects of this project. This is also an opportunity to bring in a financial planner as a guest speaker.

### TEACHING TIP

Point out to students that the tax rates given here are for a single person in 2011. The 33% bracket is between $174,400 and $379,150. For all income above $379,150, the rate is 35%. Consult the Internal Revenue Service for the current tax rates in any year.

## Sample Answer

Answers will vary depending on the types of investments chosen. Each student's plan should adhere to the guidelines provided for the project, and should reflect what the student has learned about budgeting, taxes, saving, and borrowing in this chapter.

---

CHAPTER

# 15

## Modeling Project

## Money for Life

Everyone faces decisions about managing money and planning for retirement. Do you buy a house or rent? If you choose to buy, then when is the best time? Do you keep your money secure and easily accessed, or do you put it in an account that pays higher interest, but with restrictions on its use? Or, do you invest in something considered to be riskier, such as stocks or bonds?

Prepare a written plan for your financial future. Use the mathematical techniques you have explored in this chapter. A spreadsheet may be helpful. Determine what kinds of investments to make and when to make them. Also determine what your net worth will be at retirement.

Include these assumptions:

- You just finished college, have no outstanding debts, and have $10,000 in a savings account.
- You just took a job at a firm where you will remain for the rest of your career. The starting salary is $40,000, and you receive pay raises of $2,500 every two years.
  - You are 25 years old and will work full time for up to 40 years.
  - The selling price of a typical house is $225,000 and is increasing by 2% per year. (The value of the house increases at the same rate.)
  - You need at least 20% of the price of a house as a down payment, and the closing costs (which must be paid when the house is purchased) are 5% of the price. The down payment must come from savings, but the closing costs can be financed with the house, which is financed at 6.5% per year compounded monthly over 30 years.
- You will be in the 25% income tax bracket until your salary reaches $83,600. For any salary amount from $83,600 to $174,400, the income tax rate is 28%.
- You need $1,400 a month in living expenses, including monthly rent on an apartment (if and until you buy a house), which is $900 but increases $100 every two years. Other expenses go up by 3% per year.
- Your savings account pays 5% interest compounded monthly.

- Certificates of deposit (CDs) pay 7% interest compounded quarterly, but you have to keep the money in the bank for two years.

- You may put up to $5,000 in an Individual Retirement Account (IRA) every year. But before making a decision, research typical options that a person has for IRA investments. These vary considerably, but can include annuities, money market accounts, mutual funds, stocks, and bonds. Any contribution to a regular IRA is not taxed until the money is taken out of the account. Other accounts (called Roth IRAs) are funded from taxable income. However, in either case, you probably cannot take out any money until you retire without paying a penalty.

# Chapter 15 Review

## You Should Be Able to:

### Lesson 15.1

- use a computer spreadsheet to record and summarize expenses for a budget.

### Lesson 15.2

- find income equivalents for different time periods.
- use federal tax tables to find withholding amounts for various income levels.
- use formulas to determine Social Security and Medicare taxes.
- identify functions that model tax calculations.

### Lesson 15.3

- include income data in a complete budget spreadsheet.
- determine whether a budget is balanced.

### Lesson 15.4

- distinguish between simple and compound interest.
- determine the future value of savings under various compounding methods.

### Lesson 15.5

- solve problems that require previously learned concepts and skills.

### Lesson 15.6

- construct and interpret an amortization schedule.
- compare the relative costs of buying and leasing. (optional)

## Key Vocabulary

budget (p. 527)

fixed expenses (p. 527)

variable expenses (p. 527)

tax withholding table (p. 534)

gross income (p. 535)

net income (p. 535)

balanced budget (p. 540)

interest (p. 543)

principal (p. 543)

interest rate (p. 543)

simple interest (p. 543)

future value (p. 544)

compound interest (p. 544)

compounding period (p. 544)

nominal rate (p. 545)

finance a loan (p. 552)

interest-only loan (p. 552)

loan principal (p. 552)

remaining balance method (p. 552)

loan term (p. 554)

amortization (p. 554)

amortization schedule (p. 554)

capitalized cost (optional) (p. 555)

adjusted capitalized cost (optional) (p. 555)

residual value (optional) (p. 555)

depreciation (optional) (p. 555)

money factor (optional) (p. 555)

## Chapter 15  Test Review

**For Exercises 1–8, fill in the blank.**

1. Income before taxes and other deductions have been taken out is _____ income.

2. Income remaining after taxes and other deductions are taken out is _____ income.

3. If you are overspending and not staying within your budget, the difference between your income and expenses is _____ (negative, positive, zero).

4. Money deposited into a savings account is called _____.

5. The total amount that accumulates in a savings account after a specified time is called _____ _____.

6. When interest is compounded quarterly, it is compounded _____ times per year.

7. Compound interest is an example of _____ growth.

8. The process of repaying a loan through regular payments of principal and interest is called _____.

**For Exercises 9–11, consider the following monthly budget.**

| Income | |
|---|---|
| Salary (less taxes) | $2,870 |
| Dividends | $30 |
| Miscellaneous Income | $80 |
| | |
| **Fixed Expenses** | |
| Mortgage Payment | $1,350 |
| Insurance | $400 |
| Savings | $150 |

| Variable Expenses | |
|---|---|
| Food | $320 |
| Utilities | $220 |
| Home Maintenance | $120 |
| Credit Cards | $130 |
| Clothing | $40 |
| Entertainment | $100 |
| Pocket Money | $150 |

9. What is the total income?
10. What are the total expenses?
11. Is the budget balanced? Explain.

## Chapter 15 Test Review Answers

1. gross income
2. net income
3. negative
4. principal
5. future value
6. 4
7. exponential
8. amortization
9. $2,980
10. $2,980
11. yes; total income – total expenses = $0

# CHAPTER REVIEW

**12a.** $510

**12b.** $27,300

**12c.** $510.92

**12d.** $\dfrac{\$2,500}{1 \text{ month}} \cdot \dfrac{12 \text{ months}}{52 \text{ weeks}} \cdot \dfrac{1 \text{ week}}{40 \text{ hours}} =$ $14.42

**12e.** $6,275

**13.** Sample answer based on 2011 withholding tables: For 0 allowances, the entire $8,274 is subject to income tax withholding. The monthly withholding amount for a married person claiming no allowances is $791.65 + 0.25($8,274 − $6,408) = $1,258.15. Net income will be $8,274 − $1,258.15 − 0.042($8,274) − 0.0145($8,274) − $127 = $6,421.37.

**14a.** a direct variation (linear) function

**14b.** Sample answer: $C = 0.07S$

**14c.** Sample answer: The company contributes an amount equivalent to 7% of an employee's income to a retirement account.

**14d.** $3,360

**14e.** $71,429

---

**12.** Calculate each of the following. Assume that 40 hours = 1 work week.

   **a.** Weekly earnings when you make $12.75 an hour.

   **b.** Yearly earnings when you make $525 a week.

   **c.** Weekly earnings when you make $26,568 a year.

   **d.** Hourly earnings when you make $2,500 a month.

   **e.** Monthly earnings when you make $75,300 a year.

**13.** Assume you are married, claim zero allowances, and your gross income for one month is $8,274. The cost of your health insurance is $127 per month and is deducted from your earnings after taxes are calculated. Federal withholding, Social Security, and Medicare taxes are also deducted. Find your net income.

**14.** Employers often contribute an amount equivalent to a percentage of a person's salary to a retirement account. The graph shows the annual retirement contribution of one company as a function of annual salary.

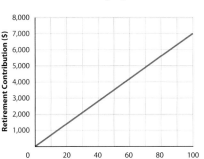

   **a.** What kind of function models the relationship in the graph?

   **b.** Write an equation that models retirement contribution $C$ as a function of salary $S$.

   **c.** Explain the real-world meaning of the constant in your equation.

   **d.** How much money would be contributed to the retirement account of a person making $48,000 under such a plan?

   **e.** What minimum amount of money would an employee have to earn in order to have $5,000 contributed to a retirement account under such a plan? Round to the nearest dollar.

15. Given that a budget is balanced and shows the following:

   Income = $6,517

   Fixed expenses = $5,162

   What are the total variable expenses?

16. Explain the difference between simple interest and compound interest.

17. Suppose $800 is deposited at a simple interest rate of 2.5%. How much interest is earned after 2 years?

18. Find the future value of $2,000 at 5% compounded annually for 10 years.

19. Find the future value of $8,300 at $3\frac{1}{2}$% compounded monthly for 4 years.

20. Find the monthly payment necessary to amortize a loan of $12,000 at 6% on the unpaid balance for 15 years.

21. Suppose you obtain a five-year loan for $32,500 at 7.5% interest on the unpaid balance through your bank.

   a. Find the monthly payment.

   b. Find the total interest.

22. The table below shows a portion of an amortization schedule for a $125,000 mortgage with an interest rate of 6%. The loan term is 30 years and the monthly payment is $749.44. Complete the first two months of the schedule.

| Payment Number | Monthly Payment | Interest Amount | Principal Paid | Remaining Principal |
|---|---|---|---|---|
| 0 | | | | $125,000.00 |
| 1 | | | | |
| 2 | | | | |

15. $1,355
16. Sample answer: Simple interest is interest that is paid on the principal alone. Compound interest is the interest that is paid on the principal plus the interest accumulated in previous periods.
17. $40.00
18. $3,257.79
19. $9,545.33
20. $101.26
21a. $651.23
21b. $6,574.04

**22.**

| Payment Number | Monthly Payment | Interest Amount | Principal Paid | Remaining Principal |
|---|---|---|---|---|
| 0 | | | | $125,000.00 |
| 1 | $749.44 | $625.00 | $124.44 | $124,875.56 |
| 2 | $749.44 | $624.38 | $125.06 | $124,750.50 |

**5e**  Elaborate

## Lesson Objective

- determine the future value of an annuity.

## Vocabulary

- annuity
- annuity due
- ordinary annuity
- simple annuity
- value of an annuity

## Materials List

## Description

Students should work in pairs or individually on this lesson. They use a formula for the future value of an ordinary annuity to explore how regular savings payments accumulate with interest.

---

# Chapter Extension
## Annuities

**Connection**

Another type of annuity, called a *contract annuity* or *retirement annuity*, is an asset that pays a constant amount each year to the holder until the annuity expires.

When people save to meet their long-range goals, they sometimes try to deposit equal amounts of money into savings plans such as Individual Retirement Accounts (IRAs) on a regular basis. These plans are often referred to as **annuities**. Most annuities are **simple** in that the compounding period and the deposit period are the same. The **value of an annuity** is the sum of all of the deposits and the interest earned.

Tables and spreadsheets provide a convenient way to explore annuities. For example, consider a situation where $500 is deposited at the *beginning* of each year for the next 5 years into an account that earns $5\frac{1}{2}\%$ compounded annually.

| Beginning of Year | Amount in the Account | Value at the End of the Year $P(1 + rt)$ |
|---|---|---|
| 1 | $500 | $500(1 + 0.055) = $527.50 |
| 2 | $527.50 + $500 = $1,027.50 | $1,027.50(1 + 0.055) = $1,084.01 |
| 3 | $1,084.01 + $500 = $1,584.01 | $1,584.01(1 + 0.055) = $1,671.13 |
| 4 | $1,671.13 + $500 = $2,171.13 | $2,171.13(1 + 0.055) = $2,290.54 |
| 5 | $2,290.54 + $500 = $2,790.54 | $2,790.54(1 + 0.055) = $2,944.02 |

This type of annuity where payments are made at the *beginning* of the compounding period is called an **annuity due**.

If the payments to an annuity are made at the *end* of each compounding period, then the annuity is generally referred to as an **ordinary annuity**. The following formula can be used to calculate the future value amount of any ordinary annuity:

**Future Value of an Ordinary Annuity**

$$A = R\left[\frac{(1 + i)^n - 1}{i}\right]$$

where
$A$ = future value amount
$R$ = regular deposit or payment at the end of each period
$i$ = interest rate per period (as a decimal)
$n$ = number of periods

1. Suppose you are starting your first job and you decide to begin saving for retirement. You deposit $1,500 in an account at the end of each year. The interest rate is 5.4% compounded annually. Use the formula for the future value of an ordinary annuity to calculate the amount in the account at the end of the first year.

2. Is the amount you calculated what you expected to be in the account? Explain.

3. Explain how the value of an annuity due would differ from your answer in Question 1.

4. What will be the value of the ordinary annuity at the end of 35 years?

5. Find the total amount of all the payments that you will have made after 35 years.

6. How much total interest will you have earned after 35 years?

7. Now suppose that the same $1,500 is saved each year, but in monthly payments of $125 to an ordinary annuity paying 5.4% interest *compounded monthly*. What is the total amount of all the payments that you will have made after 35 years?

8. What will be the value of the annuity at the end of 35 years?

9. How much total interest will you have earned after 35 years?

## Chapter 15 Extension Answers

1. $A = \$1,500\left[\dfrac{(1 + 0.054)^1 - 1}{0.054}\right]$

   $= \$1,500$

2. Yes; since the first deposit is made at the end of the first year, there has been no time for interest to accumulate.

3. For an annuity due, a payment would be made at the beginning of the first year. Interest would accumulate during the year, and the amount at the end of the year would be $1,581.

4. $A = R\left[\dfrac{(1 + i)^n - 1}{i}\right]$

   $= 1,500\left[\dfrac{(1 + 0.054)^{35} - 1}{0.054}\right]$

   $= \$147,254.80$

5. $35(\$1,500) = \$52,500$

6. $\$147,254.80 - \$52,500 = \$94,754.80$

7. $52,500

8. $A = R\left[\dfrac{(1 + i)^n - 1}{i}\right]$

   $= 125\left[\dfrac{(1 + 0.0045)^{420} - 1}{0.0045}\right]$

   $= \$155,315.65$

9. $\$155,315.65 - \$52,500 = \$102,815.65$

# Appendices

A **fraction** is a number that represents:

- a part of a whole. For example, $\frac{2}{3}$ of this rectangle is gray.

- a part of a set. For example, $\frac{2}{3}$ of the squares in this set are gray.

A fraction has a **numerator** and a **denominator**. The numerator counts the number of parts considered. The denominator tells the total number of parts.

$$\frac{2}{3} \begin{array}{l} \to \text{ numerator} \\ \to \text{ denominator} \end{array}$$

## WRITING A FRACTION IN SIMPLEST FORM

**To write a fraction in simplest form**, divide both the numerator and denominator by their common factor(s) until the only common factor of both is 1.

### Example

**1.** Simplify.

$$\frac{80}{120}$$

**Solution:**

10 is a common factor of 80 and 120.

Divide 80 and 120 by 10.    $\dfrac{80}{120} = \dfrac{80 \div 10}{120 \div 10} = \dfrac{8}{12}$

4 is a common factor of 8 and 12.

Divide 8 and 12 by 4.    $\dfrac{8}{12} = \dfrac{8 \div 4}{12 \div 4} = \dfrac{2}{3}$

Since the only factor common to both 2 and 3 is 1, $\frac{2}{3}$ is in simplest form. Notice, to write the fraction in simplest form, you could have divided the numerator and the denominator of $\frac{80}{120}$ by 40, the greatest common factor.

# Appendix A

## Writing a Fraction in Simplest Form Practice Answers

1. $\dfrac{3}{7}$

2. $\dfrac{3}{5}$

3. $\dfrac{3}{4}$

4. $\dfrac{5}{6}$

5. $\dfrac{5}{7}$

6. $3\dfrac{2}{3}$

## Writing an Equivalent Fraction Practice Answers

1. $\dfrac{3}{24}$

2. $\dfrac{15}{30}$

3. $\dfrac{24}{56}$

4. $\dfrac{28}{48}$

5. $\dfrac{3}{7}$

6. $5\dfrac{2}{9}$

*Practice*  **Simplify.**

1. $\dfrac{12}{28}$    2. $\dfrac{9}{15}$    3. $\dfrac{6}{8}$    4. $\dfrac{20}{24}$    5. $\dfrac{50}{70}$    6. $3\dfrac{18}{27}$

## WRITING AN EQUIVALENT FRACTION

**To find an equivalent fraction**, multiply (or divide) both the numerator and denominator by the same non-zero number.

### Example

2. $\dfrac{2}{3} = \dfrac{?}{12}$

**Solution:**

Since $3 \times 4 = 12$, multiply the numerator and
    denominator by 4.               $\dfrac{2}{3} = \dfrac{2 \times 4}{3 \times 4}$

Simplify.                                                    $= \dfrac{8}{12}$

*Practice*  **Write an equivalent fraction having the given denominator.**

1. $\dfrac{1}{8} = \dfrac{?}{24}$    2. $\dfrac{5}{10} = \dfrac{?}{30}$    3. $\dfrac{6}{14} = \dfrac{?}{56}$

4. $\dfrac{7}{12} = \dfrac{?}{48}$    5. $\dfrac{6}{14} = \dfrac{?}{7}$    6. $5\dfrac{4}{18} = 5\dfrac{?}{9}$

## ADDING AND SUBTRACTING FRACTIONS

**To add (or subtract) fractions with like denominators**, write the denominator, add (or subtract) the numerators, and then rewrite the answer in simplest form.

### Examples

3. Add.
    $\dfrac{2}{7} + \dfrac{3}{7}$

**Solution:**

Add the numerators.                    $\dfrac{2}{7} + \dfrac{3}{7} = \dfrac{2 + 3}{7}$

Simplify.                                                  $= \dfrac{5}{7}$

**4.** Subtract.

$$\frac{7}{8} - \frac{3}{8}$$

**Solution:**

Subtract the numerators.
$$\frac{7}{8} - \frac{3}{8} = \frac{7-3}{8}$$

Simplify the numerator.
$$= \frac{4}{8}$$

Write the fraction in simplest form.
$$= \frac{1}{2}$$

*Practice*    **Add or subtract. Write your answer in simplest form.**

**1.** $\frac{1}{5} + \frac{3}{5}$     **2.** $\frac{9}{15} - \frac{6}{15}$     **3.** $\frac{10}{21} + \frac{8}{21}$

**4.** $\frac{3}{12} + \frac{5}{12}$     **5.** $\frac{9}{10} - \frac{5}{10}$     **6.** $\frac{7}{8} - \frac{1}{8}$

**To add (or subtract) fractions with unlike denominators**, find the least common denominator (LCD). Rewrite the fractions as equivalent fractions with that LCD. Add (or subtract) and simplify, if possible.

### Example

**5.** Add.

$$\frac{3}{10} + \frac{8}{15}$$

**Solution:**

Rewrite the fractions using the LCD of $\frac{3}{10}$ and $\frac{8}{15}$.
$$\frac{3}{10} + \frac{8}{15} = \frac{9}{30} + \frac{16}{30}$$

Add the numerators.
$$= \frac{9+16}{30}$$

Simplify.
$$= \frac{25}{30}$$

Write the fraction in simplest form.
$$= \frac{5}{6}$$

*Practice*    **Add or subtract. Write your answer in simplest form.**

**1.** $\frac{3}{14} + \frac{2}{7}$     **2.** $\frac{5}{6} - \frac{1}{2}$     **3.** $\frac{2}{5} + \frac{3}{4}$

**4.** $\frac{4}{9} - \frac{1}{6}$     **5.** $\frac{2}{7} + \frac{1}{3}$     **6.** $\frac{9}{10} - \frac{2}{6}$

FRACTIONS    **Appendix A**    **571**

## Adding and Subtracting Fractions with Like Denominators
## Practice Answers

1. $\frac{4}{5}$

2. $\frac{1}{5}$

3. $\frac{6}{7}$

4. $\frac{2}{3}$

5. $\frac{2}{5}$

6. $\frac{3}{4}$

## Adding and Subtracting Fractions with Unlike Denominators
## Practice Answers

1. $\frac{1}{2}$

2. $\frac{1}{3}$

3. $\frac{23}{20}$ or $1\frac{3}{20}$

4. $\frac{5}{18}$

5. $\frac{13}{21}$

6. $\frac{17}{30}$

To add (or subtract) mixed numbers, rewrite the fractions as equivalent fractions with a common denominator. (When subtracting, if the fraction in the subtrahend is greater than the fraction in the minuend, it will be necessary to regroup.) Add (or subtract) the fractions. Add (or subtract) the whole numbers. Then rewrite the answer in simplest form.

## Examples

**6.** Add.

$$2\frac{2}{5} + 5\frac{7}{10}$$

**Solution:**

Rewrite the fractions using the LCD of $\frac{2}{5}$ and $\frac{7}{10}$.

$$2\frac{2}{5} + 5\frac{7}{10} = 2\frac{4}{10} + 5\frac{7}{10}$$

Add the fractions. Then add the whole numbers.

$$= 7\frac{11}{10}$$

Write $\frac{11}{10}$ as a mixed number.

$$= 7 + 1\frac{1}{10}$$

Add the whole numbers.

$$= 8\frac{1}{10}$$

**7.** Subtract.

$$4\frac{1}{8} - 1\frac{1}{6}$$

**Solution:**

Rewrite the fractions using the LCD of $\frac{1}{8}$ and $\frac{1}{6}$.

$$4\frac{1}{8} - 1\frac{1}{6} = 4\frac{3}{24} - 1\frac{4}{24}$$

Regroup $4\frac{3}{24}$ as $3\frac{27}{24}$.

$$= 3\frac{27}{24} - 1\frac{4}{24}$$

Subtract the fractions and the whole numbers.

$$= 2\frac{23}{24}$$

*Practice*    **Add or subtract. Write your answer in simplest form.**

**1.** $5\frac{3}{10} + 3\frac{7}{10}$     **2.** $6\frac{2}{5} - 2\frac{3}{5}$     **3.** $1\frac{3}{7} + 9\frac{2}{3}$

**4.** $8\frac{1}{2} - 6\frac{2}{3}$     **5.** $9\frac{2}{3} - 4\frac{3}{4}$     **6.** $10\frac{2}{5} + 8\frac{3}{4}$

## Adding and Subtracting Mixed Numbers Practice Answers

1. $9$

2. $3\frac{4}{5}$

3. $11\frac{2}{21}$

4. $1\frac{5}{6}$

5. $4\frac{11}{12}$

6. $19\frac{3}{20}$

**To multiply a fraction by a fraction**, multiply the numerators to find the numerator of the product. Multiply the denominators to find the denominator of the product. Then rewrite the answer in simplest form.

### Example

**8.** Multiply.

$$\frac{2}{3} \times \frac{5}{8}$$

**Solution:**

| | |
|---|---|
| Multiply the numerators. | $\frac{2}{3} \times \frac{5}{8} = \frac{10}{}$ |
| Multiply the denominators. | $= \frac{10}{24}$ |
| Simplify the fraction. | $= \frac{5}{12}$ |

*Practice* **Multiply. Write your answer in simplest form.**

**1.** $\frac{1}{3} \times \frac{4}{5}$  **2.** $\left(\frac{5}{6}\right)\left(\frac{4}{7}\right)$  **3.** $\frac{1}{2} \times \frac{1}{3} \times \frac{3}{4}$

**4.** $\frac{3}{8} \times \frac{7}{8}$  **5.** $\frac{4}{9} \cdot \frac{1}{4}$  **6.** $\frac{15}{2} \cdot \frac{4}{5}$

**To multiply mixed numbers**, write all mixed numbers as improper fractions. Multiply the numerators to find the numerator of the product. Multiply the denominators to find the denominator of the product. Then write the product in simplest form.

### Example

**9.** Multiply.

$$2\frac{3}{4} \times 3\frac{1}{3}$$

**Solution:**

Write the mixed numbers as improper fractions. $\quad 2\frac{3}{4} \times 3\frac{1}{3} = \frac{11}{4} \times \frac{10}{3}$

Multiply the numerators. Multiply the denominators. $\quad = \frac{110}{12}$

Write as a mixed number in simplest form. $\quad = 9\frac{1}{6}$

*Practice* **Multiply. Write your answer in simplest form.**

**1.** $1\frac{3}{5} \times \frac{3}{4}$  **2.** $1\frac{1}{3} \times 2\frac{4}{5}$  **3.** $2 \times 1\frac{3}{8}$  **4.** $2\frac{1}{2} \cdot 4\frac{1}{2}$  **5.** $\left(1\frac{5}{6}\right)\left(2\frac{3}{4}\right)$

## Multiplying a Fraction by a Fraction Practice Answers

1. $\frac{4}{15}$

2. $\frac{10}{21}$

3. $\frac{1}{8}$

4. $\frac{21}{64}$

5. $\frac{1}{9}$

6. $6$

## Multiplying Mixed Numbers Practice Answers

1. $1\frac{1}{5}$

2. $3\frac{11}{15}$

3. $2\frac{3}{4}$

4. $11\frac{1}{4}$

5. $5\frac{1}{24}$

# Appendix A

## Dividing a Fraction by a Fraction Practice Answers

1. $\dfrac{1}{4}$

2. $1\dfrac{1}{8}$

3. $\dfrac{2}{11}$

4. $1\dfrac{7}{8}$

5. $\dfrac{1}{9}$

6. $\dfrac{8}{21}$

## Dividing Mixed Numbers Practice Answers

1. $3\dfrac{3}{10}$

2. $\dfrac{3}{8}$

3. $\dfrac{13}{27}$

4. $2\dfrac{1}{4}$

5. $\dfrac{5}{9}$

**To divide a fraction by a fraction,** multiply by the reciprocal of the divisor. Then rewrite the answer in simplest form.

### Example

**10.** Divide.

$$\dfrac{3}{5} \div \dfrac{7}{10}$$

**Solution:**

Multiply by the reciprocal of the divisor. $\quad \dfrac{3}{5} \div \dfrac{7}{10} = \dfrac{3}{5} \times \dfrac{10}{7}$

Multiply the numerators. Multiply the denominators. $\quad = \dfrac{30}{35}$

Simplify the fraction. $\quad = \dfrac{6}{7}$

*Practice* **Divide. Write your answer in simplest form.**

**1.** $\dfrac{1}{5} \div \dfrac{4}{5}$  **2.** $\dfrac{1}{2} \div \dfrac{4}{9}$  **3.** $\dfrac{1}{3} \div \dfrac{11}{6}$

**4.** $\dfrac{3}{8} \div \dfrac{1}{5}$  **5.** $\dfrac{4}{9} \div 4$  **6.** $\dfrac{2}{7} \div \dfrac{3}{4}$

**To divide mixed numbers,** write all mixed numbers as improper fractions. Change the divisor to its reciprocal. Multiply the resulting fractions. Then rewrite the answer in simplest form.

### Example

**11.** Divide.

$$1\dfrac{1}{4} \div 4\dfrac{2}{3}$$

**Solution:**

Write the mixed numbers as improper fractions. $\quad 1\dfrac{1}{4} \div 4\dfrac{2}{3} = \dfrac{5}{4} \div \dfrac{14}{3}$

Multiply by the reciprocal of the divisor. $\quad = \dfrac{5}{4} \times \dfrac{3}{14}$

Multiply the numerators. Multiply the denominators. $\quad = \dfrac{15}{56}$

*Practice* **Divide. Write your answer in simplest form.**

**1.** $2\dfrac{1}{5} \div \dfrac{2}{3}$  **2.** $\dfrac{1}{2} \div 1\dfrac{1}{3}$  **3.** $1\dfrac{4}{9} \div 3$  **4.** $6\dfrac{3}{8} \div 2\dfrac{5}{6}$  **5.** $2\dfrac{1}{2} \div 4\dfrac{1}{2}$

**Appendix B** | **Decimals**

Numbers that are expressed using a decimal point are called **decimal numbers** or simply **decimals**.

Each digit of a decimal number has a value based on its place in the number. Each place has a value of 10 times the place to its right.

83.94 is read *eighty-three and ninety-four hundredths.*

## ADDING AND SUBTRACTING DECIMALS

**To add (or subtract) decimals,** line up the decimal points. Insert zeros when necessary. Add (or subtract) as you would with whole numbers. Place the decimal point in the answer in line with those above.

### Examples

**1.** Add.

13.4 + 8.1

**Solution:**

Write the numbers vertically with the decimal points aligned.

$$\begin{array}{r} 13.4 \\ +\phantom{0}8.1 \end{array}$$

Add. Place the decimal point.

$$\begin{array}{r} 13.4 \\ +\phantom{0}8.1 \\ \hline 21.5 \end{array}$$

# Appendix B

## Adding and Subtracting Decimals Practice Answers

1. 98.1
2. 0.36
3. 10.53
4. 728.84
5. 4.57
6. 0.228

**2.** Subtract.

8.9 − 3.25

**Solution:**

| Write the numbers vertically with the decimal points aligned. | 8.9<br>− 3.25 |
| Insert a zero. | 8.90<br>− 3.25 |
| Subtract. Place the decimal point. | 8.90<br>− 3.25<br>5.65 |

*Practice*   **Add or subtract.**

**1.** $87.3 + 10.8$   **2.** $0.75 − 0.39$   **3.** $9.5 + 1.03$

**4.** $823.7 − 94.86$   **5.** $0.17 + 0.5 + 3.9$   **6.** $0.6 − 0.372$

## MULTIPLYING DECIMALS

**To multiply decimals**, multiply as with whole numbers. The number of decimal places in the product is the sum of the number of decimal places in the factors. When necessary, insert zeros in the product to place the decimal point.

### Examples

**3.** Multiply.

$2.47 \times 1.3$

**Solution:**

$$
\begin{array}{r}
2.47 \\
\times\ 1.3 \\
\hline
741 \\
2470 \\
\hline
3.211
\end{array}
$$

⇐ 2 decimal places
⇐ 1 decimal place

⇐ 3 decimal places

**4.** Multiply.

$43.5 \times 0.0009$

**Solution:**

$$
\begin{array}{r}
43.5 \\
\times\ 0.0009 \\
\hline
0.03915
\end{array}
$$

⇐ 1 decimal place
⇐ 4 decimal places

⇐ 5 decimal places (Insert zeros when necessary.)

*Practice*  **Divide.**

**1.** $5.88 \div 0.6$    **2.** $0.1296 \div 5.4$    **3.** $625 \div 2.5$

**4.** $2.08 \div 0.16$    **5.** $18.43 \div 0.4$    **6.** $0.6572 \div 4.24$

## CHANGE A DECIMAL TO A FRACTION

**To change a decimal to a fraction,** write the digits in the number over the place value of the last digit of the decimal.

### Examples

**9.** Write 0.45 as a fraction.

**Solution:**

0.45 is read "45 hundredths." Write 45 over 100. Simplify. $\frac{45}{100} = \frac{9}{20}$

So, $0.45 = \frac{9}{20}$.

**10.** Write 0.003 as a fraction.

**Solution:**

0.003 is read "3 thousandths." Write 3 over 1,000. $\frac{3}{1,000}$

So, $0.003 = \frac{3}{1,000}$.

**11.** Write $0.\overline{72}$ as a fraction.

**Solution:**

Since $0.\overline{72}$ is a repeating decimal, let $N = 0.\overline{72}$. Then $100N = 72.\overline{72}$.

$$100N = 72.\overline{72}$$

Subtract $N$ from $100N$. $\quad \dfrac{-N = -0.\overline{72}}{99N = 72.00}$

Divide each side by 99. $\quad N = \dfrac{72}{99}$

Simplify. $\quad N = \dfrac{8}{11}$

So, $0.\overline{72} = \dfrac{8}{11}$.

*Practice*  **Change the decimal to a fraction.**

**1.** 0.75    **2.** 0.008    **3.** $0.\overline{16}$    **4.** 1.7

**5.** 0.463    **6.** 0.18    **7.** $0.\overline{2}$    **8.** 25.382

## Dividing by a Decimal Number Practice Answers

1. 9.8
2. 0.024
3. 250
4. 13
5. 46.075
6. 0.155

## Changing a Decimal to a Fraction Practice Answers

1. $\dfrac{3}{4}$

2. $\dfrac{1}{125}$

3. $\dfrac{16}{99}$

4. $1\dfrac{7}{10}$

5. $\dfrac{463}{1,000}$

6. $\dfrac{9}{50}$

7. $\dfrac{2}{9}$

8. $25\dfrac{191}{500}$

**To change a fraction to a decimal,** divide the numerator by the denominator.

## Examples

**12.** Write $\frac{7}{8}$ as a decimal.

**Solution:**

Divide 7 by 8.

$$
\begin{array}{r}
0.875 \\
8\,\overline{)7.000} \\
\underline{6\,4} \\
60 \\
\underline{56} \\
40 \\
\underline{40} \\
0
\end{array}
$$

So, $\frac{7}{8} = 0.875$.

**13.** Write $\frac{5}{12}$ as a decimal.

**Solution:**

Divide 5 by 12.

$$
\begin{array}{r}
0.4166\ldots \\
12\,\overline{)5.0000} \\
\underline{4\,8} \\
20 \\
\underline{12} \\
80 \\
\underline{72} \\
80 \\
\underline{72} \\
8
\end{array}
$$

This decimal repeats. When a decimal repeats, the quotient is written with a bar over the digit or group of digits that repeat.

So, $\frac{5}{12} = 0.41\overline{6}$.

*Practice*   **Change the fraction to a decimal.**

**1.** $\frac{3}{5}$   **2.** $\frac{9}{100}$   **3.** $\frac{257}{1,000}$   **4.** $\frac{6}{11}$   **5.** $1\frac{4}{8}$   **6.** $\frac{7}{22}$

## Changing a Fraction to a Decimal Practice Answers

**1.** 0.6
**2.** 0.09
**3.** 0.257
**4.** $0.\overline{54}$
**5.** 1.5
**6.** $0.3\overline{18}$

A **ratio** is a comparison of two numbers by division. Ratios can be written in three ways. For example, the ratio of the number of red squares to the number of gray squares is 3 to 4 or 3 : 4 or $\frac{3}{4}$.

## FINDING A RATIO

**To find the ratio between two quantities**, show the two quantities as a fraction. Then write the fraction in simplest form.

### Examples

**1.** Your class has 20 books and 25 students. Find the ratio of the number of books to the number of students.

**Solution:**

Write the ratio of the number of books to the number of students.

$$\frac{20 \text{ books}}{25 \text{ students}}$$

Simplify.

$$\frac{20}{25} = \frac{20 \div 5}{25 \div 5}$$

$$= \frac{4}{5}$$

The ratio can be written in three ways.    4 to 5, 4 : 5, or $\frac{4}{5}$

**2.** There are 14 girls and 12 boys in a class. Find the ratio of the number of boys to the number of students in the class.

**Solution:**

Write the ratio of the number of boys to the number of students.

$$\frac{12 \text{ boys}}{(14 + 12) \text{ students}}$$

Simplify.

$$\frac{12}{26} = \frac{12 \div 2}{26 \div 2}$$

$$= \frac{6}{13}$$

The ratio can be written in three ways. 6 to 13, 6 : 13, or $\frac{6}{13}$

# Appendix D

## Finding a Ratio Practice Answers

1. 2 to 3, 2 : 3, $\frac{2}{3}$

2. 50 to 1, 50 : 1, $\frac{50}{1}$

3. 2 to 5, 2 : 5, $\frac{2}{5}$

4. 3 to 1, 3 : 1, $\frac{3}{1}$

*Practice*　　**Find the ratio. Then write the ratio in three ways.**

1. A recipe calls for 3 cups of flour and 2 cups of sugar. Find the ratio of the number of cups of sugar to the number of cups of flour.

2. Tom drives 400 miles in 8 hours. Find the ratio of the number of miles to the number of hours.

3. One pet store sells cats, dogs, and birds. Today, there are 24 cats, 25 dogs, and 11 birds for sale at the pet store. Find the ratio of the number of cats to the total number of animals for sale today.

4. A grocery store determined that 45 out of 60 customers spent over $50 on Monday. Find the ratio of the number of customers who spent over $50 to the number of those who spent $50 or less.

## Appendix D　　Proportions

A statement that two ratios are equal is called a **proportion**. For example, the equation $\frac{1}{2} = \frac{4}{8}$ is a proportion because the two ratios are equal.

In the proportion $\frac{1}{2} = \frac{4}{8}$, the cross products $1 \times 8$ and $2 \times 4$ are equal. This is true for all proportions.

### SOLVING A PROPORTION

One way **to solve a proportion** is to use the properties of equality.

#### Example

1. Solve for $x$.

$$\frac{5}{6} = \frac{x}{36}$$

**Solution:**

| | |
|---|---|
| Original equation | $\frac{5}{6} = \frac{x}{36}$ |
| Multiply each side of the equation by 36. | $36 \cdot \frac{5}{6} = 36 \cdot \frac{x}{36}$ |
| Multiply. | $\frac{36 \cdot 5}{6} = x$ |
| Simplify. | $30 = x$ |

Another way **to solve a proportion** is to use cross products and the properties of equality.

### Example

**2.** Solve for $n$.

$$\frac{4}{7} = \frac{28}{n}$$

**Solution:**

| | |
|---|---|
| Original equation | $\frac{4}{7} = \frac{28}{n}$ |
| Use cross products. | $4n = 7 \cdot 28$ |
| Divide each side of the equation by 4. | $\frac{4n}{4} = \frac{7 \cdot 28}{4}$ |
| Simplify. | $n = 49$ |

*Practice*　　**Solve the proportion.**

**1.** $\frac{3}{n} = \frac{5}{20}$　　　　**2.** $\frac{1}{4} = \frac{n}{16}$　　　　**3.** $\frac{x}{8} = \frac{3}{12}$

**4.** $\frac{6}{5} = \frac{18}{y}$　　　　**5.** $\frac{8}{3} = \frac{14}{n}$　　　　**6.** $\frac{x}{16} = \frac{22.5}{15}$

## Solving a Proportion Practice Answers

1. $n = 12$
2. $n = 4$
3. $x = 2$
4. $y = 15$
5. $n = 5.25$
6. $x = 24$

| **Appendix E** | **Percents as Fractions or Decimals** |
|---|---|

The word **percent** means "per hundred" or "parts per hundred." The symbol for percent is %. A percent can be written with a percent symbol (%), as a fraction, or as a decimal.

For example, 95% of this square is red.

You can also write 95% as a fraction $\left(\frac{95}{100}\right)$ or as a decimal (0.95).

## Appendix E

### Changing a Decimal to a Percent Practice Answers

1. 19%
2. 270%
3. 50%
4. 0.54%
5. 68%
6. 100%

### Changing a Percent to a Decimal Practice Answers

1. 0.13
2. 0.02
3. 0.50
4. 1.45
5. 0.021
6. 0.169

## CHANGING A DECIMAL TO A PERCENT

**To change a decimal to a percent,** multiply by 100 and write the % sign after the number.

### Examples

**1.** Write 0.8 as a percent.

**Solution:**

| | |
|---|---|
| Multiply by 100. | 0.80. |
| Write a % sign after the number. | 80% |

So, 0.8 = 80%.

**2.** Write 0.004 as a percent.

**Solution:**

| | |
|---|---|
| Multiply by 100. | 0.00.4 |
| Write a % sign after the number. | 0.4% |

So, 0.004 = 0.4%.

*Practice*    **Write the decimal as a percent.**

**1.** 0.19    **2.** 2.7    **3.** 0.5    **4.** 0.0054    **5.** 0.68    **6.** 1.00

## CHANGING A PERCENT TO A DECIMAL

**To change a percent to a decimal**, divide by 100 and remove the % sign.

### Examples

**3.** Write 8% as a decimal.

**Solution:**

| | |
|---|---|
| Divide by 100 and remove the % sign. | 0.08 = 0.08 |

So, 8% = 0.08.

**4.** Write 6.3% as a decimal.

**Solution:**

| | |
|---|---|
| Divide by 100 and remove the % sign. | 0.06.3 = 0.063 |

So, 6.3% = 0.063.

*Practice*    **Write the percent as an equivalent decimal.**

**1.** 13%    **2.** 2%    **3.** 50%    **4.** 145%    **5.** 2.1%    **6.** 16.9%

## CHANGING A FRACTION TO A PERCENT

**To change a fraction to a percent**, first write the fraction as a decimal. Then change the decimal to a percent.

### Example

**5.** Write $\frac{2}{5}$ as a percent.

**Solution:**

Write the fraction as a decimal.

$$\frac{2}{5} = 5\overline{)2.0}^{\,0.4}$$

Multiply by 100.

$0.40.$

Write a % sign after the number.

$40\%$

So, $\frac{2}{5} = 40\%$.

*Practice*  **Write the fraction as a percent.**

**1.** $\frac{7}{20}$  **2.** $\frac{53}{100}$  **3.** $6\frac{3}{4}$  **4.** $\frac{8}{1}$  **5.** $\frac{6}{15}$  **6.** $\frac{11}{25}$

## CHANGING A PERCENT TO A FRACTION

**To change a percent to a fraction**, write the percent as a decimal. Then change the decimal to a fraction. Rewrite as a fraction in simplest form.

### Examples

**6.** Write 25% as a fraction.

**Solution:**

Write the percent as a decimal.

$25\% = 0.25$

Write the decimal as a fraction.

$= \frac{25}{100}$

Simplify.

$= \frac{1}{4}$

So, $25\% = \frac{1}{4}$.

**7.** Write 150% as a fraction.

**Solution:**

Write the percent as a decimal.

$150\% = 1.50$

Write the decimal as a fraction.

$= 1\frac{5}{10}$

Simplify.

$= 1\frac{1}{2}$ or $\frac{3}{2}$

So, $150\% = 1\frac{1}{2}$ or $\frac{3}{2}$.

## Changing a Fraction to a Percent Practice Answers

1. 35%
2. 53%
3. 675%
4. 800%
5. 40%
6. 44%

## Changing a Percent to a Fraction Practice Answers

1. $\dfrac{9}{20}$

2. $\dfrac{1}{20}$

3. $\dfrac{49}{100}$

4. $1\dfrac{1}{4}$

5. $\dfrac{3}{4}$

6. $3$

**Practice**   Write the percent as an equivalent fraction in simplest form.

**1.** 45%    **2.** 5%    **3.** 49%    **4.** 125%    **5.** 75%    **6.** 300%

Proportions can often be used to solve percent problems. These problems involve finding one of three numbers: the *whole*, the *part*, or the *percent*. For example,

- finding a part of a whole.

$$\underset{\substack{\uparrow \\ \text{percent}}}{\underline{30\%}} \quad \text{of} \quad \underset{\substack{\uparrow \\ \text{whole}}}{\underline{70}} \quad = \quad \underset{\substack{\uparrow \\ \text{part}}}{\underline{?}}$$

- finding what percent one number is of another.

$$\underset{\substack{\uparrow \\ \text{percent}}}{\underline{?\%}} \quad \text{of} \quad \underset{\substack{\uparrow \\ \text{whole}}}{\underline{20}} \quad = \quad \underset{\substack{\uparrow \\ \text{part}}}{\underline{2}}$$

- finding the whole when the part is known.

$$\underset{\substack{\uparrow \\ \text{percent}}}{\underline{4\%}} \quad \text{of} \quad \underset{\substack{\uparrow \\ \text{whole}}}{\underline{?}} \quad = \quad \underset{\substack{\uparrow \\ \text{part}}}{\underline{8}}$$

Each of these types of problems can be solved using the proportion:

$$\frac{\text{part } (a)}{\text{whole } (b)} = \frac{\text{percent } (p)}{100}$$

### FINDING A PERCENT OF A WHOLE

### Example

**1.** What is 30% of 40?

**Solution:**

| | |
|---|---|
| Write the general form. | $\dfrac{\text{part}}{\text{whole}} = \dfrac{\text{percent}}{100}$ |
| Substitute. | $\dfrac{a}{40} = \dfrac{30}{100}$ |
| Use cross products. | $100a = 30 \cdot 40$ |
| Divide each side by 100. | $\dfrac{100a}{100} = \dfrac{30 \cdot 40}{100}$ |
| Simplify. | $a = 12$ |

So, 30% of 40 is 12.

*Practice* **Solve.**

**1.** What is 20% of 40?　**2.** What is 24% of 9?　**3**. What is 150% of 60?

**4.** What is 6.5% of 92?　**5.** What is 0.5% of 10?　**6.** What is 90% of 12?

## FINDING WHAT PERCENT ONE NUMBER IS OF ANOTHER

### Example

**2.** What percent of 150 is 30?

**Solution:**

Write the general form.

$$\frac{\text{part}}{\text{whole}} = \frac{\text{percent}}{100}$$

Substitute.

$$\frac{30}{150} = \frac{p}{100}$$

Use cross products.

$$150p = 30 \cdot 100$$

Divide each side by 150.

$$\frac{150p}{150} = \frac{30 \cdot 100}{150}$$

Simplify.

$$p = 20$$

The percent is 20. So, 20% of 150 is 30.

*Practice* **Solve.**

**1.** What percent of 200 is 36?　**2.** What percent of 48 is 24?

**3.** What percent of 80 is 152?　**4.** What percent of 46 is 6.9?

**5.** What percent of 20 is 5?　**6.** What percent of 1,000 is 90?

## FINDING THE ORIGINAL NUMBER WHEN A PERCENT OF IT IS KNOWN

### Example

**3.** 24% of what number is 144?

**Solution:**

Write the general form.

$$\frac{\text{part}}{\text{whole}} = \frac{\text{percent}}{100}$$

Substitute.

$$\frac{144}{b} = \frac{24}{100}$$

Use cross products.

$$24b = 100 \cdot 144$$

Divide each side by 24.

$$\frac{24b}{24} = \frac{100 \cdot 144}{24}$$

Simplify.

$$b = 600$$

So, 24% of 600 is 144.

## Finding a Percent of a Whole Practice Answers

**1.** 8
**2.** 2.16
**3.** 90
**4.** 5.98
**5.** 0.05
**6.** 10.8

## Finding What Percent One Number Is of Another Practice Answers

**1.** 18%
**2.** 50%
**3.** 190%
**4.** 15%
**5.** 25%
**6.** 9%

# Appendix G

## Finding the Original Number When a Percent of It Is Known Practice Answers

1. 240
2. 22
3. 40
4. 600
5. 100
6. 2.5

*Practice*        **Solve.**

**1.** 35% of what number is 84?        **2.** 50% of what number is 11?

**3.** 130% of what number is 52?        **4.** 2% of what number is 12?

**5.** 95% of what number is 95?        **6.** 30% of what number is 0.75?

| Appendix G | Absolute Value |

The set of **integers** consists of the counting numbers, their opposites, and zero. The number line below represents this set.

### FINDING ABSOLUTE VALUE

The **absolute value** of a number is the distance between the number and 0 on a number line.

- The absolute value of $a$ is written as $|a|$.
- The absolute value of 0 is 0.

### Examples

**1.** Find the absolute value.

$$|-6|$$

**Solution:**

Find the distance from 0.

6 units from 0

So, $|-6| = 6$.

**2.** Find the absolute value.

$|+6|$

**Solution:**

Find the distance from 0.

6 units from 0

-6  -5  -4  -3  -2  -1   0   1   2   3   4   5   ⑥

So, $|+6| = 6$.

*Practice*    **Find the absolute value.**

**1.** $|-5|$        **2.** $|5|$        **3.** $|-14|$        **4.** $|+20|$

**5.** $|-9|$        **6.** $|8|$        **7.** $|0|$        **8.** $\left|-\frac{1}{2}\right|$

## Finding Absolute Value Practice Answers

1. 5
2. 5
3. 14
4. 20
5. 9
6. 8
7. 0
8. $\frac{1}{2}$

---

## Appendix H    Order of Operations

To avoid confusion in situations where expressions contain more than one operation, guidelines have been established. These guidelines indicate the order in which mathematical operations must be performed.

### ORDER OF OPERATIONS GUIDELINES

To find the value of an expression containing more than one operation, the following order is used:

**1.** Perform the operations within the grouping symbols such as parentheses ( ), brackets [ ], braces { }, and the fraction bar.

**2.** Raise numbers to powers.

**3.** Perform multiplications and divisions from left to right.

**4.** Perform additions and subtractions from left to right.

## Examples

**1.** Evaluate.

$2(3 + 5) + 100 \div 2$

**Solution:**

Add inside the parentheses. $\quad 2(3 + 5) + 100 \div 2 = 2(8) + 100 \div 2$

Multiply and divide from left to right. $\qquad\qquad = 16 + 50$

Add. $\qquad\qquad\qquad\qquad\qquad\qquad\qquad = 66$

**2.** Evaluate.

$\dfrac{3(20)}{18 - 6}$

**Solution:**

Evaluate the expressions grouped by the fraction bar. $\quad \dfrac{3(20)}{18 - 6} = \dfrac{60}{12}$

Divide. $\qquad\qquad\qquad\qquad\qquad\qquad\qquad = 5$

**3.** Evaluate.

$(7 - 1)^2 + 6 \div 3$

**Solution:**

Subtract inside the parentheses. $\quad (7 - 1)^2 + 6 \div 3 = 6^2 + 6 \div 3$

Evaluate the power. $\qquad\qquad\qquad\qquad = 36 + 6 \div 3$

Divide. $\qquad\qquad\qquad\qquad\qquad\qquad = 36 + 2$

Add. $\qquad\qquad\qquad\qquad\qquad\qquad\qquad = 38$

## Order of Operations Guidelines Practice Answers

1. 1
2. 1
3. 9
4. 23
5. 24
6. 2

*Practice* **Evaluate.**

**1.** $73 - 8(8 + 1)$ $\quad$ **2.** $(14 \div 2) - 3 \cdot 2$ $\quad$ **3.** $3^2 + 5 \div 5 \times (4 + 2) - 6$

**4.** $25 - 10 \div 5$ $\quad$ **5.** $(1 + 7) \times 12 \div 2^2$ $\quad$ **6.** $\dfrac{6^2 - 2(4 + 3)}{2 \cdot 3 + 1 + 2^2}$

## Appendix I | Operations with Positive and Negative Numbers

### ADDITION

- **When adding two numbers with the same sign**, add their absolute values and write the common sign of the numbers.
- **When adding two numbers with different signs**, find the absolute value of each number. Subtract the smaller absolute value from the larger absolute value. Then write the sign of the number with the larger absolute value.

### Examples

**1.** Add.

$$-12 + (-13)$$

**Solution:**

The two numbers have the same sign:

$$\text{Add } |-12| \text{ and } |-13|.$$
$$\downarrow$$
$$-12 + (-13) = -25$$
$$\uparrow$$

The sum is negative.

**2.** Add.

$$-22 + 8$$

**Solution:**

The two numbers have different signs:

$$\text{Subtract } |8| \text{ from } |-22|.$$
$$\downarrow$$
$$-22 + 8 = -14$$
$$\uparrow$$

The sum is negative.

*Practice*    **Add.**

**1.** $8 + (-9)$      **2.** $-12 + 3$      **3.** $-100 + 50$

**4.** $-12 + (-3)$    **5.** $100 + 50$     **6.** $-25 + (-32)$

**7.** $6 + (-4)$      **8.** $-6 + (-4)$    **9.** $25 + (-32)$

## Addition with Positive and Negative Numbers Practice Answers

1.  $-1$
2.  $-9$
3.  $-50$
4.  $-15$
5.  $150$
6.  $-57$
7.  $2$
8.  $-10$
9.  $-7$

## Subtraction with Positive and Negative Numbers Practice Answers

1. 17
2. −15
3. −150
4. 10
5. −28
6. 55
7. 22
8. −3
9. −14

**To subtract any number from another**, add its opposite.

### Examples

**3.** Subtract.

$4 - (-5)$

**Solution:**

To subtract, add the opposite.    $4 - (-5) = 4 + 5$

Use the guidelines for adding signed numbers.    $= 9$

**4.** Subtract.

$-4 - 6$

**Solution:**

To subtract, add the opposite.    $-4 - 6 = -4 + (-6)$

Use the guidelines for adding signed numbers.    $= -10$

**5.** Subtract.

$(-13) - (-15)$

**Solution:**

To subtract, add the opposite.    $(-13) - (-15) = -13 + 15$

Use the guidelines for adding signed numbers.    $= 2$

*Practice*    **Subtract.**

**1.** $8 - (-9)$        **2.** $-11 - 4$        **3.** $-100 - 50$

**4.** $6 - (-4)$        **5.** $-20 - 8$        **6.** $20 - (-35)$

**7.** $24 - 2$        **8.** $-8 - (-5)$        **9.** $6 - 20$

**To multiply or divide two numbers,** use the following:

- The product or quotient of two positive numbers is positive.
- The product or quotient of two negative numbers is positive.
- The product or quotient of two numbers with different signs is negative.

## Examples

**6.** Multiply.

$-4(-5)$

**Solution:**

Both factors are negative, so the product is positive.
So, $-4(-5) = 20$.

**7.** Divide.

$14 \div (-7)$

**Solution:**

The numbers have different signs, so the quotient is negative.
So, $14 \div (-7) = -2$.

*Practice*  **Multiply or divide.**

**1.** 0(9)　　　　**2.** $-2(3)$　　　　**3.** $4 \div 1$

**4.** $6(-4)$　　　　**5.** $-24 \div 8$　　　　**6.** $5(-2)$

**7.** $18 \div (-9)$　　**8.** $-8(-5)$　　　**9.** $6(2)$

**10.** $-4(-2)$　　　**11.** $-12 \div (-3)$　　**12.** $-40 \div 4$

---

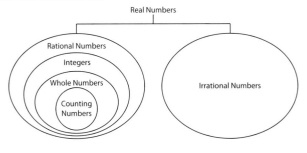

## Multiplication and Division with Positive and Negative Numbers Practice Answers

**1.** 72
**2.** $-6$
**3.** 4
**4.** $-24$
**5.** $-3$
**6.** $-10$
**7.** $-2$
**8.** 40
**9.** 12
**10.** 8
**11.** 4
**12.** $-10$

---

**Appendix J | Properties of Real Numbers**

The **real numbers** fall into two categories, the **rational numbers** and the **irrational numbers.**

- A *rational number* can be expressed as a ratio $\frac{a}{b}$, where $a$ and $b$ are integers and $b$ is not 0. Rational numbers can be written as a decimals that either terminate or repeat. Examples: $-25$, $48$, $\frac{2}{3}$, $0.38$, $0$, and $0.1\overline{6}$
- An *irrational number* cannot be written as a ratio of integers. When an irrational number is written as a decimal, it neither terminates nor repeats. Examples: $0.121121112\ldots$, $\sqrt{7}$, and $\pi$.

## PROPERTIES OF ADDITION AND MULTIPLICATION

The table below summarizes some of the properties of real numbers. Let $a$, $b$, and $c$ be real numbers.

| Property | Addition | Multiplication |
|---|---|---|
| Commutative | $a + b = b + a$ | $a \times b = b \times a$ |
| Associative | $a + (b + c) = (a + b) + c$ | $a \times (b \times c) = (a \times b) \times c$ |
| Identity | $a + 0 = a$ and $0 + a = a$ | $a \cdot 1 = a$ and $1 \cdot a = a$ |
| Inverse | $a + (-a) = 0$ | $a \cdot \frac{1}{a} = 1, a \neq 0$ |
| The **Distributive Property** involves both multiplication and addition. | | |
| | $a(b + c) = ab + ac$ and $a(b - c) = ab - ac$ | |
| Zero Property of Multiplication | $a \cdot 0 = 0$ and $0 \cdot a = 0$ | |

## Properties of Addition and Multiplication Practice Answers

1. Commutative Property of Addition
2. Distributive Property
3. Inverse Property of Multiplication
4. Associative Property of Addition
5. Commutative Property of Multiplication
6. Identity Property of Addition
7. Distributive Property
8. Zero Property of Multiplication
9. Associative Property of Multiplication
10. Identity Property of Multiplication
11. Inverse Property of Addition
12. Commutative Property of Addition

*Practice*    **Identify the property illustrated by the equation.**

1. $3 + 7 = 7 + 3$
2. $4(8 + 6) = 4(8) + 4(6)$
3. $8 \cdot \frac{1}{8} = 1$
4. $1 + (4 + 12) = (1 + 4) + 12$
5. $59 \times 893 = 893 \times 59$
6. $0 + 8 = 8$
7. $5(26 - 17) = (5)(26) - (5)(17)$
8. $10 \cdot 0 = 0$
9. $(35 \cdot 7) \cdot 4 = 35 \cdot (7 \cdot 4)$
10. $24 \cdot 1 = 24$
11. $5 + (-5) = 0$
12. $(4 + 2) + 8 = 8 + (4 + 2)$

A number is written in standard **scientific notation** if it is written in the form $a \times 10^n$, where $1 \le a < 10$ and $n$ is an integer.

| Standard Form | Written as a Product | Scientific Notation |
|---|---|---|
| 42,000,000 | $4.2 \times 10,000,000$ | $4.2 \times 10^7$ |

$\qquad\qquad\qquad\qquad\qquad\qquad\qquad\quad\downarrow\qquad\qquad\downarrow$

$\qquad\qquad\qquad\qquad\qquad$ a number $\ge 1$ and $< 10$ $\quad$ a power of 10

## CHANGING A NUMBER TO SCIENTIFIC NOTATION

**To change a number to scientific notation**, count the number of places the decimal point must be moved to produce a number that is at least 1 and less than 10. This will tell you the power of 10.

### Examples

**1.** Write 6,238.9 in scientific notation.

**Solution:**

Count the number of places the decimal point must be moved. 6238.9
The decimal point must be moved 3 places to the left.
So, 6,238.9 in scientific notation is $6.2389 \times 10^3$.

**2.** Write 100,000,000 in scientific notation.

**Solution:**

Count the number of places the decimal point must be moved.

$\qquad\qquad\qquad$ 100,000,000.

The decimal point must be moved 8 places to the left.
So, 100,000,000 in scientific notation is $1 \times 10^8$.

**To change a number in scientific notation to standard form,** write the number as a product of two factors. Then multiply.

### Example

**3.** Write $5.0391 \times 10^2$ in standard form.

**Solution:**

Write the number as a product. $\qquad\qquad$ $5.0391 \times 100$
Multiply the factors. $\qquad\qquad\qquad\qquad$ 503.91
So, $5.0391 \times 10^2$ in standard form is 503.91.

# Appendix L

## Changing a Number to Scientific Notation and Changing a Number in Scientific Notation to Standard Form Practice Answers

1. $3 \times 10^4$
2. $5.18 \times 10^1$
3. $1.24 \times 10^4$
4. $3.6 \times 10^1$
5. $4.8 \times 10^5$
6. $1.25 \times 10^{11}$
7. 8,700,000
8. 4,000
9. 6,172,900
10. 30,000
11. 520
12. 26,000,000,000

*Practice*  **Write the number in scientific notation.**

**1.** 30,000   **2.** 51.8   **3.** 12,400

**4.** 36   **5.** 480,000   **6.** 125,000,000,000

**Write the number in standard form.**

**7.** $8.7 \times 10^6$   **8.** $4 \times 10^3$   **9.** $6.1729 \times 10^6$

**10.** $3 \times 10^4$   **11.** $5.2 \times 10^2$   **12.** $2.6 \times 10^{10}$

| Appendix L | Solving One- and Two-Step Linear Equations |
|---|---|

A mathematical sentence with an equal sign (=) is called an **equation**. You **solve an equation** when you find a value for a variable that makes an equation true. The value (or values) that makes an equation true is called a **solution** of the equation.

### SOLVING ONE-STEP LINEAR EQUATIONS USING MODELS

Models called *algebra tiles* can be used to solve one-step equations. Note that there are two shapes that you will use, the small square tile, called the 1-tile, and the rectangular-shaped tile, called the *x*-tile.

1-tile    *x*-tile

**To solve a one-step equation using models**, first model the equation with 1-tiles and *x*-tiles. Then, isolate the *x* to find the solution.

### Examples

**1.** Solve for *x*.

$x + 2 = 6$

**Solution:**

**Step 1** To model $x + 2 = 6$, place one *x*-tile and two 1-tiles on one side of an equal sign and six 1-tiles on the other side.

**Step 2** To find the value of $x$, isolate $x$ on one side of the equation by taking away two 1-tiles from each side of the equation.

**Step 3** The model now shows that one $x$-tile is equal to four 1-tiles.

So, the solution to the equation $x + 2 = 6$ is 4.

**2.** Solve for $x$.

$$2x = 6$$

**Solution:**

**Step 1** To model $2x = 6$, place two $x$-tiles on one side of an equal sign and six 1-tiles on the other side.

**Step 2** To find the value of $x$, isolate $x$ on one side of the equation by dividing the two $x$-tiles and six 1-tiles into two equal groups.

# Appendix L

## Solving One-Step Linear Equations Using Models Practice Answers

1. $x = 4$
2. $x = 3$
3. $x = 7$
4. $x = 5$
5. $x = 2$
6. $x = 1$

**Step 3** The model now shows that one $x$-tile is equal to three 1-tiles.

$$\boxed{\phantom{xx}} = \boxed{\phantom{}}\,\boxed{\phantom{}}\,\boxed{\phantom{}}$$

So, the solution to the equation $2x = 6$ is 3.

*Practice*   **Use algebra tiles to model and solve the equation.**

**1.** $x + 1 = 5$    **2.** $x + 4 = 7$    **3.** $9 = x + 2$

**4.** $2x = 10$    **5.** $4x = 8$    **6.** $3 = 3x$

### SOLVING A ONE- OR A TWO-STEP LINEAR EQUATION ALGEBRAICALLY

To solve a one-step or two-step linear equation, isolate the variables by

- adding the same number to each side of the equation,
- subtracting the same number from each side of the equation,
- multiplying each side of the equation by the same nonzero number, and/or
- dividing each side of the equation by the same nonzero number.

### Examples

**3.** Solve for $x$.

$x - 3 = 12$

**Solution:**

| | |
|---|---|
| Write the equation. | $x - 3 = 12$ |
| Add 3 to each side of the equation. | $x - 3 + 3 = 12 + 3$ |
| Simplify. | $x = 15$ |

**4.** Solve for $x$.

$\dfrac{x}{4} = 3$

**Solution:**

| | |
|---|---|
| Write the equation. | $\dfrac{x}{4} = 3$ |
| Multiply each side of the equation by 4. | $4 \cdot \dfrac{x}{4} = 4 \cdot 3$ |
| Simplify. | $x = 12$ |

**5.** Solve for $x$.

$$5x - 11 = -1$$

**Solution:**

| | |
|---|---|
| Write the equation. | $5x - 11 = -1$ |
| Add 11 to each side of the equation. | $5x - 11 + 11 = -1 + 11$ |
| Simplify. | $5x = 10$ |
| Divide each side of the equation by 5. | $\dfrac{5x}{5} = \dfrac{10}{5}$ |
| Simplify. | $x = 2$ |

*Practice*  **Use algebra to solve the equation.**

**1.** $3x + 5 = 11$  **2.** $3x - 4 = -13$  **3.** $8 = 3x - 7$

**4.** $\dfrac{x}{3} - 2 = 1$  **5.** $9x - 20 = 25$  **6.** $\dfrac{x}{4} + 5 = 3$

---

## Appendix M | Simplifying Radicals

### SIMPLEST RADICAL FORM

A radical is in simplest form if

- there are no perfect square factors except 1 in the radicand,
- there are no fractions in the radicand, and
- there are no radicals in the denominator.

### PROPERTIES OF RADICALS

For $a \geq 0$ and $b \geq 0$,

$$\sqrt{ab} = \sqrt{a} \cdot \sqrt{b} \qquad \text{Product Property of Square Roots}$$

For $a \geq 0$ and $b > 0$,

$$\sqrt{\dfrac{a}{b}} = \dfrac{\sqrt{a}}{\sqrt{b}} = \dfrac{\sqrt{ab}}{b} \qquad \text{Quotient Property of Square Roots}$$

## Solving a One- or a Two-Step Linear Equation Algebraically Practice Answers

1. $x = 2$
2. $x = -3$
3. $x = 5$
4. $x = 9$
5. $x = 5$
6. $x = -8$

## Simplifying Radicals Practice Answers

1. $2\sqrt{5}$

2. $\dfrac{1}{5}$

3. $9\sqrt{2}$

4. $\dfrac{\sqrt{6}}{3}$

5. $\dfrac{\sqrt{7}}{6}$

6. $\dfrac{\sqrt{10}}{4}$

7. $6\sqrt{5}$

8. $5\sqrt{3}$

9. $4\sqrt{3}$

10. $\dfrac{2\sqrt{2}}{3}$

11. $3\sqrt{7}$

12. $\dfrac{\sqrt{30}}{6}$

### Examples

**1.** Simplify $\sqrt{44}$.

**Solution:**

| | |
|---|---|
| Product Property of Square Roots | $\sqrt{44} = \sqrt{4} \cdot \sqrt{11}$ |
| Simplify. | $= 2\sqrt{11}$ |

**2.** Simplify $\sqrt{\dfrac{5}{9}}$.

| | |
|---|---|
| Quotient Property of Square Roots | $\sqrt{\dfrac{5}{9}} = \dfrac{\sqrt{5}}{\sqrt{9}}$ |
| Simplify. | $= \dfrac{\sqrt{5}}{3}$ |

**3.** Simplify $\sqrt{\dfrac{2}{7}}$.

| | |
|---|---|
| Quotient Property of Square Roots | $\sqrt{\dfrac{2}{7}} = \dfrac{\sqrt{2}}{\sqrt{7}}$ |
| Multiply numerator and denominator by $\sqrt{7}$. | $= \dfrac{\sqrt{2}}{\sqrt{7}} \cdot \dfrac{\sqrt{7}}{\sqrt{7}}$ |
| Multiply fractions. | $= \dfrac{\sqrt{14}}{\sqrt{49}}$ |
| Simplify. | $= \dfrac{\sqrt{14}}{7}$ |

*Practice*   **Simplify the expression.**

**1.** $\sqrt{20}$    **2.** $\sqrt{\dfrac{1}{25}}$    **3.** $\sqrt{162}$    **4.** $\sqrt{\dfrac{2}{3}}$

**5.** $\sqrt{\dfrac{7}{36}}$    **6.** $\sqrt{\dfrac{5}{8}}$    **7.** $\sqrt{180}$    **8.** $\sqrt{75}$

**9.** $\sqrt{48}$    **10.** $\sqrt{\dfrac{8}{9}}$    **11.** $\sqrt{63}$    **12.** $\sqrt{\dfrac{5}{6}}$

| Appendix N | Mean, Median, Mode, and Range |
|---|---|

There are times when you are given a set of data and you want to find a single number to describe the entire set. Such a number is called a *measure of center*. There are three common measures of center: the *mean*, the *median*, and the *mode*.

## FINDING THE MEAN

The **mean** or **(arithmetic) average** of a data set is the sum of the values divided by the number of values in the set.

### Example

**1.** Find the mean.

24, 35, 45, 22, 13, 27, 44

**Solution:**

Add the data values.        $24 + 35 + 45 + 22 + 13 + 27 + 44 = 210$

Count the number of values in the set.        7

Divide.                $210 \div 7 = 30$

The mean of the data is 30.

*Practice*        **Find the mean of the data set.**

**1.** 4, 4, 7, 1, 8, 2, 3, 4, 4, 3

**2.** 100, 120, 135, 112, 118

**3.** 1,250; 1,245; 1,237

**4.** 5.5, 6.5, 3.4, 1.22, 8.6, 7.45

## FINDING THE MEDIAN

The **median** of a set of data is the middle value of the data set when it is arranged in numerical order. If there is an even number of values in the data set, then the median is the mean of the two middle values.

### Examples

**2.** Find the median.

13, 18, 19, 17, 18, 14, 16

**Solution:**

There is an odd number of values. So there will be only one middle number.

Order the values.            13, 14, 16, 17, 18, 18, 19

Find the value in the middle.        13, 14, 16, ⟨17⟩, 18, 18, 19

The median of the data is 17.

**Finding the Mean Practice Answers**

**1.** 4

**2.** 117

**3.** 1,244

**4.** 5.445

**3.** Find the median.

20, 24, 19, 25, 22, 28, 26, 21, 18, 29

**Solution:**

There is an even number of values. So there is no single middle number.

Order the values.      18, 19, 20, 21, 22, 24, 25, 26, 28, 29

Find the values in the middle.      18, 19, 20, 21, 22, 24, 25, 26, 28, 29

Find the mean of the two middle numbers.      $\frac{22 + 24}{2} = 23$

The median of the data is 23.

*Practice*      **Find the median of the data set.**

**1.** 4, 4, 7, 1, 8, 2, 3, 4, 4, 3      **2.** 100, 120, 135, 112, 118

**3.** 1,250; 1,245; 1,237      **4.** 5.5, 6.5, 3.4, 1.22, 8.6, 7.45

## FINDING THE MODE

The **mode** of a set of data is the value or values of a data set that occur most often. A data set may have *no*, *one*, or *more than one* mode.

### Examples

**4.** Find the mode.

13, 18, 19, 17, 18, 14, 16

**Solution:**

Order the values.      13, 14, 16, 17, 18, 18, 19

Which number occurs most often?      13, 14, 16, 17, 18, 18, 19

The mode of the data is 18.

**5.** Find the mode.

20, 24, 19, 25, 22, 28, 26, 21, 18, 29

**Solution:**

Order the values.      18, 19, 20, 21, 22, 24, 25, 26, 28, 29

Which number occurs most often?      They each appear the same number of times.

There is no mode for this data set.

## Finding the Median Practice Answers

1. 4
2. 118
3. 1,245
4. 6.0

**6.** Find the mode.

30, 34, 30, 35, 30, 34, 28, 28, 34, 29

Solution:

Order the values.                28, 28, 29, 30, 30, 30, 34, 34, 34, 35

Which number occurs most often?   28, 28, 29, <u>30, 30, 30</u>, <u>34, 34, 34</u>, 35

The modes of the data are 30 and 34.

*Practice*   **Find the mode of the data set.**

**1.** 4, 4, 7, 1, 8, 2, 3, 4, 4, 3          **2.** 100, 118, 135, 112, 118

**3.** 1,250; 1,245; 1,237               **4.** 5.5, 6.5, 5.5, 1.22, 6.5, 7.45

## FINDING THE RANGE

The **range** of a set of data is used to describe how spread out the data are. The range is the difference between the greatest value and the least value in the data set.

### Example

**7.** Find the range.

13, 18, 19, 17, 18, 14, 16

Solution:

Order the values.                13, 14, 16, 17, 18, 18, 19

Find the greatest and the least values.   13, 14, 16, 17, 18, 18, 19

Subtract.                        $19 - 13 = 6$

The range of the data is 6.

*Practice*   **Find the range of the data set.**

**1.** 4, 4, 7, 1, 8, 2, 3, 4, 4, 3          **2.** 100, 120, 135, 112, 118

**3.** 12, 50, 32, 45, 85, 37             **4.** 5.5, 6.5, 3.4, 1.22, 8.6, 7.45

## Finding the Mode Practice Answers

1. 4
2. 118
3. no mode
4. 5.5 and 6.5

## Finding the Range Practice Answers

1. 7
2. 35
3. 73
4. 7.38

A **coordinate plane** provides a way to locate points in a plane. It consists of two number lines or axes. The horizontal number line, generally called the *x*-**axis**, and the vertical number line, called the *y*-**axis**, intersect at a point called the **origin**. Notice that the axes divide the plane into four **quadrants**.

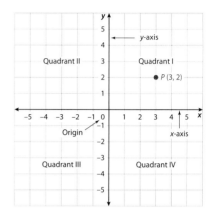

### NAMING THE COORDINATES OF POINTS

You can represent any point on the plane with an **ordered pair**, $(x, y)$.

The first number in the ordered pair is called the *x*-**coordinate**.

The second number is called the *y*-**coordinate**.

The ordered pair (3, 2) describes the location of the point $P$ on the coordinate plane shown above. The *x*-coordinate of the point, 3, indicates the horizontal distance from the *y*-axis (the distance left or right). The *y*-coordinate, 2, indicates the vertical distance from the *x*-axis (the distance up or down). Point $P$ lies in Quadrant I.

## Examples

Use the coordinate plane below to answer each of the following.

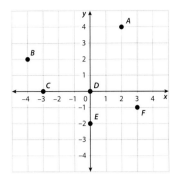

**1.** Name the coordinates of point *A*.

**Solution:**

To locate point *A*, move 2 units to the right of the origin. And then move up 4 units.

So, the coordinates of *A* are (2, 4).

**2.** Name the coordinates of point *C*.

**Solution:**

To locate point *C*, move 3 units to the left of the origin. There is no movement up or down.

So, the coordinates of *C* are (−3, 0).

**3.** In which quadrant does point *B* lie?

**Solution:**

Point *B* lies in Quadrant II.

**4.** In which quadrant does point *E* lie?

**Solution:**

Point *E* lies on the *y*-axis. A point that is on an axis is not considered to be in any quadrant.

# Appendix O

## Naming the Coordinates of Points Practice Answers

1. $(3, -1)$
2. $E$
3. $D$

*Practice*    **Use the coordinate plane above to answer the question.**

1. What are the coordinates of point $F$?

2. Which point has the coordinates $(0, -2)$?

3. Which point is located at the origin?

## GRAPHING POINTS ON THE COORDINATE PLANE

**To graph (or plot) a point on the coordinate plane**, begin at the origin. The $x$-coordinate indicates the distance from the $y$-axis (number of units to count left or right). The $y$-coordinate indicates the distance from the $x$-axis (number of units to count up or down).

### Examples

**5.** Graph $M(-4, -2)$.

**Solution:**

Start at the origin. Move 4 units to the left. Then move down 2 units. Label $M$ on the graph.

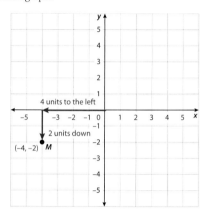

**6.** Graph $N(0, 3)$.

**Solution:**

Start at the origin. Make no movement to the right or left. Move up 3 units. Label $N$ on the graph.

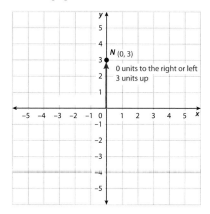

N (0, 3)
0 units to the right or left
3 units up

*Practice*   **Draw a coordinate plane and graph the point.**

**1.** $(1, 4)$   **2.** $(-2, 3)$   **3.** $(4, 0)$   **4.** $(-4, -4)$

**5.** $(-1, 3)$   **6.** $(2, 5)$   **7.** $(-1, -1)$   **8.** $(0, -1)$

---

## Appendix P

## Graphing Points on the Coordinate Plane Practice Answers

1.–8.

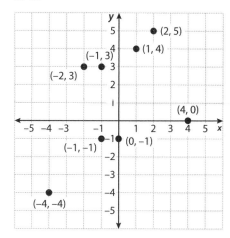

---

| Appendix P | Square Roots |
| --- | --- |

### SQUARE ROOTS

The **square** of a number $n$ is $n^2$. The inverse operation of squaring a number is finding the **square root** of the number. The square root of a given number $n$ is a number that, when multiplied by itself, results in the number $n$.

Since $5^2 = 25$ and $(-5)^2 = 25$, the square roots of 25 are 5 and –5. The symbol for square root, $\sqrt{\phantom{x}}$, is called the *radical sign*. It indicates the nonnegative square root. So, $\sqrt{25} = 5$. To indicate the negative square root, use $-\sqrt{\phantom{x}}$. So, $-\sqrt{25} = -5$.

# Appendix P

## Square Roots Practice Answers

1. 7
2. −10
3. 9
4. 0
5. 1
6. 20

## Approximating Square Roots Practice Answers

1. 5 and 6
2. 9 and 10
3. 9 and 10
4. 3 and 4
5. 1 and 2
6. 8 and 9

### Example

**1.** Find each square root.

    **a.** $\sqrt{144}$      **b.** $-\sqrt{16}$

**Solution:**

    **a.** $\sqrt{144} = 12$      **b.** $-\sqrt{16} = -4$

*Practice*      **Find the square root.**

**1.** $\sqrt{49}$    **2.** $-\sqrt{100}$    **3.** $\sqrt{81}$    **4.** $\sqrt{0}$    **5.** $\sqrt{1}$    **6.** $\sqrt{400}$

Any number that has a whole number as its square root is a **perfect square**.

Some perfect squares are shown in the table below.

| Perfect Square | 0 | 1 | 4 | 9 | 16 | 25 | 36 | 49 | 64 | 81 | 100 | 121 | 144 |
|---|---|---|---|---|---|---|---|---|---|---|---|---|---|
| Square Root | 0 | 1 | 2 | 3 | 4 | 5 | 6 | 7 | 8 | 9 | 10 | 11 | 12 |

You can use the square roots of perfect squares to help you **approximate the square roots** of numbers that are not perfect squares.

### Example

**2.** Tell which two consecutive whole numbers $\sqrt{15}$ is between.

**Solution:**

Find the two perfect squares that 15 is between.     $9 < 15 < 16$

Write the square roots.     $\sqrt{9} < \sqrt{15} < \sqrt{16}$

Simplify.     $3 < \sqrt{15} < 4$

So, $\sqrt{15}$ is between 3 and 4.

*Practice*      **Tell which two consecutive integers the square root is between.**

**1.** $\sqrt{29}$        **2.** $\sqrt{99}$        **3.** $\sqrt{83}$

**4.** $\sqrt{12}$        **5.** $\sqrt{2}$        **6.** $\sqrt{65}$

# Photo Credits

## Chapter 1

Getty Images/Vetta
corepics/Shutterstock
Getty Images/Vetta
© Tetra Images/SuperStock
Rob Cousins/Alamy
Steve Nudson/Alamy
John Foxx/Thinkstock
Z.H. Chen/Shutterstock

## Chapter 2

© Look Photography/Beateworks/Corbis
© SuperStock/Alamy
Pakhnyushcha/Shutterstock
Steve Nudson/Alamy
© Nikada/istockphoto
Gary Simundza
© Image Source/Corbis
© Feng Yu/Alamy
Stuart McClymont/Stone/Getty Images

## Chapter 3

© Markus Botzek/Corbis
Christopher Meder/Shutterstock
Andrey Shchekalev/Shutterstock
© Momatiuk-Eastcott/Corbis
© Markus Botzek/Corbis
© Jupiter Images/Thinkstock/Getty Images
© Todd Gipstein/CORBIS
Yellow Dog Productions/Lifesize/Getty
    Images
Wikipedia Commons
© ParkerDeen/istock
© Alexey Stiop/Alamy

## Chapter 4

Mashe/Shutterstock
© Aardvark/Alamy
© Jill Fromer/istockphoto
Fermilab/U.S. Department of Energy
Inti St Clair/Getty Images
Hemera/Thinkstock
corepics/Shutterstock
© Michael Dwyer/Alamy
Caitlin Mirra/Shutterstock
Picsfive/Shutterstock
Hemera/Thinkstock
© Manor Photography/Alamy

## Chapter 5

© Ocean/Corbis
Deborah Anderson

© Floortje/istockphoto
istockphoto/Thinkstock
AbleStock.com/Thinkstock
Crok Photography/Shutterstock
istockphoto/Thinkstock
© Lee Foster/Alamy
© Richard Lord/PhotoEdit
istockphoto/Thinkstock

## Chapter 6

S. Meltzer/PhotoLink/Getty Images
Carolyn Kaster/AP Images
© Gong Zhihong/Xinhua Press/Corbis
© Dana Fry/istockphoto
Dennie Cody/Workbook Stock/Getty
    Images
© JLP/Jose L. Pelaez/Corbis
U.S. Census Bureau, Public Information
    Office
© Enigma/Alamy
Steve Estvanik/Shutterstock

## Chapter 7

AFP/Getty Images
Hulton Archives/Getty Images
© Marilyn Angel Wynn/Nativestock.com
© Arco Images GmbH/Alamy
iStockphoto/Thinkstock
© Bill Gozansky/Alamy
© FRONTIER Henri/istockphoto
© Mark Evans/istockphoto
SSPL via Getty Images

## Chapter 8

© Jen Grantham/istockphoto
Andrey Shadrin/Shutterstock
© Roger Bamber/Alamy
iStockphoto/Thinkstock
© Andre Jenny/Alamy
Alistair Berg/Digital Vision/Getty Images
iStockphoto/Thinkstock
Courtesy of Jerry Cunningham, Woodland
    Mills, Glenville, PA
Shawn Gearhart/istockphoto
© Radius/SuperStock
Schalke fotografie/Melissa Schalke/
    Shutterstock
U.S. Air force photo by Senior Airman
    Jenifer Calhoun
Zave Smith/Getty Images
© imagebroker/Alamy
iStockphoto/Thinkstock
Rich Pilling/MLB Photos via Getty
    Images

## Chapter 9

Martin Bureau/AFP/Getty Images
Stones and Bones
National Park Service
Brand X Pictures/Thinkstock
©YURIKO NAKAO/Reuters/Corbis
Rubberball/istockphoto

## Chapter 10

Kateryna Larina/Shutterstock
Chepko Danil/istockphoto
Lori Labrecque/Shutterstock
NASA/JPL/USGS
Hemera/Thinkstock
iStockphoto/Thinkstock
Gene Anderson
Ron Paik, Hawaii IGERT
Kevin Horan/Getty Images
© Jan Tadeusz/Alamy
© Joseph Sibilsky/Alamy
Kateryna Larina/Shutterstock
Will van Overbeek

## Chapter 11

© Robert Glusic/Corbis
Arto/Fotolia
chantal de bruijne/Shutterstock
Marty Ellis/Shutterstock
Photodisc/Getty Images
© Greg Vaughn/Alamy
Paul Brennan/istockphoto
Wikipedia Commons
jcpjr/Shutterstock
© John Elk III/Alamy
Peter Chigmaroff/Flickr/Getty Images
© Robert Glusic/Corbis
Richard Cummins/agefotostock
© Robert Glusic/Corbis

## Chapter 12

onfilm/istockphoto
duckycards/istockphoto
Adrin Shamsudin/Shutterstock
Chase Jarvis/Corbis
David Madison/Getty Images
fotek/istockphoto
HuHu/Shutterstock
onfilm/istockphoto
© Peter Titmuss/Alamy
© Joshua Roper/Alamy
shutswis/Shutterstock
waterboyVT/istockphoto
iStockphoto/Thinkstock
Christina Richards/Shutterstock

# Index

## Lesson 5.2 Activity Answers (page 144)

1. Independent variable: the number of objects in the container; dependent variable: weight; Since the total weight depends on the number of objects in the container, weight is the dependent variable.

**2a, 2b, & 2c.** Sample table

| Number of Objects | 0 | 1 | 2 | 3 | 4 | 5 | 6 |
|---|---|---|---|---|---|---|---|
| Weight (oz) | 6.3 | 6.5 | 6.7 | 6.9 | 7.1 | 7.3 | 7.5 |

| Number of Objects | 7 | 8 | 9 | 10 |
|---|---|---|---|---|
| Weight (oz) | 7.7 | 7.9 | 8.1 | 8.3 |

3.

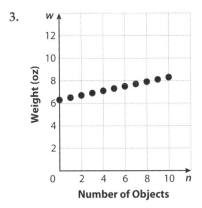

4. Yes; the points in the scatter plot appear to lie along a straight line.

5. Sample answer: Domain: whole numbers 0 to 10 (the number of objects placed in the container and weighed); range: real numbers 6.3 oz, 6.5 oz, 6.7 oz, 6.9 oz, 7.1 oz, 7.3 oz, 7.5 oz, 7.7 oz, 7.9 oz, 8.1 oz, and 8.3 oz, where 6.3 oz is the weight of the container with 0 objects in it and 8.3 oz is the weight of the container with 10 objects in it

6. Sample answer: This is not a proportional relationship, even though it is a linear relationship, since the ratio of weight to the number of objects is not constant. Also, the graph does not pass through the origin (0, 0).

7. Yes, for each input value, there is exactly one output value

## Lesson 7.2 Investigation Answers (page 225)

1. Sample answers: No, the ratios of height to forearm length are not constant. They are generally less for points toward the right than for points toward the left. A line drawn through the origin would not fit the scatter plot well.

2. Answers will vary.

3. It is possible to find a line with *any* slope that will satisfy the rule.

4. Sample answer: Draw a line through the center of the scatter plot. Adjust its slope so that the points near the right end are split evenly by the line, and the points near the left end are also split evenly by the line.

5. Sample answer:

6. Sample answer: Using (25.0, 165) and (31.0, 185), the slope is $\frac{185 - 165}{31.0 - 25.0} = \frac{20}{6} = \frac{10}{3}$.

7. Small errors in measurement of the coordinates will have less of an effect on the value of the slope.

8. Sample answer: From $h = \frac{10}{3} f + b$, use the point (25.0, 165) to get $b = 81\frac{2}{3} \approx 81.7$. The equation is $h = \frac{10}{3} f + 81\frac{2}{3}$, or $h = 3.33 f + 81.7$.

9. Sample answer: $h = 3.33(22.5) + 81.7 \approx 156.6$, or about 157 cm

10. Sample answer: A student whose forearm is 1 centimeter longer than another student's forearm will be about 3.3 centimeters taller.

11. A student with a forearm length of 0 centimeters will be 81.7 centimeters tall. This does not make sense.

12. all real numbers

13. Sample answer: $f > 0$; Students may suggest a more restricted problem domain based on what they think are reasonable for the shortest and longest forearms for any person.

## Practice for Lesson 7.2 Answers (page 228)

**12c.** Sample window:

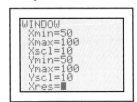

# EXTRA ANSWERS

**12d.** Sample plot:

[50, 100] × [50, 100]

**12e.** Sample graph:

[50, 100] × [50, 100]

**12f.** Sample answer: Using (57, 56) and (100, 89) gives
$y = 0.767x + 12$.

## Lesson 7.3 Investigation Answers (page 229)

2. Sample answer: The residuals for (24.0, 164) and
   (24.5, 166) are positive and those for (24.0, 157) and
   (27.0, 164) are negative. If a data point is above the line,
   the residual is positive, and if a point is below the line,
   the residual is negative.

3. Sample answer: Using $h = 3.33f + 81.7$, a person with
   a forearm length of 27.0 cm should have a height of
   $3.33(27.0) + 81.7 \approx 171.6$ cm.

4. $164 - 171.6 = -7.6$ cm

## Practice for Lesson 7.7 Answers (page 249)

**10.** $t = -0.327n + 46.0$

[0, 15] × [−15, 15]

The model is much better for the reduced data set, with
small and random residuals.

**11.** $-0.327(15) + 46.0 \approx 41.1$ seconds

**12.** Times decrease by 0.327 seconds per race. The pattern
cannot continue indefinitely because eventually the time
would be 0, which is impossible.

## Practice for Lesson 8.1 Answers (page 265)

9. Sample answer: The slope of each line is $\frac{3}{2}$. The lines are
   parallel, so they have no points in common.

[−5, 5] × [−5, 5]

10. Sample answer: The graphs are the same line, so the
    equations are equivalent. Every solution of one equation
    is a solution of the other.

[−5, 5] × [−5, 5]

## Practice for Lesson 8.5 Answers (page 286)

**6a.**

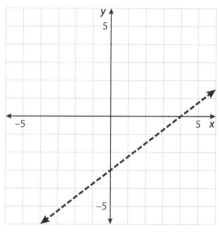

**6b.** The points (0, −5) and (5, 0) satisfy the inequality.
The others do not.

**7a.**

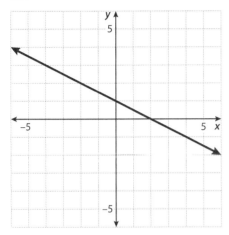

**7b.** The points (0, 5) and (5, 0) satisfy the inequality. The others do not.

**7c.**

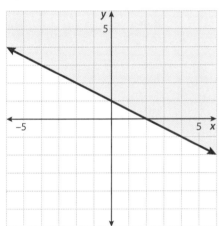

## Lesson 11.6 Investigation Answers (page 399)

**16.** $y = 0.4(x + 4)(x - 2)$; Students will either use trial and error by adjusting the value for $a$ to match the vertex point coordinates, or they will substitute $-1$ for $x$ and $-3.6$ for $y$ in the equation $y = a(x + 4)(x - 2)$ and solve for $a$.

**17.** $y = 0.4x^2 + 0.8x - 3.2$; Only one graph appears which means that the two functions are equivalent.

## Lesson 13.2 Activity Answers (page 475)

**4a.** Sample answer: The first minimum occurs at 0.0004 second, and the fifth at 0.0184 second. So, the period is $\frac{0.0184 - 0.0004}{4} = 0.0045$ second.

**4b.** Sample answer: The frequency is $\frac{1}{period} = \frac{1}{0.0045} \approx 222$ cycles per second or Hz. This means that the pressure oscillates up and down about 222 times a second.

**5.** Sample answer: $5\frac{1}{2}$ inches

**6.** Sample answer: A musical tone with a higher pitch than before is heard.

**7.** Sample answer:

[−0.002, 0.022] × [−0.1595, 0.2199]

**8.** Sample answer: The first maximum occurs at 0.0018 second, and the fifth at 0.0127 second. The period is $\frac{0.0127 - 0.0018}{4} = 0.002725$ second. So, the frequency is $\frac{1}{0.002725} \approx 367$ Hz.

**9.** Sample answer: Greater frequencies result in higher-pitched sounds. Lesser frequencies result in lower-pitched sounds.

## Lesson 13.3 Investigation Answers (page 479)

**1.** See the completed table in the answer for Question 2.

**2.** Sample answers: Measurements are based on an $8\frac{3}{4}$-inch bottle.

| Water Height (inches) | Frequency (Hz) | Length of Air Column (in.) | Period (s) |
|---|---|---|---|
| $\frac{5}{8}$ | 200 | $8\frac{1}{8}$ | 0.0050 |
| $1\frac{3}{8}$ | 222 | $7\frac{3}{8}$ | 0.0045 |
| 2 | 244 | $6\frac{3}{4}$ | 0.0041 |
| $2\frac{3}{4}$ | 263 | 6 | 0.0038 |
| $3\frac{1}{2}$ | 303 | $5\frac{1}{4}$ | 0.0033 |
| $4\frac{1}{4}$ | 370 | $4\frac{1}{2}$ | 0.0027 |

**3a.** Sample graph:

[0, 9] × [0, 800]

**3b.** Sample graph:

[0, 9] × [0, 0.0060]

# EXTRA ANSWERS

**3c.** Sample graph:

[0, 9] × [0, 800]

**3d.** Sample graph:

[0, 9] × [0, 0.0060]

## Lesson 15.1 Investigation Answers (page 529)

**5.** Sample answer:

| Number of Months | Total Rent Paid |
|---|---|
| 0 | $0 |
| 1 | $350 |
| 2 | $700 |
| 3 | $1,050 |
| 4 | $1,400 |
| 5 | $1,750 |
| 6 | $2,100 |
| 7 | $2,450 |
| 8 | $2,800 |
| 9 | $3,150 |
| 10 | $3,500 |
| 11 | $3,850 |
| 12 | $4,200 |

**6.** direct variation function; $R = 350n$

**7.** Entries showing the formula and the result of the formula evaluation are shown in the spreadsheets below.

|  | A | B | C |
|---|---|---|---|
| 1 | **Fixed Expenses** | | **Yearly Expenses** |
| 2 | Rent | $350 | =12*B2 |
| 3 | Tuition | $1,400 | |
| 4 | Subtotal | $1,750 | |
| 5 | | | |
| 6 | **Variable Expenses** | | |
| 7 | Food | $280 | |
| 8 | Utilities | $150 | |
| 9 | Books | $165 | |
| 10 | Credit Card | $100 | |
| 11 | Clothing | $50 | |
| 12 | Personal Items | $30 | |
| 13 | Entertainment | $50 | |
| 14 | Pocket Money | $50 | |
| 15 | Subtotal | $875 | |
| 16 | | | |
| 17 | **Total Expenses** | $2,625 | |

|  | A | B | C |
|---|---|---|---|
| 1 | **Fixed Expenses** | | **Yearly Expenses** |
| 2 | Rent | $350 | $4,200 |
| 3 | Tuition | $1,400 | |
| 4 | Subtotal | $1,750 | |
| 5 | | | |
| 6 | **Variable Expenses** | | |
| 7 | Food | $280 | |
| 8 | Utilities | $150 | |
| 9 | Books | $165 | |
| 10 | Credit Card | $100 | |
| 11 | Clothing | $50 | |
| 12 | Personal Items | $30 | |
| 13 | Entertainment | $50 | |
| 14 | Pocket Money | $50 | |
| 15 | Subtotal | $875 | |
| 16 | | | |
| 17 | **Total Expenses** | $2,625 | |

**8.** Sample answer: Each of the monthly expenses is multiplied by 12. The product for each is given in column C.

|  | A | B | C |
|---|---|---|---|
| 1 | **Fixed Expenses** | | **Yearly Expenses** |
| 2 | Rent | $350 | $4,200 |
| 3 | Tuition | $1,400 | $16,800 |
| 4 | Subtotal | $1,750 | $21,000 |
| 5 | | | $0 |
| 6 | **Variable Expenses** | | $0 |
| 7 | Food | $280 | $3,360 |
| 8 | Utilities | $150 | $1,800 |
| 9 | Books | $165 | $1,980 |
| 10 | Credit Card | $100 | $1,200 |
| 11 | Clothing | $50 | $600 |
| 12 | Personal Items | $30 | $360 |
| 13 | Entertainment | $50 | $600 |
| 14 | Pocket Money | $50 | $600 |
| 15 | Subtotal | $875 | $10,500 |
| 16 | | | $0 |
| 17 | **Total Expenses** | $2,625 | $31,500 |

## Practice for Lesson 15.1 Answers (page 531)

**4.**

| | A | B | C | D | E | F | G |
|---|---|---|---|---|---|---|---|
| 1 | Fixed Expenses | | Yearly Expenses | Year 2 | Year 3 | Year 4 | Year 5 |
| 2 | Savings | $690 | $8,280 | $8,280.00 | $8,280.00 | $8,280.00 | $8,280.00 |
| 3 | Mortgage | $1,460 | $17,520 | $17,520.00 | $17,520.00 | $17,520.00 | $17,520.00 |
| 4 | Student Loans | $345 | $4,140 | $4,140.00 | $4,140.00 | $4,140.00 | $4,140.00 |
| 5 | Auto Loan | $313 | $3,756 | $3,756.00 | $3,756.00 | $3,756.00 | $3,756.00 |
| 6 | Taxes | $815 | $9,780 | $9,780.00 | $9,780.00 | $9,780.00 | $9,780.00 |
| 7 | Property Taxes | $168 | $2,016 | $2,016.00 | $2,016.00 | $2,016.00 | $2,016.00 |
| 8 | Health Insurance | $348 | $4,176 | $4,176.00 | $4,176.00 | $4,176.00 | $4,176.00 |
| 9 | Homeowner's Insurance | $147 | $1,764 | $1,764.00 | $1,764.00 | $1,764.00 | $1,764.00 |
| 10 | Auto Insurance | $86 | $1,032 | $1,032.00 | $1,032.00 | $1,032.00 | $1,032.00 |
| 11 | Subtotal | $4,372 | $52,464 | $52,464.00 | $52,464.00 | $52,464.00 | $52,464.00 |
| 12 | | | $0 | | | | |
| 13 | Variable Expenses | | $0 | | | | |
| 14 | Food | $480 | $5,760 | $5,932.80 | $6,110.78 | $6,294.11 | $6,482.93 |
| 15 | Utilities | $435 | $5,220 | $6,376.60 | $6,697.30 | $5,704.05 | $5,875.16 |
| 16 | Home Repair | $80 | $960 | $988.80 | $1,018.46 | $1,049.02 | $1,080.49 |
| 17 | Gas/Oil/Car Repairs | $215 | $2,580 | $2,657.40 | $2,737.12 | $2,819.24 | $2,903.81 |
| 18 | Credit Cards | $275 | $3,300 | $3,399.00 | $3,500.97 | $3,606.00 | $3,714.18 |
| 19 | Personal Items | $60 | $720 | $741.60 | $763.85 | $786.76 | $810.37 |
| 20 | New Clothing | $125 | $1,500 | $1,545.00 | $1,591.35 | $1,639.09 | $1,688.26 |
| 21 | Gifts | $50 | $600 | $618.00 | $636.54 | $655.64 | $675.31 |
| 22 | Vacation Savings | $100 | $1,200 | $1,236.00 | $1,273.08 | $1,311.27 | $1,350.61 |
| 23 | Emergency Savings | $325 | $3,900 | $4,017.00 | $4,137.51 | $4,261.64 | $4,389.48 |
| 24 | Entertainment | $380 | $4,560 | $4,696.80 | $4,837.70 | $4,982.84 | $5,132.32 |
| 25 | Pocket Money | $350 | $4,200 | $4,326.00 | $4,455.78 | $4,589.45 | $4,727.14 |
| 26 | Subtotal | $2,875 | $34,500 | $35,535.00 | $36,601.05 | $37,699.08 | $38,830.05 |
| 27 | | | $0 | | | | |
| 28 | Total Expenses | $7,247 | $86,964 | $87,999.00 | $89,065.05 | $90,163.08 | $91,294.05 |

## Lesson 15.3 Investigation Answers (page 539)

1. See the answer to Question 2.

2. Sample entries showing formulas and results of formula evaluations are shown in the two spreadsheets on the left and right below, for 2011 withholding tables.

| | A | B | C | D | E |
|---|---|---|---|---|---|
| 1 | Fixed Expenses | | | Income | |
| 2 | Rent | $350 | | Salary | $960 |
| 3 | Tuition | $1,400 | | Withholding | $47.67 |
| 4 | Subtotal | $1,750 | | Social Security | =0.042*E2 |
| 5 | | | | Medicare | =0.0145*E2 |
| 6 | Variable Expenses | | | | |
| 7 | Food | $280 | | | |
| 8 | Utilities | $150 | | | |
| 9 | Books | $165 | | | |
| 10 | Credit Card | $100 | | | |
| 11 | Clothing | $50 | | | |
| 12 | Personal Items | $30 | | | |
| 13 | Entertainment | $50 | | | |
| 14 | Pocket Money | $50 | | | |
| 15 | Subtotal | $875 | | | |
| 16 | | | | | |
| 17 | Total Expenses | $2,625 | | | |

| | A | B | C | D | E |
|---|---|---|---|---|---|
| 1 | Fixed Expenses | | | Income | |
| 2 | Rent | $350 | | Salary | $960 |
| 3 | Tuition | $1,400 | | Withholding | $47.67 |
| 4 | Subtotal | $1,750 | | Social Security | $40.32 |
| 5 | | | | Medicare | $13.92 |
| 6 | Variable Expenses | | | | |
| 7 | Food | $280 | | | |
| 8 | Utilities | $150 | | | |
| 9 | Books | $165 | | | |
| 10 | Credit Card | $100 | | | |
| 11 | Clothing | $50 | | | |
| 12 | Personal Items | $30 | | | |
| 13 | Entertainment | $50 | | | |
| 14 | Pocket Money | $50 | | | |
| 15 | Subtotal | $875 | | | |
| 16 | | | | | |
| 17 | Total Expenses | $2,625 | | | |

3. Sample entries showing the formula and the result of formula evaluation are shown in the two spreadsheets below, for 2011 withholding tables.

| | A | B | C | D | E |
|---|---|---|---|---|---|
| 1 | **Fixed Expenses** | | | Income | |
| 2 | Rent | $350 | | Salary | $960 |
| 3 | Tuition | $1,400 | | Withholding | $47.67 |
| 4 | Subtotal | $1,750 | | Social Security | $40.32 |
| 5 | | | | Medicare | $13.92 |
| 6 | **Variable Expenses** | | | Salary after Deductions | =E2-(E3+E4+E5) |
| 7 | Food | $280 | | | |
| 8 | Utilities | $150 | | | |
| 9 | Books | $165 | | | |
| 10 | Credit Card | $100 | | | |
| 11 | Clothing | $50 | | | |
| 12 | Personal Items | $30 | | | |
| 13 | Entertainment | $50 | | | |
| 14 | Pocket Money | $50 | | | |
| 15 | Subtotal | $875 | | | |
| 16 | | | | | |
| 17 | **Total Expenses** | $2,625 | | | |

| | A | B | C | D | E |
|---|---|---|---|---|---|
| 1 | **Fixed Expenses** | | | Income | |
| 2 | Rent | $350 | | Salary | $960 |
| 3 | Tuition | $1,400 | | Withholding | $47.67 |
| 4 | Subtotal | $1,750 | | Social Security | $40.32 |
| 5 | | | | Medicare | $13.92 |
| 6 | **Variable Expenses** | | | Salary after Deductions | $858.09 |
| 7 | Food | $280 | | | |
| 8 | Utilities | $150 | | | |
| 9 | Books | $165 | | | |
| 10 | Credit Card | $100 | | | |
| 11 | Clothing | $50 | | | |
| 12 | Personal Items | $30 | | | |
| 13 | Entertainment | $50 | | | |
| 14 | Pocket Money | $50 | | | |
| 15 | Subtotal | $875 | | | |
| 16 | | | | | |
| 17 | **Total Expenses** | $2,625 | | | |

4. See the answer to Question 5 for 2011 withholding tables.

5. Sample entries showing the formula and the result of formula evaluation are shown in the next two spreadsheets (the one below and the one at the top of the column at the right), for 2011 withholding tables.

| | A | B | C | D | E |
|---|---|---|---|---|---|
| 1 | **Fixed Expenses** | | | Income | |
| 2 | Rent | $350 | | Salary | $960 |
| 3 | Tuition | $1,400 | | Withholding | $47.67 |
| 4 | Subtotal | $1,750 | | Social Security | $40.32 |
| 5 | | | | Medicare | $13.92 |
| 6 | **Variable Expenses** | | | Salary after Deductions | $858.09 |
| 7 | Food | $280 | | | |
| 8 | Utilities | $150 | | Scholarship | $617 |
| 9 | Books | $165 | | Student Loans | $650 |
| 10 | Credit Card | $100 | | Gifts | $500 |
| 11 | Clothing | $50 | | | |
| 12 | Personal Items | $30 | | Total Net Income | =E6+E8+E9+E10 |
| 13 | Entertainment | $50 | | | |
| 14 | Pocket Money | $50 | | | |
| 15 | Subtotal | $875 | | | |
| 16 | | | | | |
| 17 | **Total Expenses** | $2,625 | | | |

| | A | B | C | D | E |
|---|---|---|---|---|---|
| 1 | **Fixed Expenses** | | | Income | |
| 2 | Rent | $350 | | Salary | $960 |
| 3 | Tuition | $1,400 | | Withholding | $47.67 |
| 4 | Subtotal | $1,750 | | Social Security | $40.32 |
| 5 | | | | Medicare | $13.92 |
| 6 | **Variable Expenses** | | | Salary after Deductions | $858.09 |
| 7 | Food | $280 | | | |
| 8 | Utilities | $150 | | Scholarship | $617 |
| 9 | Books | $165 | | Student Loans | $650 |
| 10 | Credit Card | $100 | | Gifts | $500 |
| 11 | Clothing | $50 | | | |
| 12 | Personal Items | $30 | | Total Net Income | $2,625.09 |
| 13 | Entertainment | $50 | | | |
| 14 | Pocket Money | $50 | | | |
| 15 | Subtotal | $875 | | | |
| 16 | | | | | |
| 17 | **Total Expenses** | $2,625 | | | |

## Practice for Lesson 15.3 Answers (page 542)

7. Sample answer:

| | A | B | C | D | E | F |
|---|---|---|---|---|---|---|
| 1 | **Fixed Expenses** | | | Income | | |
| 2 | Savings | $690 | | Net Salaries | | $6,850 |
| 3 | Mortgage | $1,460 | | Interest and Dividends | | $47 |
| 4 | Student Loans | $345 | | Misc. Income | | $100 |
| 5 | Auto Loan | $313 | | | | |
| 6 | Taxes | $815 | | Total Income | | $6,997 |
| 7 | Property Taxes | $168 | | | | |
| 8 | Health Insurance | $348 | | | | |
| 9 | Homeowner's Insurance | $147 | | | | |
| 10 | Auto Insurance | $86 | | Difference (I - E) | | -$250 |
| 11 | Subtotal | $4,372 | | | | |
| 12 | | | | | | |
| 13 | **Variable Expenses** | | | | | |
| 14 | Food | $480 | | | | |
| 15 | Utilities | $435 | | | | |
| 16 | Home Repair | $80 | | | | |
| 17 | Gas/Oil/Car Repairs | $215 | | | | |
| 18 | Credit Cards | $275 | | | | |
| 19 | Personal Items | $60 | | | | |
| 20 | New Clothing | $125 | | | | |
| 21 | Gifts | $50 | | | | |
| 22 | Vacation Savings | $100 | | | | |
| 23 | Emergency Savings | $325 | | | | |
| 24 | Entertainment | $380 | | | | |
| 25 | Pocket Money | $350 | | | | |
| 26 | Subtotal | $2,875 | | | | |
| 27 | | | | | | |
| 28 | **Total Expenses** | $7,247 | | | | |

## Lesson 15.6 Investigation Answers (page 553)

**8.** Sample answer:

| | A | B | C | D | E |
|---|---|---|---|---|---|
| 1 | Payment Number | Payment | Interest | Principal Paid | Remaining Principal |
| 2 | 0 | | | | $15,000 |
| 3 | 1 | $200 | $75.00 | $125.00 | $14,875.00 |
| 4 | 2 | $200 | $74.38 | $125.63 | $14,749.38 |
| 5 | 3 | $200 | $73.75 | $126.25 | $14,623.12 |
| 6 | 4 | $200 | $73.12 | $126.88 | $14,496.24 |
| 7 | 5 | $200 | $72.48 | $127.52 | $14,368.72 |
| 8 | 6 | $200 | $71.84 | $128.16 | $14,240.56 |
| 9 | 7 | $200 | $71.20 | $128.80 | $14,111.77 |
| 10 | 8 | $200 | $70.56 | $129.44 | $13,982.32 |
| 11 | 9 | $200 | $69.91 | $130.09 | $13,852.24 |
| 12 | 10 | $200 | $69.26 | $130.74 | $13,721.50 |
| 13 | 11 | $200 | $68.61 | $131.39 | $13,590.10 |
| 14 | 12 | $200 | $67.95 | $132.05 | $13,458.05 |
| 15 | 13 | $200 | $67.29 | $132.71 | $13,325.34 |
| 16 | 14 | $200 | $66.63 | $133.37 | $13,191.97 |
| 17 | 15 | $200 | $65.96 | $134.04 | $13,057.93 |
| 18 | 16 | $200 | $65.29 | $134.71 | $12,923.22 |
| 19 | 17 | $200 | $64.62 | $135.38 | $12,787.84 |
| 20 | 18 | $200 | $63.94 | $136.06 | $12,651.78 |
| 21 | 19 | $200 | $63.26 | $136.74 | $12,515.04 |
| 22 | 20 | $200 | $62.58 | $137.42 | $12,377.61 |
| 23 | 21 | $200 | $61.89 | $138.11 | $12,239.50 |
| 24 | 22 | $200 | $61.20 | $138.80 | $12,100.70 |
| 25 | 23 | $200 | $60.50 | $139.50 | $11,961.20 |
| 26 | 24 | $200 | $59.81 | $140.19 | $11,821.01 |

## Practice Lesson 15.6 Answers (page 558)

**2.** Sample answer:

| | A | B | C | D | E |
|---|---|---|---|---|---|
| 1 | Payment Number | Payment | Interest | Principal Paid | Remaining Principal |
| 2 | 0 | | | | $1,850 |
| 3 | 1 | $474.12 | $18.50 | $455.62 | $1,394.38 |
| 4 | 2 | $474.12 | $13.94 | $460.18 | $934.20 |
| 5 | 3 | $474.12 | $9.34 | $464.78 | $469.43 |
| 6 | 4 | $474.12 | $4.69 | $469.43 | $0.00 |

**14.** Sample answer: It will take 29 months to pay off the credit card balance, but only 23 months to save $2,400.

Option A:

| | A | B | C | D |
|---|---|---|---|---|
| 1 | Month | Deposit | Interest | Balance |
| 2 | | | | $0 |
| 3 | 1 | $100 | $0.42 | $100.42 |
| 4 | 2 | $100 | $0.84 | $201.25 |
| 5 | 3 | $100 | $1.26 | $302.51 |
| 6 | 4 | $100 | $1.68 | $404.18 |
| 7 | 5 | $100 | $2.10 | $506.28 |
| 8 | 6 | $100 | $2.53 | $608.81 |
| 9 | 7 | $100 | $2.95 | $711.76 |
| 10 | 8 | $100 | $3.38 | $815.15 |
| 11 | 9 | $100 | $3.81 | $918.96 |
| 12 | 10 | $100 | $4.25 | $1,023.21 |
| 13 | 11 | $100 | $4.68 | $1,127.89 |
| 14 | 12 | $100 | $5.12 | $1,233.00 |
| 15 | 13 | $100 | $5.55 | $1,338.56 |
| 16 | 14 | $100 | $5.99 | $1,444.55 |
| 17 | 15 | $100 | $6.44 | $1,550.99 |
| 18 | 16 | $100 | $6.88 | $1,657.86 |
| 19 | 17 | $100 | $7.32 | $1,765.19 |
| 20 | 18 | $100 | $7.77 | $1,872.96 |
| 21 | 19 | $100 | $8.22 | $1,981.18 |
| 22 | 20 | $100 | $8.67 | $2,089.85 |
| 23 | 21 | $100 | $9.12 | $2,198.98 |
| 24 | 22 | $100 | $9.58 | $2,308.56 |
| 25 | 23 | $100 | $10.04 | $2,418.59 |

Option B:

| | A | B | C | D |
|---|---|---|---|---|
| 1 | Month | Payment | Interest | Balance |
| 2 | | | | $2,400 |
| 3 | 1 | $100 | $27.00 | $2,327.00 |
| 4 | 2 | $100 | $26.18 | $2,253.18 |
| 5 | 3 | $100 | $25.35 | $2,178.53 |
| 6 | 4 | $100 | $24.51 | $2,103.04 |
| 7 | 5 | $100 | $23.66 | $2,026.69 |
| 8 | 6 | $100 | $22.80 | $1,949.49 |
| 9 | 7 | $100 | $21.93 | $1,871.43 |
| 10 | 8 | $100 | $21.05 | $1,792.48 |
| 11 | 9 | $100 | $20.17 | $1,712.65 |
| 12 | 10 | $100 | $19.27 | $1,631.91 |
| 13 | 11 | $100 | $18.36 | $1,550.27 |
| 14 | 12 | $100 | $17.44 | $1,467.71 |
| 15 | 13 | $100 | $16.51 | $1,384.22 |
| 16 | 14 | $100 | $15.57 | $1,299.80 |
| 17 | 15 | $100 | $14.62 | $1,214.42 |
| 18 | 16 | $100 | $13.66 | $1,128.08 |
| 19 | 17 | $100 | $12.69 | $1,040.77 |
| 20 | 18 | $100 | $11.71 | $952.48 |
| 21 | 19 | $100 | $10.72 | $863.20 |
| 22 | 20 | $100 | $9.71 | $772.91 |
| 23 | 21 | $100 | $8.70 | $681.60 |
| 24 | 22 | $100 | $7.67 | $589.27 |
| 25 | 23 | $100 | $6.63 | $495.90 |
| 26 | 24 | $100 | $5.58 | $401.48 |
| 27 | 25 | $100 | $4.52 | $306.00 |
| 28 | 26 | $100 | $3.44 | $209.44 |
| 29 | 27 | $100 | $2.36 | $111.79 |
| 30 | 28 | $100 | $1.26 | $13.05 |
| 31 | 29 | $100 | $0.15 | ($86.80) |